CNC Machining and Programming: An Introduction

SECOND EDITION

CNC Machining
and
Programming:
An Introduction

SECOND EDITION

Thomas M. Crandell

Director
Corporate and Professional Development
Associate Professor
Manufacturing Engineering Technologies Department
Ferris State University

Industrial Press Inc.

Library of Congress Cataloging-in-Publication Data

Crandell, Thomas M.
    CNC machining and programming : an introduction / Thomas M. Crandell.—2nd ed.
        p. cm.
    First ed. by David Gibbs published under title: An introduction to CNC machining
    and programming. New York : Industrial Press, 1991.
    ISBN 0–8311–3118–7
        1. Machine-tools—Numerical control—Programming.   I. Gibbs, David
    (David A. W.). An introduction to CNC machining and programming.   II. Title.

TJ1189.C73 2002
621.9'023—dc21
                                                                    2002024224

INDUSTRIAL PRESS INC.
200 Madison Avenue
New York, New York 10016-4018

2   3   4   5   6   7   8   9   10

DEDICATION

I would like to dedicate my work on this textbook in loving memory of my grandfather, Edgar L. Crandell. I also dedicate my work to my parents Gale and Beverly Crandell. It was these three individuals who taught me to work hard to complete a task and to do it to the best of my ability. I thank them for their time and patience during my upbringing.

My thanks goes to the following: My family—Linda, Chad, and Todd—for time spent away from them; Ferris State University for equipment support; and Ferris Faculty and Staff that provided assistance.

Thomas M. Crandell

CONTENTS

PREFACE

CNC Machining and Programming is intended to support the essentially practical activity of preparing and proving computer numerical control (CNC) part programs for turning, milling, and drilling. It will be of value to students in a wide range of courses dealing with CNC programming and calculations of all forms, tooling for CNC, and fixturing for CNC whether in a major or related course in a college, university, technical center, or industrial organization.

The preparation and proving of CNC part programs requires access to machinery and computer installations in order to obtain the necessary practical experience. Using such equipment, and understanding particular programming languages and techniques, requires instruction, examples, and exercises from a competent instructor. Students undertaking a course of study devoted to part programming will therefore find it necessary to attend a college or training center with adequate resources. The student must also have a good understanding of basic machining techniques, and should ideally have previous experience in turning, milling, and drilling operations. In preparing this text, these fundamental requirements have been borne in mind.

CNC part programming is an absorbing and time-consuming activity—it is one of the few areas of study where students complain that time has passed too quickly! Thus a primary objective of this book is to ensure that limited course time available can be used to the best advantage by providing the opportunity to devote as much time as possible to preparing programs and using the associated equipment. Accordingly, an attempt has been made to include sufficient information to provide the student with much of the theoretical knowledge needed to support the more practical elements of study, thereby reducing the time spent on formal lectures and unnecessary note taking. The text also provides the student with the opportunity to study specific aspects of interest or needs.

This text is essentially practical in nature and is intended to provide adequate material for a variety of course work. It contains a series of assignments that provide the student with a practical understanding of CNC processing, fixturing, tooling, and programming by various means. Throughout the book there are numerous fully detailed drawings of components in inch and metric units that, while primarily included to complement the text, may also be used as programming exercises in the early stages of a course. An additional series of projects, of varying degrees of complexity and intended for later use, should satisfy most levels of ability.

It is the author's experience that many mature people returning to college or retraining, also many younger students, are hampered in their programming work by never being taught how to apply their calculation skills in algebra, geometry, and trigonometry. It is generally outside the scope of a course of study devoted to part programming to spend much time rectifying this state of affairs, and yet it cannot be ignored. To assist both instructors and students there is a chapter devoted entirely to the type of calculations that will be encountered when preparing or checking part programs manually; it is hoped that the completion of this material, supported by on-the-spot tutoring by faculty, will be of value.

This text will be of on-going value to students, faculty, and industrial programmers alike.

Thomas M. Crandell
Director
Corporate and Professional Development
Ferris State University

Chapter 1

AN INTRODUCTION TO THE CONCEPT OF COMPUTER NUMERICAL CONTROL

Definition of Numerical Control

Numerical control (NC) is the term used to describe the control of machine movements and various other functions by instructions expressed as a series of numbers and initiated via an electronic control system.

Computerized numerical control (CNC) is the term used when the control system utilizes an internal computer. The internal computer allows for the following: storage of additional programs, program editing, running of programs from memory, machine and control diagnostics, special routines, and inch/metric–incremental/absolute switchability.

The two systems are shown diagrammatically in Figure 1.1. The control units may be free-standing or built into the main structure of the machine. The operating panel of an integrated control unit is shown in Figure 1.2.

The Application of Computer Numerical Control

Computer numerical control is applied to a wide range of manufacturing processes such as metal cutting, woodworking, welding, flame cutting, sheet metal forming, sheet metal punching, water jet cutting, electrical discharge machining and laser cutting. The text that follows is restricted to its application to common machine-shop engineering processes, namely, turning, milling, and drilling, where it has been particularly successful.

The Advantages of Computer Numerical Control over Conventional Machining

Computer numerical control is economical for mass, batch, and, in many cases, single-item production. Many factors contribute to this economic viability, the most important of these being as follows:

(a) high productivity rates
(b) uniformity of the product
(c) reduced component rejection

1

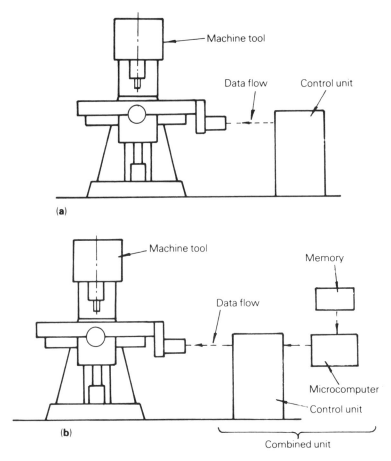

Figure 1.1 Basic control systems: (a) numerical control and (b) computerized numerical control.

(d) reduced tooling costs
(e) less operator involvement
(f) machining of complex contours can now be produced.

It is also found in most cases that fewer machine operators will be required as conventional machines are replaced by modern CNC technology, but those employees that remain will of necessity be high caliber technicians with considerable knowledge of metal-cutting methods, cutting speeds and feeds, work-holding, and tool-setting techniques and who are familiar with the control systems and programming for computer numerical control.

The Capability of Computer Numerical Control

The dramatic effect computer numerical control has already had on traditional engineering production techniques is now well appreciated. Machines controlled in this way

Figure 1.2 Integrated control unit.

are capable of working for many hours every day virtually unsupervised. They are readily adaptable to facilitate production of a wide range of components. Every function traditionally performed by the operator of a standard machine tool can be achieved via a computer numerical control machining program.

To appreciate just how versatile computer numerical control can be, it is only necessary to examine very briefly the human involvement in the production of a simple component such as the one shown in Figure 1.3. The hole only is to be produced by drilling on a conventional vertical milling machine. The activities of the operator in producing the component would be as follows:

1. Select a suitable cutting tool.
2. Locate the cutting tool in the machine spindle.

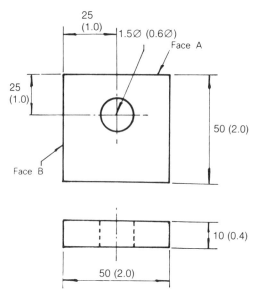

Figure 1.3 Component detail. (Inch units are given in parentheses.)

3. Secure the cutting tool.
4. Locate the component in the work-holding device.
5. Clamp the component.
6. Establish a datum in relation to face A.
7. Determine the amount of slide movement required.
8. Determine the direction of slide movement required.
9. Move the slide, monitoring the movement on the graduated dial allowing for leadscrew backlash, or digital readout if available.
10. Lock the slide in position.
11. Establish a second datum in relation to face B.
12. Determine the amount of slide movement required.
13. Determine the direction of slide movement required.
14. Move the slide, monitoring the movement on the graduated dial allowing for leadscrew backlash, or digital readout if available.
15. Lock the slide in position.
16. Select a suitable spindle speed.
17. Determine the direction of spindle rotation.
18. Select a suitable feed rate.
19. Switch on the spindle motor.
20. Switch on the coolant supply motor.
21. Engage the feed and machine the hole.
22. Disengage feed and withdraw tool.
23. Switch off the coolant supply motor.
24. Switch off the spindle motor.
25. Remove the component.
26. Verify the accuracy of the machine movement by measuring the component.

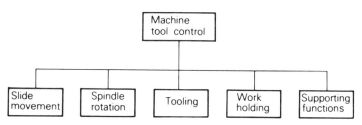

Figure 1.4 Elements of machine control.

From this list it can be seen that even the simplest of machining operations involves making a considerable number of decisions that influence the resulting physical activity. A skilled machinist operating a conventional machine makes such decisions and takes the necessary action almost without thinking. Nevertheless, the decisions *are* made and the action *is* taken.

It is not possible to remove the human involvement totally from a machining process. No automatic control system is yet capable of making a decision in the true sense of the word. Its capability is restricted to responding to a manually or computer-prepared program, and it is during the preparation of the program that the decisions are made. Via that program the machine controller is fed with instructions that give effect to the decisions. In this way all the functions listed above, and many others not required in such a simple example of machining, may be automatically and repeatedly controlled. Figure 1.4 lists the elements of total machine control.

Slide Movement

The success of any manual machining exercise is dependent on many factors, not least of which is the experienced worker's practical skills. These skills are most in evidence when they affect the accuracy of the finished product, such as when they are involved in positioning, via the machine slides, the cutting tool and workpiece in the correct relationship to each other. This aspect of machining skill is also the crucial factor when the machine is electronically controlled.

Slide movement on computer numerically controlled machines is achieved by:

(a) hydraulically operated pistons
(b) electric servo motors attached to screw drives
(c) magnetic linear motor drive systems.

The use of electric motors is by far the most common technique. The motor is either directly coupled, or connected via a toothed belt drive, to the slide leadscrew. The servo motor, in effect, replaces the conventional handwheel and this is illustrated in Figure 1.5, which shows conventional machines, a center lathe and a vertical milling machine, fitted with servo motors. A few machine designs have retained handwheels as an aid to setup or to provide for both numerical and manual control.

Machine tools have more than one slide and so the slide required to move will have to be identified. The plane in which movement can take place may be longitudinal,

Figure 1.5(a) Conventional center lathe fitted with servo motors.

transverse, or vertical. These planes are referred to as axes and are designated by the letters X, Y, Z, and sometimes U, V, W. Rotary axes A, B, and C can also be applied to a machine around a center axis mentioned previously. A rotary axis has as its centerline one of the three standard axes (X to A, Y to B, and Z to C). Their location on common machine tools is shown in Figure 1.6. Note that the Z axis always relates to a sliding motion parallel to the spindle axis.

The direction in which a slide moves, in rotary motor drive systems, is achieved by the direction of rotation of the motor, either clockwise or counterclockwise, and the movement would be designated as plus or minus in relation to a given datum. Figure 1.6 also shows how the direction of travel is designated on common machine tools. Hydraulic or linear drive systems produce motion through a push or pull (linear force) activation on one side or the other of the machine slide. Slide movement and relative tool and work movement occur from the push or pull. Slide movement and relative tool and work movement are discussed in more detail in Chapter 6.

The rate or speed at which slide movement takes place, expressed in feet/meters per minute or inches/millimeters per revolution of the machine spindle, will be proportional to the revolutions per minute of the servo motor; the higher the revolutions per minute, the faster the rate of slide travel. In the case of hydraulic drives the rate of motion is controlled by regulating the flow of fluid into the drive cylinder. Linear motor drives are controlled electronically by the activation of magnetic force fields along the motor magnet strip.

Figure 1.5(b) Conventional milling machine fitted with servo motors.

On rotary drives the length of slide movement is controlled by either the number of revolutions or the number of part revolutions the motor is permitted to make, one complete revolution being equal to the lead of the leadscrew, in the same way as one turn of a handwheel is equal to the lead of a leadscrew. In some cases there may be reduction pulleys or gears between the motor and the leadscrew, as shown in Figure 1.7, in which case the linear movement obtained in relation to the motor revolutions would be proportionally reduced. The length of travel made, or required to be made, by a slide is referred to as a coordinate dimension. In the case of linear drive mechanisms such as hydraulic or electro-magnetic drives, movement is not dependent on a rotation and accuracy of a screw. In these drives movement is tracked through a measurement device such as a precision linear scale or laser feedback system.

Since the slide movement is caused by the servo motor (or drive system), control of that motor (or drive system) will in turn control the slide movement. The drive is controlled electronically via the machine control unit. All the relevant information, that is the axis, direction, feed rate, and length of movement, has to be supplied to the control unit in an acceptable numerical form. The input of information to the machine controller is achieved in a variety of ways: in the past perforated tape or magnetic tape was used. Today input is achieved via a direct computer link, computer disk, or manually entered. Data input is covered in more detail in Chapter 5.

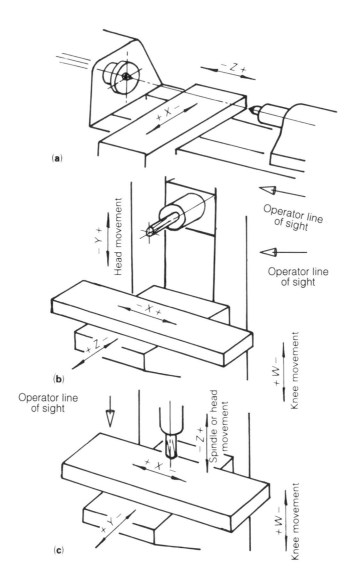

Figure 1.6 Identification of slides and direction of the slide movement on common machine tools: (a) center lathe (turning center); (b) horizontal milling machine (horizontal machining center); (c) vertical milling machine (vertical machining center).

Complex Slide Movement

So far, consideration has been given to simple linear movement involving one slide. There are, however, many instances when two or more slides have to be moving at the same time. It is possible to produce a 45° angle as shown in Figure 1.8 by synchronizing the slide movements in two axes, but to produce the 30° angle in Figure 1.9 would require a different rate of movement in each axis, and this may be outside the scope of

Figure 1.7 Cogged belt drive from servo motor to leadscrew.

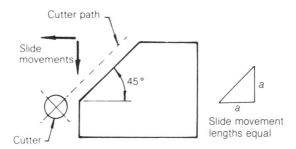

Figure 1.8 Effect of equal rates of slide movement.

a simple NC system unless it is capable of accurately responding to two precalculated feed rates.

Similarly, the curve shown in Figure 1.10 would present problems, since ideally its production would require constantly changing feed rates in two axes. The curve could be designated by a series of coordinate dimensions as shown in Figure 1.11, and, providing the machine were capable of responding to the minute variations in size, a satisfactory result would be obtained, but the calculations necessary to approach the task in

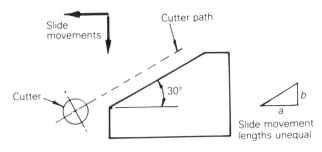

Figure 1.9 Effect of unequal rates of slide movement.

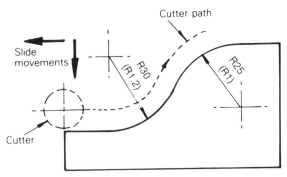

Figure 1.10 Profile requiring constantly changing rates of slide movement. (Inch units are given in parentheses.)

this way would be considerable. Complex slide movements such as those required to produce the curve can readily be achieved by the inclusion in the system of a computer capable of making the necessary calculations from the minimum of input data. Of course, the calculation of slide movements to produce complex profiles is not the only function of a computer. The other facilities it provides, in particular its ability to store data that can be used as and when required, will be considered later.

Verification of Slide Movement

An important function of the skilled worker operating a conventional machine is to monitor the slide movement and verify its accuracy by measuring the component. A similar facility is desirable on computer numerically controlled machines.

Control systems without a facility to verify slide movements are referred to as "open-loop" systems, while those with this facility are called "closed-loop" systems. A closed-loop system is shown diagrammatically in Figures 1.12 and 1.13.

One method that the exact position of the slide is monitored is by a transducer attached to the drive screw system with its information fed back to the control unit, which in turn will, via the feed motor, make any necessary corrections. As mentioned

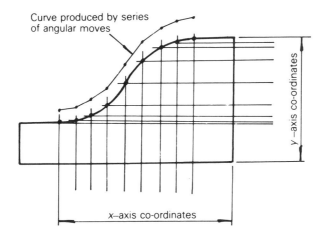

Figure 1.11 Designation of a curved profile by a series of coordinate dimensions.

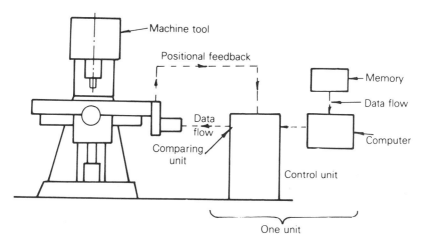

Figure 1.12 Closed-loop control system. (Courtesy of AIMTECH.)

other drive systems will use high precision linear scale devices or laser measurement systems.

In addition to positional feedback some machines are equipped with "in-process mea-surement." This consists of probes that touch the machined surface and respond to any unacceptable size variation. The data thus gathered are fed back to the control system and corrections to the slide movement are made automatically.

Rotary Movements

Sometimes the production of a component requires rotary movement in addition to the linear movement of the machine-tool slides. This movement is provided by ancillary equipment such as rotary tables and indexers. These movements are controllable via

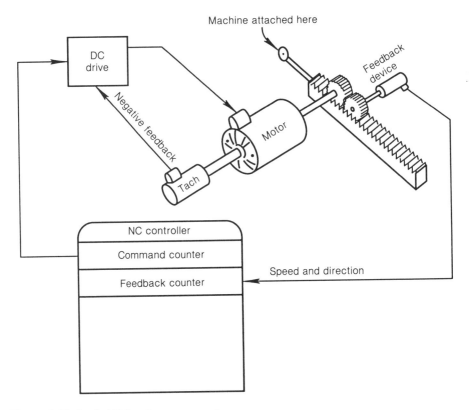

Figure 1.13 Basic NC hardware concept.

the machining program. They are identified by the letters *A*, *B*, and *C* as indicated in Figure 1.14.

Control of Machine Spindles

Machine spindles are driven directly or indirectly by electric motors, and a few by hydraulic drive. The degree of automatic control over this motion usually includes stopping and starting, and the direction and speed of rotation. Some very early systems, and perhaps a few inexpensive modern systems, do not include control of the spindle motions at all, switching on and off and gear selection being a totally manual operation. On the other hand, on some very modern control systems the torque or horsepower necessary to carry out the machining operation can be monitored and compared with a predetermined value included in the machining program; when necessary, the spindle speed will be varied automatically to provide optimum cutting conditions. (See "Adaptive Control," Chapter 11.)

The speed of the spindle is often infinitely variable, and may automatically change as cutting is taking place to maintain a programmed surface speed. Thus, when facing the end of a bar on a lathe as the tool nears the work center, the spindle speed will increase. In this way material removal is achieved at the fastest possible rate with due regard to tool life and the surface finish required.

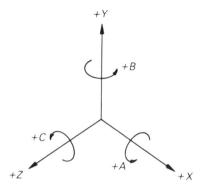

Figure 1.14 Identification of rotary movements.

The direction of spindle rotation required can be determined as follows: Remember that in lathe or turning operations the piece part will be rotating about it's axis with the cutting tool traversing into the part to perform the cutting action. In milling/drilling operations, on the other hand, the tool revolves around it's center axis, and the part advances into it.

1. Clockwise (CW). When the spindle rotates a right-handed screw would advance into the workpiece, or if the machine operator looked through the tool toward the workpiece, he would see it moving clockwise.
2. Counterclockwise (CCW). When the spindle rotates a right-handed screw would retract from the workpiece, or if the machine operator looked through the tool toward the workpiece, he would see it moving counterclockwise.

Control of Tooling

Computer numerically controlled machines may incorporate in their design turrets or magazines that hold a number of cutting tools. The machine controller can be programmed to cause indexing of the turret or magazine to present a new cutting tool to the work or to facilitate tool removal and replacement where automatic tool-changing devices are involved.

Simpler machines rely on manual intervention to effect tool changes. In these cases the control unit is programmed to stop the automatic sequence at the appropriate time and the operator will make the change. There is sometimes a connection between the control unit and the tool-storage rack and the correct tool to be used is indicated by an illuminated lamp.

Tooling is dealt with in more detail in Chapter 3.

Control of Work Holding

Work holding is another aspect of computer numerically controlled machining that can include manual intervention or be totally automatic. The work-holding devices themselves can be fairly conventional: vices, chucks, collets, and fixtures are all used. The computer numerical control can extend to loading the workpiece by the use of robots and securely clamping it by activating hydraulic or pneumatic clamping systems.

Again, as with tool changing, on simpler machines, a programmed break in a machining cycle can facilitate manual intervention as and when required.

Work holding is dealt with in detail in Chapter 4.

Supporting Functions

The various supplementary functions a skilled worker would perform during a manually controlled machining operation are, of course, vital to the success of the operation. For example, it may be necessary to clamp a slide, apply coolant, clear away swarf before locating a component, monitor the condition of tooling, and so on. Slide clamping is usually hydraulic, and hydraulic pressure provided by an electrically driven pump with the fluid flow controlled by solenoid valves has long been a feature of machine tool design. With the new technology the control of the electrical elements of such a system is included in the machining program. Similarly, it is a simple matter to control the on–off switching of a coolant pump and the opening or closing of an air valve to supply a blast of cleaning air. Tool monitoring, however, is more complex and is the subject of much research and innovation ranging from monitoring the loads exerted on spindle motors to recording variations in the sound the cutting tool makes. Some of these more advanced features of computer numerical control are discussed further in Chapter 9.

QUESTIONS

1 Explain with the aid of a simple block diagram the difference between an NC and a CNC machining system.

2 State two advantages of CNC control systems over manual control.

3 The common axes of slide movement are X, Y, and Z. What is significant about the Z axis?

4 How are rotary movements about a given axis identified and when are they likely to be used?

5 What data are required to initiate a controlled slide movement?

6 On a vertical machining center the downward movement of the spindle is designated as a Z minus. From a safety aspect this is significant. Why is this so?

7 How is an angular tool path achieved?

8 With the aid of simple block diagrams to show data flow, explain the difference between an open-loop and a closed-loop control system.

9 How would a manual tool change be accommodated in a machine program?

10 Explain what is meant by "constant cutting speed" and how this is achieved on CNC machines.

Chapter 2

MACHINE DESIGN

Repeatability

The quality of conventional machine tools varies considerably. They are built to a price to meet a wide-ranging market. Generally speaking, the more expensive the machine is, the higher the quality of work that can be expected to be produced on it. However, an expensive conventional machine does not guarantee high-quality work. The key to success lies in the skills of the operator. The cheapest of machines is capable of producing very accurate work in the hands of the right person.

Skilled workers get to know their machines and make allowances for their failings. During the production of a component a skilled worker can, for example, compensate for leadscrew backlash, slide friction, lack of power, and so on. He or she can vary spindle speeds, feed rates, and tooling arrangements. The approach to a final cut can be gradual until it is correct and before a final commitment is made.

With a computer numerically controlled machine tool responding to a predetermined program, the capacity for readily varying the conditions when machining is under way is limited, and to make changes is inconvenient. As far as possible conditions have to be correctly determined at the time the program is produced and the machine is set up.

The slide movements are of prime importance. The movement must be precise, and this precision must continue throughout a machining program, which may involve thousands of components. The ability of the machine to produce continually accurate slide movement is called repeatability.

A precise definition of repeatability is as follows: the maximum difference that can occur between the shortest and longest positions achieved in a number of attempted moves to any programmed target position.

Repeatability is expressed as the mean of a number of attempted moves. A typical figure for repeatability would be ± 0.0003 in. or ± 0.008 mm. It follows that some moves must be well within those figures.

Repeatability is dependent on the following features being incorporated in the design of the machine:

(a) adequate strength
(b) rigidity
(c) minimum of vibration
(d) dimensional stability
(e) accurate control of the slide movements

Although many conventional machines have been, and continue to be, converted to computer numerical control, such conversions being referred to as "retrofits," their design in

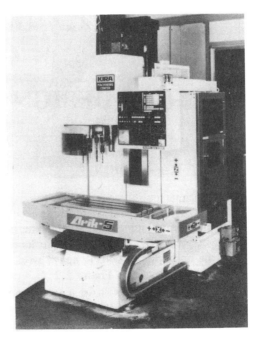

Figure 2.1(a) Vertical machining center.

Figure 2.1(b) Horizontal machining center.

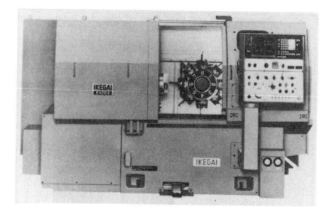

Figure 2.1(c) Turning center.

general does not meet the exacting requirements necessary to achieve a high standard of repeatability, while at the same time catering to the needs for high rates of metal removal that modern tooling and electronic control have made possible. Radical changes in design were inevitable and have resulted in the machines now generally known as vertical machining centers, horizontal machining centers, and turning centers. These are shown in Figure 2.1.

Static and Dynamic Loading

A simple analysis of the function of a machine tool reveals that it is subjected to certain loading which may be described as:

(a) static
(b) dynamic

Static loading is the term used to describe a situation where forces are acting on a structure when the machine, or that part of the machine, is not in motion. For example, due to its mass, a milling machine table exerts a static load on the knee. If the table is offset on the knee, that static load could cause the table to drop slightly at the unsupported end. A heavy workload would exacerbate the problem, which is illustrated in Figure 2.2.

Dynamic loading is the term used to describe a situation where forces are acting on a structure when movement is taking place. An example of this, shown in Figure 2.3, is the radial force exerted on a milling machine spindle as the cutter is fed into the work. The spindle could deflect.

Deflections such as those illustrated need only be quite small to affect the dimensional accuracy of the workpiece, so the machine structure and its subassemblies must be so designed to ensure that movement of this nature cannot occur.

Basic Structure

For many years cast iron was considered to be the only material suitable for the basic structure of a machine tool. It possessed adequate strength and rigidity and tended to absorb

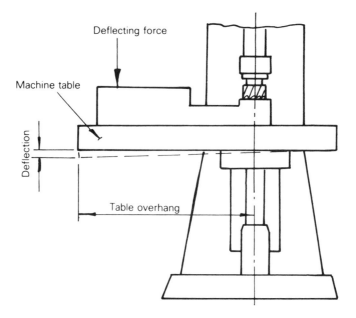

Figure 2.2 Example of the possible effect of static loading.

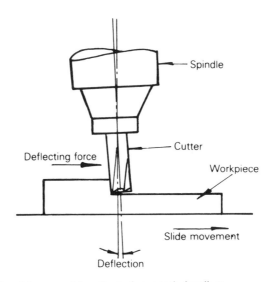

Figure 2.3 Example of the possible effect of dynamic loading.

vibration. In addition, the complex shapes required were easier to produce by casting than by any other method. Cast iron is still extensively used, but its traditional position as the most suitable material is now challenged by steel and, more recently, by concrete.

When castings are used, they are generally of one-piece box construction, heavily ribbed and stabilized by heat treatment.

Fabricated steel structures are increasingly being favored for very large machines. Steel plates of the same thickness as a cast iron structure have approximately twice the

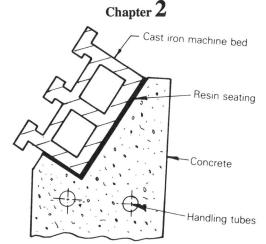

Figure 2.4 Concrete base for a machine tool.

strength. By reducing the plate thickness, the weight of the structure can be considerably reduced, yet still provide the necessary strength. In use, the rigidity of such structures has proved to be more than adequate. However, the general use of steel is limited by the problems of making complex shapes and by its resonant quality, which is not conducive to effective damping of vibration.

The use of concrete or ceramics as a machine base is a comparatively new development. The advantages of concrete are its low cost and good damping characteristics. Very large structures can be cast on site, thus reducing the overall cost even further, since no transport is involved. Smaller structures can be provided with steel tubing cast into the concrete to permit easier handling. The cast iron bed of the machine is set on a cushion of air-setting resin and attached to the concrete by steel studs. The diagram in Figure 2.4 illustrates the concept.

Machine Spindles

The machine spindle is a very important design feature. The possibility of deflection has already been noted. In addition to the radial loads that cause deflection, a spindle assembly is also subjected to a thrust load acting along its axis. The design of the spindle assembly must be such that these loads are adequately contained. Inadequate support results not only in dimensional inaccuracies but also in poor surface finish and chatter. A well-supported spindle assembly is shown in Figure 2.5. Note that the spindle overhang has been kept to a minimum, a common feature of turning and horizontal machines.

The spindle of vertical machining centers presents additional problems, since it is a traditional feature of this type of machine for the spindle to move up and down. Obviously, the more the spindle is extended, the greater the risk of deflection. Some manufacturers have now moved away from the moving-spindle concept and instead the whole head assembly moves up and down.

Another design feature problem of vertical machining centers is that in order to provide an adequate work area, the spindle head must overhang. The length of overhang must be kept to a minimum, and Figure 2.6 shows how one manufacturer has improved on the traditional design without reducing the work area.

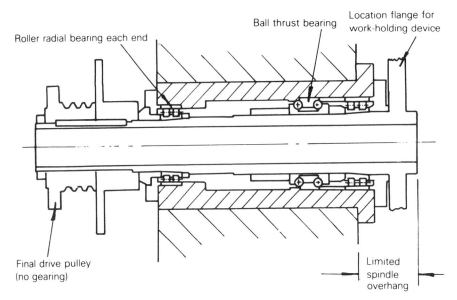

Figure 2.5 Spindle assembly for turning center.

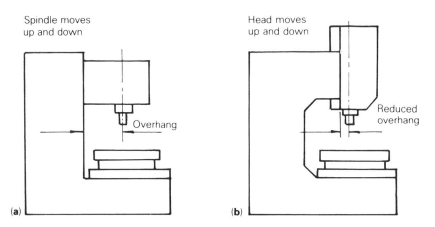

Figure 2.6 Variations in the design of vertical machining centers: (a) conventional design; (b) improved design.

The forces that cause deflection of the spindle also result in a tendency for the complete spindle-housing assembly to twist. This has resulted in an increased use of bifurcated or two-pillar structures where the spindle housing is located between two substantial slideways that reduce the tendency to twist. A bifurcated structure is shown in Figure 2.7.

Spindle Drives

Two types of electric motors are used for spindle drives: direct current (DC) and alternating current (AC). They may be coupled direct to the spindle or via belts and/or gears.

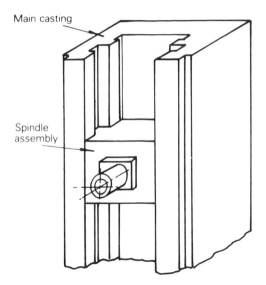

Figure 2.7 Bifurcated structure.

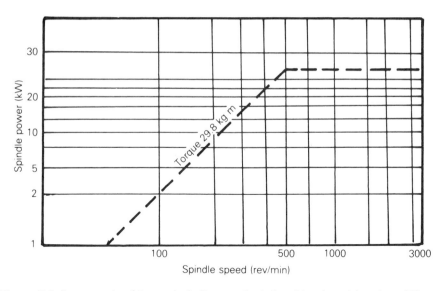

Figure 2.8 An example of torque/spindle speed relationship when driven by a DC motor: constant torque after 500 rev/min.

Many machines have a final belt drive which is quieter and produces less vibration than a geared drive.

The majority of modern machines use DC motors. By varying the voltage input, their speeds are infinitely variable as they rotate and so a constant cutting speed can be maintained. The torque available from a DC motor is constant throughout most of the speed range, as illustrated in Figure 2.8.

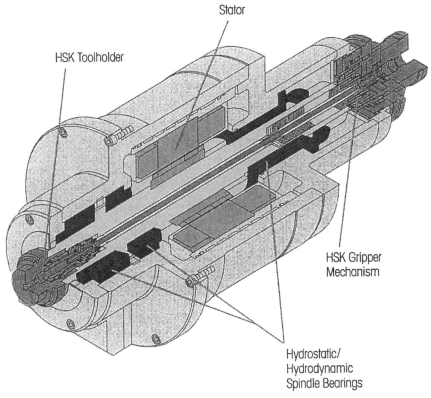

Figure 2.8(a) Hydrostatic/Hydrodynamic spindle. (Ingersoll Machine Company.)

There are some machines fitted with specially designed AC motors that also provide for variable spindle speeds, but the use of AC motors usually involves a stepped drive, that is, a series of spindle speeds will be available and the selection of a particular speed may involve switching from one speed range to another, high or low, for example, a feature that is common to many conventional machines. On computer numerically controlled machines the switching will be carried out as and when programmed via the control unit and may also include an automatic engagement or disengagement of an electrically operated clutch.

New spindle drive and bearing designs are now allowing high-speed machining using RPMs of tens of thousands. Ingersoll Milling Machine Company has developed a fluid bearing high-speed spindle that provides: higher stiffness, better running accuracies, full range of operation with high horsepower, lower runout, better dampening and lower vibration, along with unlimited bearing life. All of this is achieved through the use of hydrostatic/hydrodynamic spindle bearing technology. Simply put, they eliminate the rolling element spindle bearings and the spindle shaft runs on a film of

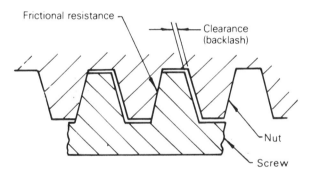

Figure 2.9 Disadvantages of conventional Acme leadscrews.

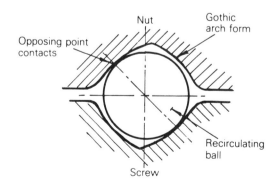

Figure 2.10 Ball screw form.

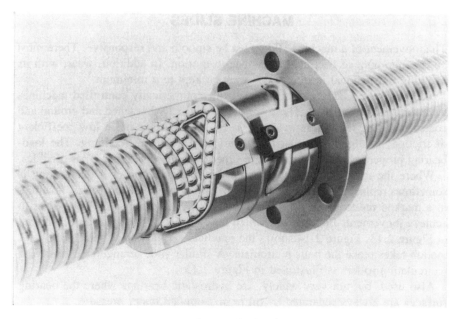

Figure 2.11 Recirculating ball screw (external return).

oil. The machine spindle becomes the motor shaft running on this film of oil, illustrated in Figure 2.8a.

Leadscrews

The Acme form of leadscrew used on conventional machines has not proved to be satisfactory for numerically controlled machines. The movement of an Acme screw is dependent on there being clearance, i.e., backlash, between two flanks. At the same time friction between the mating flanks of the screw means that considerable resistance to motion is present. These two disadvantages are illustrated in Figure 2.9.

Computer numerically controlled machines, except perhaps for a few cheaper training machines, are commonly fitted with recirculating ballscrews, which replace sliding motion with rolling motion, resulting in reduced frictional resistance. The balls, which in effect form the nut, recirculate in and out of the thread. The thread form is referred to as a Gothic arch and is illustrated in Figure 2.10. The balls make opposing point contact which virtually eliminates backlash. Figure 2.11 shows an external ball return and Figure 2.12 an internal return. The internal ball return is more compact.

The advantages of recirculating ball screws over Acme screws are:

(a) longer life
(b) less wear
(c) low frictional resistance
(d) less drive power required due to reduced friction
(e) higher traversing speeds can be used

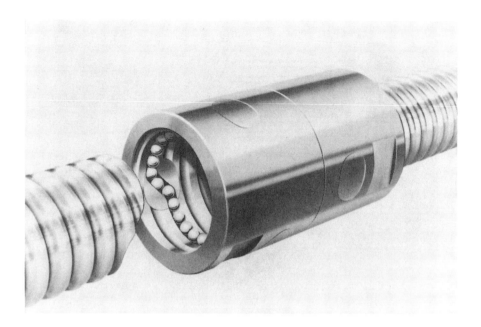

Figure 2.12 Recirculating ball screw (internal return).

(f) no stick slip effect

(g) more precise positioning over the total life of the machine

Leadscrews are usually of substantial diameter and centrally positioned to avoid twisting the slide and thus reducing the efficiency of the movement.

Machine Slides

The movement of a machine slide must be smooth and responsive. There must be the minimum of frictional resistance to motion. In addition, wear, with its resulting dimensional inaccuracies, must be kept to a minimum.

The slides of a large number of computer numerically controlled machines have flat bearing surfaces. These surfaces are usually hardened and ground and coated with polytetrafluorethylene (PTFE). This surface has a low coefficient of friction, is slightly porous, and therefore is lubricant retaining. The load-bearing properties of flat surfaces are superior to those of other types of slides.

Where the machine loading permits, the sliding action of a flat bearing is sometimes replaced by a rolling action, in the form of balls or rollers, resulting in a marked reduction in the frictional resistance and requiring less power to achieve movement. Ball bushes, which may be circular or split, are illustrated in Figure 2.13. Figure 2.14

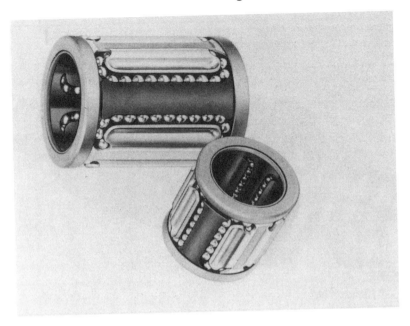

Figure 2.13(a) Ball bush.

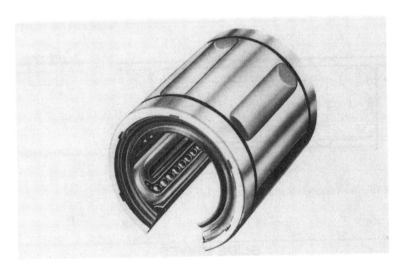

Figure 2.13(b) Split ball bush.

shows the practical application of split bushes. As motion takes place the balls recirculate. A similar slide arrangement involving recirculating rollers is illustrated in Figure 2.15.

Also used, but not very widely, are hydrostatic bearings where the bearing surfaces are always separated by oil or air supplied under pressure.

Figure 2.14 Application of split ball bushes.

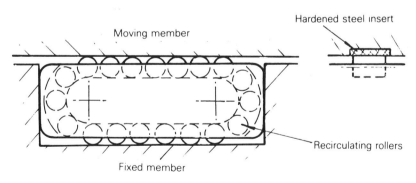

Figure 2.15 Recirculating roller slide.

The automatic forced lubrication of slides is common, and protection is provided by telescopic or accordion way covers.

Newer machine slide designs are now applying more of the bifurcated structure for strength and rigidity. Ingersoll Milling has developed a box-in-a-box design to eliminate overhangs and deflections. They have done this by applying drive forces and bearing support for each axis symmetrically around the spindle and work zone. See Figure 2.15a.

Figure 2.15(a) Box-in-a-box slide design (Ingersoll Machine Company.)

Slide Drives

It was stated in Chapter 1 that both electric and hydraulic power are used to achieve slide motion. There are a number of very effective, responsive, and thoroughly proved hydraulic systems currently in use, but by far the most common power source is the electric motor, and so the text will be confined to dealing only with this method.

Three types of DC motor are used:

(a) stepping motors (rotary)
(b) conventional, nonstepping motors (rotary)
(c) magnetic linear drive motors

Stepping motors are a special type of motor designed so that they rotate in sequential finite steps when energized by electrical pulses. Open-loop stepping motor drive systems have two major limitations: (1) there are limited horsepower and torque ratings to meet requirements; (2) the increment size-versus-slide velocity requirements needed. An example would be an 8000 pulse per second stepper motor with a system requiring 0.0001 in. slide accuracy would have a velocity of 48 in. per minute. Therefore, the higher the machine slide accuracy required, the slower the feedrate obtainable. See open-loop servo control diagram in Figure 2.16a. This type of motor was fitted to the earlier generation of machines but has now been largely superseded by the closed-loop servo drive system, which in recent years has been the subject of much research, resulting in vastly improved designs that, together with improvements in control systems technology, make them much more responsive and easier to control than open-loop stepping motor systems.

The speeds of DC motors are infinitely variable. Constant torque is available throughout most of the speed range, which means that relatively small motors can be used, and when

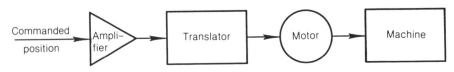

Figure 2.16(a) Open-loop servo control (block diagram). (From Fundamentals of Numerical Control, Publication SD-100, Allen Bradley Corp., Milwaukee, WI.)

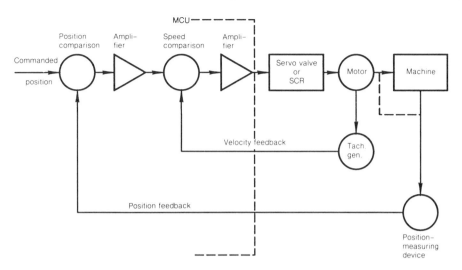

Figure 2.16(b) Closed-loop servo system, servo block diagram. (From Fundamentals of Numerical Control, Publication SD-100, Allen Bradley Corp., Milwaukee, WI.)

they are directly coupled to the machine leadscrew a torsionally stiff drive is provided. The motors provide regenerative braking, resulting in a virtually nonexistent slide overrun.

The closed-loop system (Figure 2.16b) is not drive-motor-dependent using stepper motors, AC motors, DC motors, SCR drives, hydraulic motors, or hydraulic cylinders. With this type of drive system, resolutions of 50 millionths and speeds higher then 400 inches per minute are possible.

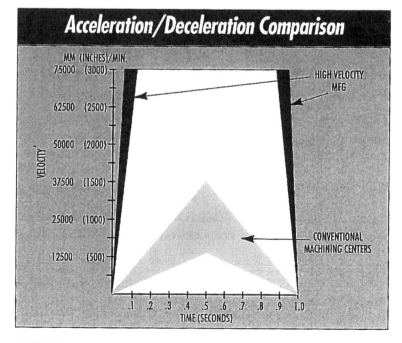

Figure 2.16(c) Acceleration/Deceleration graph. (Courtesy of Ingersoll Machine Company.)

Considerable research is being carried out with AC servo motors. At present they are larger than DC motors providing equivalent power, and are also more costly. However, they need less maintenance and this is a factor very much in their favor.

The newest slide drive system to appear on machinery is the magnetic linear drive system found on Ingersoll Milling Machine Company's High Velocity equipment. Machine movement is obtained through the activation of magnetic forces alone, using high force linear motors (see Figure 2.16c, d, e). Using this direct axis drive system allows much higher machine acceleration/deceleration and velocity, as well as being stiffer and allowing improved control performance. The improved performance allows:

1. More constant chipload with higher acceleration/deceleration rates reducing tool wear.

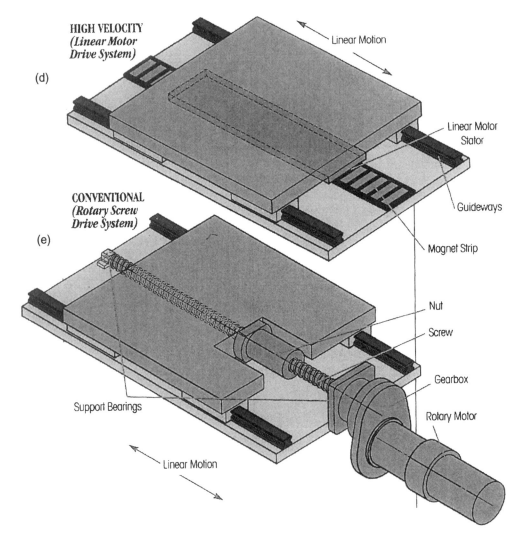

Figure 2.16(d–e) (d) Linear motor drive system. (e) Conventional rotary drive system. (Courtesy of Ingersoll Machine Company.)

2. Power transmission devices are removed, reducing or eliminating end play, backlash, drive train friction, and elasticity in conventional drive trains.
3. Improved path accuracy and reduced following error.
4. Feedrates up to 3,000 IPM increase production capability and reduce non-cutting time.

Positional Feedback

In Chapter 1 reference was made to the concept of open-loop and closed-loop slide positioning systems. The closed-loop positioning system is an important feature of any good computer numerically controlled machine. The concept can be summarized as instruction–movement–information–confirmation. The crucial feedback information is provided by a transducer.

A transducer can be described as a device that receives and transmits information. This information is received in one form, converted, and then transmitted in another form acceptable to the receiver.

A variety of transducers have been applied, with varying success, to computer numerically controlled machines. Two of the more common types are described below.

Rotary-Type Transducers

A rotary-type transducer transmits angular displacement as a voltage. The transducer creates electrical pulses and transmits them back to the control by use of electrical windage in resolvers/synchro resolvers or photoelectric disk encoders. Physically, this transducer is attached to one end of the leadscrew either by direct means or through the use of precision gears (Figures 2.17a and 2.17b). Within this relatively small package there are a series of electrical windings. One of these windings, referred to as a rotor, rotates with the leadscrew. Around the periphery of the leadscrew are a series of interconnected windings that do not rotate and that are referred to as the stator.

The stator windings or photocells are fed with electrical power at a voltage rate that has been determined by the machine control unit in response to digital information relating to the required slide movements it has received via the part program. As the servo motor rotates the leadscrew, a voltage is induced in the rotor photocells, and this voltage will vary according to the angular position of the leadscrew in relation to the stator windings or photo encoder disk. Information relating to the induced voltage is fed back to the control unit, which, in effect, counts the number of complete revolutions and part revolutions the leadscrew has made, thus confirming that the movement achieved corresponds to the original instruction.

Optical Gratings

An optical grating transducer transmits linear movement as a voltage signal in the form of a series of pulses.

The principle of the optical grating can be shown in a practical way as follows. Figure 2.18 represents a pair of optical gratings, each consisting of a number of evenly spaced parallel lines. One grating is fixed and the other is caused to move

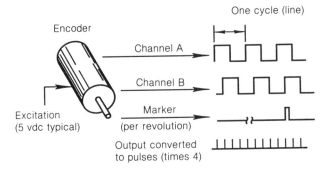

Using channels A or B or both permits encoder signals to be 1, 2, or 4 times the number of lines; marker signal occurs once per revolution and is used for reference

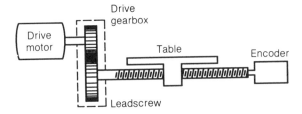

Encoder feedback coupled directly to leadscrew

Figure 2.17(a) Encoder. (From Fundamentals of Numerical Control, Publication SD-100, Allen Bradley Corp., Milwaukee, WI.)

along. The reader is invited to reproduce the moving grating on either a piece of tracing paper or clear plastic film. Place the second grating over the first and, with the lines inclined at a slight angle, move the second grating across the first. A fringe pattern similar to the one shown will be observed moving across the fixed grating. This pattern is referred to as Moiré fringe.

There is a mathematical connection between the spacing of the gratings, the angle of inclination and the apparent fringe movement. This principle is applied to measuring the movement of machine slides.

For practical purposes the gratings are etched either on gelatine-coated glass or on stainless steel. The fixed grating is attached to the main casting of the machine and the moving grating is positioned immediately above the fixed grating, but is attached to the moving slide. Gratings for applications of this nature have 100 to 200 spacings per inch or 25 mm.

If glass is used, a light source is directed through the grating; if stainless steel is used, the light is reflected off the surface. This light is focused onto a phototransistor, which responds according to whether the projected light is uninterrupted or interrupted, that is, a fringe is present or not present. The electrical pulses produced in this way each represent a known linear value. The number of pulses is counted and this information is fed back to the control unit as confirmation that the correct movement has been made.

Both the transducers described have a weakness. One monitors revolutions of the leadscrew, the other movements made by a slide. Neither of these factors may be a precise indication of the position of the tool in relation to the work, which would be the

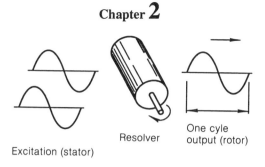

Excitation (stator)   Resolver   One cyle output (rotor)

Output phase angle indicates shaft-angle position of the rotor

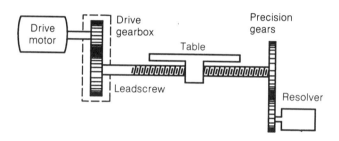

Precision gearing in the proper ratio must be used when the feedback device is not compatible with leadscrew pitch

Figure 2.17(b) Resolver. (From Fundamentals of Numerical Control, Publication SD-100, Allen Bradley Corp., Milwaukee, WI.)

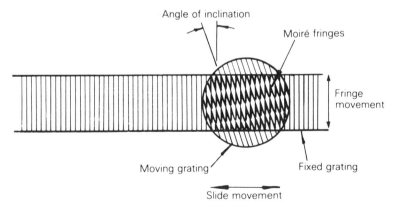

Figure 2.18 Principle of optical grating.

function of a perfect transducer. Such a transducer poses many design problems and has yet to be developed.

The locations of a linear and a rotary transducer on machine tools are illustrated in Figure 2.19.

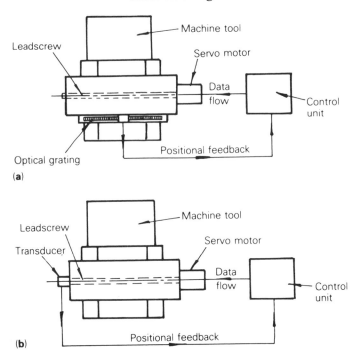

Figure 2.19 Location of positional transducers on machining centers: (a) linear transducer; (b) rotary transducer.

Laser Feedback

The newest form of feedback systems are the high resolution lasers and they can be used for positional and velocity feedback. Lasers offer benefits in the area of feedback resolution, ease of set-up, ease of service, contamination resistance, thermal compensation and self diagnostics. See Figure 2.19a.

Temperature Variations That Affect Dimensional Stability

Manufacturers design their machines so that the correct alignments are achieved at a stated temperature. "Warm up" times are often quoted and sometimes warning lights are built into the control system. Deviation from the stated temperature can cause twisting or distortion of the machine castings and can have a considerable effect on the accuracy of the work produced.

Heat sources that have to be accommodated in the design of the machine, or otherwise eliminated, are as follows:

(a) heat due to friction in motors, bearings and slides
(b) heat due to the metal-cutting action
(c) heat due to accumulated chips or swarf
(d) heat in the environment

Figure 2.19(a) Laser feed-back system. (Ingersoll Machine Company.)

Heat due to friction is eliminated or its effect reduced in a variety of ways. For example, main drive motors are sometimes placed outside the main structure (which also helps to reduce vibration) and the final drive to the spindle is via belts. Motors that are attached to the machine body have heat radiation facilities in the form of vanes built into their structure. Some are cooled by a ducted air flow. Spindles may be air or oil cooled; sometimes when oil is used there are cooling facilities for the recirculating oil. Heat produced by slide movement is virtually eliminated by the efforts made to produce frictionless slides, as mentioned earlier.

Heat produced by the cutting action is kept to a minimum by ensuring that the correct cutting conditions prevail, that is, by using tools with the correct geometry for the material being cut and the operation being carried out, and by ensuring that the correct cutting speed and feed rates are employed. In addition, coolant, as a flood or as spray mist, can be applied to the cutting area. Some machines provide each cutting tool with an individual coolant supply, as illustrated in Figure 2.20.

Heat due to chip accumulation can be a major problem, especially when the machines are totally enclosed for safety. The ideal situation is to have the chips falling away from the machine. Figure 2.21a illustrates how the sloping bed of a turning center permits the chips to fall away, while Figure 2.21b shows a horizontal machining center with the same facility. An added refinement is to have the chips continuously removed by conveyor.

Figure 2.20 Individual coolant supply to cutting tools.

It is best if the room temperatures for workshops containing computer numerically controlled machines are maintained at a constant 20°C or 72°F, but with recent control upgrades this is no longer mandatory. The presence of a radiator or a constantly opening and closing door close to a machine can have a detrimental effect, and very warm summer days have been known to halt production in factories where the air conditioning was inadequate.

It is also worth noting that excesses in temperature not only affect the dimensional stability of a machine but can also cause malfunctioning of the electronic control systems. To prevent control overheating air circulation or air conditioning devices may be provided on controls.

Additional Machining Facilities

A number of machines currently available have special design features that extend their capabilities by providing machining facilities not generally available. They include the following.

1. Turning centers with two turrets positioned in such a way that two tools can cut simultaneously. An example is shown in Figure 2.22.

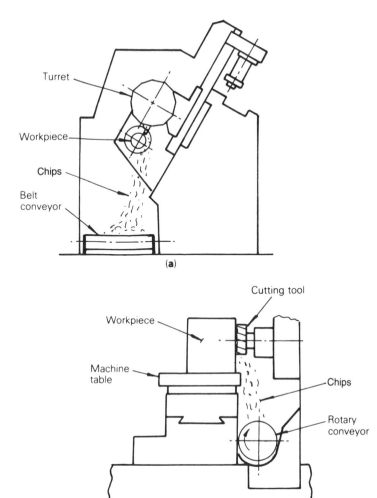

Figure 2.21 Chip removal arrangements: (a) turning center; (b) horizontal machining center.

2. Turning centers which use special tool holders that are power driven and can be programmed to rotate when the machine spindle is stationary, thus permitting the milling of flats, keyways, and slots and the drilling of holes offset from the machine axis as illustrated in Figure 2.23.

3. A turning center with a similar facility to that described above, but where the rotating holders are located in a separate turret. In addition the spindle, when clamped to prevent rotation, can be caused to slide in the Y axis, thus giving four-axis control: X, Y, Z, and C (rotary).

4. A milling machine with two spindles providing for machining operations in the vertical and horizontal planes, a facility that is particularly useful and time

Figure 2.22 Additional machining facilities provided by second turret.

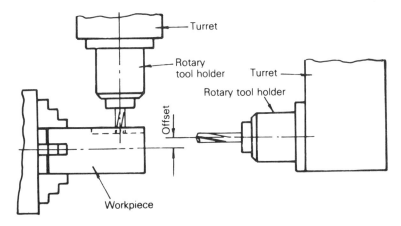

Figure 2.23 Example of additional machining facilities on a turning center.

saving when machining large components that cannot be readily reset. This feature is illustrated in Figure 2.24.

5. A turning center using a tooling magazine, as opposed to a turret, to provide for a greatly extended tooling range.

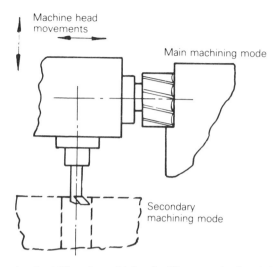

Figure 2.24 Example of additional machining facilities on a horizontal machining center.

Safety

The safety aspects of computer numerically controlled machines have to be related not only to the machine operator but also to the very costly equipment. There are two problem areas: the high voltage involved and the extreme mechanical forces resulting from high spindle speeds and rapid slide movements.

The electrical services are protected by lockable covers, and access should be limited to authorized persons.

The mechanical dangers are greatly reduced by total enclosure, a common feature of computer numerically controlled machines. This affords protection from flying chips and broken tooling, reduces noise level and prevents contamination of the atmosphere by coolant, the latter being a considerable problem when spray cooling is employed.

When machines are not totally enclosed guards are used, these being fitted with interlocking switches so that there is no machine movement until the guard is correctly positioned.

The electrical control of mechanical features is also extended to work-holding devices. If the work is not correctly held, there is no machine movement.

Excessive slide movement, which could damage the machine or workpiece, is prevented by limit switches, and this can also be extended further by programmable safety zones that fall into three categories: safe, warning, and fault. Tool movement in the safe zone is unrestricted; in the warning zone it is only possible by the operator making a conscious response to a power cut-off; in the fault zone no movement at all is possible. The whole machine can, of course, be instantly immobilized by activating the obligatory emergency switch.

Reference was made earlier to conventional machines being retrofitted with computer numerical control systems. These machines often do not have the built in safety features referred to above and because of this the utmost care must be taken in their use.

The reader should appreciate that, on all computer numerically controlled machines, whether purpose built or retrofitted, slide movements can be very rapid, and movements made at the wrong time or in the wrong direction can have disastrous results both for the operator and for the equipment. Accidents of this nature are more likely to happen during machine setting and program proving, and when restarting after a program stop.

A clearly defined code of operation, with the accent on safety, is desirable for all remote controlled machine tools, particularly those used in educational and training establishments, and the student should be made fully aware of the inherent dangers.

QUESTIONS

1 Define repeatability as applied to CNC machine tools.

2 List five qualities which need to be incorporated in a machine design if repeatability is to be maintained.

3 What are bifurcated structures and why are they used?

4 Why is it desirable that slide leadscrews should be centrally positioned?

5 What do you understand by the term dimensional stability as applied to CNC machine tools?

6 List four factors that can affect the dimensional stability of a CNC machine tool.

7 Explain the difference between static and dynamic loading by quoting examples of where they occur in a CNC machine tool.

8 Why do some manufacturers recommend a warm up period before a CNC machine tool is used?

9 How do some machine designs eliminate the problems caused by the heat present in chips?

10 List the various techniques that are used on machine-tool slides to reduce the frictional resistance to motion.

11 List the advantages of using DC servo motors for slide movement on CNC machines.

12 Why is it that gearboxes are not necessary when machine spindles are driven by DC motors?

13 Why is the traditional Acme form of leadscrew unsuitable for CNC machines?

14 List the advantages of using recirculating ball screws to facilitate slide movement.

15 What is the name given to the thread form of ball screw?

16 What is a positional transducer and where and why it is used on a CNC machine?

17 What are the two problem areas that make safety an important consideration in the design of CNC machine tools?

18 Many CNC machines are totally enclosed. List three advantages of such an arrangement.

19 How can the danger of inadequate work holding be eliminated?

20 Explain the differences among safe, warning, and fault safety zones and their purpose in CNC machine tool control systems.

TOOLING FOR COMPUTER NUMERICALLY CONTROLLED MACHINING

To the onlooker one of the most startling aspects of computer numerically controlled machining is the rapid metal-removal rates used. That there are cutting tools capable of withstanding such treatment can seem quite incredible. Add to this indexing times of less than one second and automatic tool changing providing a "chip-to-chip" time of around five seconds and it is easy to understand why many production engineers consider tooling to be the most fascinating aspect of computer numerically controlled machining.

Materials for Cutting Tools

Although high-speed steel (HSS) is used for small-diameter drills, taps, reamers, end mills, and spot drills, the bulk of tooling for computer numerically controlled machining involves the use of cemented carbide.

The physical properties necessary in a cutting tool are hardness at the metal-cutting temperature, which can be as high as 600°C, and toughness. High-speed steel is tougher than cemented carbide but not as hard and, therefore, cannot be used at such high rates of metal removal. On the other hand, the lack of toughness of cemented carbide presents problems, and this has meant that a tremendous amount of research has gone into developing carbide grades that, when adequately supported, are able to meet the requirements of modern machining techniques. It is only necessary to observe a computer numerically controlled machine in action to see how successful this research has been.

The hardness of cemented carbide is almost equal to that of diamond. It derives this hardness from its main constituent, tungsten carbide. In its pure form tungsten carbide is too brittle to be used as a cutting tool, so it is pulverised and mixed with cobalt.

The mixture of tungsten carbide and cobalt powder is pressed into the required shape and then sintered. The cobalt melts and binds the tungsten carbide grains into a dense, nonporous structure.

In addition to tungsten carbide, other hard materials such as titanium and tantalum carbides are used, and by providing tungsten carbide tools with a thin layer of titanium carbide, resistance to wear and useful life are increased by up to five times.

The Practical Application of Cemented Carbides

Solid Tools

Solid carbide tools are somewhat restricted in their use owing to their lack of toughness. However, they are particularly useful when the work material is difficult to machine with high-speed steel, thus precluding the use of this material even for the small sizes referred to earlier. Solid carbide milling cutters as small as 1/32 in. diameter, drills as small as 1/64 in. or No. 80 (0.0135 in.) diameter and reamers as small as 1/16 in. diameter are available. The successful application of solid carbide tooling depends greatly on the tool being short and mounted with the minimum of overhang, and the machines on which they are used being vibration free and having no play or misalignment. The correct speeds and feeds have to be determined with great care, often by experiment on the particular work in hand.

Brazed Tips

When the shank size of a cutting tool is large enough, a more viable technique is to braze the carbide tip to a medium carbon steel shank. Drills, reamers, milling cutters, and turning tools produced in this way are available.

Indexable Inserts

While both types of tooling previously referred to have their particular uses, by far the most widely used application of cemented carbides is as inserts located in special holders or cartridges.

The advantages of inserts are as follows:

1. correct cutting geometry
2. precise dimensions
3. no resharpening
4. rapid replacement

The first two factors are particularly relevant where preset tooling is concerned. (Preset tooling is discussed subsequently in the text.)

The inserts are indexable, that is, as a cutting edge becomes dull the insert is moved to a new position to present a new edge to the work. The number of cutting edges available depends on the design of the insert.

The control of chips is an essential requirement when high metal-removal rates are involved, and this can be a built-in feature of the insert itself, in the form of a groove, or of the holder, in the form of a chip-breaking pad clamped on the top of the insert.

American National Standards Institute and International Standards Organization Codes

Although there is still a wide range of cemented carbide grades, insert shapes, and toolholder designs currently available, the initially somewhat confusing situation was greatly helped by the introduction of the American National Standards Institute (ANSI) and International Standards Organization (ISO) codes. Manufacturers' literature usually states where their particular products correspond with the ANSI/ISO recommendations.

Carbide Grades

Carbide grades vary according to their wear resistance and toughness. As the wear resistance increases, the toughness decreases. The ANSI/ISO systems differ in how they handle grade classification, but suppliers of carbide can provide either set of information. The ANSI system allows carbide manufacturers to create their own grade coding system, which they in turn explain in their catalog. (See example in Figure 3.1a.) The

Cutting Material Grade Selection

The Kennametal grade system consists of four basic material groups: tungsten carbide, cermet, ceramic and polycrystalline. Each group contains a variety of cutting grades to accommodate various metalcutting needs.

tungsten carbide
This group consists of uncoated, CVD coated (chemical vapor deposition) and PVD coated (physical vapor deposition) materials. Each coated grade is made with various substrates of unalloyed (straight WC/Co), and alloyed (WC/TaC/TiC/NbC/Co) compositions.

cermet
Cermets contain mostly titanium carbide (TiC) and titanium nitride (TiN) with a metallic binder.

ceramic
Ceramic cutting tools can be divided into two basic families: alumina-base (aluminum oxide) and silicon nitride-base (sialon) compositions.

diamond
This material can also be divided into two basic families: polycrystalline diamond (PCD) and thin film diamond coatings.

Carbide Grades

uncoated—carbide		
grade	composition and application	ISO
K313	composition: An uncoated WC/Co fine-grained grade. application: Exceptional edge wear resistance, combined with very high edge strength and abrasion resistance, delivers high-speed metal removal rates with lighter chip loads when machining non-metals and non-ferrous metals including aluminum, stainless steels and titanium.	K05-K15 M10-M20

coated—tri-phase CVD		
grade	composition and application	ISO
KC850	composition: TiC/TiCN/TiN coating on a strengthened, cobalt-enriched substrate. application: Milling of carbon, alloy and certain stainless steels in a variety of feed and speed combinations. Balance of wear resistance and toughness is due to enriched substrate.	M25-M40 P25-P45

coated—alumina CVD		
grades	composition and application	ISO
KC992M	composition: A multi-layered TiCN/Al$_2$O$_3$ CVD coated carbide. application: For milling of gray cast iron, with or without coolant, at medium feeds and speeds. Inserts with T-land geometries can machine nodular irons. Chip loads will be equivalent to those found when machining cast irons.	K10-K25
KC994M	composition: CVD Al$_2$O$_3$ coating on a tough carbide substrate. application: For wet or dry milling of high tensile nickel alloys and ductile irons. Tough, high wear resistant companion to KC730.	K10-K35 M15-M35

Figure 3.1(a) Manufacturer's ANSI carbide insert grade classification system for milling (for complete listing see Appendix "B"). (Note: Different manufacturer's use different coding systems.) (Kennametal/8040 Catalog Copyright 1998. Kennametal Inc., Advertising Dept., P.O. Box 231, Latrobe, PA 15650-9984.)

Cutting Material Grade Selection

Carbide Grades (Cont'd.)

coated—titanium nitride PVD		
grades	**composition and application**	**ISO**
KC610M	**composition:** PVD TiN coated carbide grade with a deformation resistant substrate. Has superior edge wear characteristics. **application:** Developed for high productivity thread milling and grooving of most carbon, alloy and stainless steels at medium to high speeds.	P10-P30
KC620M NEW!	**composition:** PVD TiN coated carbide grade with a tough, thermal shock resistant substrate. **application:** Excellent thread milling and grooving grade for non-ferrous alloys, cast iron, high-temperature alloys and aluminum. Thermal and mechanical shock resistance, along with superior edge strength, gives this grade a good combination of properties for thread milling of difficult-to-machine materials.	K10-K20 M15-M25
KC705M NEW!	**composition:** PVD TiAlN coated carbide on a deformation resistant substrate. **application:** Primarily designed for milling aluminum. However, exceptional heat and wear resistance qualities make this grade an excellent choice for milling of hardened steel, cast iron and heat-resistant alloys.	K01-K10 M01-M15
KC709M NEW!	**composition:** PVD TiAlN coating with superior hot hardness and chemical inertness. **application:** Designed for milling of all ductile iron materials with or without coolant. Capable of higher metal removal rates than conventional CVD coated carbides.	K05-K20
KC715M NEW!	**composition:** PVD TiCN coated carbide grade with excellent toughness and wear resistance. **application:** Long and consistent tool life in milling of carbon and alloy steels at moderate to high speeds, preferably without coolant. The hard PVD TiCN coating provides compressive residual strength for abrasion resistance and edge security.	M15-M25 P15-P25
KC720	**composition:** A tough, durable PVD TiN coated carbide grade. **application:** Developed for cutting high-temperature alloys, stainless steels and low-carbon steels at low to moderate speeds. Its unique mechanical and thermal shock resistant properties, and resistance to edge build-up, enable KC720 to deliver superior performance and reliability on difficult operations, in severe interrupted cuts and when milling high-temperature alloys with coolant.	K25-K35 M30-M40 P25-P45
KC721M NEW!	**composition:** New generation PVD TiAlN coating on a tough, thermal shock resistant carbide substrate. **application:** The synergistic combination of tough carbide substrate and highly wear resistant TiAlN coating provides long and reliable tool life when milling titanium, hard stainless steels and other high-temperature alloys. Can be applied with or without coolant.	M15-M35 P20-P35
KC725M	**composition:** A patented, multi-layer PVD TiN/TiCN/TiN coated carbide. **application:** A new milling grade engineered for high productivity wet and dry milling of carbon, alloy and austenitic stainless steels. The high thermal shock resistance of the tough carbide substrate, combined with the patented multi-layer coating, provides long and reliable tool life in aggressive milling operations with or without coolant. It is the higher speed companion to KC720 in wet milling of steel.	M15-M35 P20-P35
KC730	**composition:** A PVD TiN coated carbide grade. **application:** For milling cast and ductile irons, high-temperature alloys, aerospace materials, refractory metals, and 200 and 300 series stainless steels. The substrate offers superior thermal deformation resistance, depth of cut notch resistance and edge strength. The uniformly dense PVD coating increases wear resistance, reduces problems with edge build-up and provides an unusually good combination of properties for machining difficult-to-machine materials and aluminum.	K05-K15 M05-M15
KC792M	**composition:** A PVD-CVD coated carbide grade. **application:** Developed for milling of steels at higher speeds. Its unique substrate design, with cobalt-enriched periphery, provides maximum wear resistance combined with the chipping resistance needed for high-speed milling operations. Applying the patented PVD coating over a CVD coated insert allows application of thicker coatings than are possible with other CVD coatings. This provides desirable compressive strength in the coatings to delay thermal crack initiation. KC792M is the higher speed companion to KC710 for dry steel milling.	M25-M30 P30

Cermet Grades

uncoated carbonitride materials		
grades	**composition and application**	**ISO**
KT175	**composition:** Titanium carbonitride based grade. **application:** Medium-to high-speed milling of steels when wear resistance and toughness requirements are balanced against light to medium chip loads at moderate to high speeds. Resists built-up edge formation.	P10-P20 M10-M20
KT195M	**composition:** Titanium carbonitride based grade. **application:** Maximum toughness and edge chipping resistance in dry milling applications on carbon and alloy steels, and stainless steels at moderate speeds and medium chip loads. Excellent hardness, strength and oxidation resistance at higher temperatures. Resists built-up edge and provides excellent surface finish.	P10-P30 M15-M25

Figure 3.1(a) (Continued)

Cutting Material Grade Selection

Ceramic Grades

alumina-base ceramics		
grade	composition and application	ISO
K090	**composition:** A composite (black) ceramic composed of alumina and 30% TiC. **application:** High toughness and thermal shock resistance for milling carbon steels, alloy steels, tool steels and stainless steels to 60 HRc.	K01-K10 M10 P01-P20

silicon nitride-base ceramics		
grade	composition and application	ISO
Kyon 3500	**composition:** An extremely tough and pure silicon nitride grade. **application:** Superior edge strength ceramic for high-speed rough milling of gray and some ductile irons.	K10-K25

Diamond Grades

diamond (PCD) and thin film diamond coating		
grades	composition and application	ISO
KD100	**composition:** This material is a polycrystalline diamond (PCD) tip brazed on a standard carbide insert. **application:** An ultra-hard grade with excellent wear resistance for improved size control (workpiece tolerance) and surface finish. It's unsurpassed for superior tool life when milling highly abrasive non-metals and non-ferrous metals.	K01-K10 M10

Figure 3.1(a) (Continued)

ISO code groups carbides according to their application, and they are designated by the letters P, M, and K and a number. A corresponding color code of blue (P), yellow (M), and red (K) is also used. An interpretation of the code is given in Figure 3.1b.

Inserts

Inserts are designated according to shape, size, geometry, cutting direction, etc. An interpretation of the ANSI/ISO codes is given in Figures 3.2a and 3.2b. Note that only slight differences in the two systems exist, one being the use of English or metric dimensions.

Holders and Cartridges

Holders and cartridges are designated according to a number of factors, which include tool style, method of holding the insert, tool height, and width.

The shanks of the holders and cartridges can be "qualified," that is, when the insert is located, the distance from the tool tip to a stated location face is guaranteed within a tolerance of ±0.003 to ±0.005 in. depending on shank size. Qualified tooling and its application are dealt with in more detail later in this chapter.

An interpretation of the ANSI/ISO codes for tool holders and cartridges is given in Figures 3.3a and 3.3b. Note again that only minor differences appear between ANSI and ISO systems.

Figure 3.4 shows the four recommended methods of locating and clamping inserts in holders and cartridges.

Kennametal Grade Application Guide–Milling

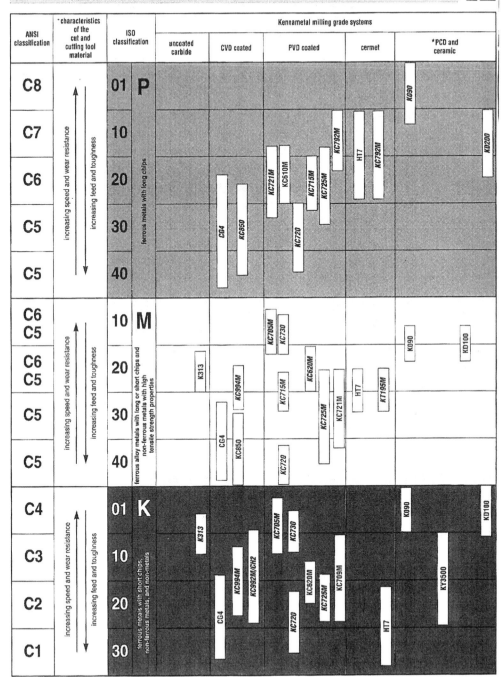

Figure 3.1(b) Selection of ISO carbide grades for metal-cutting applications.

Kennametal Milling Insert Identification System

ANSI Inserts (inch)

NOTE:

Kennametal's milling insert identification system is provided as a general reference. The dimensional tables associated with each insert should be used for specific values. This system is based on the latest ANSI and ISO insert identification guidelines.

Dimensions shown in this catalog are prior to supplemental coating and edge modifications.

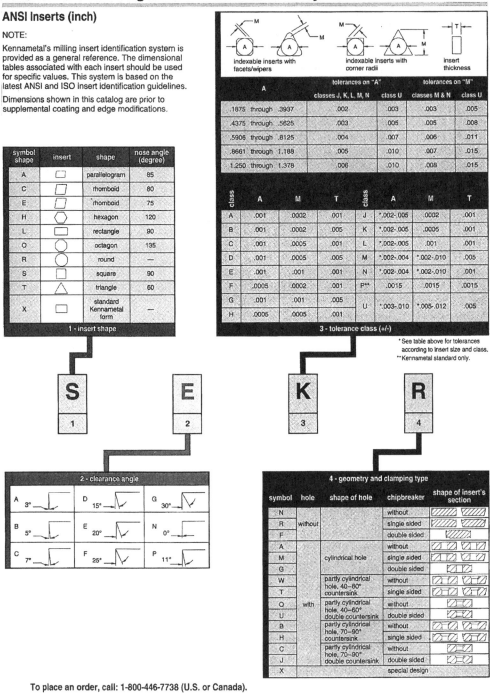

To place an order, call: 1-800-446-7738 (U.S. or Canada).

Figure 3.2(a) ANSI indexable inserts identification system. (Kennametal/8040 Catalog Copyright 1998. Kennametal Inc., Advertising Dept., P.O. Box 231, Latrobe, PA 15650-9984.)

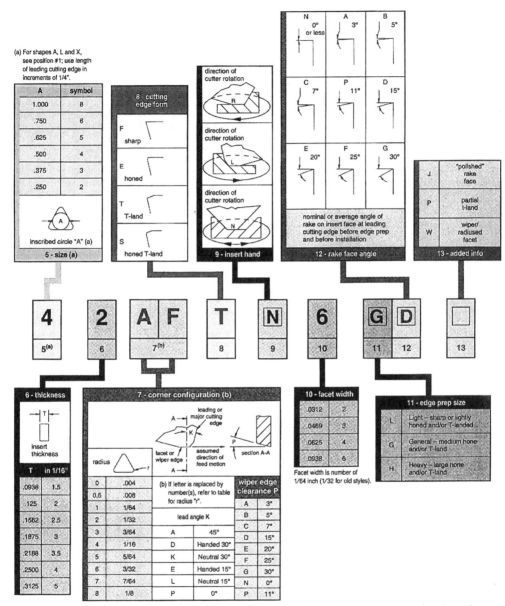

To place an order, call: 1-800-446-7738 (U.S. or Canada).

Figure 3.2(a) (Continued)

Kennametal Milling Insert Identification System

ISO Inserts (metric)

NOTE:

Kennametal's milling insert identification system is provided as a general reference. The dimensional tables associated with each insert should be used for specific values. This system is based on the latest ANSI and ISO insert identification guidelines.

Dimensions shown in this catalog are prior to supplemental coating and edge modifications.

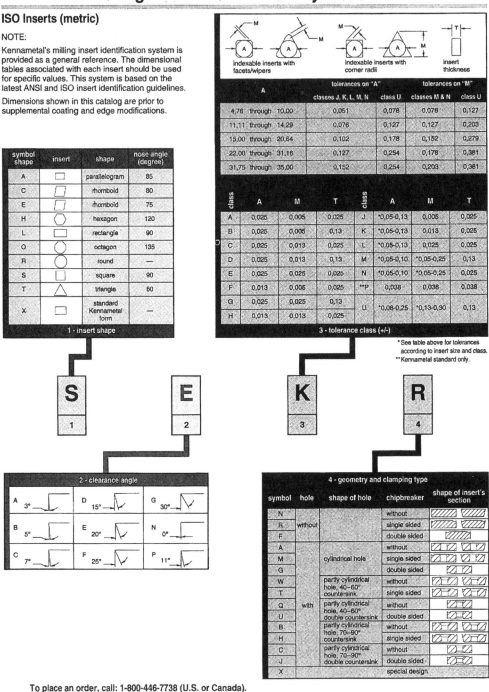

Figure 3.2(b) Interpretation of ISO Insert identification.

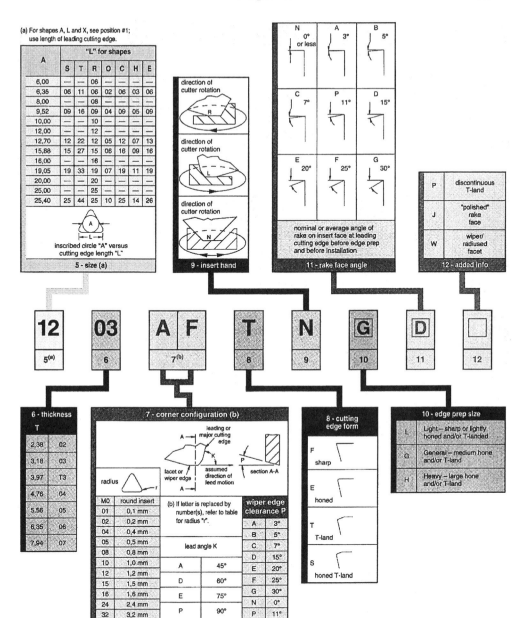

Figure 3.2(b) (Continued)

Kenloc Combination Toolholders

Toolholder Identification System

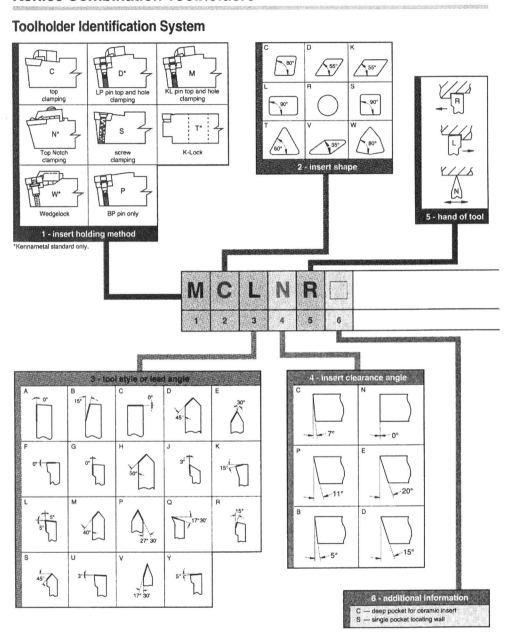

Figure 3.3(a) ANSI toolholder identification system. (Kennametal/6000 Catalog Copyright 1996. Kennametal Inc., Advertising Dept., P.O. Box 231, Latrobe, PA 15650-9984.)

Kenloc Combination Toolholders

Toolholder Identification System

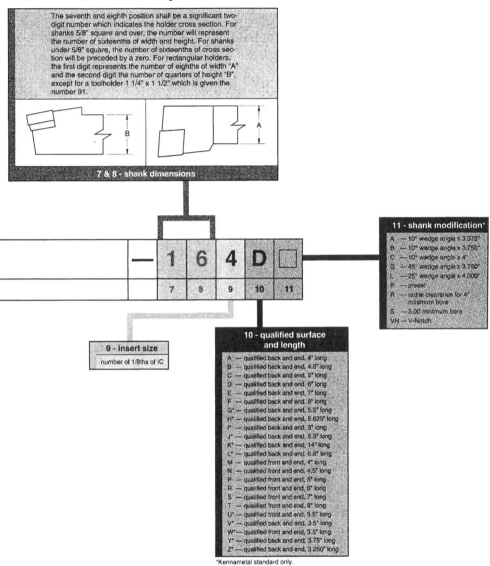

Figure 3.3(a) (Continued)

ANSI/ISO Cartridges

Cartridge Identification System

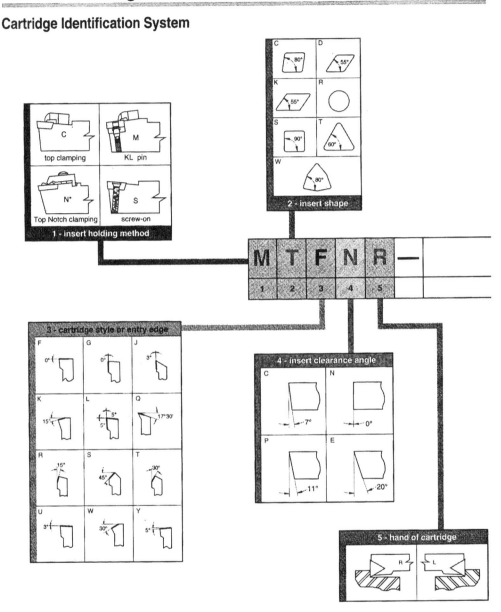

Figure 3.3(b) ANSI/ISO cartridge identification system. (Kennametal/6000 Catalog Copyright 1996. Kennametal Inc., Advertising Dept., P.O. Box 231, Latrobe, PA 15650-9984.)

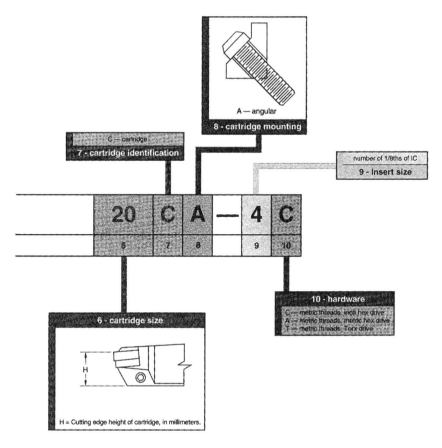

Figure 3.3(b) (Continued)

The Practical Application of Indexable Carbide Inserts

Figure 3.5 shows how a variety of insert shapes may be applied to produce external and internal turned profiles, while Figure 3.6 shows a range of holders and inserts. Figures 3.7 and 3.8 show applications of inserts to milling operations. Figures 3.9a and 3.9b show the application of cartridges to boring while Figure 3.9c shows their application to a face milling cutter body.

Metalcutting Safety

Modern metalcutting operations involve high energy, high spindle or cutter speeds, and high temperatures and cutting forces. Hot, flying chips may be projected from the work-piece during metalcutting. Although the nonductile cemented carbide and ceramic cutting tools used in metalcutting operations are designed and manufactured to withstand the high cutting forces and temperatures that normally occur in these operations, they are susceptible to fragmentating in service, particularly if they are subjected to over-stress or severe impact, or are otherwise abused. Therefore, precautions should be taken to protect

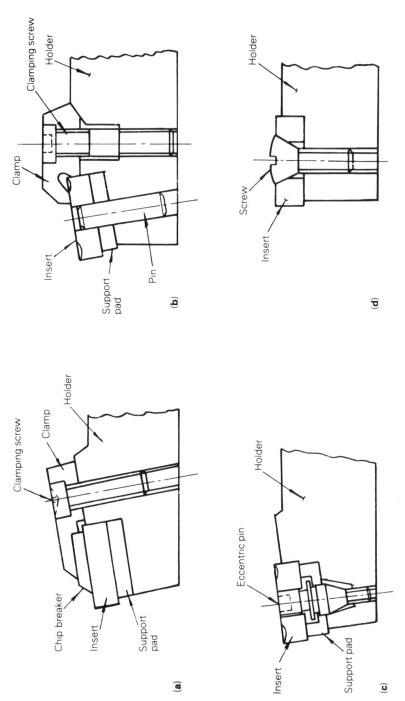

Figure 3.4 Insert clamping arrangements: (a) clamp only, (b) clamp and pin, (c) pin only, (d) screw.

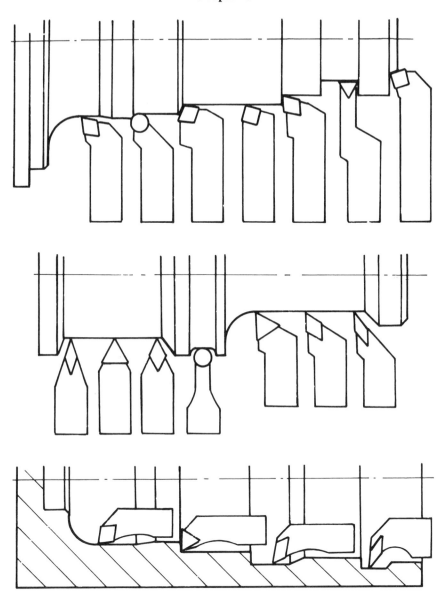

Figure 3.5 Use of insert shapes for various turning operations.

adequately workers, observers, and equipment against hot, flying chips, fragmented cutting tools, broken workpieces, carbide particles, or other similar projectiles. Machines should be fully guarded and personal protective equipment should be used at all times.

When grinding carbide and ceramic cutting tools, or otherwise fabricating cemented carbide, a suitable means for collection and disposal of dust, mist, or sludge should be provided. Inhalation of dust or mist containing metallic particles can be hazardous, particularly if exposure continues over an extended period of time. Therefore, adequate ventilation should be provided. General Industry Safety and Health Regulations, Part 1910, U.S. Department of Labor, published in Title 29 of Federal Regulations, particularly

Figure 3.6 Range of indexable insert turning tools.

those sections dealing with ventilation, local exhaust systems, and occupational health and environmental control as it relates to cobalt (Co), metal fume and dust, and tungsten (W), as well as other government regulations, should be consulted.

Tungsten carbide and ceramic cutting edges, and related supporting holders such as milling cutters and boring bars, are only one part of the man–machine–tool system. Many variables exist in machining operations, including the metal removal rate; the workpiece size, shape, strength, and rigidity; the chucking or fixturing; the load carrying capability of machine and part centers; the cutter and spindle speed and torque limitations; the holder and boring bar overhang; the available power; and the condition of the tooling and the machine. A safe metalcutting operation must take all of these variables, and others, into consideration.

Tooling Systems

The production of a machined component invariably involves the use of a variety of cutting tools, and the machine has to cater for their use. The way in which a range of cutting tools can be located and securely held in position is referred to as a tooling system and is usually an important feature of the machine tool manufacturers' advertising literature.

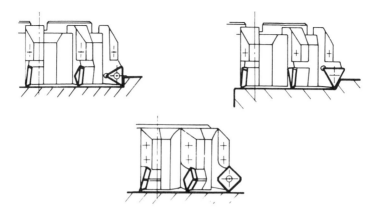

Figure 3.7 Application of various insert shapes to face milling cutters.

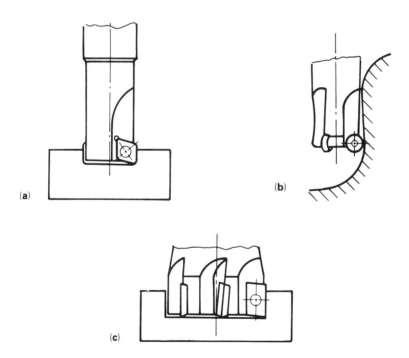

Figure 3.8 Application of insert cutters to various milling operations: (a) boring, (b) contouring, and (c) slot milling.

Figure 3.9(a) ANSI/ISO cartridges in boring bar applications. (Kennametal/85 Copyright 1994. Kennametal Inc., Advertising Dept., P.O. Box 231, Latrobe, PA 15650-9984.)

Figure 3.9(b) Tenthset precision boring cartridge with front adjustment of 0.0001 in. (Kennametal/85 Copyright 1984. Kennametal Inc., Advertising Dept., P.O. Box 231, Latrobe, PA 15650-9984.)

The tooling system for a machining center is illustrated in Figure 3.10. Note the use of tool holders with standard tapers, a feature that can be very helpful in keeping tooling costs to a minimum.

The types of tool holders shown in Figure 3.10 are retained in and released from the machine spindle by a hydraulic device, an arrangement that lends itself to automation, since it is relatively simple to control hydraulic systems using electrically activated solenoid valves which themselves can be controlled via the machine control system. The hydraulic force retaining the holder is supplemented by a mechanical force exerted by powerful disk springs, as illustrated in Figure 3.11, for added safety. It should be noted that less expensive machines may use a mechanical device in conjunction with pneumatics or hydraulics for tool changes.

Figure 3.9(c) Applications of cartridges to a face milling cutter.

Not all machines have automatic tool-changing arrangements and when manual tool changing is involved, mechanical retaining devices are used. Conventional tool holders for milling situations use the tried and tested screwed drawbar arrangement, but unfortunately their use is not in keeping with modern machining techniques, where the accent is on speed. Because of this, several machine tool manufacturers have introduced tool holders of their own design that have dispensed with the need to undo a drawbar each time a tool holder is changed and as a result they have greatly speeded up the replacement process.

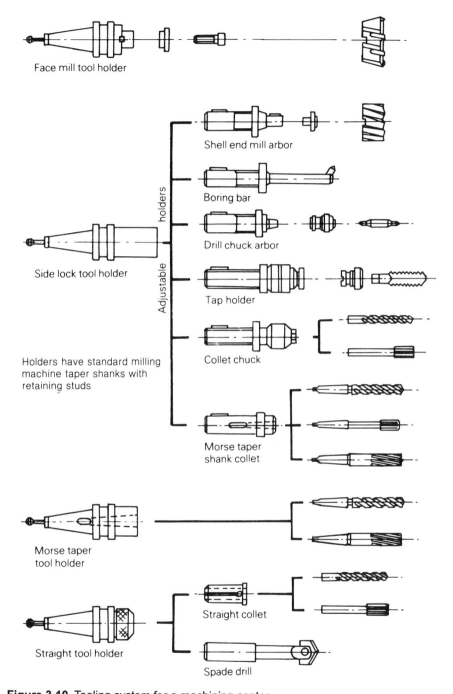

Figure 3.10 Tooling system for a machining center.

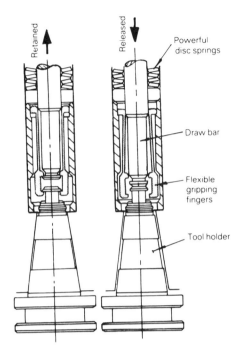

Figure 3.11 Hydraulic–mechanical draw bar assembly used on machining centers.

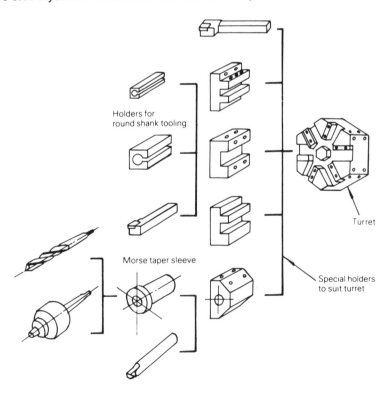

Figure 3.12 Tooling system for turning center.

As with milling, a tooling system for a turning center will indicate the range of tooling which can be accommodated on the machine. One such system is illustrated in Figure 3.12.

Tool Identity

The automatic selection and presentation of a cutting tool to the workpiece is a prime function of computer numerically controlled machining. To achieve this there must be a link between programming and machine setup. Tool stations are numbered according to the tooling stations available (see Figures 2.1 and 3.13), and when writing a program, the programmer will provide each tool with a corresponding numerical identity, usually in the form of the letter T followed by two digits: T01, T02, T03 and so on. The machine setter will need to know the type of tool required and will set it in its allocated position. The transfer of information between the programmer and the machine setter is discussed in more detail in Chapter 8.

Indexable Turrets

The turret is the part of some machines in which the cutting tools are located. They are automatically indexable, that is, they can be programmed to rotate to a new position so that a different tool can be presented to the work. Indexable turrets are used on the majority of turning centers and on some milling/drilling machines.

There are a number of turret configurations currently available on turning centers. Several different types appear in the illustrations used throughout this book. The number of tools that can be accommodated varies with machine type, but eight or ten tool positions are usually sufficient to satisfy most machining requirements, and in many cases a standard setup consisting of a range of external and internal turning tools is advised.

There are some machines in which the turret is removable and, if two turrets are available, the spare one can be loaded with tools for a particular job before they are needed and then the turret is attached to the machine when required, a technique that reduces the machine down time considerably during setup.

A variation of the rotating turret is the indexable slide on which the tools are mounted. The manufacturers of this particular arrangement claim that linear tool indexing is much more rapid than rotary indexing. An optional extra available is a subbase plate to which the tools may be attached away from the machine. As with the removable turret referred to, this base plate is interchangeable and so a spare one can be loaded with tools in advance and then quickly attached to the machine when required.

Turrets generally fitted to milling/drilling machines are somewhat different from those fitted to turning centers, because each tooling position is in fact a spindle that has to rotate at a predetermined speed. Only the tool in the machining position will rotate, the others remaining stationary. A turret of this type, with ten tooling positions, is shown in Figure 3.13. (The concept of individually rotating tool holders has been extended more recently to turning centers. See Chapter 2.)

Tool Magazines

A tool magazine is an indexable storage facility used on machining centers to store tools not in use. The most common types of magazines are the rotary drum type illustrated in Figures 2.1a and 2.1b, the turret type in Figure 3.13, and the chain type illustrated in Figure 3.14. When a tool is called into use, the magazine will index, on most machines by the shortest route, to bring the tool to a position where it is accessible to a mechanical handling device. When the tool is no longer required, it is returned to its allotted position in the magazine prior to the magazine indexing to the next tool called.

The position of the tool magazine in relation to the spindle varies from one machine to another. There are also variations in the design of the tool-handling devices. The two features are, of course, interrelated. Two arrangements are shown in Figure 3.15.

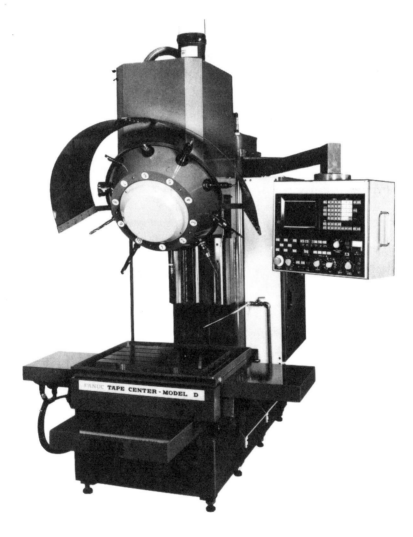

Figure 3.13 Milling/drilling center with indexable turret.

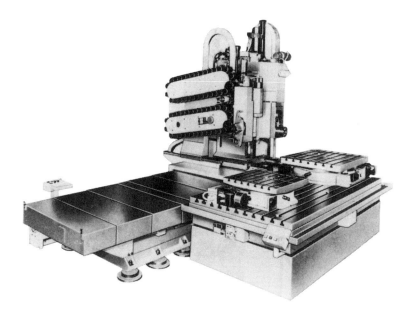

Figure 3.14 Horizontal machining center with chain-type tooling magazines.

The capacity of magazines is another variable feature, with 12 to 24 stations being typical numbers for the rotary drum magazines and from 24 to 180 for the chain type.

Replacement Tooling

From time to time, owing to wear or breakage, cutting tools have to be replaced. Such changes need to be rapid, with the minimum loss of machining time.

If the machining program is to remain valid, one of two requirements must be met:

1. The replacement tool must be dimensionally identical to the original.
2. The program must be capable of temporary modification to accommodate the tool variations.

Identical replacement tooling can be achieved by using qualified or preset tooling. Temporary program modifications are achieved by offsetting the tool from its original datum.

Qualified Tooling

The ISO code illustrated in Figure 3.3c refers to qualified tooling. The dimensions from up to three datum faces to the tool tip can be guaranteed within ± 0.08 mm (± 0.003 in.). Thus if the tolerance on the dimension being machined is such that a variation in size within ± 0.08 mm (± 0.003 in.) is acceptable, one tool can readily be replaced by another. Precise location of the holder or cartridge in the machine turret or spindle is an essential feature of replacing tooling of this type. The qualified dimensions are illustrated in Figure 3.16.

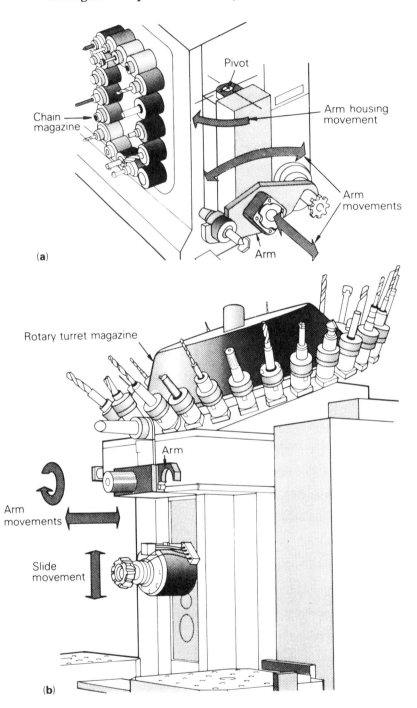

Figure 3.15 Auto tool changers.

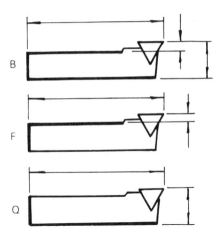

Figure 3.16 Qualified tooling. Dimensions indicated guaranteed to within ±0.08 mm (0.003 in.).

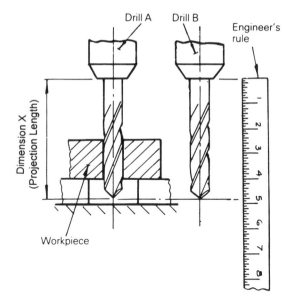

Figure 3.17 Simple presetting of tool length.

Preset Tooling

Preset tooling involves setting the cutting edge of the tool in relation to a datum face to predetermined dimensions, these dimensions having been taken into consideration when the part program was written. A simple explanation of presetting is given in Figure 3.17. The through hole in the component is produced by drilling, and drill A is to be replaced by drill B. Since the depth of travel on a through hole is not precise, it would be sufficient to set the projecting length of the drill with a rule and, providing dimension X is the same for the replacement drill as it was for the original, the program would still be valid.

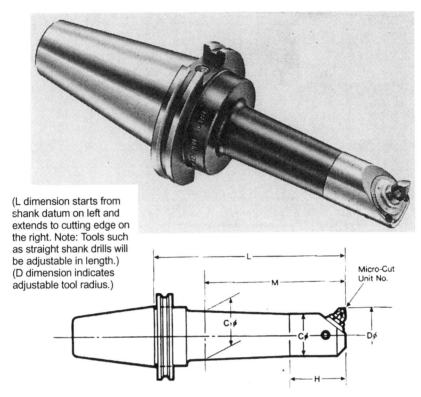

(L dimension starts from shank datum on left and extends to cutting edge on the right. Note: Tools such as straight shank drills will be adjustable in length.)
(D dimension indicates adjustable tool radius.)

Figure 3.18a Presetting tools from shank datum and centerline.

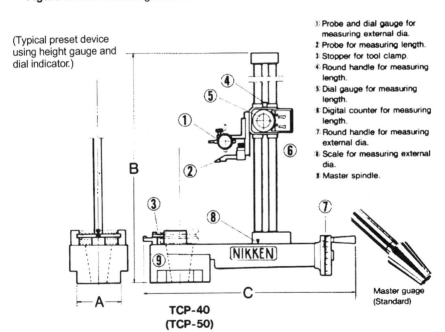

(Typical preset device using height gauge and dial indicator.)

1. Probe and dial gauge for measuring external dia.
2. Probe for measuring length.
3. Stopper for tool clamp.
4. Round handle for measuring length.
5. Dial gauge for measuring length.
6. Digital counter for measuring length.
7. Round handle for measuring external dia.
8. Scale for measuring external dia.
9. Master spindle.

TCP-40
(TCP-50)

Master guage
(Standard)

Figure 3.18a Presetting tools continued—Typical preset device using height gage and dial indicator.

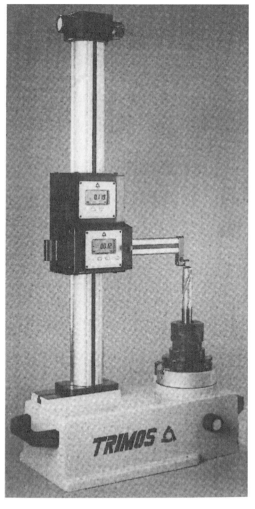

Figure 3.18a Digital Touch Probe Presetter (Continued)

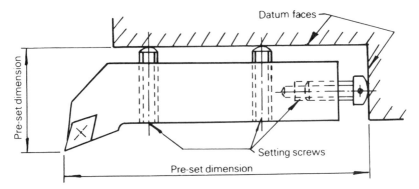

Figure 3.18b Principle of presetting a tool holder.

When closer tolerances are involved, the setting technique will need to be more precise. A wide range of specialized equipment is commercially available, the basic requirements of such equipment being a dummy tool locating/holding device with datum faces and appropriate measuring instruments. The tip of the tool is then set to predetermined dimensions in relation to datums as illustrated in Figure 3.18a and 3.18b.

The more elaborate tool-setting equipment uses optical projection. An example is shown in Figure 3.19.

Cutter Compensation

The basis of computer numerical control is programming machine slide movements to occur over a stated distance in relation to a predetermined datum. Generally there is one datum for each axis of movement. However, most machining operations involve the use of more than one tool, varying in length or diameter, which means that if the cutting edge of one tool is set to the datum to which slide movements are to be related, tools that have dimensional variations from the set tool will not start their movements from the same datum. Some compensation in slide movement is necessary to accommodate the dimensional variations of the tools. This compensation is referred to as tool offset and the offset facility is available only on computerized numerically controlled machines. Once the offset has been established, the slide movement is automatically adjusted as required during the program run.

An offset is therefore a dimensional value defining the position of the cutting edge, or edges, of a tool in relation to a given datum.

Tool Length Offsets

Consider the component shown in Figure 3.20a. The programmer has decided that the Z datum clearance plane will be 0.1 in. (2 mm in Figure 3.20b) above the top face of the work. All tool movement in the Z axis will be in relation to that datum. The machine setter or operator will establish the datum either by "touching on" to the work surface and moving away 0.1 in. (2 mm in Figure 3.20b) or by touching on to

Figure 3.19 Presetting tooling on a replacement turret using optical projection.

a suitable 0.1 in. (2 mm in Figure 3.20b) thick setting block, and then setting the Z axis readout to zero.

Now consider the tooling shown in Figure 3.20b and assume the tool T01 has been set as described above. This is now the master tool. However, the machining that is required also involves using tools T02 and T03 and the position of their cutting edges in the Z axis does not correspond to that of tool T01. Tool T02 is too short and tool T03 is too long. Any movements in relation to the Z zero axis involving these tools must take into account their starting position.

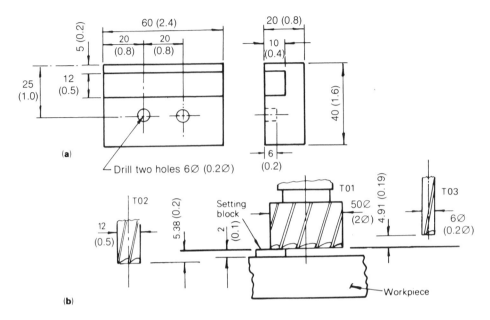

Figure 3.20 (a) Component detail and (b) tool length offsets for the milling/drilling operation. (Inch units are given in parentheses.)

The tool setter or machine operator must therefore establish the length and direction of movement which is necessary to bring the end of each tool to the zero position. This can be done by touching each tool on to the setting block and noting on the digital readout its variation from zero. Tool T02 will require a movement in the Z axis of 0.2 in. (5.38 mm) and tool T03 a movement of -0.19 in. (-4.91 mm). These dimensions are the tool length offsets.

Having established the offsets, the operator records them by entering them via the control panel key pad into an offset file or page, which can be displayed on the controller visual display screen. The method of entering offsets and the display format vary according to the control unit. The entry for the offsets relating to the tooling in Figure 3.20 could appear as shown in Figure 3.21.

With the tool length offsets being established at the machine, the part programmer is now able to ignore the variations in tool length and write the program on the assumption that all tools are starting their movements from the Z axis zero datum.

Tool length offsets are not confined to milling. They are also applicable to turning, but in this case two offset lengths are involved, one in the X axis and the other in the Z axis. The set of tools with varying lengths shown in Figure 3.22 illustrates the situation, while Figure 3.23 shows how the necessary offsets would be entered in an offset file.

Tool Radius Offsets

Just as cutting tools vary in length, they may also vary in diameter or, in the case of turning tools, in the radius of the tool tip.

T	Length	Diameter
1	0.0000	2.0000
2	−0.2000	0.5000
3	0.1900	0.2000
4	0.0000	0.0000
5	0.0000	0.0000
6	0.0000	0.0000
(a) 7	0.0000	0.0000
8	0.0000	0.0000
9	0.0000	0.0000
10	0.0000	0.0000
11	0.0000	0.0000
12	0.0000	0.0000
13	0.0000	0.0000
14	0.0000	0.0000

T	Length	Diameter
1	0.0000	50.0000
2	−5.3800	12.0000
3	4.9100	6.0000
4	0.0000	0.0000
5	0.0000	0.0000
6	0.0000	0.0000
(b) 7	0.0000	0.0000
8	0.0000	0.0000
9	0.0000	0.0000
10	0.0000	0.0000
11	0.0000	0.0000
12	0.0000	0.0000
13	0.0000	0.0000
14	0.0000	0.0000

Figure 3.21 (a) Inch and (b) metric tool offset file for milling.

Consider the profile shown in Figure 3.24. This profile could be machined by a cutter of, say, 15 mm (0.6 in.) diameter or 30 mm (1.2 in.) diameter and the path of each cutter will vary as indicated. Similarly, the profile of the component shown in Figure 3.25 could be turned using a tool with a tip radius of 1 or 2 mm (0.04 or 0.08 in.) and again the cutter paths will vary.

Without a cutter radius compensation facility the programmer would have to state the precise size of the cutting tools to be used and program the machine slide movements accordingly. With the facility the cutter size can be ignored and the work profile programmed. The exact size of the cutting tool to be used for machining is entered by the operator into the offset file and when the offset is called into the program, automatic compensation in slide movement will be made. Radius compensation also would allow the programmer to program nominal sized cutters and compensate for tool diameter variations or effects of machining cutter deflections. This type of programming may be necessary owing to limits on the amount of compensation available.

For milling machines the cutter size is entered as a diameter, in the example shown in Figure 3.21, and the machine slide movement is compensated by half of the dimensional

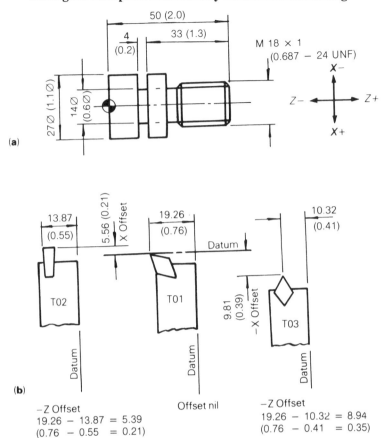

Figure 3.22 (a) Component detail and (b) tool length offsets for a turning operation. (Inch units are given in parentheses.)

entry. Note, depending on the control, the information could be entered as a radius with full amount of compensation occurring. For turning centers the offset will be entered as a radius alongside the tool length offsets, as shown in Figure 3.23.

Cutter radius compensation can be to the right or left of a profile. To determine which is applicable the programmer should imagine a position above the tool facing the direction in which cutting is taking place. Thus cutter radius compensation to machine the profile shown in Figure 3.24 would be to the left. Compensation direction will be determined by a special program code discussed in the programming area.

Tool offsets can be entered, modified or erased by the machine operator at will and so it is possible to use the facility to:

(a) accommodate replacement tooling which varies dimensionally from the original;
(b) make variations to the component size;
(c) initiate a series of cuts, say roughing and finishing, using the same dimensional program data.

While offsets have a direct effect on the machining currently being carried out, they do not affect the basic part program.

T	X	Z	Radius
1	0.0000	0.0000	0.0800
2	0.2100	-0.2100	0.0000
3	0.3900	-0.3500	0.0600
4	0.0000	0.0000	0.0000
5	0.0000	0.0000	0.0000
6	0.0000	0.0000	0.0000
(a) 7	0.0000	0.0000	0.0000
8	0.0000	0.0000	0.0000
9	0.0000	0.0000	0.0000
10	0.0000	0.0000	0.0000
11	0.0000	0.0000	0.0000
12	0.0000	0.0000	0.0000
13	0.0000	0.0000	0.0000
14	0.0000	0.0000	0.0000

T	X	Z	Radius
1	0.0000	0.0000	2.0000
2	5.5600	-5.3900	0.0000
3	-9.8100	-8.9400	1.5000
4	0.0000	0.0000	0.0000
5	0.0000	0.0000	0.0000
6	0.0000	0.0000	0.0000
(b) 7	0.0000	0.0000	0.0000
8	0.0000	0.0000	0.0000
9	0.0000	0.0000	0.0000
10	0.0000	0.0000	0.0000
11	0.0000	0.0000	0.0000
12	0.0000	0.0000	0.0000
13	0.0000	0.0000	0.0000
14	0.0000	0.0000	0.0000

Figure 3.23 (a) Inch and (b) metric tool offset file for turning.

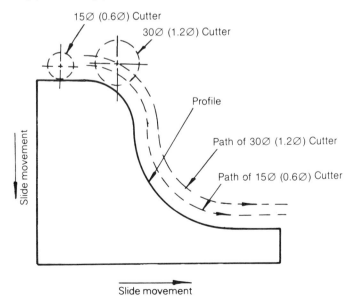

Figure 3.24 Cutter radius offset for milling operation. (Inch units are given in parentheses.)

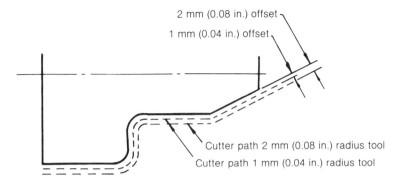

Figure 3.25 Cutter radius offset for turning operation. (Inch units are given in parentheses.)

Identification of Cutter Offsets

Reference again to Figures 3.21 and 3.23 will show that the offsets are numbered. In a similar way tooling used in any part program is given a numerical identity. The two, tools and offsets, have to be related to each other when the part program is being made. The number of tool stations on any one machine is limited, perhaps 12 to 16 on a turning center to rather more on machining centers equipped with magazines. The number of offsets available will be greater than the number of tools available so that any tool can be used with any offset. Thus if the tools are numbered T01, T02, T03, T04, and so on, and the offsets are numbered 01 to 32, the programmer may call for tool number one to be used with offset number one. The data entry in the part program could read T0101, sometimes special codes like H01 may call the offset active. It follows that, since there are more offsets available than tools, the program could well call for the same tool to be used elsewhere with yet another offset, say T0106. It is imperative that the programmer's intentions are clearly relayed to the shop floor. (See Chapter 8.)

Tool Control

The efficient use of expensive computer numerically controlled machining facilities requires a very methodical approach to the provision of tooling. It is essential that the tooling, both original and replacement, available at the machine correspond to the tooling required by the part program. Close cooperation between personnel concerned with programming, tool preparation, and machining must be maintained.

Efficient tool control should provide for the following functions:

(a) reconditioning, including regrinding when appropriate, replacing damaged or worn inserts, etc.;
(b) preparation, including sizing, presetting, identifying, etc.;
(c) storage until required for use;
(d) transportation;
(e) storage alongside the machine.

The concept is illustrated diagrammatically in Figure 3.26.

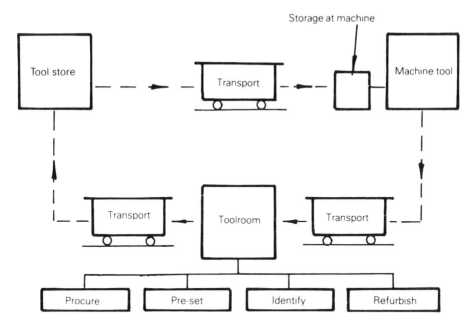

Figure 3.26 Tool control system.

Tools that can be reconditioned by grinding require skilled attention. Cutting efficiency over long periods of machining at very high rates of metal removal demands exact tool geometry. The less than precise methods often applied to tooling used on conventional machines are not acceptable for computer numerically controlled machining.

The accuracy demanded and the nature of the equipment used when presetting or establishing the precise size of tools call for skilled personnel working in clean conditions.

As tooling is prepared it must immediately be marked to facilitate identification, which can be done in a number of ways. Identification will of course correspond to the tool identity allocated by the part programmer and the tool preparation will be based on instructions he or she has prepared.

The storage of tooling not immediately needed requires the use of heavyduty steel racks in which the tools are identified as to future machine magazine location.

Stored tooling may be for a specific job or it may be for general use. Either way, the tooling available should be fully documented regarding its dimensional features, application, etc. It is also helpful if the available tooling is listed in a manner that provides a ready reference facility for part programmers, machine setters, and others associated with the practicalities of the production process. The tooling list itself is often referred to as the "tool library."

Transport of sets of tooling about the plant will require suitable carts. In some cases, to reduce handling, such carts are used for storage at the machine. If space on the shop floor is restricted, transfer to a stand may be more appropriate. One example of such a stand is referred to as a "tool wheel," since it rotates to facilitate access to each tool; this is shown in Figure 3.27.

Figure 3.27 Tool storage wheel.

QUESTIONS

1 When are high-speed steel-cutting tools likely to be used in CNC machining?

2 When are solid carbide tools, as opposed to tips, likely to be used in CNC machining?

3 Why are solid carbide tools not widely used?

4 State three advantages of using indexable inserts.

5 State two methods used to control chips when using indexable inserts.

6 What is the significance of the letters P, M, and K in relation to the classification of carbide grades?

7 How are carbide inserts classified?

8 What is the difference between a holder and a cartridge?

9 Make an outline sketch of a tool suitable for use on a turning center and explain the meaning of the term "qualified."

10 How many methods of locating and clamping inserts in holders and cartridges are included in the ISO code?

11 The following is the specification for a tool holder: M P D F L 40 40 D 24 F. What is the meaning of each letter and number?

12 Explain the difference between a tool turret and a tool magazine.

13 If a machining program is to remain valid when tool replacement is carried out, one of two conditions must be met. What are those conditions?

14 Explain with the aid of a simple diagram what is meant by preset tooling.

15 What is a tool length offset and when is it likely to be necessary?

16 What is cutter radius compensation, and how does it simplify programming?

17 How is it possible to determine whether cutter compensation is to the right or left of a machined profile?

18 List the functions of an efficient tool control system.

19 What is the function of a tool library?

20 What is a tool wheel and when is it used?

WORK HOLDING AND LOADING FOR COMPUTER NUMERICALLY CONTROLLED MACHINING

The Application of Common Work-Holding Devices

The basic requirements of any work-holding device are that it must

- (a) securely hold the work;
- (b) provide positive location;
- (c) be quick and easy to operate.

There are a variety of devices in general use that have been tried and tested in conventional machining situations. Chucks, collets, and vices are obvious examples, and these are also used on computer numerically controlled machines. Work-holding devices such as these may be mechanical, pneumatic, or hydraulic in operation. Mechanically operated devices usually involve manual intervention and, although it is not uncommon to see workpieces being loaded and clamped in this way, it is not a practice that is in keeping with automatic machining processes. Because of this, hydraulically or pneumatically operated devices, especially the latter, are favored. The operation of hydraulic or pneumatic clamping is easily controlled electronically via the machine control unit and also provides for rapid operation and uniform clamping pressure. The application of a power-operated collet is shown in Figure 4.1 and a power-operated chuck is shown in Figure 4.2.

Conventional devices such as these are more suited to machining where the component or the stock material is uniform in shape, that is, rectangular, round, hexagonal, etc. Components of irregular shape, such as castings, can be accommodated, as with conventional machining, on specially built fixtures sometimes incorporating pneumatic or hydraulic clamping arrangements.

The Importance of Accurate Location

It is established working practice that, wherever possible, work should be positively located, that is, it should be positioned in such a way that, when the cutting forces are applied, no movement can take place.

Figure 4.3 shows two applications of a conventional machine vice. In both cases the work is located against the fixed jaw but in Figure 4.3a the security of the workpiece

Figure 4.1 Use of collet for work holding on a turning center.

depends on a frictional hold and the cutting force could result in movement of the work-piece. In Figure 4.3b no movement is possible since the fixed jaw of the vice not only locates the workpiece but also absorbs the forces resulting from the cutting action.

Similarly, in Figure 4.4a it can be seen that it is possible for the workpiece held in the chuck to move, since it is not positively located. Figure 4.4b shows how the possibility of movement is eliminated by using the back face of the chuck for positive location.

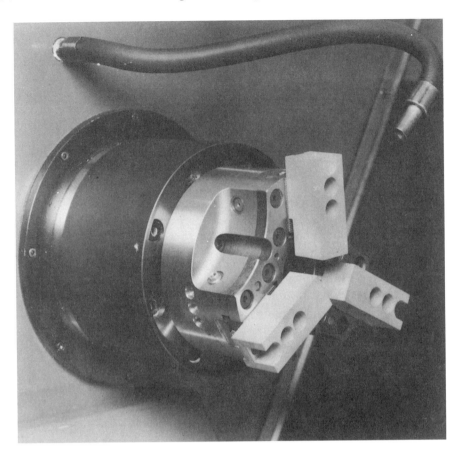

Figure 4.2 Use of power-operated chuck on a turning center.

In any machining process the possibility of movement of the workpiece is unacceptable for safety reasons. In computer numerically controlled machining processes there is also the problem that movement, however slight, means a loss of dimensional accuracy, since there is generally no constant monitoring of the workpiece size as machining proceeds. Additionally, the location of the component is often directly related to the part program, since the programmer, when writing the program, will establish datums on which all numerical data controlling the machine slide movements will be based. If the component is not precisely positioned in relation to those datums, then the machining features required will not be achieved.

Figure 4.5a shows a component that is to be machined on a vertical machining center and the datum in the X and Y axes that the programmer has established as a basis for the part program.

The machine setter will be informed of the position of the datum, either by written instructions or possibly by messages included as part of the program and visually displayed

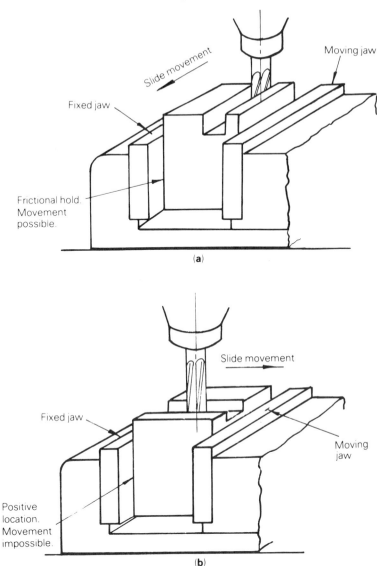

Figure 4.3 Positive location of a milled component: (a) unsatisfactory and (b) satisfactory.

on the machine control unit, and he or she will be required to set the work-holding device, which in turn provides the precise location for the component, accordingly.

To illustrate the need for accurate component location, again consider Figure 4.5. Clearly a workpiece positioned as shown in (b) will not have the same dimensional features in the X axis as the component position shown in (c). In this particular case the logical thing to do would be to place all components as shown in (d), thus using the end of the vice jaw as a locating position, and set the machine datum accordingly. A stop plate attached to the side of the fixed jaw is a method which can be used to ensure perfect location.

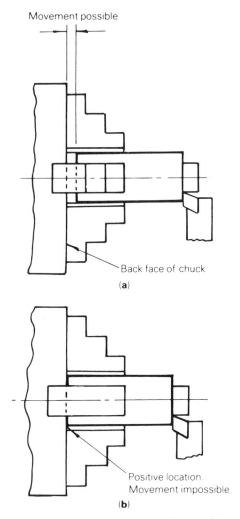

Figure 4.4 Positive location of a turned component: (a) unsatisfactory and (b) satisfactory.

Figure 4.6 shows the use of a self-centering chuck where the back face provides the datum and location face in the Z axis and the self-centering action provides the datum and location in the X axis. The positioning of the workpiece to establish positive location in the X axis is automatic, but the machine setter will need to be informed that the work is to be located against the back face of the chuck to maintain the dimensional validity of the part program in the Z axis.

When the bar size is smaller than the machine spindle bore, accurate location may still be achieved by using a special part stop placed inside the chuck or spindle and against which the component is located prior to clamping. The internal stop is not removed before machining commences so the positive location is maintained. An alternative to using an internal stop is to use soft jaws bored to suit, with a shoulder acting as a stop.

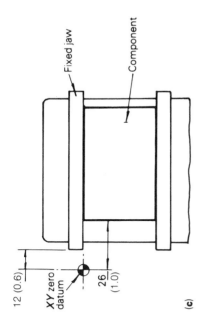

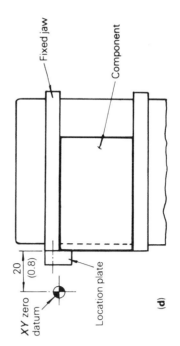

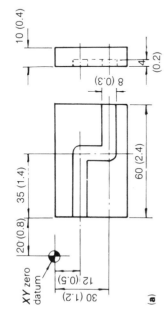

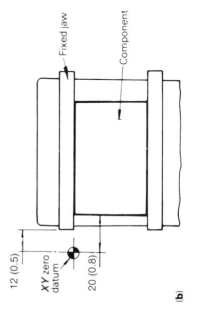

Figure 4.5 Relationship between setting position and part program for a milled component: (a) component detail; (b) initial setting; (c) second setting; (d) setting position constant, no variation in component size. (Inch units are given in parentheses.)

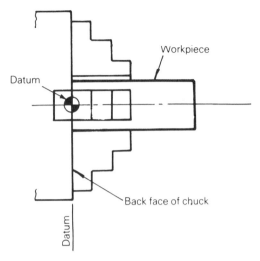

Figure 4.6 Accurate location of a turned component providing constant datum position.

The Use of Grid Plates for Milling and Drilling

A method of work holding and location that has gained wide acceptance for computer numerically controlled milling and drilling setups is the grid plate.

A grid plate is simply a base plate made of steel or cast iron that is drilled with a series of accurately positioned holes. These holes may be tapped to facilitate clamping, plain reamed to accommodate location dowels, or tapped and counterbored to provide for clamping and location. Each hole can be identified using the grid system illustrated in Figure 4.7.

The grid plate is attached to the machine table, often permanently, and since the part programmer can identify the exact position of any hole and will know the dimensions of any locating dowels or blocks used in the work-holding arrangement, he or she can establish datums when writing the program and instruct the machine setter accordingly.

The setting of a grid plate does not involve the use of dial indicators, edge finders, etc., and therefore is not demanding on manual skills on the shop floor. Once set, it provides for quick, simple, and accurate location of the workpiece.

It is often possible to load more than one component at each setting and at known pitches. By using the "zero shift" facility (see Chapter 6), the machining program can be repeated in a new position with a resulting saving in machine downtime.

Apart from clamping directly to the grid plate, components can be held in fixtures, vises, or a set of vises and fixtures, which themselves are accurately located and clamped in position. Complex shapes can be accommodated by using specially shaped locators, while fixtures can be provided with locating devices so that they may be accurately located and clamped in a known position.

Through cutting is possible by using stepped locators that raise the workpiece from the grid plate.

Examples of commercially available grid plates for both horizontal and vertical applications are shown in Figures 4.8 and 4.9.

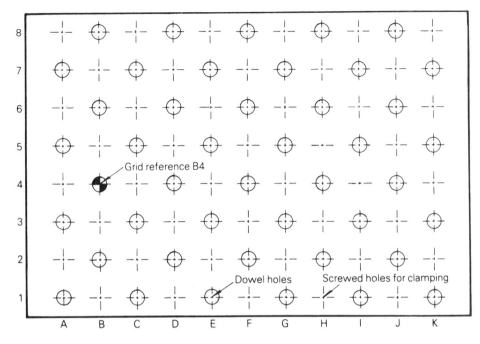

Figure 4.7 Principle of grid plate location.

Figure 4.8 Grid plate showing three components in position.

Figure 4.9 Vertical application of a grid plate.

The Use of Rotary Tables and Indexers
for Milling and Drilling

Many of the conventional uses of a rotary table have become redundant with the introduction of numerical control. Radial profiles are now achieved by circular interpolation, and the positioning of holes or slots in angular relationship to each other, possibly using polar coordinates, has been reduced to nothing more complex than a simple one-block data entry in the machine program. Circular interpolation and polar coordinates are discussed in more detail in Chapter 6.

Rotary tables are still used on horizontal machines for rotating work to facilitate machining in a new position in the vertical plane. An angle of rotation of 90°, for example, permits machining on four sides of a cube, but the indexer can be used to rotate the work through much smaller angles. An angle of rotation as small as 1° or 360 circular positions are common.

Rotary tables of this type may be attached to the machine bed in the normal way or be a built-in feature of the machine table, as illustrated in Figure 4.10.

Conventional dividing heads are also redundant as far as computer numerical control is concerned. They have been replaced by indexers, fully programmable and controlled via the machining program. Simple versions allow up to 24 positions, or increments of 15°, rather like the direct indexing plate fitted to conventional dividing heads.

For more complex indexing or where continual rotation is required, for example when cutting a helix, a rather more sophisticated version is needed, with up to 360,000 positions and feedrate controls. Some of these devices are capable of rotating in two

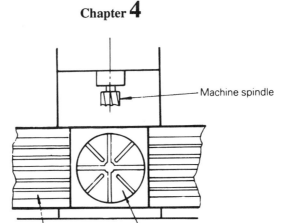

Machine spindle

Machine table   Integral rotary table

Figure 4.10 Integral rotary table.

planes. (Rather confusingly, they are referred to as "tilting rotary tables" by one manufacturer.) When the two-axis version is used in conjunction with three axes of table movement, thus providing a five-axis machining capability, it permits the production of components so complex that they may well be incapable of being produced by conventional means.

The Use of Pallets for Milling and Drilling

An aim of production engineers is to minimize downtime, that is, the time when the machine is not fulfilling its prime function of cutting metal. A major source of downtime is work loading and unloading. The use of preloaded pallets considerably improves the situation.

A pallet is simply a table, which, like the grid plate, is provided with a series of holes or slots to facilitate location and clamping of the component. Pallets are fitted to the machines, shown in Figures 2.1b and 3.14, and can be shuttled in and out of the machining area.

The most simple arrangement will involve the use of just two pallets. A workpiece is located and clamped on the first pallet in a position predetermined by the part programmer and the pallet is then moved into the machining position. As machining is taking place, the second pallet is loaded. When machining of the first component is complete, the pallets are interchanged and, as the second component is being machined, the first pallet is unloaded and reloaded with another component.

Pallets can be interchanged in several ways. Two such methods, one involving a shuttle system and the other a rotary movement, are illustrated in Figures 4.11a and 4.11b. Some machining systems involve more than two pallets (see Chapter 9).

Work Support for Turning Operations

Most turned components are relatively small. The work-holding arrangements used in their production are conventional, that is, chucks and collets are used and there is no

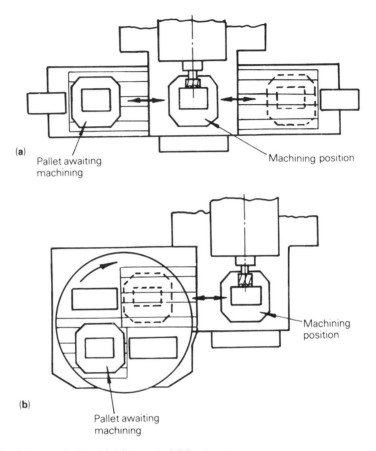

Figure 4.11 Pallet shuttles: (a) linear and (b) rotary.

need for further work support. Because of this, a number of the smaller turning centers available do not have tailstocks. They are no longer essential for drilling, reaming, etc., as this work is carried out from the turret.

When the capacity of the machine is such that the work overhang can be considerable, then tailstock support becomes essential. It is also necessary, of course, for turning between centers. Figure 4.12 illustrates a tailstock being used on a computer numerically controlled turning center.

On some machines the tailstock is very similar to that of a conventional center lathe. It is positioned and clamped solely by manual intervention. On others, it is partially controlled, being manually positioned and clamped on the machine bed but with a programmable hydraulic quill movement. Some machines provide for a fully programmable tailstock, that is, both its position along the bed and the quill movement, together with the necessary clamping, can be included in the part program and automatically controlled.

If a fully programmed tailstock movement is to be used, it is essential that, as the quill moves forward, the workpiece is in the correct position, that is, on center in order to receive the center support. Acknowledging that this condition may be difficult to obtain,

Figure 4.12 Use of a tailstock for work support on a turning center.

Figure 4.13 Bar steady rest providing pressure-controlled support.

Figure 4.14 Mechanically adjusted bar steady rest.

some manufacturers offer hydraulic self-centering steady rest to position the work prior to the tailstock movement being made.

Steady rests are also available to prevent the deflection of slender work, these being located on the machine bed in a manner similar to the way steady rests are used on conventional lathes. Two types of steady rests are illustrated in Figures 4.13 and 4.14.

Work Loading for Turning Operations

Work loading into turning centers may be manual or automatic. The choice of method to be used will be affected by various factors such as component size, component shape, and quantity required.

Manual loading detracts from the benefits in terms of increased production rates and reduced labor costs inherent in computer numerically controlled machining. However, it is quite acceptable for small-batch production and indeed may be essential when the component shape is irregular, for example, a casting, or when nonstandard work-holding devices, such as a fixture clamped to a face plate, are being used.

When automatic loading is applicable, the cost of the necessary equipment is likely to be the determining factor in the final choice. The possibilities range from relatively inexpensive bar feeders to arrangements involving conveyors and robots.

Bar feeders have been applied to turning machines for many years. One of the disadvantages associated with earlier designs was that they were noisy in operation, the noise being created by the bar rotating in the feeder tube. Modern designs have eliminated this problem by various methods, perhaps the most successful one being where the bar is completely surrounded by oil. The bar is fed into the machine under pressure (hydraulic and pneumatic systems are available) when the work-holding device releases its grip. The bar extends to a preset stop located in the turret before the work-holding device closes again.

Bar feeders do not provide total automation, since they have to be reloaded manually from time to time. A modern bar feeder is shown in Figure 4.15.

Components that are too large for bar feeders to be suitable are often produced from preprepared "billets," that is, the material is supplied in short lengths, sometimes

Figure 4.15 Silent bar feeder. Bar is supported in oil.

already faced to size. Material in this form, and partly machined components of similar size requiring further machining, are usually suitable for robot handling. Many machine manufacturers offer robot handling equipment as an optional extra, the robot being adaptable to various component shapes and sizes by fitting interchangeable end effectors (grippers).

QUESTIONS

1 Explain what is meant by positive location as applied to work holding.

2 Why is it especially important that components are positively located for computer numerically controlled machining operations?

3 Explain how a workpiece can be positively located in a self-centering power-operated chuck.

4 State three reasons why pneumatic or hydraulically operated work-holding devices are particularly suitable for use on computer numerically controlled machines.

5 List the advantages of the grid plate as a means of holding workpieces.

6 Describe how the positioning of a workpiece on a grid plate is identified.

7 How would components of irregular shape, such as castings or forgings, be held on a grid plate?

8 Much of the work carried out on a rotary table using conventional machines is achieved in other ways on computer numerically controlled machines. Quote examples where the facilities provided by a rotary table are still useful.

9 What is the main advantage of using preloaded pallets?

10 Describe two ways in which pallets are interchanged on a machining center.

11 Why is the accurate location of a pallet essential before machining commences?

12 Explain what is meant by a fully programmable tailstock as used on a turning center and briefly describe the alternative types of tailstock.

13 What is the main disadvantage of having manual work loading in a computer numerically controlled machining situation? Give an example of a situation where there is unlikely to be an economically viable alternative.

14 What are the advantages and disadvantages of using bar feeders for turning centers?

15 What are billets and what are the advantages in their use?

Chapter 5

DATA PREPARATION AND INPUT TO MACHINE CONTROL UNITS

Data Preparation

The preparation of numerical data prior to input to the machine control unit is referred to as programming. The extent of the preparation will depend on the complexity of the component. It is possible that the data necessary to produce a simple component may require nothing more than an examination of a detailed drawing followed by a direct manual entry to the control unit. On the other hand, programming very complex components may require computing facilities to determine appropriate tool paths. The vast majority of components require an approach similar to that outlined diagrammatically in Figure 5.1.

From the diagram it can be seen that the program is central to the whole process. It is compiled after taking into account a number of essential interrelated factors and then, having been compiled, it totally controls the machining process. Efficient programming requires considerable practical knowledge on the part of the programmer together with a full understanding of the control system to be employed.

The approach to programming must be methodical, and because of this it usually involves compiling a special form or listing the data on a computer screen, preferably followed by a checking process, before recording the data in a form acceptable to the machine control unit. Even at this late stage a further checking process, referred to as "program proving," is essential before a final commitment to machining is made.

Data Input

Data can be entered into machine control units by the following methods:

1. Manual data input (MDI).
2. Conversational manual data input.
3. Perforated tape (obsolete method once used extensively).
4. Magnetic tape (obsolete method once used).
5. Portable electronic data storage unit via an interfaced computer.
6. Magnetic disk via an interfaced computer.
7. Master computer (direct numerical control, DNC).

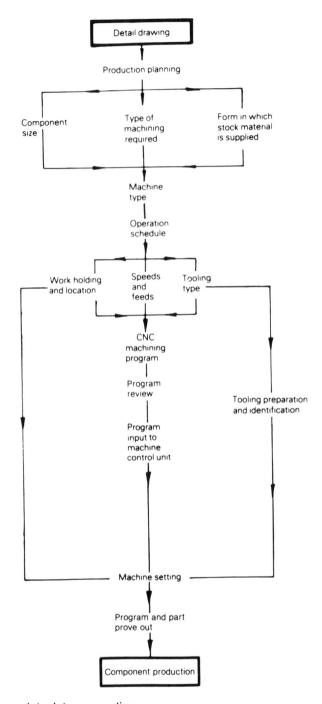

Figure 5.1 Approach to data preparation.

Manual Data Input

Manual data input is used when setting up the machine and editing programs, and for entering complete programs, although the latter should be restricted to relatively simple programs so that the machine is not idle for too long as the data entry is being made. **Manual Data Input to NC Machines** In the past to input data on noncomputerized control units the operator has to set dials, position switches, etc., before finally activating the machine tool to carry out the required movements. Only a limited amount of data can be entered at any one time. Data-recording facilities were often not available. **Manual Data Input to CNC Machines** On computerized control units, by pressing the appropriate buttons on the control console keyboard a limited amount of data or a complete part program may be entered and the machine activated accordingly. The computer will retain the data and it can be transferred to a recording medium such as computer disk and/or transferred back to the company host computer as and when required.

Conversational Manual Data Input

Conversational manual data input involves the operator pressing the appropriate keys on the control console in response to questions in everyday English, which appear on the visual display unit (CRT, cathode ray tube) screen. This method of manual data input is quicker than methods requiring the use of data codes, and manufacturers of these control units claim that to make the first chip takes one tenth of the time and that operator training is just a matter of hours as opposed to up to two weeks for nonconversational input.

The basis of conversational data input is the preprogramming of the computer with standard data stored in files within the computer memory, each item of data being numerically identified and called into the program by the appropriate operator response. Some machines maintain files of data from which the operator makes his or her final selections; other machines only ask questions to remind the operator what is needed.

Consider the turning of a bar of metal on a turning center. Before any consideration can be given to slide movements, the basic metal-cutting data would have to be ascertained. For example, the correct spindle speed and feed rate are of vital importance. The spindle speed is affected by the work diameter and the cutting speed. The cutting speed is related to the material being machined. The feed rate would depend on the depth of cut, tool type, and surface finish required. From this it can be seen that the necessary data to machine the metal successfully can be related to four factors:

(a) the material being cut;
(b) the material diameter;
(c) the surface finish required;
(d) the tool type.

The computer will be programmed to select the appropriate spindle speed and feed rate from an input of information relating to these factors. To assist the input of information

MATERIAL STOCK FILE	
CODE	MATERIAL
1	MILD STEEL
2	MED. CARBON STEEL
3	STAINLESS STEEL
4	CAST IRON
5	ALUMINUM

SURFACE ROUGHNESS FILE	
CODE	Microinches
1	100
2	50
3	25
4	12.5
5	6.3

Figure 5.2 Material file and surface roughness file.

there will be a material file and surface roughness file within the computer memory, as shown in Figure 5.2.

Cutting tools available will also be numerically identified. A simple question-and-answer routine will extract from the computer memory all the necessary data to give the correct cutting conditions; the programmer then enters the axes calculations or parameters to finish the program. An example of a question-and-answer routine is as follows:

CRT question	Operator's keyed response	
Material?	5	input
Material diameter?	2.0	input
Surface code?	4	input
Tool number?	8	input

The preceding illustrates just a small part of the total data input necessary to make a component, and, having established basic cutting conditions, the programmer would proceed to feed in additional data relating to slide movement, etc. However, slide movement data input can be reduced to a question-and-answer routine, even when the movements are complex, such as when machining a radius or cutting a screw thread.

Consider the production of a thread on a work diameter that has just been produced by the preceding data entry. The required data input may be restricted to the following questions:

> Thread root diameter?
> Lead?
> Number of starts?
> Start location?
> Finish location?

From this the control will determine the number of passes necessary, the depth of cut taken by each pass, and the feed rate needed to produce the required pitch. Even the spindle speed may vary automatically to allow for roughing and finishing cuts.

Routines such as the one described are commonly known as "canned cycles" and are not restricted to conversational MDI but may also form part of other programming systems. The use of such routines is described in more detail in Chapter 6.

Data entered in response to questions can be recorded, usually on computer disk or in computer memory, for future use. Some advanced conversational MDI systems incorporate the use of computer graphics (see "Graphical Numerical Control," Chapter 8).

Perforated Tape Input

Sometime ago numerical control was generally referred to as tape control, an indication of the important part this input medium has played in the development of the technology. The expression is not common today as it was, years ago, but perforated tape played a large role in the history of CNC.

The basis of tape control was the transfer of coded information contained on a perforated tape to the machine control unit via a tape reader.

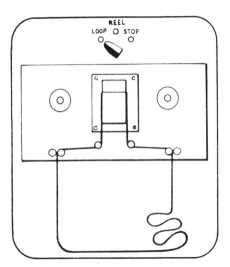

Loop
The tape is joined at its ends to produce a continuous loop.

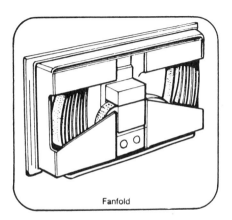

Fanfold or random length
The tape is drawn across the reader and passed from one compartment to the other.

Figure 5.3 CNC tape configurations.

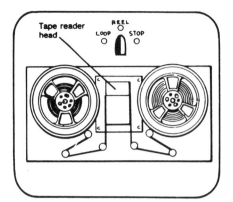

Reel

The tape is wound from one reel to another across the tape reader head.

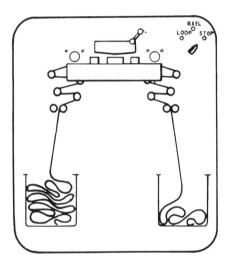

Tape Tumble Box

The tape is left loose at both ends and is allowed to fall freely into a tumble box. Although this was an original configuration, it is rarely used today.

Figure 5.3 (Concluded)

The standard tape width was 1 in./25 mm. Originally only paper tape was used, a factor very much in its favor being its low cost. It was available in rolls or precisely folded in a concertina or fanlike arrangement (Figure 5.3). The rolls were most commonly used, but the folded paper was possibly easier to store.

One of the problems with paper tape was that the sprocket drive holes that are used to carry the tape through some tape readers tended to wear or even tear. Also, a tape was easily damaged by contact with oil, which is always likely in a shop atmosphere. This led to the introduction of other materials or combinations of materials; but, while these tapes were more durable, they were more expensive, and still bulky to store.

Examples of tape materials other than paper include polyester film, paper–polyester–paper laminates, polyester–aluminum-foil–polyester laminates, metallized polyester, and aluminum laminate or Mylar. Some of these tapes can cause excessive punch wear and the adhesives used to produce some laminates have also presented punching problems.

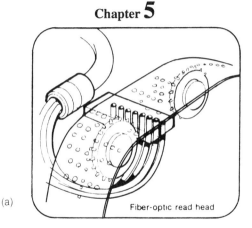

(a)

Fiber-optic read head

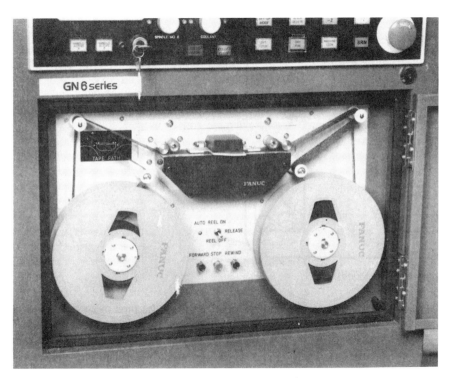

Figure 5.4 (a) Fiber-optic and (b) photoelectric tape reader.

The choice of tape was also affected by the tape reader being used. The prime function of the reader was to detect the presence and position of the perforations in the tape. Tape readers were first mechanical, then became fiber optic or photoelectrical. Various tape readers are shown in Figure 5.4.

Fiber optic and photoelectric readers have light either passing through the perforations or being reflected off a reflector positioned behind the tape. Having detected a perforation, the reader converts this information into an electrical signal that is transmitted to the control unit.

The advent of the computerized control system has eliminated the use of punched tapes and their inherit strength and wear problems. On older control units the tape was run through the reader each time a component was machined. For short programs it could be spliced to form a continuous loop, thus eliminating the need for rewinding. For longer programs the tape was wound from reel to reel. With computerized controls it became common practice to use the tape more as a storage medium, feeding the data it contained into the control unit computer by just one pass through the tape reader. The computer retained the data in its memory and this facilitated data retrieval as and when required. When data was transferred from tape to the computer memory, the tape could be removed from the reader to avoid contamination.

Tape Standards and the Binary Code When a tape reader detected a perforation, the transmission of an electrical signal to the control unit resulted. The simplest way an electrical signal can be meaningful is by its presence or absence, creating an on–off effect. The detection of a perforation registers an "on" signal, and this signal will be given further meaning by the position of the perforation that caused it, as will be explained subsequently. Simply put this is also the basic principle that computers and their memory have been built on. Many of the terms used to describe the units found in CNC programming originated in the tape programs and carried over to the computerized versions.

Whatever the type of CNC reader, the switching effect is achieved by using binary arithmetic, a system that has 2 as a base and can convey numerical values in terms of 1 and 0: "on" and "off."

To understand the binary system of numbers it is helpful to look more closely at the familiar decimal system, which uses 10 as a base. In this system numerical values are constructed from multiples of units, tens, hundreds, thousands, etc.

$$
\begin{array}{ll}
\text{Unit} & 1 = 10^0 \\
\text{Ten} & 10 = 10^1 \\
\text{Hundred} & 100 = 10^2 \\
\text{Thousand} & 1000 = 10^3 \\
\end{array}
$$

Thus the number 2345 is made up as follows:

Thousand	Hundred	Ten	Unit
(10^3)	(10^2)	(10^1)	(10^0)
2	3	4	5

This is a convenient, well-understood method of expressing numbers, but unfortunately it does not readily relate to the requirements of electrical switching control.

Now consider the application of the binary system using two as the base—2^0, 2^1, 2^2, 2^3, and so on—and then relate this to certain decimal values as follows:

$$\text{Let} \quad 2^0 = 1$$

$$
\begin{array}{l}
\text{Then } 2^1 = 2 \\
\text{Then } 2^2 = 4 \\
\text{Then } 2^3 = 8 \text{ and so on}
\end{array}
$$

By using this small range of binary values any decimal digit can be expressed as shown in Table 5.1.

Table 5.1 Decimal digits expressed in binary.

Decimal Digit	Binary equivalent				Composition
	2^3	2^2	2^1	2^0	
1				1	$2^0 = 1$
2			1	0	$2^1 + 0 = 2$
3			1	1	$2^1 + 2^0 = 3$
4		1	0	0	$2^2 + 0 + 0 = 4$
5		1	0	1	$2^2 + 0 + 2^0 = 5$
6		1	1	0	$2^2 + 2^1 + 0 = 6$
7		1	1	1	$2^2 + 2^1 + 2^0 = 7$
8	1	0	0	0	$2^3 + 0 + 0 + 0 = 8$
9	1	0	0	1	$2^3 + 0 + 0 + 2^0 = 9$

Now if the holes in the perforated control tape are arranged in columns or tracks corresponding to the binary values indicated in Table 5.1 it is possible to express the required decimal values by making perforations in the appropriate places:

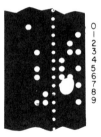

The tape shown above has, eight tracks or vertical columns where a hole might be punched. Five columns are all that is required to express numbers, columns one through four indicate binary values and six indicates a zero. However, the numbers used in numerical control need an identity; for example, a slide movement not only has a dimensional value but the axis in which movement is required has to be defined. This definition is achieved by using letters, as explained in Chapter 1.

There were two tape standards in general use, the ISO (International Standards Organization or ASCII, American Standard Code for Information Interchange) and the EIA (Electrical Industries Association); the latter was developed in the United States of America and gained wide acceptance before the introduction of the ISO standards. The two tapes identify letters in different ways, but both use the binary coded decimal system for numbers. The following description is applicable only to the ISO standard.

The 26 letters of the alphabet are identified numerically from 1 to 26. We have seen that the digits 1 to 9 can be expressed using four binary columns. To include the numbers 10 to 26 requires a fifth column, a fifth track in the tape, so that the decimal value can be expressed *in one row* of punched holes as shown in Table 5.2.

Table 5.2 Letters of the alphabet expressed numerically.

Letter	Decimal Digit	Binary equivalent					Composition
		2^4	2^3	2^2	2^1	2^0	
J	10		1	0	1	0	$2^3 + 0 + 2^1 + 0 = 10$
K	11		1	0	1	1	$2^3 + 0 + 2^1 + 2^0 = 11$
L	12		1	1	0	0	$2^3 + 2^2 + 0 + 0 = 12$
M	13		1	1	0	1	$2^3 + 2^2 + 0 + 2^0 = 13$
N	14		1	1	1	0	$2^3 + 2^2 + 2^1 + 0 = 14$
O	15		1	1	1	1	$2^3 + 2^2 + 2^1 + 2^0 = 15$
P	16	1	0	0	0	0	$2^4 + 0 + 0 + 0 + 0 = 16$
Q	17	1	0	0	0	1	$2^4 + 0 + 0 + 0 + 2^0 = 17$
R	18	1	0	0	1	0	$2^4 + 0 + 0 + 2^1 + 0 = 18$
S	19	1	0	0	1	1	$2^4 + 0 + 0 + 2^1 + 2^0 = 19$

There is, of course, a conflict as far as the first nine decimal digits are concerned. Does the value 7, for example, indicate a numerical value or the seventh letter, G? This is clarified by increasing the number of tracks in the tape from five to seven. Digits are indicated by additional holes being punched in both tracks five and six, while letters are indicated by holes punched in track 7.

The control system will require other characters as well as numbers and letters. For instance, a minus $(-)$ sign may be necessary to indicate the direction of slide movement. These additional symbols have been allocated combinations of punched holes not used otherwise. Thus all the data required for CNC part programming purposes can be expressed via a seven-bit code. The term "bit," incidentally, is derived from BInary digiT.

Finally, to check the accuracy of the tape punching and tape reading, there was an eighth track referred to as a parity track. The ISO standard requires that each row contain an even number of holes. If the required character was expressed by an odd number of holes, an extra hole would be punched in track eight. If the required character was expressed by an even number of holes, there would be no extra hole in track eight. This system is referred to as "even parity." The EIA system also uses an eighth track, but as an end-of-block code. The fifth track is a parity punch to give odd parity in EIA-244-D standards. The newer EIA-358-B standard required even parity and became widely used in conjunction with computer applications. A visual check that each line of the tape contains an even number of holes (ISO) or an odd number of holes (EIA) is one method of ascertaining that there are no errors as a result of the equipment malfunctioning.

By reference to Figure 5.5 the reader can see the variations between the two tape standards. Most modern control systems of that time would accept either standard EIA or ISO. (EIA standards 244 and 358 can be found in Appendix A.)

Tape Format Each horizontal row of holes in the tape was termed a "character." Each set of characters was termed a "word." Each set of words was termed a "block." This is illustrated in Figure 5.6.

Blocks are identified by the letter N or O followed by three or four digits. A block could contain information on the type of slide movement required, length of slide

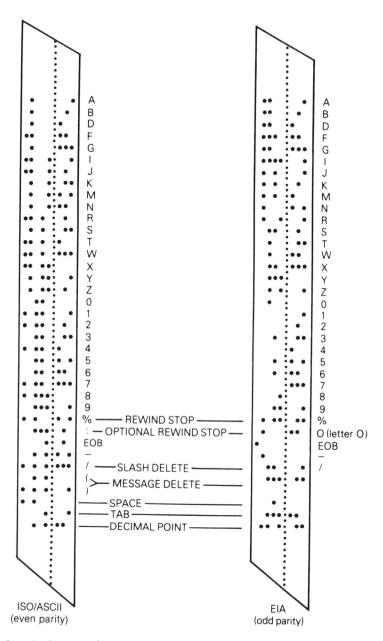

Figure 5.5 Standard tape codes.

movement, rate of slide movement, spindle speed, tool identity, etc., and would terminate with an "end of block" character.

The order in which words are entered in a block may be fixed or variable. The fixed
block format requires each block to have the correct number of entries and they must

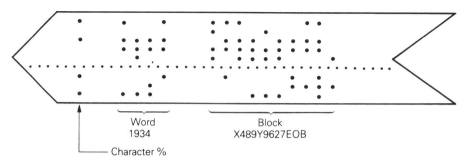

Word
1934

Block
X489Y9627EOB

Character %

Figure 5.6 Perforated tape format.

Figure 5.7 Automatic tape punch for interfacing with computer.

appear in a set sequence. This meant that data had to be reentered in each block even if there has been no change from the previous block and even if the numerical value of the entry is zero. On some systems each word has to be separated by the *tab* function, this type of format being referred to as *tab sequential*.

Much more commonly used is the variable block format in which words can be entered in any order. Their meaning or function is determined by the letter preceding the data, a system referred to as *word address*. Data that remain unchanged in following blocks need not be reentered, and this leads to more rapid programming and a considerable reduction in the resulting tape length.

Production of Punched Tape Punched tapes were produced either from a teletypewriter or by an automatic tape punch interfaced (connected) with a computer. An automatic tape punch is shown in Figure 5.7.

The teletypewriter was similar in many ways to an electric typewriter. It had an alphanumeric (letters and numbers) keyboard, and the prewritten program was typed in the normal way either onto conventional teletype paper or onto a blank program sheet. A teletypewriter is shown in Figure 5.8.

Figure 5.8 Teletypewriter used for production of perforated tape.

Attached to the side of the teletypewriter was the punching device. The blank tape fed automatically from a roll into the punching head and, as each character was typed on the keyboard, a row of holes were punched in the tape.

Additional copies of the tape or of the typewritten program could than be made automatically.

The facility to produce additional copies could also be used for tape correcting. The original tape was run through the machine, and while it was running through, a replica of the tape and a printout were being made. At the point where the correction was to be made the automatic process was stopped. The new data was then typed into the program in the normal way. When the correction was completed the original tape was inched forward to the point where the original entry was still valid and the automatic reproduction process was restarted.

With computer-linked tape preparation facilities, editing became much simpler. The listed part program appeared on the display screen, where it could readily be examined, and any necessary alterations were made via the keyboard. When the programmer was satisfied that all was correct, the tape punch was activated to produce a complete new tape. Additional copies of the tape could readily be made and an interfaced printer would provide copies for filing for future reference.

Tape Proving Before any punched tape was used for machining, it should have been "proven," that is, checked that the desired machine movements will be achieved. This was normally done on the machine tool, although the wisdom of wasting valuable machining time in nonproductive testing was questioned, it was shown to be the proper thing to do to prevent errors from causing machine crashes.

On basic numerically controlled machines, that is, those not computer controlled, testing facilities are limited to a "dry run," where all machine feedrates are changed to rapid transverse. Owing to the inherent danger present here from the flip of a switch, no part is placed in the machine and tooling may also be removed. It should be noted that a dry run only checks for command format errors, and after machine setup, the program should be cycled through in a block by block or single cycle mode to check for physical errors. On computer controlled machines the dry run can be complemented by a "test run," that is, all axis and spindle movements are inhibited, but the visual display is continually updated as demanded by the program in real time, that is, the actual time it would take to machine the component. Errors in the program, like no spindle speed stated would be indicated by an appropriate error message appearing on the CRT screen.

To avoid incurring the nonproductive downtime referred to, other test facilities remote from the machine may be more appropriate; for example, a plotter was used. A plotter was in effect an automatic drawing device. The profile of the cutter path was traced out by the machine according to the data supplied via the tape. The result is, of course, a "flat" view; depth, that is, the third axis, is achieved by using colors and different views if available. An interfaced printer was used to provide a copy of the program and a drawing of the tool path.

The tape-proving facilities referred to were made obsolete when computer graphics became available for use as part of the programming preparation process. The preprepared program was fed into the computer via keyboard, floppy disk, or tape, the entry appearing on the CRT. Incorrect entries, for example, an unrealistic feed rate, can be stalled and the operator informed by a displayed error message. When the program is complete, it can be transferred to storage and the computer graphics are then used to simulate a test run. The correct blank size appears and, using animated tool movements, is "machined" according to the program requirements. The use of a computer for program proving is illustrated in Figure 5.9. A computer printout of a program, together with a graphical representation of the component, is shown in Figure 5.10. It should be noted that graphic types of prove-out do not eliminate the need for a slowed down single step mode run through the program after each setup on the machine.

When the programmer was satisfied that the entry was correct, a tape was than produced very rapidly at the touch of a key via an automatic tape punch interfaced with the computer. Similarly, an interfaced printer will produce a printout. These forms of advanced proveout introduced us to the computer age of programming.

Figure 5.9 (a) Use of computer for program proving: program listing. (Metric output example for unidentified machine tool.)

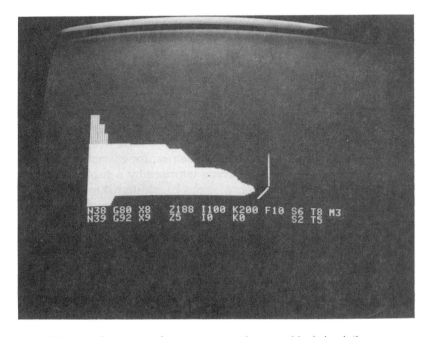

Figure 5.9 (b) Use of computer for program proving: graphical simulation.

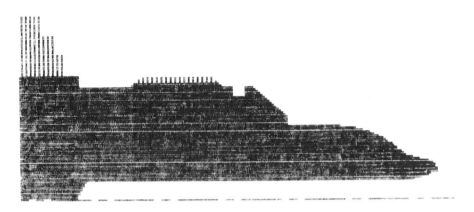

Optional stop out.   Single step out.

Time Taken = 11.93 min.
================================

PROGRAM USED TO GENERATE WORKPIECE
================================

Figure 5.10 (a) Computer printout and graphical representation of component in metric output form for unidentified machine tool.

Magnetic Tape Data Input

Magnetic tape, in the form of cassettes, was the next widely used means of transmitting data (Figure 5.11). The advantages claimed for it were:

(a) easier handling;
(b) more rapidly produced and read;
(c) the program can be erased and the tape re-used;
(d) simpler editing;
(e) more storage space than a paper tape of the same length;
(f) more durable than paper tapes.

Early applications of magnetic tape involved a recording being made as machining of the first component was being carried out "manually" from the control console, a form of manual data input. A major drawback of this system was that the final program was only as rapid as the human reactions producing it and, with all the dial setting and switching involved, it was inevitably rather slow compared with modern techniques.

It was the advent of computer-controlled machining and computer-aided program proving that resulted in a more general application of magnetic tape. To record a part

Figure 5.10 (b) Program used to generate workpiece.

N	G	X	Z	I	K	F	S	T	M
N1	G96							S1000	
N2	G95								
N3	G92	X10	Z0	I0	K1	F99	S9	T1	M8
N4	G82	X61	Z188	I61	K91				M3
N5	G81	X68	Z84	I68	K188				M6
N6	G84	X56	Z188	I56	K109				M3
N7		X51		I51	K114				
N8		X46		I46	K119				
N9	G0	X41							
N10	G83		Z119	I45					
N11	G81	X63	Z101	I63	K188				
N12	G84	X36	Z188	I36	K159				
N13		X31		I31	K165				
N14		X27		I27	K170				
N15	G82	X23		I23	K181				
N16	G3	X29	Z167	I41					
N17	G2	X41	Z139	I1	K139				
N18	G80	X43	Z187	I16	K187				
N19	G1	X22	Z181						
N20	G3	X28	Z167	I42	K181				
N21	G2	X40	Z139	I0	K139				
N22	G83		Z119	I44	K119				
N23		X60	Z103	I60	K90				
N24		X65	Z85	I65	K45				
N25	G0	X145	Z230						
N26	G97								
N27	G92	X10	Z0	I0	K0	F12	S3	T12	M8
N29	G81	X0	Z153		K162				M3
N30			Z121		K130				
N31			Z89		K98				
N32			Z57		K66				
N33			Z25		K200				
N35	G92	X11	Z0	I1	K0	F10	S6	T8	M8
N36	G82	X15	Z188	I15	K185				M3
N37	G3	X10	Z173	I49	K164				
N38	G80	X8	Z188	I100	K200				
N39	G92	X9	Z5	I0	K0		S2	T5	
N40	G82	X62	Z95	I55	K95				
N41	G4			I1000					
N42	G80	X68		I68	K40				
N43	G81	X60	Z40						
N44	G85	X68	Z36	I60	K36				
N45			Z31		K31				
N46			Z27		K27				
N47	G0		Z53						
N48	G1	X60	Z45						
N49	G80	X68	Z30	I100	K200				
N50	G92	X5	Z3	I0	K1	F99	S5	T6	
N51	G0	X66	Z100						
N52	G34	X64	Z37		K50				
N53		X63							
N54		X62							
N55	G0	X100	Z200						M2

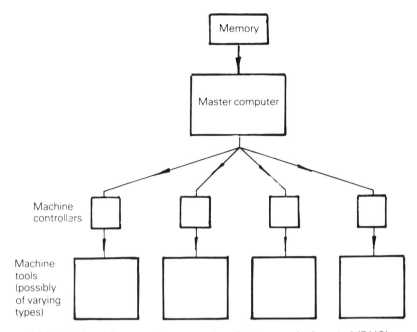

Figure 5.11 Data input from master computer: direct numerical control (DNC).

program in this way involves entering a program by MDI either at the machine control unit or through a computer keyboard. After the program has been entered it can be listed, edited and proved by using computer graphics, as discussed earlier. Finally, the program was recorded in much the same way as a tape recording of a piece of music can be made from a record or the radio.

Magnetic tape recordings do have the disadvantage of not being visible without the use of special CRT screens, printers, or plotters. Their other major disadvantage is that the magnetic information can be easily scrambled or destroyed if placed near magnetic fields or machine tools.

Data Input via Portable Electronic Storage Unit

There were problems associated with the use of paper and magnetic tape in what may be a dirty, and therefore potentially damaging, environment such as may be encountered in a machine shop. These problems were eliminated by the use of a portable electronic storage unit. The data are first transferred into the unit away from the machine shop. The unit is then carried to the machine, connected to the machine control unit via data cable, and the data then transferred. Similarly data already in the machine control unit may be transferred into the portable unit for downloading and storage elsewhere. Data transfer is very rapid. The capacity of the portable units is such that a number of programs can be accommodated at any one time.

Magnetic Disk Input via an Interfaced Computer

Providing the distance is not too great, it is possible to directly cable-link microcomputer to a machine tool or, alternatively, to have a computer mounted on a trolley that can be brought alongside the machine and temporarily interfaced. It is then possible to transfer data stored on a magnetic diskette, commonly referred to as a "floppy disk," into the computer and hence into the machine control unit. Data already in the control unit can also be extracted an recorded. Newer CNC machine tool controls are now also appearing with portable or built in disk drives, or personal computer (PC) based controls.

Disks have the same disadvantage as magnetic tape in that the program is not visible but, as with tapes, a program may be transferred into the computer for visual display, and printing and graphic tool path display facilities may be included.

The rate at which data can be transferred or retrieved using a disk is much faster than when using a tape and, size for size, the storage capacity of the disk is much greater.

Master Computer Data Input

An extension of the concept described previously of linking a computer to a machine tool is when a computer, usually a mini or mainframe, is permanently linked to a series of machines. Prepared programs stored in the memory of master computer are then transferred to the microcomputer of the control unit of the selected machine tool as and when required. The concept is illustrated in Figure 5.11 and is referred to as direct numerical control (DNC).

Buffer Storage

Most modern control systems have a buffer storage, which is a capability to hold data extracted from the computer memory in an intermediate position. As one block of information is being processed the next is ready for instant transmission, the object being to speed the rate at which data are processed so that there is a minimum loss of machining time. Also the elimination of a dwell between blocks avoids marking the machined surface.

QUESTIONS

1 When would it be economically inadvisable to enter data manually into a machine control unit?

2 What is conversational manual input and what are the advantages and disadvantages of entering a machining program by this method?

3 Name three types of materials, or combinations of materials, used for perforated tape and state the advantages of each.

4 Name three types of tape readers. Which of these is most commonly used?

5 How is the reverse loading of perforated tape into a tape reader prevented?

6 Why is the binary system of numbers used to indicate the meaning of data input on a perforated tape?

7 What is the origin of the expression "eight bit" as applied to perforated tape?

8 Name the two tape standards in general use and explain how, by a visual check, you could identify them.

9 Explain what is meant by "character," "word," and "block" as applied to perforated tape format.

10 What is the difference between tab sequential and variable block tape format?

11 Describe two ways in which a tape can be proved away from the machine tool.

12 What is the difference between a dry run and a test run when checking data input?

13 What are the advantages of magnetic tape as a data storage medium?

14 What are the advantages of the floppy disk as a data storage medium?

15 What is a buffer storage and why is it necessary?

TERMS AND DEFINITIONS ASSOCIATED WITH PART PROGRAMMING AND MACHINE CONTROL

Part Programming

The expression "part programming" causes some confusion, since "part" is often thought to mean something that is incomplete. In numerical control terms a part program is, in fact, a complete program. The word "part" means component.

Preparatory Functions

Preparatory functions are used to inform the machine control unit of the facilities required for the machining that is to be carried out. For example, the control unit will need to know if the axis movements stated dimensionally in the program are to be made in inch or metric units, and whether the spindle is to rotate in a clockwise or counterclockwise direction.

The way in which machine controllers are provided with such information depends on the type of control unit. On conversational MDI systems, it may simply involve pressing the appropriate button on the control panel. For systems using the word address programming method, the various preparatory functions were originally standardized (ANSI/EIA RS274-D: 1979; BS 3635:1972), each function being identified by the address letter G followed by two digits. Thus preparatory functions came to be referred to generally as "G codes." The Standard has been adopted and is widely used, although variations in the allocation of special G codes will be encountered.

The preparatory functions, as they appear in the Standard, are shown in Table 6.1. The codes used for any particular control system will depend on the machine type and the sophistication of the system and, although a complete list such as the original standard is rather extensive, it should be appreciated that the number of codes included in any one system will be considerably fewer in number.

Table 6.1 Preparatory functions codes (M = modal).

Code Number	Function	Modal[a]
G00	Rapid positioning, point to point	(M)
G01	Linear positioning at controlled feed rate	(M)
G02	Circular interpolation CW—two dimensional	(M)
G03	Circular interpolation CCW—two dimensional	(M)
G04	Dwell for programmed duration	
G05	Unassigned EIA code may be used as hold. Cancelled by operator	
G06	Parabolic interpolation	(M)
G07	Unassigned EIA code reserved for future standardization	
G08	Programmed slide acceleration	
G09	Programmed slide deceleration	
G10 G11 G12	Unassigned EIA code sometimes used for machine lock and unlock devices	
G13–G16	Axis selection	(M)
G17	XY plane selection	(M)
G18	ZX plane selection	(M)
G19	YZ plane selection	(M)
G20	Unassigned EIA code	
G21 G22 G23	Unassigned EIA code sometimes used for nonstop blended interpolation movements	
G24	Unassigned EIA code	
G25–G29	Permanently unassigned. Available for individual use	
G30 G31 G32	Unassigned EIA code	
G33	Thread cutting, constant lead	(M)
G34	Thread cutting, increasing lead	(M)
G35	Thread cutting, decreasing lead	(M)
G36–G39	Permanently unassigned. Available for individual use	
G40	Cutter compensation/offset, cancel	(M)
G41	Cutter compensation, left	(M)
G42	Cutter compensation, right	(M)
G43	Cutter offset inside corner	(M)
G44	Cutter offset outside corner	(M)
G45 G46 G47 G48 G49	Unassigned EIA code	
G50	Reserved for adaptive control	
G51	Cutter compensation +/0	
G52	Cutter compensation −/0	
G53	Linear shift cancel	(M)
G54	Linear shift X	(M)

Table 6.1 *(Continued)*

Code Number	Function	Modal[a]
G55	Linear shift Y	(M)
G56	Linear shift Z	(M)
G57	Linear shift XY	(M)
G58	Linear shift XZ	(M)
G59	Linear shift YZ	(M)
G60–G69	Unassigned EIA codes	
G70	Inch programming	(M)
G71	Metric programming	(M)
G72	Circular interpolation—CW (three dimensional)	(M)
G73	Circular interpolation—CCW (three dimensional)	(M)
G74	Cancel multiquadrant circular interpolation	(M)
G75	Multiquadrant circular interpolation	(M)
G76–G79	Unassigned EIA code	
G80	Fixed cycle cancel	(M)
G81	Fixed cycle 1	(M)
G82	Fixed cycle 2	(M)
G83	Fixed cycle 3	(M)
G84	Fixed cycle 4	(M)
G85	Fixed cycle 5	(M)
G86	Fixed cycle 6	(M)
G87	Fixed cycle 7	(M)
G88	Fixed cycle 8	(M)
G89	Fixed cycle 9	(M)
G90	Absolute dimension input	(M)
G91	Incremental dimension input	(M)
G92	Preload registers	
G93	Inverse time feedrate (V/D)	(M)
G94	Inches (millimeters) per minute feedrate	(M)
G95	Inches (millimeters) per revolution feedrate	(M)
G96	Constant surface speed, feet (meters) per minute	(M)
G97	Revolutions per minute	(M)
G98 } G99	Unassigned EIA code	

[a] Function retained until cancelled or superceded by subsequent command of same letter.

Many preparatory functions are modal, that is, they stay in operation until changed or cancelled.

Miscellaneous Functions

In addition to preparatory functions there are a number of other functions that are required from time to time throughout the machining program. For example, coolant may be required while metal cutting is actually under way but will need to be turned off during a tool-changing sequence. Operations such as this are called "miscellaneous functions."

Table 6.2 Miscellaneous functions codes.

Code number	Function	With	After Completion	Modal[a]
			Function Starts Relative To Commanded Motion In Its Block	
M00	Program stop		X	
M01	Optional stop		X	
M02	End of program		X	
M03	Spindle on CW	X		X
M04	Spindle on CCW	X		X
M05	Spindle off		X	X
M06	Tool change			
M07	Coolant 2 on	X		X
M08	Coolant 1 on	X		X
M09	Coolant off		X	X
M10	Clamp			X
M11	Unclamp			X
M12	Synchronization code		X	X
M13	Spindle on CW, coolant on	X		X
M14	Spindle on CCW, coolant on	X		X
M15	Motion in the positive direction	X		
M16	Motion in the negative direction	X		
M17 ⎫ M18 ⎬	Unassigned EIA code. Reserved for future standardization			
M19	Oriented spindle stop			X
M20–M29	Permanently unassigned. Available for individual use			
M30	End of tape/data		X	X
M31	Interlock bypass	X		X
M32–M35	Unassigned EIA code			
M36 ⎫ M37 ⎪ M38 ⎬ M39 ⎭	Permanently unassigned. Available for individual use			
M40–M46	Gear changes if used otherwise unassigned	X		X
M47	Return to program start			
M48	Cancel M49	X		X
M49	Feed/speed bypass override	X		X
M50–M57	Unassigned EIA code			
M58	Cancel M59	X		X
M59	Bypass constant surface speed updating	X		X
M60–M89	Unassigned EIA code			
M90–M99	Reserved for user			

[a] Function retained until cancelled or superceded by subsequent command of same letter.

Conversational MDI control systems will, as with preparatory functions, have their own particular way of initiating miscellaneous functions, but for word address systems the EIA standards have been adopted except for special options on particular machine tools. The functions are referred to as "M functions" and are identified by the address letter M followed by two digits.

The original standardized miscellaneous functions are listed in Table 6.2. The functions available will vary from one control system to another, the number available being fewer than the complete list.

Positioning Control

The basis of numerically controlled machining is the programmed movement of the machine slides to predetermined positions. This positioning is described in three ways:

(a) point-to-point
(b) line motion or linear interpolation
(c) contouring or circular interpolation.

Point-to-Point Positioning

Point-to-point positioning involves programming instructions that only identify the next position required. The position may be reached by movement in one or more axes. When more than one axis is involved, the movements are not coordinated with each other, even though they may occur simultaneously. The rate of movement is usually, although not necessarily, the maximum for the machine slide.

Figure 6.1 shows a component the machining of which would involve point-to-point positioning, the holes being drilled in the sequence A to D. Note that it is the positioning prior to drilling that is point-to-point, not the drilling operation itself.

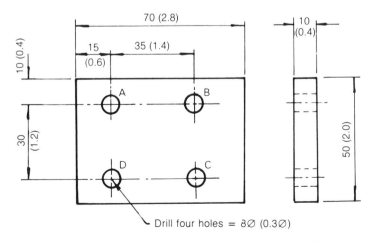

Figure 6.1 Component detail involving point-to-point positioning. (Inch units are given in parentheses.)

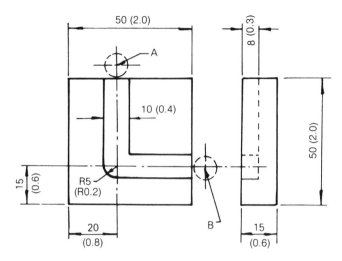

Figure 6.2 Component detail involving line motion control. (Inch units are given in parentheses.)

Line Motion Control

Line motion control is also referred to as linear interpolation. The programmed movement results from instructions that specify the next required position and also the feed rate to be used to reach that position. This type of positioning would be involved in machining the slot in the component shown in Figure 6.2, the cutter moving in relation to the workpiece from point A to point B. Although a continuous cutter path appears to be the result, two distinct slide movements are involved, each slide movement being independent of the other.

Linear interpolation was initially defined as slide movement at programmed feed rates parallel to the machine axes. More recently it has also been used to describe linear movement when two, or sometimes three, slides are moving at the same time at programmed feed rates, a facility not available on earlier control systems. When two slides are moving simultaneously, an angular tool path results, and when three slides are involved, the result would be as indicated in Figure 6.3.

Contouring

Contouring also involves two or more controlled slide movements resulting from program data that specify the next position required and the required feed rates to reach that position, so there is some overlap between linear interpolation and contouring. However, contouring can also be much more complex, involving combinations of angular movement and curves with one feature moving without interruption in the cutting process into another. This type of movement gives rise to the expression continuous path machining, which is often used to describe contouring.

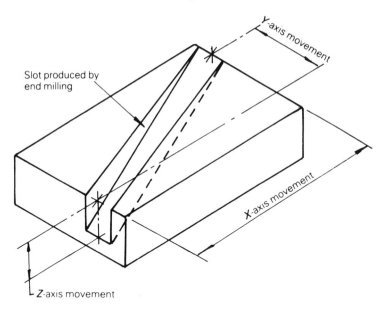

Figure 6.3 Resulting tool path when three slides move simultaneously.

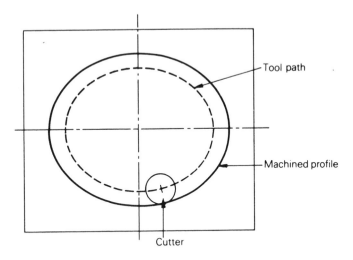

Figure 6.4 Component profile produced by contouring.

Machining of the elliptical profile shown in Figure 6.4 would involve continuous path movement. Likewise, the radii shown on the components in Figure 6.5 would be produced in a similar manner. The elliptical shape is not readily defined in numerical terms, and to produce the necessary cutter path would present an interesting, although not insurmountable, problem to the part programmer unless the control system was specially

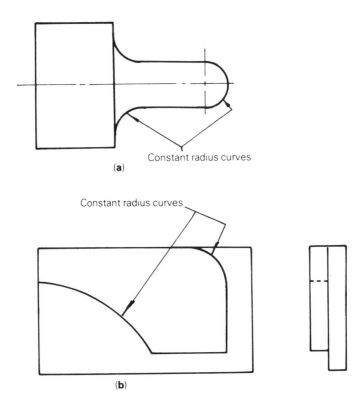

Constant radius curves

(a)

Constant radius curves

(b)

Figure 6.5 Components with radial features requiring circular interpolation: **(a)** turned component and **(b)** milled profile.

equipped with a canned cycle to deal with such a situation. On the other hand, the two radii shown in Figure 6.5 are an everyday occurrence and most control systems can readily accommodate the production of a radius, or a combination of radii. Such a facility is referred to as circular interpolation.

Circular arcs may be programmed in the *XY*, *XZ*, and *YZ* planes. In exceptional cases three axes may be involved, resulting, in effect, in a helical tool path.

Programming Positional Moves

In practice the three types of positioning referred to previously are rarely isolated. The production of the majority of components will involve a combination of the techniques. However, it will be necessary to clearly identify in the part program the type of positioning required at each stage of the machining process.

Manual data input systems will vary from one control system to another. For example, a widely used training machine specifies all linear movement as linear interpolation and differentiates by linking the movement to an appropriate feed rate. The program entry is reduced to pressing a linear interpolation key followed by the dimensional detail and the feed rate. Similarly, a radius is simply defined by pressing a circular interpolation key, followed by a data entry of the dimensional value of the target position, the radius, and the direction of rotation as either clockwise or counterclockwise.

Control systems using the recommendations contained in EIA RS-274-D or BS 3635:1972 will specify the type of positioning involved by using the appropriate preparatory function or G code, the common ones being as follows:

G00	Point-to-point
G01	Linear interpolation
G02	Circular interpolation clockwise
G03	Circular interpolation counterclockwise

Having defined the type of positioning in this way the instruction is completed by including dimensional details of the move together with the feed rate for G01, G02, and G03. G00 moves are usually made at the maximum slide traverse rate for the machine.

Dimensional Definitions of Slide Movement

In Chapter 1 it was explained that the axes in which slide movement can take place are designated by a letter and either a plus $(+)$ or minus $(-)$ sign to indicate the direction of movement. Unfortunately, these designated slide movements, owing to the different design configurations of machine tools, do not always coincide with the movement of the tool in relation to the work, and as a result this can cause some confusion when slide movements are being determined. In the case of a turning center with a conventional tool post there is no problem, since the slide movement and the tool movement in relation to the work are identical. But on a vertical machining center, for example, to achieve a positive $(+)$ movement of the tool in relation to the work, the table, not the cutter, has to move, and this movement is in the opposite direction. Since a move in the wrong direction, especially at a rapid feed rate, could have disastrous results, this fact should be clearly understood.

A sound technique when determining slide movements is to program the tool movement in relation to the work. In other words, on all types of machines, imagine it is the tool moving and not, as is sometimes the case, the workpiece. To do this it is necessary to redefine some, but not all, of the machine movements. A simple diagram such as the one alongside the components shown in Figures 6.6 and 6.9 is usually very helpful.

Once the direction of movement has been established it will need to be dimensionally defined. There are two methods used, and they are referred to as:

(a) absolute;
(b) incremental.

Figure 6.6 shows the profile of a component to be machined on a turning center using the machine spindle center line and the face of the workpiece as datums in the X and Z axes respectively. Assume the sequence of machining is to commence with the 1.4 in.

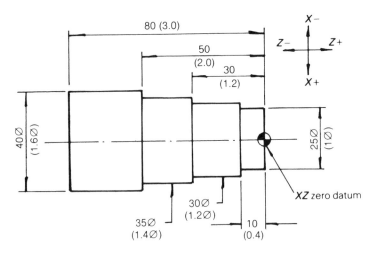

Figure 6.6 Component detail. (Inch units are given in parentheses.)

(35 mm) diameter, followed by the 1.2 in. (30 mm) diameter and finishing with the 1 in. (25 mm) diameter.

To machine the profile using absolute dimensions, it is necessary to relate all the slide movements to a preestablished datum. The movements required in absolute terms are indicated in Figure 6.7. Note that all position commands are the actual distance that the tool tip is from the datum point.

Incremental positioning involves relating the slide movement to the final position of the previous move. The slide movements, expressed in incremental terms, which would be necessary to machine the profile are indicated in Figure 6.8. Note position commands indicate the direction and the exact amount of slide motion required.

Note that each dimension in the X axis in Figure 6.7 is equal to the work radius. When turning, some control systems will require dimensions in the X axis to be stated as a diameter, other machines may allow the programmer to select radius or diameter programming.

Figure 6.9 shows a component that is to be milled in the sequence A to C on a vertical machining center using datums as indicated. Assume that the movement in the Z axis to give a slot depth of 0.4 in (10 mm) has already been made. The necessary slide movements in the X and Y axes in absolute and incremental terms are indicated in Figures 6.10 and 6.11, respectively.

On the more sophisticated control systems, it is possible to use absolute and incremental dimensional definition within the same program, the distinction being achieved by using the G91 preparatory function code when the switch from absolute (G90) to incremental (G91) is to be made.

Circular Interpolation

It was stated earlier that circular arc programming, particularly on conversational data input systems, has been reduced to simply dimensionally defining the target position,

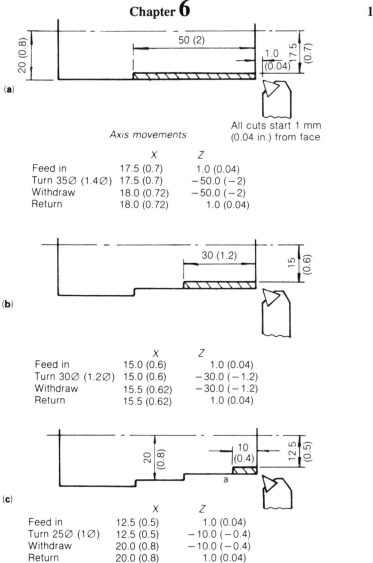

Figure 6.7 Turning using absolute positioning. (Inch units are given in parentheses.)

the radius, and the direction in which movement is to take place. On control systems using the word address format, it is rather more complex and there are slight variations in approach. Two of these variations will be considered later.

Common to all systems used to program circular movement is the need to determine whether the relative tool travel is in a clockwise (CW) or counterclockwise (CCW) direction. The following approach is usually helpful.

1. For milling operations look along the machine spindle toward the surface being machined.
2. For turning operations look on to the top face of the cutting tool. (For inverted tooling this involves looking at the tool from below.)

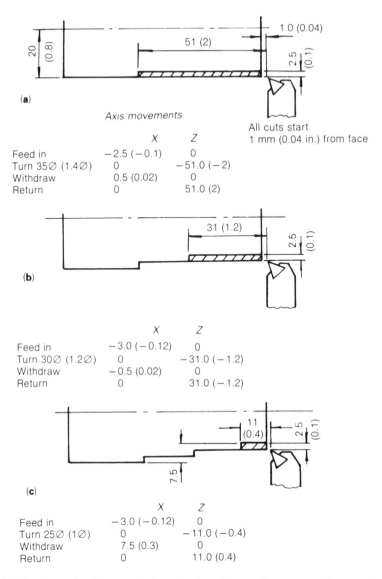

Figure 6.8 Turning using incremental positioning. (Inch units are given in parentheses.)

The standard G codes for circular interpolation are G02 (CW) and G03 (CCW). However, not all systems adopt this recommendation and there is at least one widely used system in which they are reversed, that is, G02 is CCW and G03 is CW. (In this case it is advisable to refer to the machine tool programming manual.)

The three variations in arc programming referred to above are as follows. Note: That machines will normally not have all three methods of circular arc programming.

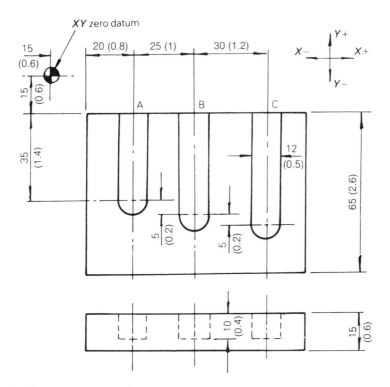

Figure 6.9 Component detail. (Inch units given in parentheses.)

Method 1

Assuming that the last programmed move brought the cutting tool to the start point, the arc is defined in the following manner:

1. The finish or target point of the arc is dimensionally defined in relation to the start point using the appropriate combination of X, Y, and Z dimensional values stated in absolute or incremental terms.
2. The center of the arc is dimensionally defined in relation to the start point using I, J, and K values measured along the corresponding X, Y, and Z axes respectively.

Thus the arc shown in Figure 6.12 would be programmed as follows. In absolute terms using diameter programming:

		X	Z	I	K
Inch	G02				
		1.6	2.0	0	0.8
Metric	G02	X	Z	I	K
		40	50	0	20

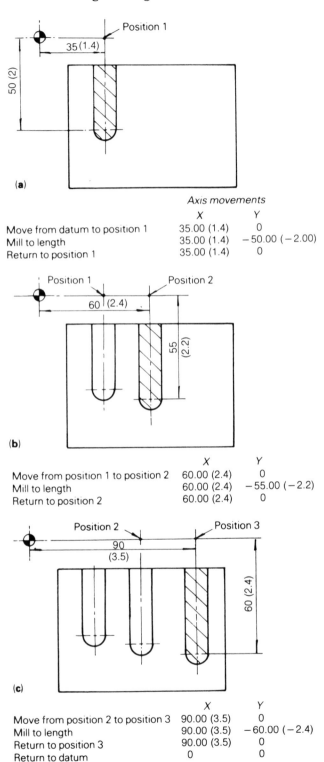

Axis movements

	X	Y
Move from datum to position 1	35.00 (1.4)	0
Mill to length	35.00 (1.4)	−50.00 (−2.00)
Return to position 1	35.00 (1.4)	0

	X	Y
Move from position 1 to position 2	60.00 (2.4)	0
Mill to length	60.00 (2.4)	−55.00 (−2.2)
Return to position 2	60.00 (2.4)	0

	X	Y
Move from position 2 to position 3	90.00 (3.5)	0
Mill to length	90.00 (3.5)	−60.00 (−2.4)
Return to position 3	90.00 (3.5)	0
Return to datum	0	0

Figure 6.10 Milling using absolute positioning. (Inch units are given in parentheses.)

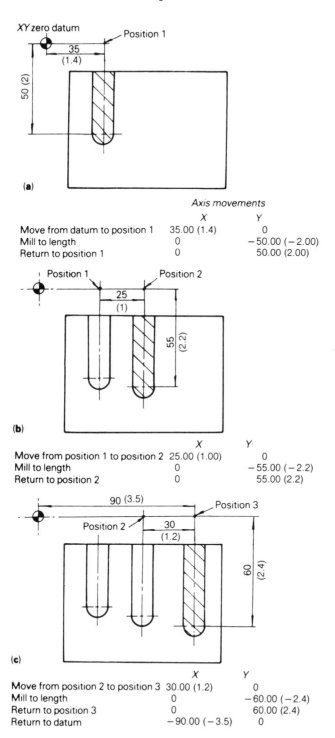

Figure 6.11 Milling using incremental positioning. (Inch units are given in parentheses.)

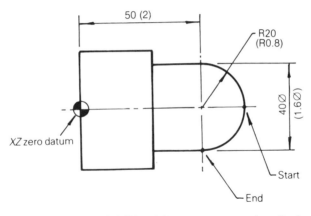

Figure 6.12 Turned component detail involving arc programming. (Inch units are given in parentheses.)

In incremental terms:

		X	Z	I	K
Inch	G02	0.8	−0.8	0	0.8
Metric	G02	20	−20	0	20

The variation in the X values in these two examples is because the absolute program assumes that X values are programmed as a diameter rather than a radius.

I has no value because the center and start point of the arc are in line with each other in relationship to the X axis. In practice, when a value is zero, it is not entered in the program.

The I, J, and K values are always positive, with I related to X, J related to Y, and K related to Z.

Complete circles and semicircles are programmed as a series of 90° quadrants in many cases. Thus a complete circle would require four lines of program entry. New pieces of equipment can now complete full circles in one line of program entry.

Figure 6.13 shows the program for a milled profile. The cutter radius has been ignored. In absolute terms:

	G	X	Y	I	J
Inch	03	2	−1.2	1.2	0
	02	3.5	−1.2	0	1.6
Metric	03	50	−30	30	0
	02	90	−70	0	40

In incremental terms:

	G	X	Y	I	J
Inch	03	1.2	−1.2	1.2	0
	02	1.6	−1.6	0	1.6

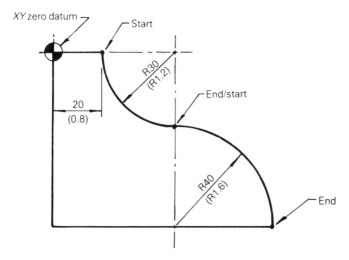

Figure 6.13 Milled component involving arc programming. (Inch units are given in parentheses.)

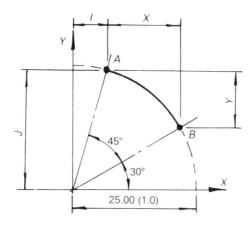

Figure 6.14 Partial arc programming. (Inch units are given in parentheses.)

Metric	G	X	Y	I	J
	03	30	−30	30	0
	02	40	−40	0	40

There are often situations where the start and/or stop points do not coincide with an X, Y, or Z axis, and it is then necessary to make a series of calculations. Such a situation is shown in Fig. 6.14. Dimensional values for X, Y, I, and J have to be determined. The necessary trigonometry is indicated in Fig. 6.15.

From A to B the magnitude of the X move is

$$\textit{Inch } 1 \times \cos 30° - 1 \times \cos 75° = 0.866 - 0.259 = 0.607$$
$$\textit{Metric } 25.00 \cos 30° - 25.00 \cos 75° = 21.65 - 6.47 = 15.18$$

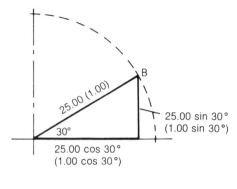

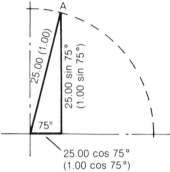

Figure 6.15 Trigonometry required to program a partial arc. (Inch units are given in parentheses.)

From *A* to *B* the magnitude of the *Y* move is

$$Inch \; 1 \times \sin 75° - 1 \times \sin 30° = 0.966 - 0.500 = 0.466$$
$$Metric \; 25.00 \sin 75° - 25 \sin 30° = 24.15 - 12.50 = 11.65$$

The magnitude of the *I* dimension in the *X* axis is

$$Inch \; 1 \times \cos 75° = 0.259$$
$$Metric \; 25 \cos 75° = 6.47$$

The magnitude of *J* in the *Y* axis is

$$Inch \; 1 \times \sin 75° = 0.966$$
$$Metric \; 25.00 \sin 75° = 24.15$$

Once the dimensions have been incorporated, they are incorporated in the program as before.

Method 2

The second method of arc programming varies from the one previously described in the way in which the arc center is defined. As in the previous method, it will be assumed that the cutting tool has arrived at the start point of the curve. To continue, the following data are required.

1. The finish or target point of the arc is dimensionally defined in relation to the start point using the appropriate combination of X, Y, and Z values stated in absolute or incremental terms.
2. The center of the arc is dimensionally defined in relation to the program datum using I, J, and K values measured along the corresponding X, Y, and Z axes respectively.

Using this method the arc shown in Fig. 6.12 would be programmed as follows.
In absolute terms:

	G	X	Z	I	K
Inch	02	1.6	2.0	0	2.0
Metric	02	40	50	0	50

In incremental terms:

	G	X	Z	I	K
Inch	02	0.8	−0.8	0	2.0
Metric	02	20	−20	0	50

Note that in this example it is I that has no value, since the center of the arc lies on the X datum and therefore I would be omitted from the program.

When the arc center is related to the program datum it is possible for the I, J, and K values to be a negative quantity, as illustrated in Figure 6.16.

The programming methods referred to above concern arcs of up to 90°. Some of the more modem control systems permit programming of arcs in excess of 90° in one data block, a facility referred to as 'multi-quadrant' programming or 360° circular interpolation.

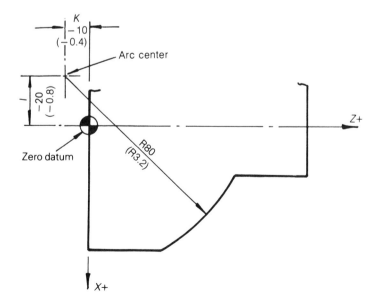

Figure 6.16 Negative I and K values. (Inch units are given in parentheses.)

Method 3

The third method of arc programming on some controls is to use absolute or incremental polar coordinates. It varies from the previous methods in that it does not use I and J values. With this method the circle center point has been defined previously with X, Y, or Z values. The arc is then programmed with a radius dimension and an angular amount of tool path from the circle center. A positive or negative angle will establish the direction of the cutter path:

1. The circle center is established with absolute or incremental dimensions.
2. The tool will have been moved to the arc start point.
3. The degrees of arc and radius are then programmed, with the sign (+ or −) on the degrees of arc establishing direction of cut.

Using the above terms the arc in Figure 6.12 would be programmed as follows:
In absolute terms:

Inch	CC *X*0 *Z*2	Define circle center
	G1 *X*0 *Z*2.8	Position cutter to starting point
	C Polar radius 0.8 polar angle 90°	Cut circle
Metric	CC *X*0 *Z*50	Define circle center
	G1 *X*0 *Z*70	Position cutter to start point
	C Polar radius 20 polar angle 90°	Cut circle

Positive angles denote clockwise motion; negative angles denote counterclockwise motion. Note: Most machines with polar coordinate circular interpolation capabilities are conversationally controlled.

In incremental terms:

Inch	CC *X*0 *Z*2	Circle center from datum
	G1 *X*0 *Z*2.8	Position tool to start from circle center
	C Polar radius 0.8 polar angle 90°	Circular movement
Metric	CC *X*0 *Z*50	Circle center from datum
	G1 *X*0 *Z*20	Position tool to start from circle center
	C Polar radius 20 polar angle 90°	Circular movement

Ramp

The starting and stopping of slide servo motors appear to be instantaneous. In fact there is, of course, a brief period of acceleration at the start of a move and a brief period of deceleration at the end of a move. This is shown graphically in Figure 6.17.

The period of acceleration is known as "ramp up" and the period of deceleration as "ramp down." The ramp is a carefully designed feature of the servo motor.

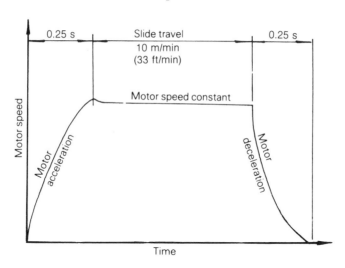

Figure 6.17 Servo motor speed/feed rate relationship.

From a metal-cutting point of view, the quicker a slide attains its correct feed rate the better, and ideally this should be maintained throughout the cut. The ramp period therefore is kept as brief as possible, but consideration has to be given to ensuring that at the end of the movement there is no motor overrun or oscillation, both of which could affect the dimensional accuracy of the component.

For linear interpolation the ramp effect is rarely of concern, but for circular interpolation, and particularly where one curve runs into another, it is preferable that there is no speed variation of the servo motor, and thus of the feed rate of the slide, however small this might be. Any such variation would not only affect the metal-removal rate but may also affect the dimensional accuracy and surface finish of the component. Because of this, many control units are equipped with a *ramp inhibit* or *ramp suppression* facility, which means there is no slowing down or acceleration of the slide movement as one programmed movement leads into a second. G codes allocated to ramp are usually G08 and G09.

Repetitive Machining Sequences

There are a number of machining sequences that are commonly used when machining a variety of components. Other less common sequences may be repetitive, but only on one particular component. It is helpful, since it reduces the program length, if such a sequence can be programmed just once and given an identity so that it can be called back into the main program as and when required. Such sequences are referred to in a variety of ways, for example, as cycles, subroutines, loops, patterns, and macros. Although this can be slightly confusing, there are instances when one particular title appears to be more appropriate than the others. Various types of repeat machining sequences are discussed here.

Standardized Fixed Cycles

A number of the basic machining sequences, or cycles, commonly used were initially standardized (ANSI/EIA RS-274-D:1979; BS 3635:1972). The recommendations were commonly adopted and continue to be employed today. The machining cycles are identified by assigned G codes, and when they are incorporated into a control system, they are referred to as "fixed" or "canned" cycles. Perhaps the most commonly used fixed cycle is that of drilling a hole. Consider the hole shown in Figure 6.18(a). The sequence of machine movements involved in drilling the hole would be:

1. Position to hole location.
2. Lower the spindle at a programmed feed rate.
3. Lift the spindle rapidly to the start position.

Now consider the process of drilling the hole shown in Figure 6.18(b). The same sequence of spindle movements is necessary; the only variation is in the depth of travel. To program such a sequence of moves is quite simple, but if there were a large number of holes to be drilled, apart from the boredom of repeating the necessary data when writing the program, the program itself would be very long. In addition, the fewer data commands that have to be handled the less likely it is that errors will be made. By standardizing the sequence of moves the only additional data requirements are the new hole location, depth of cut, feed rate, and spindle speed. This information, with the appropriate G code, is entered only once. Each time the slide moves to bring

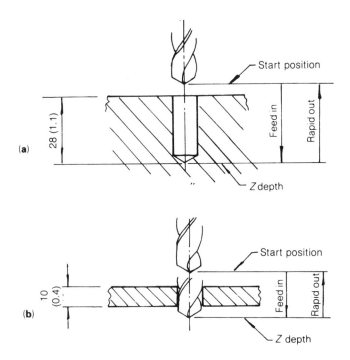

Figure 6.18 Movements required to drill holes. (Inch units are given in parentheses.)

the spindle to a new position in relation to the work another hole is drilled to the programmed depth.

Nonstandardized Fixed Cycles

It is often the case that manufacturers of machine control units wish to include in their systems cycles that are not necessarily widely applicable and therefore do not fit into the "standardized" category, but the inclusion of which considerably enhances their control system. The cycles they choose to include will depend on the machine type to which the control is to be fitted. Some of the more common cycles of this nature are discussed below.

Loops The term "loop" is particularly relevant when reducing raw material to size by making a series of roughing cuts. Consider the component shown in Figure 6.19, which is to be reduced from 50 mm (2 in.) to 26 mm (1 in.) diameter by a series of cuts each of 2 mm (0.08 in.) depth. Assuming that the starting point for the tool is as shown, the tool will first move in a distance of 2.5 mm (0.1 in.), thus taking a 2 mm (0.08 in.) depth of cut, travel along a length of 50 mm (2 in.), retract 0.5 mm (0.02 in.), and return to the Z datum, thereby completing the loop. It will then move in a distance of 2.5 mm (0.1 in.), feed along 50 mm (2 in.), retract 0.5 mm (0.02 in.), and return to the Z datum, and so on.

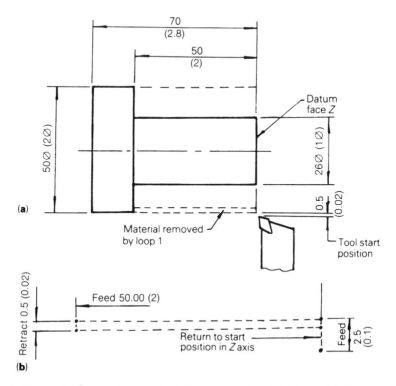

Figure 6.19 Looping or roughing cycle: **(a)** component and **(b)** loop details, repeated six times. (Inch units are given in parentheses.)

The loop, including the feed rate, is programmed just once, but is repeated via the "loop count" command in the main program as many times as necessary to reduce the work to the required diameter. Note: some controls will do this with special "G" codes, while other controls will use special command codes, but the results are the same.

Face Milling Cycle Figure 6.20 shows details of a face milling cycle. After programming the appropriate G code, together with spindle speed and feed rate, the only other information required are the X and Y dimensions of the face to be milled. The control unit computer will determine the number of passes necessary and the appropriate cutter step-over to machine the face. The cutter diameter will be picked up automatically from previously entered information. This type of cycle is very commonly found on conversationally programmed controls.

Slot Milling Cycle Figure 6.21 illustrates a slot milling routine. As with face milling, the programmer has to state spindle speed, feed rate, and slot dimensions in the X and Y axes. The first pass made by the cutter passes through the middle of the slot and then returns to the start. Further passes are made until the correct depth is achieved, the number of passes necessary being determined by the axis increment depth programmed in the cycle. When the correct depth is reached, the cutter path is that of a series of cycles increasing in size with each pass. Some controls vary this process by cutting the entire slot at each depth except the finish pass. Again, as with the face milling, the computer will determine the step-over and the number of cycles necessary to machine the slot to size.

Pocket Milling Figure 6.22 illustrates the pocket milling cycle. This cycle starts at the center of the pocket, the cutter feeding in the Z axis to a programmed depth. There follows a series of cycles until the programmed X and Y dimensions are reached, the step-over of up to 80% of the cutter diameter will ensure that a flat surface is produced by providing overlap of passes. Some systems provide for a cycle that roughs out the main

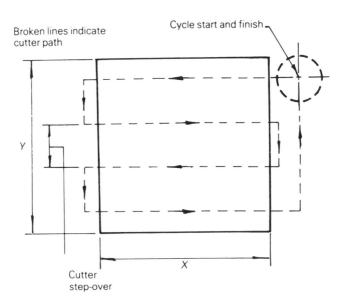

Figure 6.20 Face milling cycle.

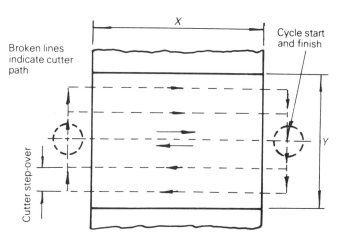

Figure 6.21 Slot milling cycle.

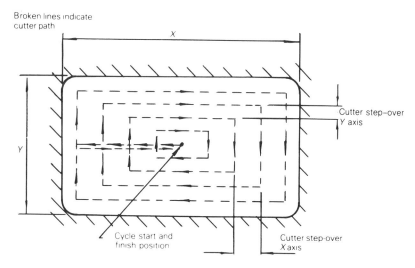

Figure 6.22 Pocket milling cycle.

pocket and then machines to size with a small finishing cut. If the pocket depth is such that more than one increment in the Z axis is necessary, the slide movement returns the cutter to the center of the pocket and the cycle is repeated at the next depth.

Bolt Hole Circles The term "bolt hole circle" means that a number of holes are required equally spaced on a stated pitch circle diameter as illustrated in Figure 6.23. Given that the program has brought the cutter to the pole position, the other dimensional data required are the position of the first hole, the Z axis movement, the pitch diameter or radius, depending on the control system, and the number of holes required. The computer makes all the necessary calculations to convert the polar coordinates to linear coordinates and to move the slides accordingly.

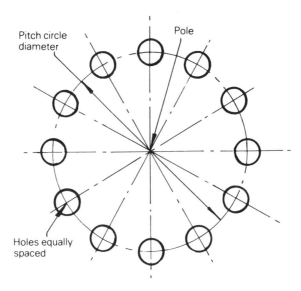

Figure 6.23 Bolt hole circle.

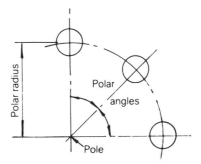

Figure 6.24 Polar coordinates.

A variation of this cycle will cater for just two or three holes positioned in an angular relationship to one another. An example is detailed in Figure 6.24. Again, the pole position is programmed and the cutter will be at this point when the cycle commences. The additional dimensional data that have to be supplied are the Z axis movement, the polar radius and the polar angle(s), and the number of holes required, the computer then converts this information to slide movement in the appropriate axes.

On some control systems it is possible to "rotate" more complex loop programmed features such as the example shown in Figure 6.25.

Cycles Devised by the Part Programmer

Cycles devised by the part programmer may be defined as follows. First, there are cycles that are devised specifically for one particular machining task. Second, there are those that may be used when machining a range of components.

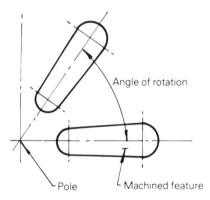

Figure 6.25 Feature rotation.

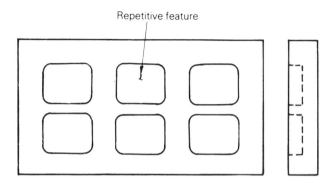

Figure 6.26 Component with repetitive feature.

Consider the component shown in Figure 6.26, which has a repetitive feature, namely, the recess. When writing a program for machining this particular component, the programmer would devise a cycle, in situations such as this being referred to as a "routine," for producing just one recess. Via an appropriate call the blocks of data defining the routine can be activated as and when required within the main machining program at new locations.

The construction of a routine may include subroutines also specifically constructed by the part programmer and may also utilize any fixed or canned cycles that are considered appropriate. The technique of programming cycles or routines within routines is referred to as "nesting" and is further described subsequently.

Assume the component shown in Figure 6.26 is quite large so that within each recess there were also a number of holes arranged in three groups, as shown in Figure 6.27. The main routine would be the data necessary for the production of the recess, as explained above. The subroutine would be the data necessary to produce a group of four holes. The subroutine would be nested within the main routine and called into the main program on three occasions.

However, the production of the four holes is repetitive, and thus it is possible to program to produce just one hole, but to repeat the sequence four times. The complete

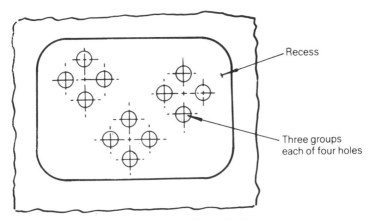

Figure 6.27 Enlarged detail of component in Figure 6.26.

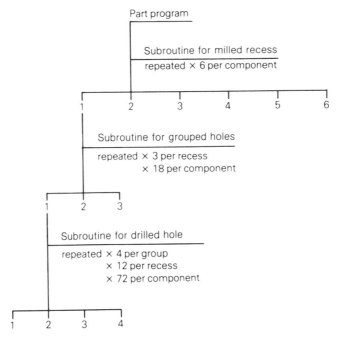

Figure 6.28 'Nesting' three deep.

sequence for producing the component is illustrated diagrammatically in Figure 6.28. On some control systems it is possible to program cycles within cycles as many as eight deep.

Programmer-devised cycles of the second type, to which reference was made above, are useful when a machined feature commonly occurs within the production schedule of a particular company, that is, a machined feature (possibly of unusual design) is required over a range of components. To accommodate this situation some control systems permit routines that are "user defined" to be prepared and "stored within the control system," so that they may be recalled and utilized as and when required as part of a more comprehensive machining program. A routine of this nature is also referred to as a "macro."

A macro may have fixed dimensions or it may have parametric variables, that is, the dimensions may be varied to produce different versions of the same basic feature or component. This technique is referred to as "parametric programming" and is described in more detail in Chapter 9.

Mirror Image

A commonly occurring aspect of mechanical engineering design is the need for components, or features of components, that are dimensionally identical but geometrically opposite either in two axes or in one axis. By using the mirror-image facility such components or features can be machined from just one set of data. The component shown in Figure 6.29 has a feature that is mirrored in two axes. Note that, to produce the second profile, the positive incremental values become negative and the negative incremental values become positive. To produce a feature of the opposite hand, as shown in Figure 6.30, the direction of slide movement changes in one axis only.

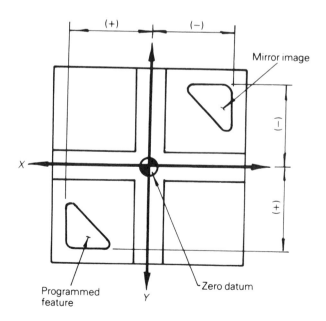

Figure 6.29 Mirror image in two axes.

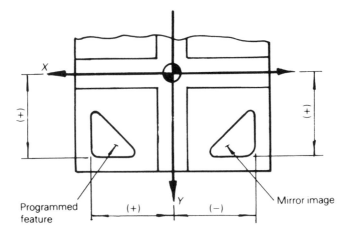

Figure 6.30 Mirror image in one axis.

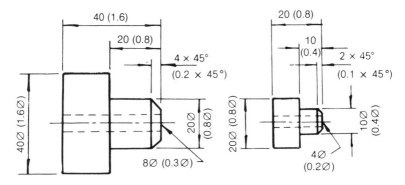

Figure 6.31 Geometrically identical components suitable for production by scaling. (Inch units are given in parentheses.)

Scaling

Another common requirement in mechanical engineering design is components with the same geometrical shape but varying dimensionally. Figure 6.31 illustrates two such components. When a control system is fitted with a scaling facility, it is possible to produce a range of components, varying in size, from one set of program data. The facility can also be used to produce geometrically identical features of components that may be required to be reproduced to different sizes.

Slash Delete

The slash or block delete facility enables part, or parts, of a program to be omitted. It is particularly useful when producing components that have slight dimensional variations. For example, a hole may be required in one version of a component but not in another, although all other details may be identical. The program data relating to the production of the hole are contained within the programmed symbols/, one at the start of each block concerned. An example is shown below. See manufacturers' programming manual for possible variations in format.

```
/N05  G01  Z1000  F  150*
/N06  G00  Z−1000*
```

To make a component *with* the hole, the operator need not take any action. To produce a component *without* the hole, the operator will have to activate the slash delete switch on the control console at the start of the program. When the slash is reached, the control unit will ignore the data that follow. On some systems, if the slash delete is not activated, the program will stop when the slash is reached and the operator then has to make a positive response either to activate the data or to delete them.

This facility is particularly useful when machining castings or forgings, where stock removal requirements may vary, the operator being given the option to include an extra cut or delete it as necessary.

Jog

The jog facility enables the machine operator to move the machine slides manually via the control console. This may need to be done for a variety of reasons, the most obvious one being when establishing datums at the initial setting of the machine. There are also two standard "G" code boring cycles that call for jog retracts after the cycle before returning to automatic operation. It may also be necessary to stop an automatic sequence and move the machine slides to facilitate work measurement, tool changing due to breakage, and so on. Whatever the reason it is desirable that the automatic program is restarted at the point at which it was interrupted, and most control systems have a *return from jog* facility that returns the machine slides to their original positions, this facility being activated manually via a button on the control console.

Program Stop

Stops in a machining sequence can be predetermined and included in the part program as a miscellaneous function (M00). Scheduled stops for measurement, tool changing (on manual tool change machines), etc., have to be notified to the machine operator so that he or she will be aware of his or her duties at this point.

Program stops can also be optional, that is, the sequence does not have to stop. Optional stops are also included in the part program as a miscellaneous function (M01) and the control will ignore the command unless the operator has previously activated a switch on the control console.

Datums

Machine Datum

The machine datum, also referred to as "zero datum" or simply as "zero," is a set position for the machine slides, having a numerical identity within the control system of

zero. All slide movements are made in dimensional relationship to this datum as indicated earlier in the chapter, when absolute and incremental positioning moves were
discussed.

On some machines the zero datum may be a permanent position that cannot be altered. On other machines a new zero is readily established by moving the slides so that
the cutting tool is placed in the desired position in relation to the workpiece and then
pressing the appropriate zero button on the control console. The facility to establish a
datum in this manner is referred to as a floating zero or zero shift. The location of the
original zero is not retained within the control memory.

A fixed machine datum may be helpful to the part programmer, especially when the
programming is carried out remote from the machining facility, since the position can
be taken into consideration when writing the program. It will be necessary, however, for
the programmer to specify the exact location of the component in relation to the machine datum if the program is to achieve the desired results.

A floating zero affords greater flexibility when machine setting, since the work can be
positioned anywhere within the range of slide movement and the zero established to
suit. But this can be time-consuming and, if incorrectly carried out, may result in machining errors or crashes.

Program Datum

The program datum or zero is established by the part programmer when writing the part
program, and the program will require all slide movements to be made in relation to that
point.

In practice, the machine zero and the program zero are often synchronized by either
accurately positioning the work or, when possible, resetting the machine zero. Any un-
avoidable variations between the two positions can be accommodated by using the zero
offset facility, if available, as described below.

Zero Offset

The zero offset facility enables a machine zero datum to be readily repositioned on a temporary basis. Once it has been repositioned, the slide movements that follow will be made
in dimensional relationship to the new datum. It is particularly useful when the original
machine datum does not coincide with the part program datum, a situation that can arise,
for instance, when a part program has been prepared without regard to the normally fixed
position of the machine datum and difficulties are encountered in positioning the workpiece to suit the part program. A simple example of this is when a part program for a
turned component has been prepared using the forward face of the workpiece as a zero
datum when the machine zero is, as is often the case, located at the back face of the chuck.
Use of the zero offset facility will reestablish the zero at the work face. The zero offset facility also enables two or more components to be machined at one setting from the same
part program. In Figure 6.32 component 1 would be machined with slide movements
made in relation to datum 1. On completion of the machining sequence, the machine table

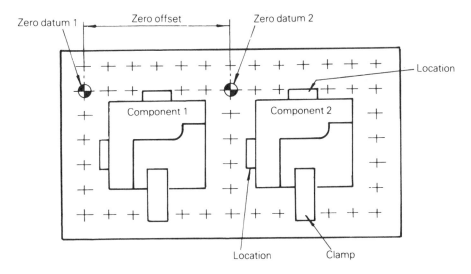

Figure 6.32 The use of zero offset facility when machining components located on a grid plate.

would be caused to move, via the part program or by manual intervention at the keyboard to datum 2 where the offset feature would be activated to the predetermined offset dimension and the machining sequence would be repeated for component 2, with all slide movements being made in relation to datum 2. The control would retain information regarding the location of the original datum, which remains a permanent feature of the part program, add the machine slide can be caused to return to that position.

The facility may also be used to machine identical features on components of different lengths. A simple example would be to cut a screw thread of particular dimensions on the ends of two bars the overall lengths of which are not the same. Similarly, the facility can also be used when turned workpieces are reversed for secondary operations and the second setting in relation to the Z axis zero differs from the first.

On the more sophisticated controls it is possible to establish a new zero, or zeros, at various stages throughout the program. All subsequent moves will be made in relation to the new datum, but these moves are not necessarily a repeat of the moves made before the new zero was established. This facility enables the features of complex or very long components to be machined by relating slide movement to more than one datum, thus simplifying programming and possibly reducing machining time by limiting the length of slide travel.

QUESTIONS

1 What is a preparatory function and how is it designated in word address programming?

2 What is a miscellaneous function and how is it designated in word address programming?

3 What is meant by the term "modal"?

4 Name and describe the three types of positioning control used on computer numerically controlled machine tools.

5 Explain, with the aid of a simple sketch, the difference between absolute and incremental dimension definition.

6 When are the letters I, J, and K used in a word address program?

7 What is meant by the term "ramp suppression"?

8 Describe what happens during a peck drill cycle.

9 What is a looping cycle and when is it used?

10 Describe what happens during a pocket milling cycle.

11 What is a bolt hole circle?

12 What is meant by the "rotation" of a machined feature?

13 With the aid of a simple sketch describe the effect of reproducing a machine feature using the mirror image programming facility in (a) two axes; (b) one axis.

14 What is the programming function that permits the production from one set of data, components geometrically identical but with proportional dimensional variations?

15 Explain the meaning of the term "nesting" as applied to machining cycles.

16 When is the block or slash delete facility likely to be used and how is it generally invoked?

17 What is the jog facility on a machine control system and when is it likely to be used?

18 Give two reasons for including an optional stop in a program.

19 Why is it necessary to inform a machine operator of the scheduled stops in a machining program?

20 With the aid of simple sketches describe the meaning of zero offset.

SPEEDS AND FEEDS FOR NUMERICALLY CONTROLLED MACHINING

Cutting Speeds and Feeds

It is difficult to determine precise data for any metal-cutting operation without knowledge of the practicalities involved. For example, the condition of the machine, the power available, the rigidity of tooling and work-holding arrangements, the volume of metal to be removed, the surface finish required, and the type of coolant to be used are all factors that have to be considered when determining the appropriate speeds and feeds to be used. The programmer is obliged to make program entries that will be, if not perfect, then at least functional.

Should it prove that the programmed speed and feed are inappropriate, machine control units have manually operated override facilities to enable the operator to increase or decrease speeds and feeds as machining proceeds. If such action is found to be necessary, the programmer should be informed so that the part program can be modified accordingly.

The selection of appropriate speeds and feeds can be based on experience when the programmer possesses the necessary practical background. Experienced craftsmen often have an instinctive ability to recognize the correct speed and feed for any particular machining task, having long forgotten any theoretical basis they may have once been taught concerning such matters. But this approach is perhaps more suitable to conventional machining processes than it is to CNC machining.

Reference to data published by the manufacturers of the cutting tools to be used is more appropriate for numerically controlled machining, since the lack of operator involvement is a feature of CNC machining it becomes imperative that optimum speeds and feeds are used. However, when reference is made to published data, the programmer should exercise caution. The figures quoted, while perfectly feasible when used under the correct conditions, can appear to be somewhat optimistic when applied to many machining situations. Examples of manufacturers' data relating to cutting speeds and feeds are included in Appendices B.

Whatever approach is used, it is essential that the programmer fully appreciates the capabilities of any machine for which he or she is preparing programs. For instance, it is pointless to program speeds and feeds that result in metal removal rates that are beyond the power capacity of the machine. Conversely, it is equally pointless to underuse the power available. If a programmer lacks essential knowledge of this nature, then liaison with those who have had practical experience of the machine should be a priority.

Unusual machining situations involving set-ups that may lack rigidity should be approached with care, and the programmed speeds and feeds should be initially on the low side. They can always be increased later in the light of experience gained at the machine when metal cutting has actually taken place.

Special attention should also be given to specific requirements regarding surface finish. Machinists are often obsessed with obtaining a "good" finish, but it should be remembered that there is no point in reducing metal removal rates to obtain a high-quality surface finish that is not necessary. A further point to remember is that a designer may specifically require a "rough" finish, so it is essential to work to the information contained on the drawing. The programmer should ensure that the setup person/operator responsible for the machining operation fully appreciates what the requirements are.

The intricate contouring capabilities of CNC machines can also present problems regarding surface finish. For example, feed rate that produces satisfactory results when machining a parallel turned surface may no longer produce acceptable results when the cutting tool changes direction to machine a tapered or radial surface. Similar situations present themselves during milling operations. When machining complex profiles that are subject to stringent surface finish requirements, the results obtained from programmed feeds and speeds, particularly feeds, should be monitored and modifications made if necessary.

Surface finish is, of course, affected by the condition of the cutting tool. Tool performance begins to deteriorate from the moment the tool is first used, and ultimately it not only affects the surface finish but may result in dimensional features not being maintained, unacceptable vibration, work deflection and eventually total failure of the tool. An unsuitable choice of cutting speeds and feeds may hasten this process, so the part programmer must give due consideration to tool life when making decisions in this respect.

It is possible to calculate the life of a cutting tool. The formula used for this purpose was derived by experimentation and, because of the many variables that exist between one machining situation and another, the results obtained from its application can only be used as a guide. The reader may reasonably ask why bother to make such a calculation if the result is only a guide, and it would be difficult to give a totally convincing answer. Nevertheless, it would be helpful to know when a tool was reaching the end of its life, so that replacement could be effected before total failure occurred. The automatic tool condition sensing devices being applied to the more complex CNC machining installations may provide the answer. In the meantime, how is the part programmer to decide what speeds and feeds to use to give an acceptable tool life, while at the same time achieving the basic objective of removing metal in the least possible time?

As stated earlier, reference can be made to the cutting tool manufacturers' literature. Their figures will have taken into account the fact that a reasonable tool life is required by the user of their products. But there is still the problem that local conditions may make their recommendations invalid. Yet again, it may be initially necessary to rely on past practical experience, and to be prepared to make modifications based on a reasoned appraisal of the situation when metal cutting is under way.

One further point relating to tool performance should be noted. The chip-breaking qualities of most carbide-tipped tools is directly related to speeds and feeds. If chip clearance becomes a problem, some modification of the cutting conditions may be appropriate.

Spindle Speeds

The program data controlling spindle speeds is expressed in one of two ways, the numerical value in both cases being preceded by the letter S. Thus a data entry of, say, S250 could indicate either a *constant surface cutting speed* of 250 ft. or m per minute or, alternatively, a *spindle speed* of 250 revolutions per minute (rev/min).

All machines have the facility to program a set spindle speed in revolutions per minute, while the alternative facility of programming a constant surface cutting speed is now commonly available on the majority of turning centers.

When both facilities are available, the machine controller differentiates between the two possibilities via a previous data entry that will establish the desired operating mode. In the case of word address programming this mode is established by a G code entry, commonly G96 (ft. or m per min) and G97 (rev/min). Feet or meters per minute will depend on whether the G70 inch programming or G71 metric programming code is active. In the case of conversational MDI, the mode is established by selection from the displayed options.

Consider the process of programming a constant surface cutting speed. The cutting speed is the rate at which the cutting tool passes over the workpiece material, or alternatively the rate at which the material is traveling as it passes the cutting tool. As indicated previously, it can be expressed in either meters or feet per minute.

Appropriate surface cutting speeds for use with cutting tools made of specific materials, when used to cut certain metals, have been determined by experiment. The figures give due regard to the maximum metal removal rates that can be obtained, while at the same time equating satisfactorily with other factors such as tool life, surface finish, and power consumption. These recommended cutting speeds are published by the manufacturers of cutting tools as a guide to users of their products (see Appendix B). As stated earlier, it may be necessary to modify these values to suit local conditions before making a program entry.

The advantage of programming a surface cutting speed as opposed to a set spindle speed in revolutions per minute is best appreciated by considering the simple operation of parting-off from bar stock during a turning operation.

During a parting-off operation the diameter of the work where metal cutting is actually taking place is steadily decreasing, and therefore the cutting efficiency is only maintained if the spindle speed increases at a corresponding rate. This steady increase, which maintains the most efficient metal cutting rate for that particular job material, is automatically achieved via the constant surface cutting speed programming facility.

The process of parting off is a convenient one to explain the value of the constant surface cutting speed programming. However, it is not a process where the use of such a facility is absolutely critical. The facility is more likely to be of value during the turning of complex profiles requiring a uniformly high standard of surface finish throughout the turned length.

In order to program a constant spindle speed in revolutions per minute, it is necessary to make a simple calculation that takes into consideration the recommended surface cutting speed referred to previously, and also the diameter of the workpiece in the case of turning operations, or the cutter in the case of milling operations. The relationship between these factors is expressed as follows.

$$\text{Spindle rev/min} = \frac{1000 \times \text{Cutting speed in m/min}}{\pi \times \text{Work or cutter diameter in mm}}$$

Multiplying the cutting speed by 1000 converts it from *meters* per minute to *millimeters* per minute, while multiplying the work or cutter diameter by π, that is, calculating the circumference, determines the relative linear travel per revolution in millimeters. Dividing the circumference in millimeters into the cutting speed in millimeters per minute determines the number of revolutions per minute required.

When inch programming, the relationship between spindle speed, work or cutter diameter and the required cutting speed is expressed as follows:

$$\text{Spindle speed in rev/min} = \frac{12 \times \text{Cutting speed in ft/min}}{\pi \times \text{Work or cutter diameter in inches}}$$

In this case multiplying the cutting speed by 12 and so converting it to in./min makes all the units in the equation compatible.

A number of cutting tool manufacturers distribute simple calculators, the use of which eliminates the need to make calculations. These devices will indicate the appropriate cutting tool material, selected from the manufacturer's range, that should be used when machining a certain material type, together with a recommended surface cutting speed for the type of operation (roughing or finishing) that is to be undertaken.

Surface Cutting Speeds

The speeds in Table 7.1 are suitable for average metal-cutting conditions. In practice it may be possible to increase these speeds considerably for light finishing cuts or, conversely, to reduce them for roughing cuts. For more accurate speed and feed tables related to operation, material, and finish refer to *Machining Data Handbook* by the Machinability Data Center (Metcut Research Associates Inc.) or *Machinery's Handbook* by Oberg, Jones, and Horton (Industrial Press Inc.).

Spindle Speeds

Example: Determine the spindle speed required to turn a 2.5-in.-diameter piece of aluminum using a high-speed tool and a surface feet per minute (SFPM) cutting speed of 300 ft/min:

$$\text{Spindle speed, rev/min} = \frac{12 \times 300}{\pi \times 2.5} = 458$$

Table 7.1 Surface cutting speeds, m/min (ft/min)

Tool Material	Part Material			
	Mild Steel	Cast Iron	Aluminum Alloy	Brass
Cemented carbide	170 (300)	100 (225)	250 (900)	180 (450)
High-speed steel	28 (90)	18 (75)	120 (300)	75 (150)

Example: Determine the spindle speed required to turn 50 mm diameter brass using a cemented carbide tool and a surface cutting speed of 180 m/min:

$$\text{Spindle speed, rev/min} = \frac{1000 \times 180}{\pi \times 50} = 1146$$

These spindle speeds will be correct for turning a 2.5 in. or 50 mm diameter bar. However, as the diameter decreases, as for instance during an end-facing operation, these spindle speeds are no longer valid or efficient. On many numerical control systems it is possible to program a surface cutting speed only, and the machine spindle speed will automatically vary within the range of the machine to compensate for changes in the work diameter, thus providing a constant cutting speed.

Feed Rates

The manufacturer's calculators referred to previously will also indicate an appropriate feed rate for the operation. The feed rate is the speed at which the cutter penetrates into the work material.

When programming data relating to feed rate, it can be expressed either as millimeters per minute (mm/min) or millimeters per revolution (mm/rev) of the machine spindle. With inch programming, the units will be inches per minute (in./min) or inches per revolution (in./rev).

The letter F is commonly used to denote the feed rate in a part program. Thus F25 could indicate a feed rate of 0.25 in. or mm/rev, while F80 could indicate a feed rate of 80 in. or mm/min, depending on the mode of expression being used. It is necessary to ensure that the data entered and the programming mode are compatible.

Although variations exist, the set-up data using the G codes common to a number or word address programming systems are as follows:

G94   feed/min
G95   feed/rev

In this situation the units to be used are established by the use of G70 for inch and G71 for metric.

Feed rates are published by cutting tool manufacturers in the same way as surface cutting speeds. Usually the rates are expressed as mm/rev or in./rev. To convert to mm/min or in./min involves making a simple calculation as follows:

Feed mm/min = Feed mm/rev × Spindle speed rev/min

or,

$$\text{Feed in./min} = \text{Feed in./rev} \times \text{Spindle speed rev/min}$$

The manufacturers of milling cutters sometimes quote recommended feed rates in millimeters or inches per tooth, in which case it is necessary, prior to making the preceding calculation, to determine the feed per revolution of the cutter. This is achieved as follows:

$$\text{Feed/rev} = \text{Feed/tooth} \times \text{Number of cutter teeth}$$

Feed Rates for Turning

Cemented carbide tools are used extensively in turning operations. It is common practice for the manufacturers to quote recommended feed rates in inches or millimeters per spindle revolution (in./rev. or mm/rev). Typical feed rates for different work materials are given in Table 7.2.

To determine the feed rate in mm/min (in./min):

$$\text{Feed mm/min (in./min)} = \text{Feed mm/rev (in./rev)} \times \text{Spindle speed (rev/min)}$$

When a constant surface cutting speed is programmed, that is, the spindle speed varies automatically to compensate for variations in the work diameter, the feed rate is programmed in in. or mm/rev to maintain a constant feed rate per spindle revolution. When the spindle speed is programmed at a constant rev/min, the feed rate can be entered either as in. or mm/rev or in. or mm/min, since both will result in a constant relationship between surface cutting speed and feed.

Feed Rates for Milling

The manufacturers of milling cutters state recommended feed rates as in. or mm/rev, in. or mm/min or in. or mm/tooth.

When feeds are quoted as in. or mm/rev or in. or mm/min, they usually refer to specific cutters in the manufacturer's product line and cannot be generally applied. For instance, if two face mills both of the same diameter, but one having five carbide inserts and the other six, were used at the same spindle speed with a feed quoted per revolution, it would mean that the cutter with the fewest teeth would be subjected to a much higher

Table 7.2 Typical feed rates for turning, mm/rev (in./rev)

Mild Steel	Cast Iron	Aluminum Alloy	Brass
0.25 (roughing 0.007–0.025) (finishing 0.002–0.007)	0.25 (roughing 0.007–0.025) (finishing 0.002–0.007)	0.3 (roughing 0.007–0.030) (finishing 0.002–0.007)	0.3 (roughing 0.007–0.030) (finishing 0.002–0.007)

volume of metal removal per tooth than the cutter with more teeth. So for general use feed rates quoted in in. or mm/tooth are more suitable. These data can then be used to determine the feed rate per revolution as follows:

Feed, mm/rev (in. /rev) = Feed, mm/tooth (in. /tooth) × Number of teeth

And from this formula,

Feed, mm/min (in./min) = Feed, mm/rev (in./rev) × Spindle speed (rev/min)

Typical feed rates are given in Table 7.3.

Feed Rates for Drilling

High-speed-steel drills are used extensively for producing smaller holes. Since small-diameter drills are liable to break, the feed rate is related to the drill size. Typical feed rates are given in Table 7.4.

Cemented carbide drills, sometimes with tips brazed to a medium carbon steel shank, but more commonly as clamped inserts, are favored for larger holes. The feed rates for

Table 7.3 Typical feed rates for milling, mm/tooth (in./tooth).

Work Material	High-Speed-Steel Cutters		Cemented Carbide Cutters	
	Face and Shell End Mills	End Mills	Face and Shell End Mills	End Mills[a]
Mild steel	0.25 (0.010)	0.15 (0.005)	0.30 (0.008–0.020)	0.18 (0.003–0.010)
Cast iron	0.30 (0.013)	0.18 (0.007)	0.50 (0.008–0.020)	0.21 (0.005–0.012)
Aluminum alloy	0.40 (0.022)	0.17 (0.011)	0.60 (0.005–0.020)	0.25 (0.005–0.020)
Brass	0.35 (0.014)	0.15 (0.007)	0.40 (0.005–0.020)	0.19 (0.003–0.012)

[a] As with high-speed-steel end mills, the design of some cemented carbide end mills provides for both plunge and side cutting.

Table 7.4 Typical feed rates for high-speed steel drills

Drill Size (mm)	2	4	6	8	10	12	14	16	18	20
Feed Rate (mm/rev)	0.05	0.10	0.12	0.15	0.18	0.21	0.24	0.26	0.28	0.30

Drill size (in.)	0.125	0.250	0.500	1.0	1.0
Feed rate (in./rev)	0.001–0.003	0.002–0.006	0.004–0.010	0.007–0.015	0.010–0.025

these drills compare with those used for carbide insert end mills. Carbide use in small holes requires a solid carbide tool, which is very expensive.

The feed rate for solid carbide drills can be determined by using tables for brazed tip as a starting point.

As with turning and milling, the feed in in. or mm/rev can be used to determine the feed in in. or mm/min, as follows:

Feed (in. or mm/min) = Feed (in. or mm/rev) × Spindle speed (rev/min)

Feed Rate and Spindle Speed Override

On the majority of control systems there are facilities that enable the operator manually to change, via a setting dial, both the feed rate and the spindle speed. Selection is usually on a percentage basis, 0–150% being fairly typical.

Changes in speed and feed may be necessary for a number of reasons. For example, the operator may judge that the rate of metal removal can be safely increased and so may increase the feed rate. Similarly, the operator may judge that a prolonged tool life would result if the spindle speed were decreased, or the surface finish being obtained from the programmed feed rate may be unsatisfactory, and so on. Manual control of speeds and feeds is also a very helpful feature during machine setting and program proving.

Changes made manually do not affect the basic program, although if an operator decides that the programmed feed rate or spindle speed for any part of a program is unsatisfactory he or she should make the fact known so that a permanent change can be made.

QUESTIONS

1 Select a suitable surface cutting speed and calculate the spindle speed required to turn a mild steel component with a diameter of 55 mm, using a cemented carbide indexable insert cutting tool.

2 If the component in question 1 has a second diameter of 24 mm, what change in spindle speed will be necessary?

3 Compare the surface speeds for machining mild steel using high-speed steel and cemented carbide cutters and express the variation as a percentage.

4 What is meant by the term "constant surface cutting speed"? Quote a situation where it may be desirable during a machining operation.

5 Select a suitable feed rate in in./rev for finish turning free-cutting mild steel using a cemented carbide tool. Using these data, determine a suitable feed rate in in./min for turning a diameter of 3.5 in.

6 Select a suitable feed rate in mm/rev for finish turning cast iron using a cemented carbide tool. Using information found in previous tables, determine a suitable feed rate in mm/min if turning a diameter of 75 mm in the same cast iron material.

7 Select a suitable surface cutting speed and determine the spindle speed required to drill a 9/16 in. diameter hole in mild steel.

8 Select a suitable surface cutting speed and determine the spindle speed required to drill a 6 mm diameter hole in free-cutting brass.

9 Why is it that the feed rate in in. or mm/rev for drilling operations varies with the drill diameter?

10 Calculate the approximate feed rate in mm/min for milling a slot in brass with a high-speed steel cutter of 15 mm diameter.

11 Calculate the approximate feed rate in in./min for milling a slot in an aluminum part with a high-speed steel two flute cutter of 0.375 in. diameter.

12 Determine a suitable spindle speed for face milling aluminum alloy using a cemented carbide cartridge-type milling cutter of 100 mm diameter.

13 Determine a suitable spindle speed for face milling cast iron using a cemented carbide insert type milling cutter with a 4.5 in. diameter.

14 If the cutter in question had six cartridges, what would a suitable feed rate be in mm/rev?

15 If the cutter in question 13 had eight inserts, what would a suitable feed rate be in in. /rev?

Chapter 8

PART PROGRAMMING FOR COMPUTER NUMERICALLY CONTROLLED MACHINING

The Part Program

The term part program is used to describe a set of instructions that, when entered into a machine control unit, will cause the machine to function in the manner necessary to produce a particular component or part. Manual part programming is the term used to describe the preparation of a part program without recourse to computing facilities to determine cutter paths, profile intersecting points, speeds and feeds, etc.

The program may be prepared manually and expressed in a coded language that is applicable to the machine controller being used. Alternatively, it may be written in another language or compiled by the use of computer graphics. The result is then post-processed, or translated, to suit the machine controller.

Included in the part program will be the necessary dimensional data relating to the features of the component itself, together with control data that will result in the machine making the slide movements required to produce the component. These data will be supplemented by instruction data that will activate and control the appropriate supporting functions.

Programs as entered into machine control units involve either of two programming concepts:

(a) word address
(b) conversational manual data input (MDI)

There are considerable variations between the two methods.

Whether a production scene incorporates total automation or merely one or two numerically controlled machines positioned among traditional machines, at the heart of successful numerical control is efficient competent part programming. The practical *skill* level requirement on the shop floor is, without doubt, in decline, but a high level of practical *knowledge* is essential if part programmers are to use costly equipment at their disposal to the best advantage. The selection of a correct sequence of operations, together with efficient cutting speeds and feeds, tooling and work holding, and the ability to express these requirements in the correct format are of paramount importance.

Unfortunately, programming methods differ and even when the basic approach is similar (for example, with word address), there are still variations and peculiarities, and conversational manual data input is very individual.

160

Thus the reader should appreciate that the ability to program with one control system, although there is much carryover, rarely means that knowledge can be used *in total* elsewhere. Specialist training is essential, and most machine-tool manufacturers respond to this by offering training courses as part of the overall package to customers buying their equipment. However, once the basic concepts involved in part programming are understood, the change from one system to another does not appear to be a major problem. Indeed, the variations encountered can be a source of much interest, while the mastery of yet another system can give considerable personal satisfaction.

Procedure

Taking as a starting point the detail drawing of the component to be manufactured, the tasks that confront the part programmer may be listed as follows:

1. Select a machine capable of handling the required work.
2. Determine the machine process to be used.
3. Determine work holding and location techniques.
4. Determine tooling requirements and their identity.
5. Document, or otherwise record, instructions relating to work holding, work location, and tooling.
6. Calculate suitable cutting speeds and feed rates.
7. Calculate profile intersecting points, arc centers, etc.
8. Determine appropriate tool paths including the use of canned cycles and subroutines.
9. Prepare the part program.
10. Prove the part program and edit as necessary.
11. Record the part program for future use.

Although these stages have been given a separate identity, they are very much interrelated and cannot be treated in isolation. A diagrammatic impression of the approach to be adopted is given in Figure 8.1.

Machine Selection

In selecting the machine to be used the first consideration is the type of work that has to be carried out. The tolerance and surface finishes required on the part will determine the type of machine and process to be used. Even when the type of machine is established, its specifications will need to be reviewed to ensure that part accuracy can be maintained.

For relatively simple components the choice will be obvious and is likely to involve just one machine. On the other hand, more complex designs may require machining to be carried out on a second or perhaps third machine. It may be necessary to move from one machine to a second before returning to the original machine for further work, and so on.

Such transfers, and the stage at which they will take place, need to be determined clearly, since they will have a direct bearing on the preparation of appropriate machining programs.

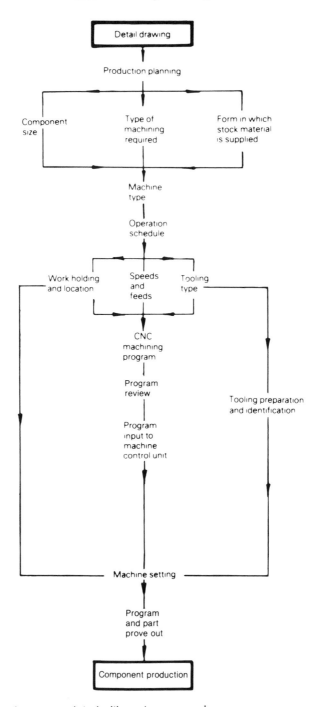

Figure 8.1 Procedures associated with part programming.

Machine selection will also be influenced by component size, and the programmer must ensure that any machine used has the necessary physical capacity to accommodate the workpiece.

Decisions made at the component design stage relating to materials—whether the form of supply will be a casting or a solid bar, for instance—will also need to be considered, since this may have some bearing on work-holding, tool selection, material removal rates, and machine-loading arrangements.

Processing of Machining Operations

Having selected a machine capable of handling the required work, the next task confronting the part programmer is to decide on a suitable sequence of operations.

In order to do this effectively the programmer should ideally have a thorough understanding of the capabilities and operating procedures associated with the particular machine to be used, and adequate knowledge of the work-holding equipment and tooling that can be employed.

It is often the case that, giving due regard to safety requirements, a machining task can be tackled in more than one way with equally good results in terms of dimensional accuracy and surface finish. But the programmer must always bear in mind one objective is to complete the machining as quickly and efficiently as possible. There are two basic planning techniques that, when carefully considered, can make a significant contribution to achieving this objective.

The first is to carry out as much machining as possible at one work setting and to avoid unnecessary repositioning of the work, since this can be a very time-consuming operation. The second is to carry out as much machining as possible with each cutting tool called, and to avoid unnecessary tool changing or indexing. The programmer should bear these points firmly in mind when listing the sequence of operations to be adopted.

The compilation of the process of operations to be used will not only be an aid to logical thinking throughout the rest of the part programming process, but it is also likely to be of value to the machine operator and may be required as a record for future reference. The more complex the component, the more vital the compilation of the process becomes.

It is likely that the operations process will form just part of the general documentation relating to a particular job, which will also contain information relating to work-holding, tooling, speeds, and feeds. The documentation relating to these aspects of part programming are discussed subsequently.

Work-Holding and Location

The part programmer's responsibilities regarding work-holding and location are as follows:

(a) determine the work-holding device or devices to be used;
(b) determine if there will be a need to use supplementary support at any stage during a machining sequence;

(c) determine the means of ensuring accurate location of the workpiece prior to machining;

(d) document all matters relating to work setting that will have a direct effect on the validity of the part program and that will, therefore, be of importance to the machine set-up person.

Decisions made in relation to these factors are greatly influenced by component shape and size. Components of regular shape are usually accommodated in standard work-holding devices such as chucks, collets, and vises. Components of irregular shape often require special work-holding arrangements, and as a result demand extra attention from the programmer. He or she may find it necessary to include special slide movements in the program, solely to avoid collisions between the cutting tools and the clamping devices.

Similarly, the programmer will need to give special attention to components requiring supplementary support—the use of a center support or steady rest, for example—and may well have to include control of these features within the part program.

Multicomponent settings will also have a direct effect on the approach adopted when preparing the part program.

A special characteristic of CNC machining involving very high rates of metal removal is that considerable cutting forces may be exerted in a number of directions during the production of a single component, with very rapid change from one direction to another, possibly occurring without the safeguard of manual observation or intervention. This variation in cutting force direction means that the prime objective in work location, that of ensuring that the cutting forces are directed against an immovable feature in the work-holding arrangement, may not always be met when using standard equipment. For example, work held in a conventional machine vise is only positively located when the cutting forces are directed against the vise jaw. If the cutting force changes direction so that it is at 90° to the fixed jaw, there will be a frictional hold only, which is not foolproof.

When confronted with the problem of multidirectional cutting forces, the programmer should give full consideration to the alternative approaches available. Devices such as the grid plate will provide for positive location in several directions, but it may be necessary to use a specially devised fixture. A number of the project components included in Appendix C will require this approach.

It is possible that the work-holding equipment available is very limited in range, such as a machine vise. In this situation the programmer will have to make the best of arrangements such as the frictional hold described previously. For example, a reduction in metal removal rates will reduce the cutting forces exerted on the workpiece. Each problem encountered will require individual assessment, and the methods used to overcome the problem should be selected with reference to the high safety standards that are so essential in CNC machining.

Another factor that must be considered is that of geometric tolerances, as listed in Appendix D. When any of these are encountered on a part drawing, the programmer must ensure that the work-holding and location arrangements being used will enable them to be achieved. It is a further area of part programming that requires the programmer to be well versed in the practical side of CNC machining, and to have a full understanding of the capabilities and limitations of the work-holding devices that may be used.

In order that specified geometric requirements are satisfied, it may be necessary to adopt a special approach to work setting, or, as is more likely, work resetting before carrying out further operations. In such cases it is imperative that the part programmer indicates to the machine set-up person or operator his or her reasons for doing so. Such information is included in the general documentation relating to that particular workpiece.

The importance of positive location of the workpiece to absorb the forces exerted by the metal-cutting action has already been stressed. There is, however, another reason why the part programmer is concerned about precise location of the work. He or she will program the slide movements in relation to a datum that will be determined when the part program is prepared, and unless the part to be machined is precisely positioned in relation to that datum the intended machining features will not be achieved. Subsequent parts must also be positioned in exactly the same way to ensure uniformity of the product.

When establishing a program zero datum, the programmer will have to take into consideration the reference zero position that is an incorporated feature of the machine control system. The machine zero may or may not be in a fixed position. If it is fixed, it may be capable of being shifted on a temporary basis via the part program using the G92 preset code. It may be capable of being established anywhere within the operating range of the machine, or there may be limitations on repositioning. Whatever the circumstances, the programmer will need to understand them completely.

Consider first a control system that permits a machine zero to be established anywhere the programmer chooses. In this situation it may be considered that the correct programming approach is to establish a machine zero that will correspond with the chosen program zero. So for a component such as the one illustrated in Figure 8.2 the programmer selects the corner of the workpiece as zero for all programmed moves in the X and Y axes, and a 2 mm (0.1 in.) clearance between the top of the work and the Z axis zero. By selecting the upper left-hand corner of the part as program zero and machine zero, the programmer can use many part print dimensions in the part program. To ensure

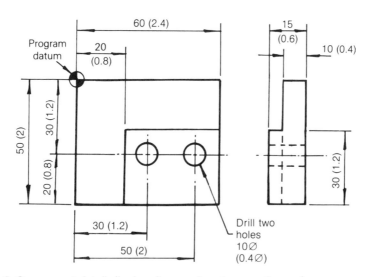

Figure 8.2 Component detail. (Inch units are given in parentheses.)

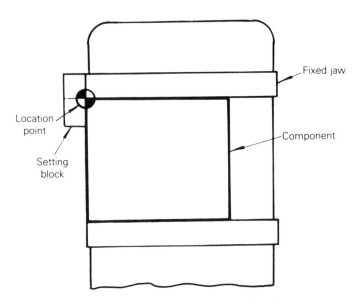

Figure 8.3 Use of stop block on fixed jaw for component location.

that there is correlation between the two zero positions the following machine setting approach will be necessary.

1. Set the corner of the vise jaw to zero in the X and Y axes (achieved by using a center locator or wiggler, or possibly an electronic probe).
2. Set the Z axis zero 2 mm (0.1 in.) above the work surface (achieved by touching on to a suitable worksetting block and calibrating the tool length offset accordingly).
3. Locate all workpieces using the corner of the fixed jaw of the vise as a reference position. (A plate attached to the vise jaw may be used to simplify this process).

The setting arrangement that accommodates the X and Y axes requirements is illustrated in Figure 8.3.

Consider now a situation involving a turned component such as that illustrated in Figure 8.4, and assume that the programmer has chosen to establish the face of the part as the Z datum zero and that the machine spindle center line is the X axis zero, as is normal. All that is required of the programmer is to ensure that the machine set-up person or operator is aware that the program datum is at the face of the work. The set-up person or operator will be required to establish the Z axis zero at the machine in the manner appropriate to that particular machine, and then ensure that all workpieces are all set to a measured overhang or to a stop as illustrated in Figure 8.5.

It is often the case that turning centers have a set zero datum for the machine, usually at the back face of the chuck or a reference surface on the spindle nose. This type of zero cannot be changed but can be shifted on a temporary basis using the G92 preset axis code.

The programmer may choose to use the back face of the component as the program zero in the Z axis, a technique often applied when work is being produced from prepared billets. Work location is simple, and simply involves ensuring the material is firmly

Figure 8.4 Component detail.
(Inch units are given in parentheses.)

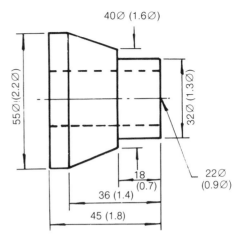

Material: medium carbon steel

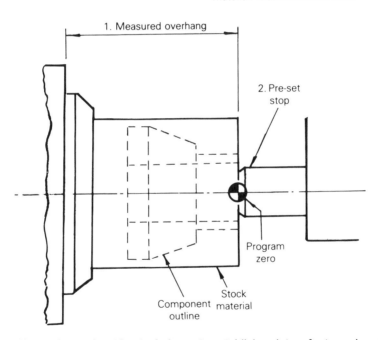

Figure 8.5 Alternative work setting techniques to establish a datum for turned work.

placed against the reference face. A further bonus is that all programmed slide movements will be positive.

To use the facility of repositioning the zero on a temporary basis—so that it corresponds to a program zero established at the workpiece face for instance—it will be necessary for the programmer to determine the amount of shift required to accommodate all the programmed movements in the Z axis. The dimensional value of the shift required, that is, the work overhang, must be documented. Eventually it will be entered into the program through the use of the G92 code followed by *X*, *Z*, and/or *Y* axis positional data as to what current slide positions should be. Some older machines may still use another method of establishing zero shifts through special offset tables, which can be activated by assigned codes like E, F, or H.

To ensure that the programmed machine movements achieve the desired effect, the work material has to be positioned accurately, either manually or automatically against stops, and this function is the responsibility of the machine set-up person or operator. The accuracy of this method of work setting can be improved if the overhang is slightly larger than the actual work requires, allowing a facing cut to be used early in the machining sequence to establish the new zero precisely.

It may be necessary to provide for more than one zero shift within the same turning program. A common situation is when the component length is such that, to ensure adequate support and to avoid chatter, part of the machining is carried out with a reduced overhang. After a programmed stop in the machining cycle, the operator repositions the work to suit the second zero position. Alternatively, the repositioning of the work may be achieved automatically through the program. This is particularly appropriate when a bar feed is utilized, the bar feeding to appropriate stops. The provision of a center support may also be a feature of such an arrangement. After the second zero shift all subsequent moves will be made in relation to that datum.

An example of a component which would involve two zero shifts during machining is shown in Figure 8.6. Because the diameter of the component is relatively small in proportion to its length, it would be advisable to use two settings and a center support for the second sequence of machining operations. The first setting involving the shift of the machine zero to the work face is illustrated in Figure 8.7(a), while the second setting requiring shifting the zero for a second time is shown in Figure 8.7(b).

The use of a second program zero is also applied to milling operations. An initial program zero is established and some machine movements will be made in relation to that datum. Then, via an appropriate program call the zero will be reestablished and all subsequent moves will be made in relation to the second datum.

One milling situation where the zero shift facility is particularly useful is when more than one component is to be machined at one setting, as illustrated in Figure 8.8. In this example a grid plate is used as a work-holding device. The advantage of the grid plate

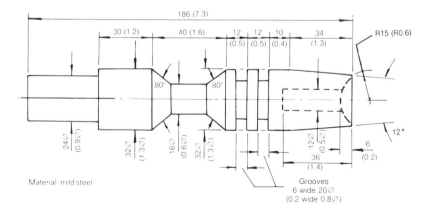

Figure 8.6 Component detail. (Inch units are given in parentheses.)

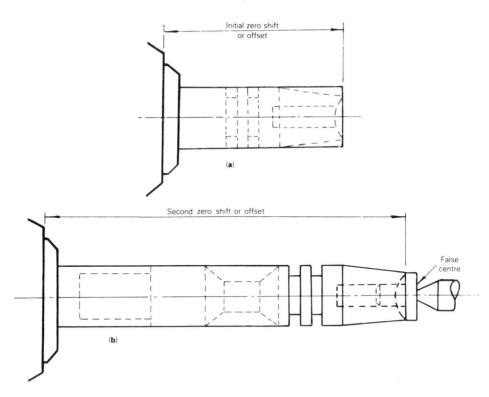

Figure 8.7 The application of a second zero shift to accommodate work resetting **(a)** first work setting **(b)** second work setting.

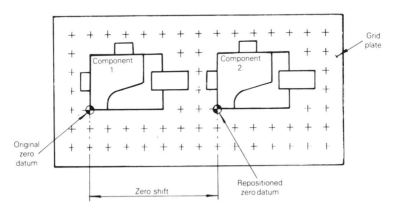

Figure 8.8 Use of zero shift for multicomponent machining at one setting.

is that all the clamping and location points can be identified using a letter/number grid reference, like using a map reference to locate a particular town. Using this reference system the part programmer can instruct the machine set-up person/operator exactly where to position each component so that their location will correspond with the selected program zeros.

OPERATION SCHEDULE		PART No.		DESCRIPTION		SHEET No. OF	
		MACHINE TYPE		COMPILED BY		DATE	
OP No.	DESCRIPTION	TOOLING TYPE AND SIZE	WORK HOLDING	CUTTING SPEED	FEED RATE	SPINDLE SPEED	

Figure 8.9 Example of an operation schedule.

Documentation Associated with Part Programming

Before a part program can be compiled it is necessary to give some thought to the practical aspects of producing the component, and in most companies this is likely to involve the completion of an operation sheet. There is no standard operation sheet, and the format will vary from company to company. One which will meet the requirements of the exercises that follow is shown in Figure 8.9.

In addition to an operation sheet there is also the need for documentation relating to machine setting and tooling, because some of the decisions made during the operation planning stage, and which in turn are taken into account when writing the part program, are of direct concern to shopfloor personnel responsible for preparing the tooling and the machine. Again, there is no standard format for such documents. Each company will have its own procedure.

Documentation Relating to Machine Setting

Information regarding work-holding and location is of vital importance to the machine set-up person. He or she will also benefit from knowing the sequence of operations that has been adopted by the programmer. Also, it will be necessary to know the form in which the material to be machined is to be supplied. Ideally, all this information should be documented, not only as an aid to efficiency on the shop floor, but also to provide a record for future reference.

The documents used to convey this information will vary from company to company, and the precise way this information is disseminated is not of major importance. The important thing is that the shop floor personnel fully understand what is required. So how detailed does the information need to be? The answer depends on the complexity of the component and the machining operations involved.

Assume that the machine set-up person knows the sequence of machining operations involved and is to proceed with setting up the machine. Consider in the first instance work loading, holding, and location. What information is required?

A simple component that is to be turned in one set up from a prefaced billet could be accommodated with a few short notes as follows:

Material:	prepared billet, part number ****
Loading:	manual
Work-holding:	chuck type, fixture number ****
Location:	back face of chuck
Zero shift:	Z direction + or −, and value

The last item would indicate that a manual data entry shifting the Z axis zero from the spindle face to the workpiece face is required.

A more complex component requiring two settings, with the second operation requiring center support activated by an entry in the program, will require a little more detail and the information may be given as follows:

Material:	diameter and length of bar stock
Loading:	bar feed to programmed stops, bar stop number
Work-holding:	collet, with programmed center support for second setting
Zero shifts:	first setting, direction + or −, and value second setting, direction + or −, and value

This information could be supplemented by two simple sketches showing the machining to be carried out at each setting.

A similar exercise can be carried out for workpieces involving milling. The exercise shown in Figure 8.10 could be produced on a "one part" basis or involve a multicomponent setting.

In the first instance the workpiece could be located using the corner of the fixed jaw of the vise as a reference point, a technique referred to on page 166. The instructions necessary to achieve this would be as follows:

Material:	prepared blank length × width × height
Work-holding:	machine vise, fixture number ****
Location:	left-corner of fixed jaw
Program datum:	X axis −25 mm (−1 in.) (axis-direction + or − value)
	Y axis 25 mm (1 in.)
	Z axis 2 mm (0.1 in.)

Again the information regarding the program datum may be more readily understood if the instructions include a sketch.

A multicomponent setup involving the same component could involve the use of a grid plate. To convey the necessary set-up information, the programmer should be familiar with the grid plate and its associated locating and clamping devices. With such knowledge he or she may be able to give detailed instructions for the complete setting, using the grid references to position the various setting blocks, locating dowels, and clamps to be used in the operation. On the other hand, a competent set-up person could manage with the basic information included in Figure 8.11.

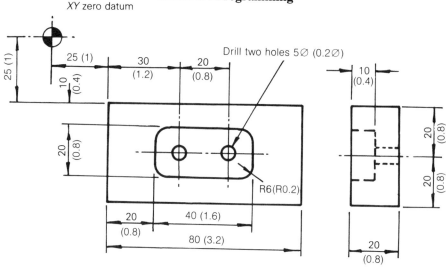

Figure 8.10 Component detail. (Inch units are given in parentheses.)

Material: aluminum alloy

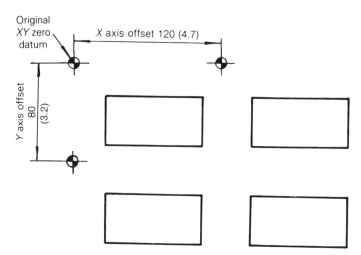

Figure 8.11 Use of grid plate. (Inch units are given in parentheses.)

Tooling Selection and Identification

The responsibilities of the part programmer concerning tooling are as follows:

(a) determine the appropriate tools to be used, including their shape and size and the material from which they will be made;
(b) allocate identification numbers to facilitate machine setting;
(c) allocate tool offset numbers;
(d) determine, when appropriate, the dimensional value of the offsets;
(e) prepare appropriate documentation.

It is essential that a programmer is fully conversant with the tooling system for the machine involved, that is, the type of tooling that can be used and the way the tools can be located and held in position.

A major feature of CNC machining is the use of standard tooling. The intricate slide movements that are possible greatly minimize the need for special tooling, particularly form tools. In many ways the tooling requirements for CNC machining are less complex than for conventional machining.

Providing the programmer is conversant with the machine tooling system, the process of selecting tooling for a particular job is largely a case of selecting and utilizing standard items.

It is important that the correct tool material is used, particularly when using carbide inserts. Reference should be made to manufacturers' literature for guidance in this respect. Pages 44 through 47 give an indication of the type of information that is available.

It is often the case that the tools available within a company for use on a particular machine will be further standardized with their details being documented. An example of a company-based tool standard is shown in Figure 8.12.

All tools are required to have a numerical identity within the part program. This identity, commonly the letter T followed by two digits, is allocated by the part programmer and will correspond with the numbered position the tool will occupy in the machine turret, magazine, or other storage facility. The position each tool will occupy is affected by factors which are discussed below.

Commonly used tools are often given an identity that is retained at all times, since this often eliminates the need to reset when jobs are changed. When this situation exists, it is essential that the part programmer knows exactly which tools are involved and their numerical identity.

Tool Storage

With automatic tool changing facilities involving turrets, the positions for the tools in the turret are numbered. Thus a tool call of, say, T06 will cause the turret to index to position number six. The tool allocated the numerical identity 6 must be set in position six.

Similarly, tools changed by automatic handling devices will be housed in readiness in a tooling magazine. When a tool is called the magazine will index to bring the appropriate tooling station into a position where the tool located in that station can be accessed by the handling device. Clearly the correct tool must be in each numbered position if the programmed tool call is to bring the desired tool into the machining position.

Even when the tool change is a manual operation, effected by a programmed stop in the machining cycle, the process is assisted if the operator has a clear indication of the next tool to be used. It is usual, therefore, to number the tool storage positions or even the tools themselves. When the programmed break in machining occurs, the operator can refer to a document provided by the programmer to determine the next tool involved; on the more sophisticated control systems the tool may be indicated by a message displayed on the visual display unit of the control.

The programmer should give due thought to the positioning of the tools in relationship to each other in the turret or magazine. Most indexing arrangements involve rotation in one direction only, so to change, say, from T03 to T06 will require three indexing moves,

TOOL HOLDER No.	
ISO CODING	PDJNL 3232P15
KENNAMETAL	
SANDVIK	PDJNL 3232P15
VALENITE	
CARBOLOY	

NOTE: ALL DIMENSIONS ARE IN INCHES UNLESS STATED OTHERWISE

TOOL No.	RN	AC	AN	XN	ZN	WN	AS	XS	ZS
T 709									
T 710	0.008	3	55	0.008	0.008		−90	3.5634	2.6795
T 711	0.0156	3	55	0.0156	0.0156		−90	3.5568	2.6788
T 712	0.0313	3	55	0.0313	0.0313		−90	3.5433	2.6772
T 713	0.0469	3	55	0.0469	0.0469		−90	3.5297	2.6756
T 714	0.0625	3	55	0.0625	0.0625		−90	3.5162	2.6741
T 715	0.0937	3	55	0.0937	0.0937		−90	3.4892	2.6710
T 716									

NOSE RADIUS	INSERT No.				Zero Rtn. Dia.	MAX. DIA.
	I.S.O. CODE	I.S.O. CODE	I.S.O. CODE	I.S.O. CODE		
0.008	DNMG150602				20.4323	25.9441
0.0156	DNMG150604	DNMM150604			20.4455	25.9573
0.0313	DNMG150608	DNMM150608			20.4725	25.9843
0.0469	DNMG150612	DNMM150612			20.4997	26.0115
0.0625	DNMG150616	DNMM150616			20.5267	26.0385
0.0937	DNMG150624				20.5807	26.0925
TITLE:	FINISH PROFILING TOOL					TOOL No.
	QUALIFIED TOOLING MORI SEIKI SL7—C.N.C. LATHE					T 709 to T 716

Figure 8.12 Company-devised tool standard. (All units are given in millimeters.)

two of which are time-consuming and unproductive. Therefore the objective should be to position the tools in the turret or magazine in the order in which they will be called into use, although this is not always possible in practice.

The problem of wasteful indexing time is considerably eased when the machine is equipped with the facility to index tooling by the shortest possible route. In other words, the turret or magazine will rotate either clockwise or counterclockwise depending on which tool is called.

Tool Changing Position

The programmer should consider carefully the position the machine slides are to be in when a tool change is made. There is a tendency, particularly among students, to return the machine slides to a set position before making a change, a practice that may have its merits from a safety point of view early in training but which, like wasteful indexing moves, can add considerably to the total time taken to machine the part.

The objective must be to keep noncutting slide movement to a minimum. For example, on a vertical machining center it is often possible to effect a tool change immediately above the point at which the tool completes the required machining, the change being carried out after an appropriate Z up-movement of the machine spindle or head. This saves making a long and unnecessary journey to a set position such as the XY zero datum. On turning centers a similar time saving can be achieved by indexing as near to the workpiece as is safely possible. The programmer should always refer to the machinery manuals to check clearances necessary to allow tool indexing mechanisms and cutting tools to clear any obstructions.

Replacement Tooling

For long production runs the programmer will need to give some thought to the provision of replacement tooling.

When tools need to be replaced it is possible for the set-up person to determine suitable offsets and make the necessary tool data entries as he or she would for the original tools, but this is time-consuming and interrupts production.

An alternative approach is to use replacement tooling which is identical to the original. Such identical tooling may be of two types, namely, "qualified" or "preset."

Qualified tooling is used on turning centers and has dimensions guaranteed by the manufacturer to within ± 0.0005 in. or ± 0.08 mm from up to three datum faces.

Preset tooling is precisely set to predetermined dimensions in the toolroom and is applied to turning tools and milling cutters.

The programmer may choose to recommend qualified or preset tools when compiling his or her tooling schedule, but if such tooling is prescribed, the programmer may need a feedback of information from the toolroom regarding the setting sizes. This information then becomes part of the overall programming and machine-setting package and should be documented for future reference.

Tooling Documentation

Documentation regarding tooling, as with machine setting instructions, may be simple or relatively complex. It depends largely on the size of the company and the degree of organization that exists.

The possibilities range from the situation where the machine set-up person has personal access to the range of tooling likely to be required, to situations where the tooling is prepared in a special-purpose tool room, issued to the set-up person as a package for that particular job, and on completion returned to the tool room for refurbishment and storage.

For each programmed tool the minimum information required on the shop floor is as follows:

(a) programmed identity—T01, T02, T03, etc.;
(b) tool type;
(c) holder type and size;
(d) insert type and size;
(e) overall dimensions (solid tools);
(f) projection of cutting tool from holder.

When presetting is involved, the tool design or program personnel usually determine the original preset dimensions. The sizes should ultimately be notified to the part programmer so that they may be recorded and included as part of the general documentation for that particular job. A well-organized tool preparation facility may well retain the data against their own job reference to facilitate the preparation of replacement tooling and to allow for the possibility of having to prepare identical tools at some future time. See Figures 8.13 and 8.14 for examples of tool data sheets.

When tooling offsets are being used to achieve a particular machining effect, as discussed on page 218, the value of the offsets must be included on the document.

It is often the situation that information regarding tooling, and sometimes information relating to machine setting, is included on the original part program form when one is used. Information documented in this way is of necessity rather brief, but in many cases is adequate.

Another practice widely adopted is to give tooling details alongside the tool call in the part program. Again, the information is brief but adequate for many situations.

The important thing is that the part programmer fully appreciates the needs of the people more directly concerned with the machining operation. There must be an efficient transfer of the relevant information. The means adopted to achieve this objective will vary, but the programmer should always remember that it is a very important aspect of his or her work.

Part Programming Procedure

The blocks of data entered in a part program are numbered N01, N02, N03, and so on. On completion of a machining program it is usually necessary to return to the beginning so that another component can be machined. The return to the program start position is usually achieved via a 'rewind" or "return to start" command included at the end of the program.

MODEL 104 TOOL SHEET

PART NO. 001-001	MATERIAL 1018 CRS	OPERATION 3	PROGRAMMED BY G. COMBS
PART NAME SAMPLE	B/P CHANGE DATE	DATE 5-6-80	SHEET 1 OF 1

SEQ	TOOL NUMBER	TOOL DESCRIPTION	TOOL DIAMETER PORG.	ACT.	#	TOOL LENGTH PROG.	ACT.	#	OPERATION DESCRIPTION	SPEED RPM	FEED IN/MIN
1	T01 / E1	HHS END MILL –4 FLUTE 4" SHANK SINGLE END/CV-49-15920 END MILL HOLDER	1.0	.750	D1 -.125	6.187	5.812	H1	FINISH MILL PERIPHERY	270	3
2	T02 / E1	HSS END MILL –4 FLUTE 3/8" SHANK DBLE END/CV-49-15915 END MILL HOLDER	.250	.250	D2	4.687	4.687	H2	Mill (4) pockets .062 Dp. Finish mill sides	1100	2
3	T03 / E1	#2 CENTER DRILL Erikson Ext Collet Chuck/#200-3/16 collet/CV-49-15923 Collet; Holder/#100-3/4 collect	.078	.078		4.875	5.000	H3 .125	SPOT (18) HOLES ON PERIMETER, (8) ON B.C. and (4) on angle. .1 DP	1180	3
4	T04 / E1	Drill CV-49-15923 collet holder/#100-1/8 collet	.125	.125		5.125	4.875	H4 -.250	Drill (8) HOLES ON B.C.	3000	6
5	T05 / E1	DRILL CV-49-15923 collet holder/with #100-7/32 collet	.205	.205		5.250	5.500	H5 .250	DRILL (18) HOLES ON PERIMETER AND (4) ON ANGLE 1" THRU	1650	5
6	T06 / E1	HCSS END MILL –2 Flute 3/8" SHANK DBLE END/CV-49-15915 END MILL HOLDER	.375	.375		4.562	4.700	H6 .138	C'BORE (18) HOLES	850	3.4

Figure 8.13 Model 104 tool sheet. Ex-Cell-O Corp., Rockford Machine Tool Company, Rockford, IL.

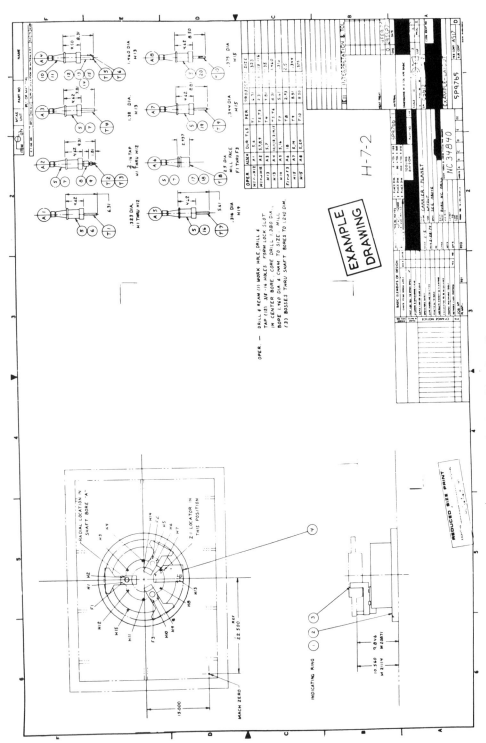

Figure 8.14 Sample tool layout. Numerical Control Society, Glenview, IL.

With word address systems, this command is entered as a miscellaneous function designated M30, which has the effect of stopping all slide and spindle movement, turning off the coolant supply and rewinding the tape. When the tape has merely been used to transfer a program into the microcomputer memory, then it rewinds the program within the microcomputer. The stage at which this rewind must cease has to be identified, and this is achieved via a "rewind stop" program entry signified by the % sign. This is usually the first entry in a word address program.

With the start of the program established, the next three or four blocks of data will concern setting the machine controller so that it interprets subsequent data in the correct manner. These set-up entries include instructions relating to the following:

(a) *units,* which may be programmed in inch or metric;
(b) *slide movement,* which may be stated as incremental or absolute dimensional values;
(c) *speed,* which may be programmed as surface speed in feet/meters per minute or spindle speed in revolutions per minute;
(d) *feed,* which may be programmed as inches/millimeters per spindle revolution or inches/millimeters per minute.

Having established the basic set-up data, it may be helpful now to list in a general way the functions and machine movements necessary to produce the component. Consider the drawing for Exercise 1 (in Appendix C) and imagine that the machine is set with the spindle in its 'home' or 'base' datum position, that is, at a point some distance above the *XY* datum indicated on the drawing. Starting from this position, the part program must provide for the following:

1. Rapid linear movement to P1 in *X* and *Y.*
2. Rapid linear movement to a clearance position above Z0.
3. Spindle on clockwise direction.
4. Coolant on.
5. Feed linear movement to *Z* depth.
6. Rapid linear movement to clearance above Z0.
7. Rapid linear movement to P2.
8. Feed linear movement to *Z* depth.
9. Rapid linear movement to clearance above Z0.
   . . . and so on.

These simple comments can, providing a space exists, be entered directly onto a program sheet or, if the program is being listed on plain paper, alongside each item of data, but it is probably a better plan to prepare a rough list in the first instance and then check carefully to ensure nothing has been overlooked. Relative codes and data can then be added to each statement.

Should it be found that, on completion of a program, omissions have inadvertently been made, the error can be rectified more easily if the block numbers are allocated in increments of five: N01, N05, N10, N15. It is then a simple matter to include additional blocks—N06, N07, N08, for instance—between N05 and N10.

If the program is being listed on a computer the blocks can be numbered consecutively, since any omission entered via the keyboard will automatically cause the existing blocks to renumber or, alternatively, renumbering can be easily effected. Many MDI control systems also have this facility.

A methodical approach to part programming is essential, and it is recommended that, even for a simple component, an operation schedule listing the tooling speeds and feeds to be used should be completed in the first instance.

Word Address Programming

Word address programming is largely based on an International Standards Organization (ISO) and Electronic Industries Association (EIA) code that require the program to be compiled using codes identified by letters, in particular G and M. Each code addresses, or directs, the item of data it precedes to perform a certain function within the control system.

The ISO and EIA Standards provided for 99G codes and an identical number of M codes, each being expressed by the address letter followed by two digits.

Not all the codes were allocated a specific function in the Standard and this gave the manufacturers of control systems the opportunity to introduce their own variations. There is, therefore, no standard word address machine programming language, although many of the recommendations made have been widely adopted.

The G codes, or preparatory functions, are used to set up the machine control unit modes of operation required for the machining that is to be carried out—whether movement is to be in a straight line/linear or radially/circular, for example. In general they relate to slide motion control. Examples of commonly used G codes are as follows:

G00	Rapid linear positioning, point to point
G01	Linear positioning at a controlled feed rate
G02	Circular interpolation, clockwise
G03	Circular interpolation, counter-clockwise
G04	Dwell for programmed duration
G33	Thread cutting, constant lead
G34	Thread cutting, increasing lead
G40	Cutter compensation, cancel
G41	Cutter compensation, left
G42	Cutter compensation, right
G70	Inch programming
G71	Metric programming
G80	Series associated with drilling, boring, tapping and reaming.

(For a complete list of G codes refer to Chapter 6.)

G codes may be "modal," that is, they remain active until cancelled. Alternatively they may be nonmodal, and are only operative for the block in which they are programmed.

The M codes, or miscellaneous functions, are used to establish requirements other than those related to slide movement. For example, they are used to activate spindle motion or to turn on a coolant supply. Examples of commonly used M codes are as follows:

M00	Program stop
M01	Optional stop
M02	End of program

M03   Spindle on clockwise
M04   Spindle on counter-clockwise
M05   Spindle off
M06   Tool change
M08 . Coolant on
M09   Coolant off
M30   End of tape

(For a complete list of M functions refer to Chapter 6.)

As with G codes, some M functions are modal, remaining active until cancelled. M functions may also become active immediately upon reading of the block or after all block commands are completed. (Refer to machinery manuals to determine how various codes operate.)

In addition to the address letters G and M there is also common usage of S, F, and T to indicate speeds, feeds, and tooling. The letter N is always used to identify block numbers.

The distinction between word address and conversational programming is best appreciated by reference to the simple movements discussed earlier.

To program the linear movement of -39.786 mm or -1.6 in. in the X axis using the word address technique, it is first necessary to establish the operating mode required. This is done by including the appropriate G code, in this case G01. Thus the complete program entry for the required move will be:

Inch   N260 G01 X–1.6

Metric   N260 G01 X–39.786

Similarly, reconsider the 0.3 in. or 8 mm radial movement through an arc of 90°. Once again the mode of operation has to be established using the appropriate G code, which for circular movement in a clockwise direction is G02. It will also be necessary to define the target position in the appropriate axes and also the start of the arc in relation to the arc center using I, J, and K address letters that correspond to the X, Y, and Z axes respectively. A word address program entry to achieve this movement would read as follows:

Inch   N350 X1.7 Z–3.0 K.3

Metric   N350 G02 X43.765 Z–75.000 K8

There are variations in procedure even when word address programming such a common machining feature as a radius. On some control systems the arc center may have to be defined—still using the I, J, and K address letters—in relation to the program datum and not the start position.

The programming of radial movements using the word address method will be returned to later in the text.

A word address program that includes a number of codes in both inch and metric is listed below. The program relates to the component detailed in Figure 8.15, and is typical of its type. The comments written alongside the data should convey to the reader an impression of how, prior to programming, the machining of a component is first broken down into operations. It also shows how the necessary machine control data are presented. Later in the text further reference will be made to the program to illustrate specific programming techniques and features.

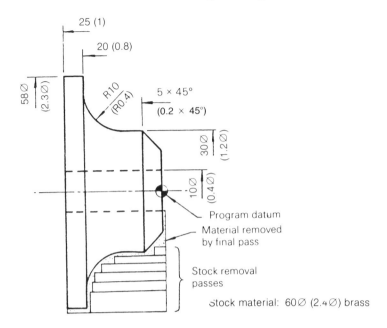

Figure 8.15 Component detail. (Inch units are given in parentheses.)

Programming Example

Figure 8.15 shows a simple turned component for which a part program is to be prepared using the following basic programming information. (Examples of more detailed programming specifications are given in Appendix C.)

Preparatory Functions (G Codes)

G00	Rapid movement
G01	Linear interpolation—movement at a programmed feed rate
G02	Circular interpolation, clockwise
G03	Circular interpolation, counter clockwise
G40	Cancel tool nose radius compensation
G41	Tool nose radius compensation left
G42	Tool nose radius compensation right
G70	Inch units
G71	Metric units
G90	Absolute positioning data ⎫ X axis values to be
G91	Incremental positioning data ⎭ programmed as diameters
G94	Feed (in. or mm)/min
G95	Feed (in. or mm)/rev
G96	Constant surface cutting speed
G97	spindle speed rev/min

Miscellaneous Functions (M Codes)

M00	Program stop
M01	Optional stop

M02   End program
M03   Spindle on clockwise
M04   Spindle on counterclockwise
M05   Spindle off
M06   Tool change
M08   Coolant on
M09   Coolant off
M30   End of program

Operation Schedule

The first stage in the programming process is to prepare an operation schedule. An operation schedule for the component is shown in Figure 8.16, where only metric units are shown. The spindle speeds and feed rates have been determined by reference to the cutting data given in Chapter 7.

Tooling Information

Although the component is a relatively simple one, it is still necessary to provide tooling information for the machine tool setter. This information is detailed on the form illustrated in Figure 8.17, where only metric units are shown.

Program Listing

Attention can now be given to listing the necessary programming data, together with appropriate remarks to ensure a logical approach is being adopted and to ensure that

OPERATION SCHEDULE		PART No. EX. 1		DESCRIPTION PLUG		SHEET No. 1 OF 1
		MACHINE TYPE HB 370		COMPILED BY A.R.C.		DATE 9-2-84
OP No.	DESCRIPTION	TOOLING TYPE AND SIZE	WORK HOLDING	CUTTING SPEED	FEED RATE	SPINDLE SPEED
1	CENTER DRILL	HSS No. 2 C/DRILL		28 m/min	.12 MM/rev	1500
2	DRILL	HSS DRILL/Ø10	Ø 60	28 m/min	.18 MM/rev	890
3	TURN PROFILE	CEM. CARB. INSERT	COLLET	170 m/min	.25 mm/rev	1350
4	PART OFF	CEM. CARB. INSERT		170 m/min	.16 mm/rev	1350

Figure 8.16 (Metric units).

TOOL PREPARATION AND SETTING DATA				PART No.	Ex. 1		
TURRET POSITION	OFFSET No.	OPERATION	INSERT TYPE	HOLDER TYPE	PRE-SET LENGTHS		
						X	Z
1	01	CENTER DRILL		RC 107			
3	03	DRILL Ø 10		RC 110	DETERMINE AND ENTER OFFSETS ON THE MACHINE		
4	04	TURN TO PROFILE	P10	TN 22-08			
5	05	PART OFF	P20	GR 18-04			

Figure 8.17 (Metric units).

nothing is overlooked. The required program is listed below. (Note that, in this particular case, a programming form is not being used, but partially completed programming exercises involving the use of a form are given in Appendix C.)

Part Program (INCH)

Data		Remarks
N10	G70 G90	Absolute inch
N15	G95 G97	Feed inches/rev Spindle speed rev/min
N20	G92 X4.0 Z8.0	Pre-set safe turret indexing position
N25	T0101 M06	Tool change. Tool No. 1. Off-set No. 1
N30	S3000 M03	Spindle on clockwise
N35	G00 X0 Z.1 M08	Rapid to start position. Coolant on
N40	G01 Z-.3 F.003	Center drill
N45	G00 Z.1	Rapid retract
N50	X4.0 Z8.0	Return to turret index position
N55	T0202 M06	Tool change. Tool No. 2 Off-set No. 2
N60	S2380 M03	Spindle Speed
N65	G00 X0 Z.1	Rapid to start position
N70	G01 Z-1.2 F.015 M08	Drill through .4ø
N75	G00 Z.1	Rapid retract
N80	X4.0 Z8.0	Return to turret index position
N85	T0303 M06	Tool change. Tool No. 3 Off-set No. 3
N90	S1430 M03	Spindle speed
N95	G00 X1.97 Z.1	Rapid to start position
N100	G01 Z-.768 F.020 M08	
N105	G00 X2.05 Z-.688	Rapid retract to clear cut surface
N110	Z.1	Second rough pass—start position
N115	X1.772	
N120	G01 Z-.748	
N125	G00 X1.85 Z-.669	
N130	Z.1	

Data	Remarks
N135 X1.575	Third rough pass—start position
N140 G01 Z-.709	
N145 G00 X1.654 Z-.63	
N150 Z.1	
N155 X1.417	Fourth rough pass—start position
N160 G01 Z-.65	
N165 G00 X1.496 Z-.57	
N170 Z.1	
N175 X1.26	Fifth rough pass—start position
N180 G01 Z-.512	
N185 G00 X1.339 Z-.433	
N190 Z.1	
N195 X.984	Sixth rough pass—start position
N200 G01 Z-.079	
N205 G00 X1.063 Z.1	
N210 G41	Cutter radius compensations
N215 X0	Rapid to X zero
N220 G01 Z0	Rapid to Z zero
N225 S1750 M03	Spindle speed and feed rate change
N230 X1.0 F.007	Machine face to 1.0ø
N235 X1.2 Z-.2	Machine chamfer
N240 Z-.4	Linear move to radius start
N245 G03 X2.0 Z.8 I.4	Circular interpolation
N250 G01 X2.3	Linear move to 2.3ø
N255 Z-1.1	Linear move to length
N260 G00 X2.5	Lift from finished surface
N265 G40	Cancel cutter radius compensation
N270 X4.0 Z8.0	Return to turret index position
N275 T0404 M06	Tool change. Tool No. 4 Parting Tool
N280 S1430 F.007	Spindle speed and feed rate change
N285 G00 X2.5 Z-1	Rapid to start
N290 G01 X.08 M08	Part off leaving stock faced
N295 G00 X4.0 Z8.0	Return to turret index position
N300 G92 X0 Z0 M30	Program end. Spindle and coolant off

Finish machine profile (N210–N300)

Note: To simplify the program, neither tool nose radius or thickness were used.

Part Program (Metric)

Data	Remarks
N10 G71 G90	Absolute metric
N15 G95 G97	Feed mm/rev Spindle speed rev/min
N20 G92 X100 Z200	Pre-set safe turret indexing position
N25 T0101 M06	Tool change. Tool No. 1. Off-set No. 1
N30 S3000 M03	Spindle on clockwise
N35 G00 X0 Z2 M08	Rapid to start position, coolant on
N40 G01 Z-8 F.1	Center drill
N45 G00 Z2	Rapid retract
N50 X100 Z200	Return to turret index position

Data	Remarks
N55 T0202 M06	Tool change. Tool No. 2 Off-set No. 2
N60 S2380 M03	Spindle speed
N65 G00 X0 Z2	Rapid to start position
N70 G01 Z-30 F.18 M08	Drill through 10ø
N75 G00 Z2	Rapid retract
N80 X100 Z200	Return to turret index position
N85 T0303 M06	Tool change. Tool No. 3 Off-set No. 3
N90 S1430 M03	Spindle speed
N95 G00 X50 Z2	Rapid to start position
N100 G01 Z-19.5 F.3 M08	
N105 G00 X52 Z-17.5	Rapid retract to clear cut surface
N110 Z2	
N115 X45	Second rough pass—start position
N120 G01 Z-19	
N125 G00 X47 Z-17	
N130 Z2	
N135 X40	Third rough pass—start position
N140 G01 Z-18	
N145 G00 X42 Z-16	
N150 Z2	
N155 X36	Fourth rough pass—start position
N160 G01 Z-16.5	
N165 G00 X38 Z-14.5	
N170 Z2	
N175 X32	Fifth rough pass—start position
N180 G01 Z-13	
N185 G00 X34 Z-11	
N190 Z2	
N195 X25	Sixth rough pass—start position
N200 G01 Z-2	
N205 G00 X27 Z2	
N210 G41	Cutter radius compensations
N215 X0	Rapid to *X* zero
N220 G01 Z0	Rapid to *Z* zero
N225 S1750 M03	Spindle speed
N230 X20 F.15	Machine face to 20ø
N235 X30 Z-5	Machine chamfer
N240 Z-10	Linear move to radius start
N245 G03 X50 Z-20 I10	Circular interpolation
N250 G01 X58	Linear move to 58ø
N255 Z-26	Linear move to length
N260 G00 X64	Lift from finished surface
N265 G40	Cancel cutter radius compensation
N270 X100 Z200	Return to turret index position
N275 T0404 M06	Tool change. Tool No. 4 parting tool
N280 S1430 F.18	Spindle speed and feed rate change
N285 G00 X64 Z-25	Rapid to start
N290 G01 X-2	Part off leaving stock faced
N295 G00 X100 Z200	Return to turret index position
N300 G92 X0 Z0 M30	Program end. Spindle and coolant off

Finish machine profile (N210–N265)

Note: To simplify the program no tool nose radius or thickness was used.

DATA FORMAT EXAMPLES

Fixed Block Example

N	G	X	Y	Z	I	J	K	F	S	M	Remarks
0250	00	05000	09000	04000	00000	00000	00000	2000	0350	03	Rapid position X, Y, Z, and start spindle.
0300	01	08500	09000	04000	00000	00000	00000	0310	0350	08	Mill in X axis—turn coolant on
0350	00	08500	09000	04500	00000	00000	00000	2000	0350	09	Retract Z axis—turn coolant off

Note: When information is placed in machine format, no spaces occur between data words.

Variable Block Example (spaced out in a form)

N	G	X	Y	Z	I	J	K	F	S	M	Remarks
N0250	G00	X05000	Y09000	Z04000	—	—	—	F2000	S0350	M03	Rapid position X, Y, Z, and start spindle
N0300	G01	X08500	—	—	—	—	—	F0310	—	M08	Mill in X axis—turn coolant on
N0350	G00	—	—	Z04500	—	—	—	F2000	—	M09	Retract Z axis—turn coolant off

Variable Block Example (without form—using decimal point format)

N0250 G00 X5 Y9 Z4 F200 S350 M03　　Rapid position X, Y, Z, and start spindle.

N0300 G01 X8.5 F31 M08　　Mill in X axis—turn coolant on.

N0350 G00 Z4.5 F200 M09　　Retract Z axis—turn coolant off.

Data Format

Data are written in blocks. The data within a block were once expressed in a fixed sequence with each block containing all data (even if they have not changed from the previous block), but now almost exclusively the commands appear in random order without the repetition of unchanged data but with each word being clearly identified by its address letter. The terminology used to describe these two methods is "fixed block" and "variable block word address," respectively. The preceding examples illustrate these formats.

It is necessary for the part programmer to be aware of the data format for the system being used, and also to be familiar with the classification of the data that dictates the way in which it may be presented within a block. For example, a programming manual could indicate that data must conform to the following classification:

$$N4, \ G2, \ X3/3, \ Y3/3, \ Z3/3, \ F4, \ S4, \ T2, \ M2 \quad \text{(METRIC)}$$
$$N4, \ G2, \ X2/4, \ Y2/4, \ Z2/4, \ F4, \ S4, \ T2, \ M2 \quad \text{(INCH)}$$

This classification indicates the following:

N4	The block sequence address letter N may be followed by up to four digits.
G2	The preparatory function address letter G may be followed by up to two digits.
X3/3, Y3/3, Z3/3 (Metric) X2/4, Y2/4, Z2/4 (Inch)	The axis identification letters X, Y, and Z may be followed by up to three digits in front of the decimal point, and up to three after in metric form. Identification letter may be followed by two digits in front of decimal point, and up to four after in inch format. (Dimensional values may be subject to other limitations as explained below.)
F4	The feed address letter F may be followed by up to four digits.
S4	The spindle speed or cutting speed address letter S may be followed by up to four digits.
T2	The tool address letter T may be followed by up to two digits.
M2	The miscellaneous function address letter M may be followed by up to two digits.

(*Note:* These formats will change from one machine control to another. For a complete list of your machine code formats refer to your machine tool manual.)

The description above has stated that up to so many digits may be used. Some systems require that leading zeros are included and some do not. Thus a linear slide movement at a programmed feed rate may be programmed as G01 or G1, depending on the system used.

Similarly, dimensional values may also have to be programmed according to certain rules. For instance, using a data classification of 3/3 it would be possible, depending on the requirements of the system, to program a value of 32 mm in a number of ways:

(a) 032000—all digits must be included but no decimal point.
(b) 32000—leading zeros are omitted, but no decimal point is required; trailing zeros must be included.

(c) 32.000—the decimal point and all trailing zeros are required.
(d) 32.—no leading or trailing zeros are required but the decimal point must be included.
(e) 32—whole numbers may be programmed without leading or trailing zeros and without a decimal point.

Slide Movements

Both word address and conversational programming require definition of the slide movements necessary to position the cutting tool correctly in relation to the work.
This positioning is described in three ways:

(a) point-to-point;
(b) linear interpolation;
(c) contouring/circular interpolation.

Point-to-point positioning involves programming instructions that identify only the next relative tool position required. The position may be reached by movement in one or more axes at a rate of travel that is generally, though not necessarily, the maximum for the machine. If metal cutting takes place during this type of motion, it must be in one axis or the cut path will not necessarily repeat cycle to cycle.

Figure 8.18 shows details of a component. To drill the holes in this component would require two-axis point-to-point positioning. Note that the positioning prior to drilling is clear of obstruction, therefore path is not important and the actual drilling is a single-axis move, so point to point can be used. Note that point-to-point positioning is not capable of machining angles or contours, because they require controlled movement of more that one axis.

Linear interpolation control requires programmed instructions that specify both the next position and the rate of travel, or feed rate, to be employed to reach that position; the resulting cutter path is a straight line. Metal cutting would normally take place

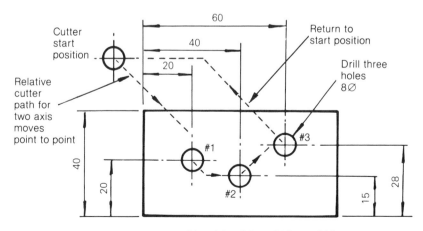

Figure 8.18 Component detail requiring point-to-point positioning to drill holes.

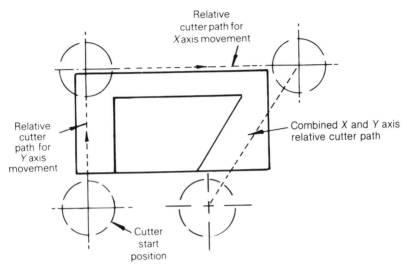

Figure 8.19 Linear interpolation.

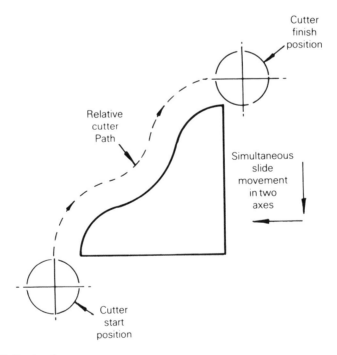

Figure 8.20 Contouring.

during such a move. Linear interpolation allows the machining of straight lines at a feed rate using one or two axes of motion. Other more expensive machines allow linear interpolation in three axes simultaneously. Figure 8.19 illustrates examples of one- and two-axis linear interpolation moves.

Contouring is used to describe movements involving at least two slides. The movements occur simultaneously and at a predetermined feed rate, and result in a continuous machining path which is not a straight line. An elliptical profile or a combination of arcs—the production of an arc being referred to as 'circular interpolation'—are good examples of contouring. Contouring will normally refer to irregular curves that must be machined using minute straight line segments to generate it. Contouring requires many data blocks and multiple axis movement capability. Circular interpolation, on the other hand, will produce uniform arc segments or circles with minimal programming owing to the machine control's ability to self-generate uniform arc data. The principle is illustrated in Figure 8.20.

Definition of the Axes of Movement

Whether conversational or word address programming is being used, the direction in which slide movement is to occur is defined by a letter, which for common machines is either X, Y, or Z for linear movement and B for rotary table movement where applicable. Axes definition codes appear together with a positive $(+)$ or negative $(-)$ sign for determining direction. In practice the $+$ sign is not actually entered, because if a sign is omitted, the control automatically assumes plus.

The definition of the axes of movement on common machine types, namely a turning center, a vertical machining center, and a horizontal machining center, are illustrated in Figure 8.21. Two points should be noted in relation to the illustrations. First, on a turning center having a rear-mounted tool post the plus $(+)$ and minus $(-)$ in the X axis would be reversed. Movement of the tool away from the spindle axis is always plus.

Second, the axes definitions shown indicate the *machine* slide movements. In the case of a turning center these movements are identical to the tool movement in relation to the work. On milling machines, where it is the table and not the cutting tool which moves, this is not the case. For programming purposes, where it is easier to imagine that the tool is moving, it is necessary to redefine some movements. On a vertical machining center, for example, in order to achieve a tool movement in relation to the workpiece in the X positive or plus direction it is necessary to build a machine slide that movement in the X axis would cause physical table movement to the right under the machine spindle viewed from the front of the machine. In determining axes directions, the programmer can always consider that the part is viewed through the tool from the shank to the tip. Right-theoretical tool motion on the part is always positive, with left being negative. Tool motion viewed this way in the up direction on the part print is positive, with down being negative. Tool motion causing penetration of the tool into the work is negative, with retraction being positive. If rotary tables are involved, clockwise direction viewed looking into the table face from outside is positive, with counterclockwise being negative.

Note: these directions are based on a normal operator position in front of the machine.

In addition to linear movement, the production of a part may also require rotary movement which is provided by the use of ancillary equipment such as rotary tables and indexers. These movements are also controlled via the machining program and are identified by the letters A, B, and C as illustrated in Figure 8.22.

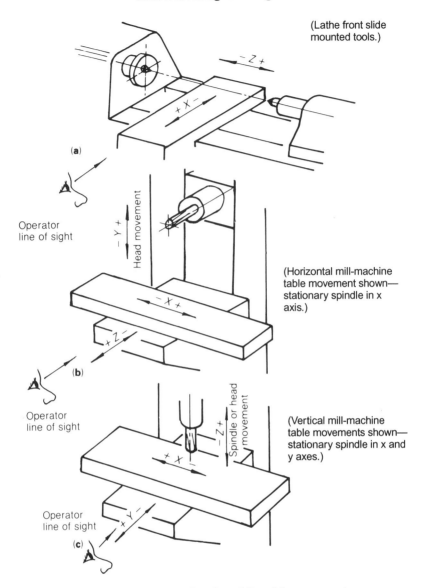

Figure 8.21 Identification of slides and direction of the slide movement on common machine tools: **(a)** center lathe (turning center), **(b)** horizontal milling machine (horizontal machining center), **(c)** vertical milling machine (vertical machining center).

Datums

There are two datums involved in CNC machining that concern the part programmer.

The first of these is the program datum, which is established by the programmer when writing the program. This datum is at the intersection of the X, Y, and Z axes when milling, and at the intersection of the X and Z axes when turning. In both cases it is given the numerical identity of zero. The actual position of this datum in relation to the workpiece is optional, although there are certain factors to be taken into consideration.

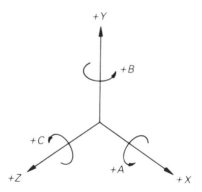

Figure 8.22 Identification of rotary movements.

The program datum is, in effect, the point from which the slide movements in each axis will be dimensionally related. It should be noted that part setup on a machine tool must allow for the proper machine zero/program zero relationship. When program data are stated in absolute terms, all subsequent moves will also be dimensionally related to that point.

The second datum that concerns the part programmer is the machine datum. This datum is a set position for the machine slides where the axes intersect, and it has a numerical identity of zero within the control system.

On some machines the machine datum is a permanently established position (referred to as a fixed zero) and cannot be altered, although it can be repositioned on a temporary basis via a zero "shift" or "offset" facility. On other machines a new datum can be established anywhere within the operating range of the machine, a facility referred to as a "floating zero."

Clearly, there must be some correlation between the machine datum and the program datum when setting the machine if the programmed slide movements are to achieve the intended effect, and the practicalities involved are discussed in more detail in Chapter 6.

Absolute and Incremental Positional Data

Once the direction of movement has been established, the distance moved by the machine slide to bring it to a desired position has to be defined dimensionally. This is achieved by the use of linear coordinates, with the dimensions being stated in absolute or incremental terms.

A third method is sometimes used, involving the use of polar coordinates. This requires a distance (the radius) stated in relation to a defined point and at an angle stated in relation to a datum axis. It generally requires the control system to include a special programming facility.

Absolute dimensional definition requires all slide movements to be related to a predetermined zero datum.

Incremental dimensional definition requires each slide movement to be related to the final position of the previous move.

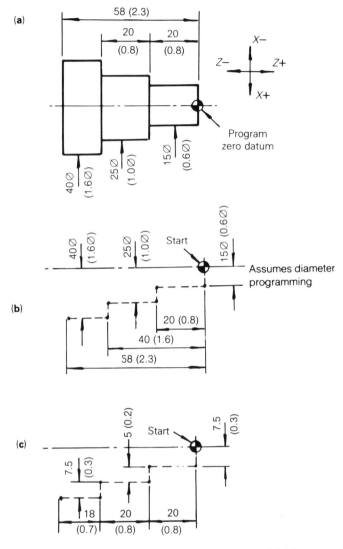

Figure 8.23 **(a)** Component detail, **(b)** absolute dimensions, and **(c)** incremental dimensions. (Inch units are given in parentheses.)

Figure 8.23(a) shows the details of a turned component. The intersection of the spindle centerline and the face of the work is the program zero datum. Assume that a final trace of the component profile is to be programmed.

The dimensional definition in absolute and incremental values that would be required to define slide movement is shown in Figures 8.23(b) and 8.23(c) respectively.

In Figure 8.24(a) the details of a milled component are given. Absolute and incremental dimensional values required to program the machining of the slot are shown in Figures 8.24(b) and 8.24(c) respectively.

Earlier programming languages required dimensional data to be stated in *either* absolute or incremental terms. Modern controllers often provide a "mix and match" facility

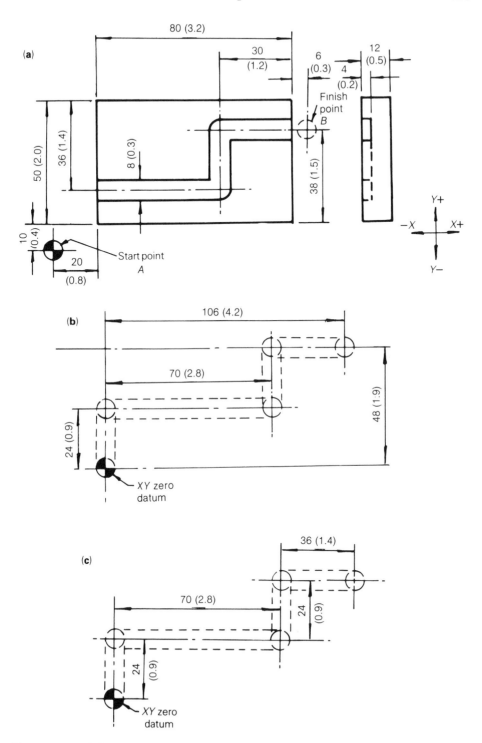

Figure 8.24 **(a)** Component detail, **(b)** absolute dimensions, and **(c)** incremental dimensions. (Inch units are given in parentheses.)

that permits the use of both within the same program, and even within the same data block. The distinction is achieved by the continued use of the G90 (absolute) and G91 (incremental) preparatory function codes, or X, Y, and Z word addresses for absolute values and U, V and W for incremental values. The use of the "G" code for changing from absolute to incremental is much more common.

Circular Interpolation

Circular interpolation allows for programming a machine to move the cutting tool in a circular path with a uniform arc, with only a few commands. Circular like motion is achieved through the machine controls capability to calculate minute cordal movements between commanded points (Figure 8.25). The basic elements of circular interpolation will deal with the following four items:

1. *Direction of rotation*—The direction of rotation that the cutter path will follow around the circle or arc segment.
2. *Start point*—The actual beginning point of the circle or arc segment where the cutter has previously been positioned.
3. *Center point*—The point of rotation in which the circle or arc segment is developed around.
4. *End point*—The finish point of the cutter path used to generate the circle or arc segment.

It was explained earlier in the text that circular arc programming on conversational MDI systems has been reduced to a simple data entry that specifies the target position, the value of the radius, and the direction of rotation. This simple method of defining

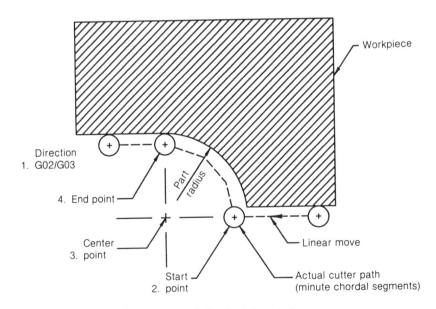

Figure 8.25 The four basic elements of circular interpolation.

circular movement in a single block with the direction of rotation being defined by the appropriate G code is also available on some word address systems (see method 3), but many systems employ one of two slightly more complex techniques of quadrant circular interpolation (methods 1 and 2).

Common to all programming systems is the need to determine whether the relative tool travel to produce a particular arc is in a clockwise (CW) "G02" or counterclockwise (CCW) "G03" direction, and the location of the arc or circle center. The following approaches are usually helpful:

1. For turning operations look down onto the top face of the cutting tool. (For inverted tooling this involves looking up at the tool from below.)
2. For milling operations look along the machine spindle centerline toward the surface being machined.

It should be noted that this technique does not always correspond with the definition adopted by the control system's manufacturer. A simple trial program entered into the machine will clarify the situation if it cannot be determined from the machinery manuals.

Determining clockwise and counterclockwise direction on milling machines with multiple plane circular interpolation capability can be done using the following rule and Figure 8.26.

Clockwise and counterclockwise are determined by looking at the plane of the circle from the positive end of the coordinate axis normal to the plane of the circle.

The arc center definition for circular interpolation is also a standard requirement. It informs the control of the point of rotation for an arc along standard axes from the arc start point or program datum. Use the following definitions and Figure 8.27 to determine proper arc center addresses needed for various planes of rotation.

Use of I, J, and K to Specify the Arc Center

I is the *increment* along the X axis from the start point of the arc to the arc center.
J is the *increment* along the Y axis from the start point of the arc to the arc center.
K is the *increment* along the Z axis from the start point of the arc to the arc center.

Note: Refer to your machinery manual to determine whether or not positive or negative signs will be required on the I, J, K values.

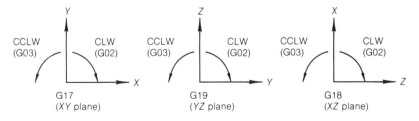

Figure 8.26 Determining clockwise and counterclockwise directions.

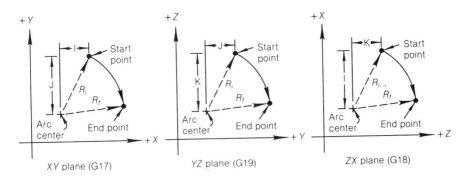

Figure 8.27 Arc centers.

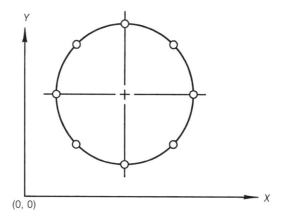

Figure 8.28 Circle quadrants.

Quadrant Circular Interpolation

Quadrant circular interpolation allows up to 90° of arc to be programmed as long as the entire segment does not cross quadrant lines; refer to Figure 8.28.

For any circle there are four quadrants that are created by axis lines which cross at the center of the circle. These axis lines are parallel to the part coordinate axes. No circular block may cross either of these axes. Starting at any point on the circle, it can be seen that the maximum number of circular controller data blocks to cut a 360° arc is five.

An individual circular controller data block cannot cross an axis line. To continue into the next quadrant, terminate the present circular controller data block and program another circular controller data block, starting on the axis. This procedure is quite straightforward.

A minimum of four sets of dimensional data are required to complete a full circle with up to four dimension words per block. Two dimension words are required to define the arc and one or two are required to define the arc center. Arc center values of zero are normally not required. Machines that are capable of either quadrant or 360°

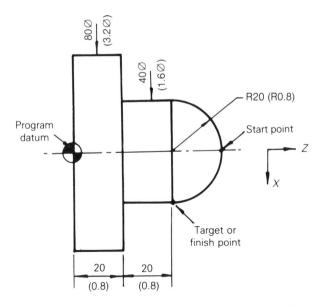

Figure 8.29 Component detail. (Inch units are given in parentheses.)

circular interpolation will require a modal G code to be programmed (G74 quadrant; G75 360°). *Note:* For exact programming format and arc size limits refer to your machinery manual.

The two arc center address programming techniques previously referred to can be described using the component detail shown in Figure 8.29, and assuming that the last programmed move has brought the cutting tool to the start point indicated.

Method 1

1. The target or finish point of the arc is dimensionally defined, using X, Y, or Z values, in relation to the program datum when using absolute mode, or to the finish position from the previous move when using incremental mode.
2. The center of the arc is dimensionally defined in relation to the start point using I, J, and K values measured along the X, Y, and Z axes respectively.

Using this method the arc shown in Figure 8.29 would be programmed as follows:

Inch:
In absolute terms: G02 X1.6 Z1.6 I0 K.8 (Diameter programming of lathe part.)
In incremental terms: G02 X.8 Z−.8 I0 K.8

Metric:
In absolute terms: G02 X40 Z40 I0 K20 (Diameter programming of lathe part.)
In incremental terms: G02 X20 Z−20 I0 K20

Note that the I code has no value because the center and start point of the arc are in line with each other. In practice, when a value is zero, it is not entered into the program. In this method of arc definition the I, J, and K values are unsigned.

Method 2

The second method of word address arc programming differs in the way the arc center is defined. The following data are required:

1. The target or finish point of the arc is dimensionally defined, using X, Y, and Z values, in relation to the program datum when using absolute mode, or to the finish position from the previous move when using incremental mode.
2. The center of the arc is dimensionally defined in relation to the program datum using I, J, and K values measured along the corresponding X, Y, and Z axes, respectively, in absolute mode. The arc center is still defined from the previously defined point in incremental mode.

Using this second method of programming the arc shown in Figure 8.30 would be programmed as follows:

Inch:
In absolute terms: G02 X1 Y2.4 I1 J1.4
In incremental terms: G02 X1 Y1 I1 J0

Metric:
In absolute terms: G02 X25 Y60 I25 J35
In incremental terms: G02 X25 Y25 I25 J0

It is possible when using this approach for the I, J, and K values to be negative, as illustrated in Figure 8.31. These values are, therefore, signed plus or minus.

The two arc programming methods described will cater for movement within one quadrant only with each block of program data. Thus programming a complete circular

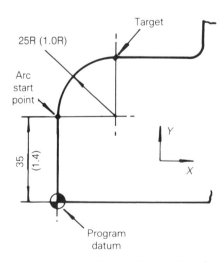

Figure 8.30 Milled component detail. (Inch units are given in parentheses.)

move would require four blocks of data minimum. Similarly, blending arcs would re-quire a separate block of data for each quadrant involved. This latter situation is illus-trated in Figure 8.32; the first block would take the tool from point A to point B, and the second block would continue the movement from point B to point C.

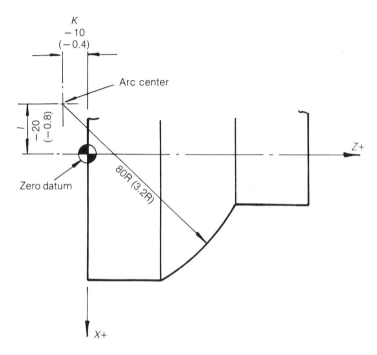

Figure 8.31 Circular interpolation: negative I and K values for an absolute program. (Inch units are given in parentheses.)

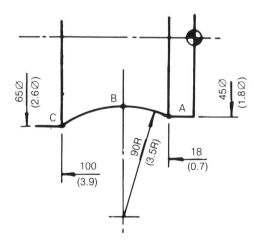

Figure 8.32 Profile detail requiring two arcs to be programmed. (Inch units are given in parentheses.)

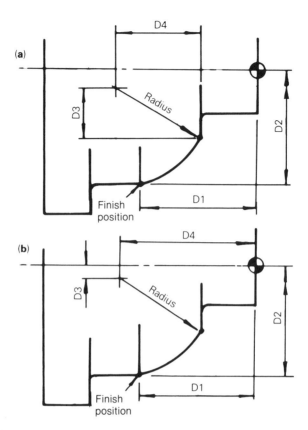

Figure 8.33 Calculations for arcs less than 90°: (**a**) method 1; (**b**) method 2. (Inch units are given in parentheses.)

When the start or stop points or both do not coincide with an X, Y, or Z axis, that is the arc is not exactly 90° or a multiple of 90°, it will be necessary to make a series of calculations.

Consider the part detail shown in Figure 8.33(a) and again in Figure 8.33(b), each diagram relating to an arc programming method as indicated. Whichever of the two methods is used, the finish arc position indicated by the dimensions D1 and D2 will have to be defined dimensionally. It will also be necessary to calculate the additional dimensions indicated on each drawing as D3 and D4, these latter dimensions being expressed in the part program as I and K values. A number of circular interpolation examples follow.

Programming Examples

The circle in Figure 8.34 will be used to illustrate programming various arcs, clockwise and counterclockwise, absolute and incremental. (All units in the following examples are in inches.)

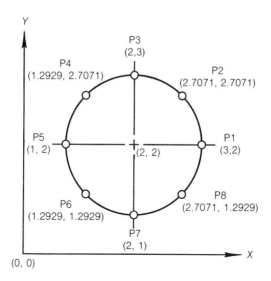

Figure 8.34 Example of programming arcs.

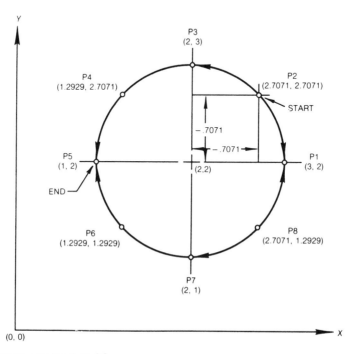

Figure 8.35 Examples 1 and 2.

Example 1 (Method 1) (Figure 8.35)

Go from P2 to P5 clockwise (absolute) (G74 default).

Signed I and J	Unsigned I and J
G17	G17
G90	G90
G2X3Y2I-.7071J-.7071 F10	G2X3Y2I.7071J.7071FI0
X2Y1I-1	X2Y1I1
X1Y2J1	X1Y2JI

Example 2 (Figure 8.35)

Go from P2 to P5 counterclockwise (incremental) (G74 default).

Signed I and J	Unsigned I and J
G17	G17
G91	G91
G3X-.7071Y.2929I-.7071J-.7071F10	G3X-.7071Y.2929I.7071J.7071F10
X-1Y-1J-1	X-1Y-1J1

Example 3 (Figure 8.36)

Go from P4 to P7 clockwise (incremental) (G74 default).

Signed I and J	Unsigned I and J
G17	G17
G91	G91
G2X.7071Y.2929I.7071J-.7071F10	G2X.7071Y.2929I.7071J.7071F10
X1Y-IJ-1	X1Y-1J1
X-1Y-1I-1	X-1Y-1I1

Example 4 (Method 1) (Figure 8.36)

Go from P4 to P7 counterclockwise (absolute) (G74 default).

Signed I and J	Unsigned I and J
G17	G17
G90	G90
G3X1Y2I.7071J-.7071F10	G3X1Y2I.7071J.7071F10
X2Y1I1	X2Y1I1

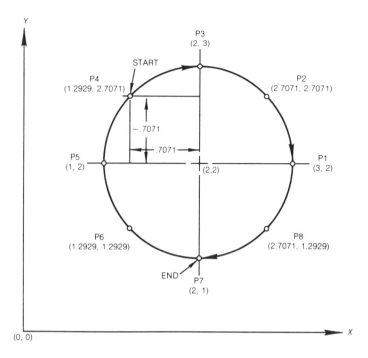

Figure 8.36 Examples 3 and 4.

Method 3

Single block or 360° circular interpolation is now available on more sophisticated CNC controls. Single block circular interpolation allows up to 360° of circular movement to be programmed in a single block of information when the modal G75 code is active. All previous circular interpolation command words defined are still used to determine rotation, finish/end position, and arc center. It should be noted, though, that in this form of circular interpolation the I, J, and K combination used must be signed to determine the circle's center.

Another difference that will be noted in this method of programming is if a full 360° of circle is to be produced, the starting and ending points of rotation will be identical. When identical starting and ending points occur, the end point of the arc does not have to be programmed, only the rotation and arc center information are required; refer to the examples with Figure 8.37.

Example 5 (Method 3) (Figure 8.37)

Go from P3 to P3 clockwise.

Incremental	Absolute
G17	G17
G91	G90
G75	G75
G2I0J-1F10	G02I0J-1F10

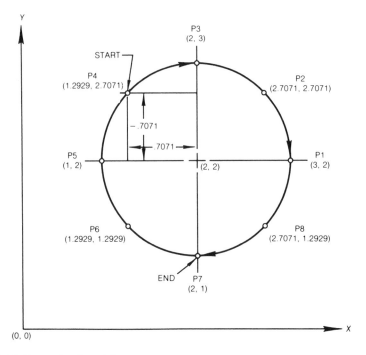

Figure 8.37 Examples 5 and 6.

Example 6 (Method 3) (Figure 8.37)

Go from P4 to P7 clockwise.

Incremental	Absolute
G17	G17
G91	G90
G75	G75
G2X.7071Y-1.7071I.7071J-.7071F10	G2X2Y1I.7071J-.7071F10

Toleranced Dimensions

It is often the case that dimensions on drawings are toleranced, thus permitting a higher and lower limit. Since it is only possible to enter one value into the control unit, it is logical that this should be the middle or mean value of the tolerance band.

Repetitive Machining Sequences

There are a number of repetitive sequences that are commonly used when machining a variety of components like drilling a hole. Other less common sequences are also repetitive, but on only one particular component (hole patterns—milling path). It is helpful, since it reduces the program length and also simplifies programming, if such a sequence can be programmed just once; it is then given an identity so that it can be recalled into the program as and when required.

Repetitive machining sequences can be generally classified as follows:

(a) Canned or fixed cycles that are a built in feature of the machine control system.
(b) User or programmer defined routines to suit the particular job in hand (custom canned cycles, program macros).

The facility for the programmer to devise special routines may be restricted, especially on small training machines. However, even the most simple system will usually include one or two canned cycles. The controls fitted to advanced machines will have many available.

Canned Cycles

In a text of this nature it would be impossible to deal in detail with all the canned cycles that are available, but the review that follows will convey a good impression of the range currently in use and likely to be encountered. More specifically, the student is advised to make a careful study of the programming methods and techniques associated with the control system he or she will be using. In this respect a close examination of the examples found in the programming manuals will be found to be helpful. The point to remember is that the use of canned cycles is an aid to programming efficiency and accuracy, and they should be used whenever possible. You will notice later in this chapter that the special cycles mentioned here are not unique to manual programming techniques. Conversational programming has many of the same options/routines that are used in place of the special "G" codes used here.

Fixed or canned G code cycles (G81–G89) were developed, as stated, to simplify the programming of hole-making operations with repetitive motions at each hole location. These codes are normally modal and must be cancelled with a G80 code (linear rapid transverse mode) before other program movements are commanded. The normal action of the canned cycles mode is to position the programmed nonspindle (tool penetration) axes, including the rotary table axes on milling machines, with the (Z) coordinate axis remaining stationary. The tool will then rapid the Z axis to the R or tool-clearance plane preceding the part surface and feed at the programmed rate to Z depth. After feeding the tool to depth, the tool will be retracted from the hole automatically as required by the cycle. Note: different codes will cause various forms of retraction (refer to your programming manual for specific retraction action). Once all of the necessary modal information is programmed (G code, depth, clearance position, spindle speed, feed, and spindle direction), additional holes can be produced by programming new axis or axes positions until the canned cycle is cancelled. Most canned cycles will pick up the last programmed spindle speed/direction and feedrate if they are not initiated in the canned cycle block of information.

Perhaps the most widely used machining sequence is that of drilling a hole, and there are few controls that fail to cater to this requirement by including a canned cycle. Indeed, with word address programming, early attempts were made to standardize a drill cycle. That this was quite successful is evident by the fact that the use of G81 for the purpose is as common as the use of G00 and G01 for linear movement control and G02 and G03 for circular interpolation.

There are a number of machining variations necessary in the production of drilled holes.

One of the most commonly used is the basic drilling movement, catered for by the drilling cycle illustrated in Figure 8.38. This involves a drill movement to the required depth at a controlled feed rate, followed by rapid withdrawal.

Also widely used is the intermittent or "peck" drill cycle for deep holes illustrated in Figure 8.39. This illustration shows a complete withdrawal to the Z axis clearance plane after each peck, but variations of this cycle provide for a smaller withdrawal that conveniently breaks the chip but does not give total retraction for chip clearance. The peck depth is established with an additional Z axis command word, which many times is a "K" value.

A further refinement of this cycle provides for automatic variation of the peck length as the hole deepens. This is achieved by including a "multiplier" in the cycle data. For example, a multiplier of 0.8 will have the effect of reducing each peck length to 0.8 of the previous peck. To avoid the reduction continuing indefinitely a minimum peck length is also programmed.

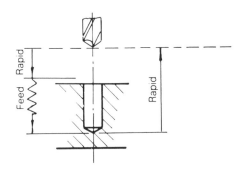

Figure 8.38 Drill cycle.

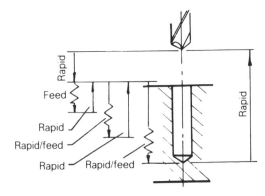

Figure 8.39 Peck drill cycle.

Closely allied to the drilling cycles are those for boring and tapping. To ensure a clean surface, boring may require special or no drag line retraction, and counterboring may require the inclusion of a time dwell at the extent of cutter travel. Tapping requires that the direction of spindle rotation is reversed to allow withdrawal of the tap.

Many turning operations involve machining chamfer or radius features illustrated in Figures 8.40(a) and 8.40(b). It is possible to program a special cycle on some machines that would normally require two data blocks in just one block. Figure 8.40(a) shows the programming case which would otherwise require a Z axis movement followed by simultaneous movement in both the X and Z axes to produce an angle or chamfer. Figure 8.40(b) shows a similar situation, but in this case the angular movement is preceded by linear movement in the X axis.

Very similar to the cycles described previously are those illustrated in Figures 8.41(a) and 8.41(b). Instead of a linear move being followed by an angular move, the linear moves are followed by radial movement. In both cases the radial movement must be a full 90°.

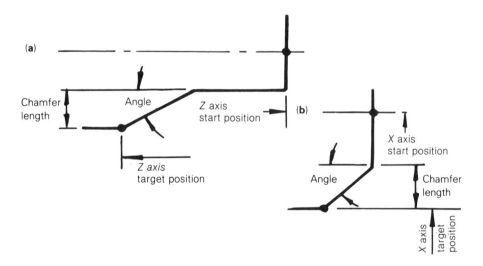

Figure 8.40 Chamfering cycles.

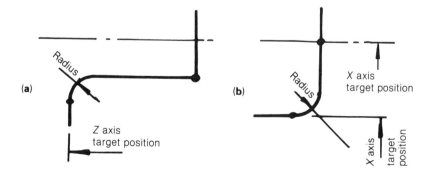

Figure 8.41 90° arc cycles.

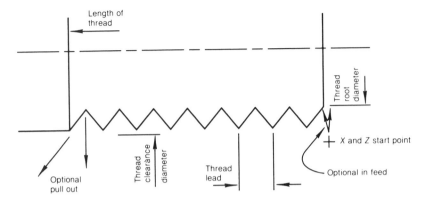

Figure 8.42 Automatic threading cycle.

Both the chamfering and radius cycles may be automatic with little or no programming required for a standard size or there may be special G code and axis information required. Refer to your specific programming manual.

Automatic threading cycles are the counterpart of the G84 tapping canned cycle for single-point threading tools. Single-point thread cutting tools require a number of passes to produce a finished thread. Special G codes, like G33, have been developed for lathe work, which allows the programmer to call thread approach and depth, cut distance, retract to clear part, and return to start point all in one·block/line of information. Various controls will handle this differently, some requiring a line of instruction for each thread pass and others allowing the entire thread cutting operation to be cut with one statement. G codes like G28 and G29 may be used to define the basic thread pass for later recall. The various codes have been developed to handle both internal and external threads as well as straight or tapered threads. Figure 8.42 shows an example of the types of program information required to make this cycle work.

User-Defined Routines

Canned cycles cater for the easy programming of machined features that are often required on a wide range of components. But the part programmer is often confronted with a feature that is repeated a number of times on a particular component but is found only on that component or a limited range of components. It is in situations such as this that the facility to devise a special routine for use as and when required is very helpful.

Consider the component detail shown in Figure 8.43. Along the length of the shaft is a series of identical recesses. If there is no facility to write a special program, or routine, to machine these recesses the programmer is faced with the rather cumbersome task of detailing each move necessary to machine one recess and then repeating the data for each of the others.

When preparing a routine to accomplish a specific machining task such as this, the programmer can include any of the available canned cycles that might be appropriate. For example, the profile of the shaft recess referred to could be machined using the cycle that permitted one-block programming of a linear move in the Z axis followed by an

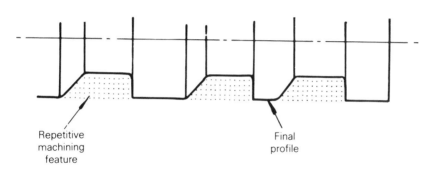

Figure 8.43 Application of a turning subroutine.

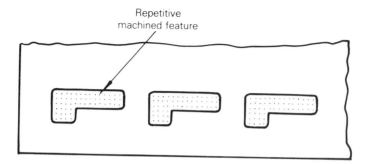

Figure 8.44 Component detail: application of a milling subroutine.

automatic chamfer or radius. When specific routines are programmed within other routines, they are said to be "nested."

Assume the component shown in Figure 8.44 has a repetitive feature as indicated that justifies using a specially devised routine to clear the recess and mill it to the required profile. Now assume that within each of these recesses there is a series of three smaller recesses as shown in Figure 8.45. Since there will be three times as many smaller recesses as larger recesses, a further specially devised routine to machine them will be justified.

The routine for machining the larger recess will therefore contain the subroutine for machining the smaller recess. The subroutine is nested within the first routine and will be activated three times during the machining of the larger recess.

It would be quite feasible for each of the smaller recesses to include a drilled hole, and this could also be produced using a canned cycle. The subroutine for the smaller recess would now include a nested drilling cycle.

There are usually some limitations regarding nesting. Some controllers permit subroutines within subroutines up to eight deep; others may accept only half this number.

Specially devised routines can also be used to control machine movements and functions not directly associated with metal cutting. For example, a special routine can be used to establish and readily recall predetermined parameters relating to machine slide positions and programming modes which may, for safety reasons, need to be established from time to time throughout the program run. The application of a programmer-devised safety routine is included in the sample program listed in Figure 8.46.

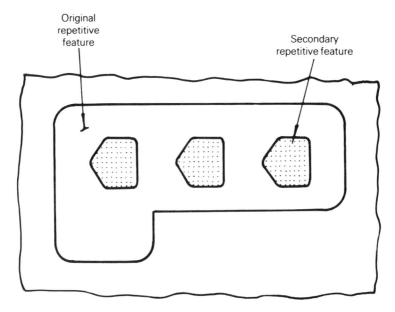

Figure 8.45 Nesting of subroutines.

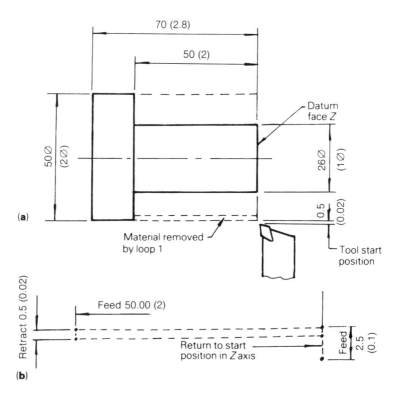

Figure 8.46 Looping cycle: (a) component detail, (b) *loop* detail, repeated six times. (Inch units are given in parentheses.)

The safety routine in this instance is determined by the blocks N10 to N70. It can be seen that, in the program, these data blocks are activated by a G25 program entry. Blocks N100 and N160 are examples where the safety routine is being called. Each time the routine appears in the program the slides return to a safe indexing position and a set of known operating modes is reestablished. This provides a basis from which the programmer can proceed with the programming of further machining operations.

Machine: Hardinge HXL Turning Center Control: GE 1050 Sample Program for Drawing Figure 8.46

N0010	G71		Metric
N0020	G40		Cancels Tool Nose Radius
			compensation (TNRC)
N0030	G95		Feed mm/rev
N0040	G97 S1000 M03	SAFETY	Spindle rev/min. CW
N0050	G00	ROUTINE	Cancels G01, G02, G03, etc.
N0060	G53X177.8Z254 T00		Return to safe indexing position,
			offsets cancelled
N0070	M01		Optional stop
N0100	G25P$_1$ 10P$_2$60		Calls safety routine
N0110	T1200		Calls tool
N0120	G54X0Z3T1212		Move in X and Y with zero shift to
			work face and tool offset active
N0130	S2500F.1	CENTER	Spindle speed and feed
N0140	G01Z-6	DRILL	Center drill
N0150	G00Z2		Drill retract
N0160	G25P$_1$ 10P$_2$70		Safety routine call with optional stop
			turret returns to safe indexing
			position

Note: In the programming areas of special canned cycles and routines, controls vary drastically and your programming manual should be reviewed.

Loops

Some control systems provide a "loop" facility. This enables the programmer to devise a routine and to repeat that routine within the part program a specific number of times. In other words, when the program reaches the end of the routine the control will return, or loop, back to the beginning of the routine again.

Consider the component shown in Figure 8.46, which is to be reduced from 50 mm (2 in.) diameter to 26 mm (1 in.) diameter by a series of cuts each of 2 mm (0.08 in.) depth. Assuming the starting point for the tool is as shown, the tool will first move in to a depth of 2.5 mm (0.1 in.), thus taking a 2 mm (0.08 in.) depth of cut, travel along a length of 50 mm (2 in.), retract 0.5 mm (0.02 in.) and return to the Z datum, so completing a loop. It will then move in a distance of 2.5 mm (0.1 in.), feed along 50 mm (2 in.), retract 0.5 mm (0.02 in.) and return to the Z datum, and so on. The loop, including the feed rate, is programmed just once, but is repeated via the loop count data included in the main program as many times as necessary to reduce the work to the required diameter.

Macros

A somewhat specialized type of programmer-devised routine is referred to as a "macro." This facility can be used for machining a complete component or a feature of a component that, while not standard in the wider sense, is nevertheless frequently required. For instance such a feature may commonly occur within the production schedule of a particular company. The macro is given an identity and stored within a separate macro file, or memory, and is called into use as and when required, possibly as an element within a much larger machining program.

A macro may have fixed dimensions, or it may have parametric variables which enable the dimensions to be varied to produce different versions of a basic component. This technique is referred to as "parametric programming." The parametric or variable version of macro programming is very useful when programming for a family of parts that have the same shape but vary in size.

Parametric Programming

A parameter is a quantity that is constant in one particular case but variable in others. A simple engineering example of a parameter is the length of a bolt. One version of the bolt will have a certain length; all other versions will be identical, that is, they will have the same thread form, diameter, and hexagon head, but they will all vary in length. Thus, the length of the bolt is a parameter, constant in one particular case but variable in others.

Parametric programming involves defining parameters and then using those parameters as the basis for one part program that may be used to machine not only the original component but a number of variations as well.

Figure 8.47(a) shows a component the dimensional features of which have been defined as parameters using the symbol # and a number: #1, #2, #3, and so on.

Figures 8.47(b)–8.47(g) show six variations of the component, the variations being indicated. A range of components such as this is referred to as a family of parts.

The machine movements necessary to machine each of the variations are all included in the original component. Some components require exactly the same movements, but with varying lengths of travel. Other components do not require all of the movements to be made. Using the more usual programming techniques, the production of each component would require a separate part program. Using the parametric part programming technique, instead of defining each dimensional movement individually in the X and Z axes, the parametric reference is programmed. Thus, to turn along the stepped diameter, the entry in the main program, referred to as the "macro," would read as follows:

```
N07    G01    X#4
N08    Z#2
```

These entries would suffice for all components requiring a stepped diameter. Equally, one entry using parametric identification would suffice for facing all the components to length or drilling the hole.

Having programmed all movements and the sequence in which they are to occur, it remains to define them dimensionally. The dimensional details are entered as a list at the

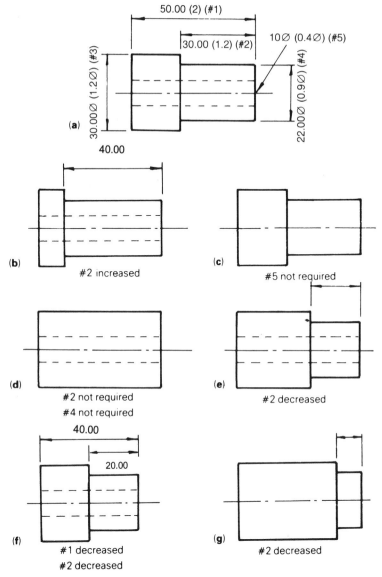

Figure 8.47 Parametric programming: a family of parts. (Inch units are given in parentheses.)

start of the part program. Thus the parameters and their metric dimensional values for the original components would read as follows:

$$\#1 = -50.00$$
$$\#2 = -30.00$$
$$\#3 = 30.00$$
$$\#4 = 22.00$$
$$\#5 = 10.00$$

As each parameter is called in the macro body, the programmed dimensional entry made previously will be invoked.

To machine any of the variations in the family of parts requires a simple amendment of the original parametric values. The parameters to machine the component shown in Figure 8.47(b) would be

$$\#1 = -50.00$$
$$\#2 = -40.00 \text{ (amended)}$$
$$\#3 = 30.00$$
$$\#4 = 22.00$$
$$\#5 = 10.00$$

and to machine the component in Figure 8.47(f)

$$\#1 = -40.00 \text{ (amended)}$$
$$\#2 = -20.00 \text{ (amended)}$$
$$\#3 = 30.00$$
$$\#4 = 22.00$$
$$\#5 = 10.00$$

Now consider the components where the programmed movements necessary for machining the basic component are not required. By using a relatively simple programming technique, the control unit can be caused to skip the redundant blocks. The necessary program entry involves the use of certain conditional expressions in which assigned abbreviations are used, such as the following:

$$EQ = \text{equal to}$$
$$NE = \text{not equal to}$$
$$GT = \text{greater than}$$
$$LT = \text{less than}$$
$$GE = \text{greater than or equal to}$$
$$LE = \text{less than or equal to}$$

Consider Figure 8.47(d) and assume the #1 and #3 have been machined. In the macro body the next call will be to machine the stepped diameter. To avoid this, blocks must be skipped and so an entry in the macro body will read as follows:

$$N15 \ \ IF \ \ [\#4 \ EQ \ 0] \ \ GO \ \ TO \ \ N18$$

This statement says that if #4 is zero, move on to block number 18. Since #4 is nonexistent in the component, the parametric value will be entered as zero and, consequently, the control unit will move ahead.

The preceding description of the use of the parametric programming technique is a very simple one. It is in fact a very powerful concept and its full application is quite complex. For instance, parameters may be mathematically related within the macro body, that is, they may be added together, subtracted from one another, and so on.

In addition, the parametric principle may be extended to include speeds and feeds, when all the likely variations for roughing, finishing, etc., may be given a parametric identity and called into the program as and when required. *Note:* parametric and macro programming, if available on particular machinery, very drastically in programming techniques, so consulting the programming manual is required.

Point Definition

Point definition is a programming facility, not widely available, which simplifies programming for drilling operations. With this facility it is possible to define dimensionally as many as 99 points or positions, and enter them into a special file within the control memory. The file can be accessed as required, the points' positions appearing in tabular form.

The points required for inclusion are entered at the start of a part program, and might look as follows:

N1	G78	P1	X15	Y20
N2	G78	P2	X20	Y20
N3	G78	P3	X50	Y30
N4	G78	P4	X65	Y60
N5	G78	P5	X75	X75
N6	G78	P6	X98	Y78

To drill a hole to a specified depth of 20 mm, using a G81 drilling cycle at points 2, 5, and 6, would require a program entry as follows:

| N095 | G81 | Z–20 | F150 | S1850 |
| N100 | G79 | P2 | P5 | P6 |

The more holes to be drilled, the more advantageous the use of the facility becomes. The dimensional data relating to each point can be modified to suit any particular job.

Mirror Image

Mirror image is the term that describes a programming facility used to machine components, or features of components, that dimensionally are identical but geometrically opposite either in two axes or one axis. By using the mirror image facility such components can be machined from just one set of data.

In Figure 8.48 an original component feature is indicated in the bottom left-hand corner of the diagram. A complete mirror image of that feature is shown in the top right-hand corner, while mirror images in the X axis and the Y axis are shown, respectively, in the bottom right- and top left-hand corners of the diagram.

To produce a complete mirror image both the X axis and Y axis dimensional values will change from negative to positive. For half mirror images the dimensional values will change from negative to positive in one axis only. Mirror imaging is normally achieved by repeating a series of program instructions after activating a X and/or Y axis switch or button on the machine controller.

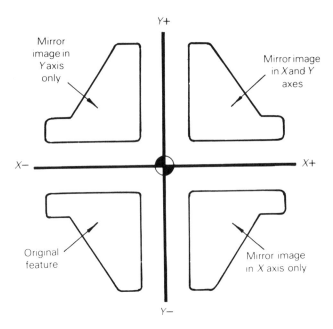

Figure 8.48 Mirror image.

Tool Offsets

Most machining operations involve the use of more than one tool, and usually they vary in length and/or diameter. To accommodate these size variations, and to permit the programmer to assume that all the tools are identical, machine controls are provided with a cutter compensation facility that will, when activated, automatically adjust the programmed slide movements. Thus, it enables the programmer to totally ignore tool size and simply program movements that are exactly the same as the profile detail, a technique referred to as "point" programming or zero-gage-length programming. Some programmers do not agree with this form of programming owing to the inherent dangers if a compensation is missed or gage length incorrectly measured. Therefore, in gage length programming techniques where tool length and radius/diameter are allowed for in program calculations, the tool compensation is used for variations in setup dimensions versus programmed tool lengths.

The task of dealing with variations in tool size is left to the tool setter or operator, since it is essentially a case of ascertaining the tool sizes or size variations and entering these numerical values into the machine control.

The numerical values that are required to be entered relate to tool length and tool radius/diameter.

The manner in which tool length variations are determined and entered varies with machine type. On some controls they are entered simply as offset values, one tool being used as a reference tool and thus having no offset value, and all other tools having data entries corresponding to their dimensional variation from the reference tool. This principle is illustrated in Figure 8.49.

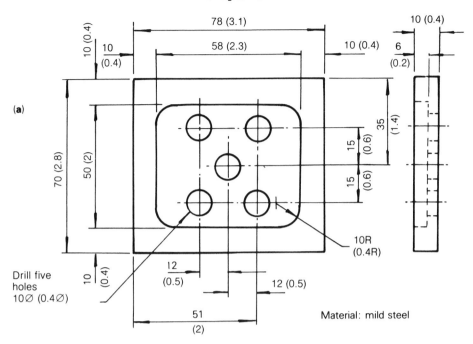

(a)

Drill five
holes
10∅ (0.4∅)

Material: mild steel

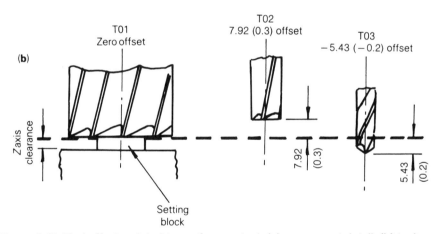

(b)

Figure 8.49 Tool offsets related to a reference tool: **(a)** component detail; **(b)** tool offsets. (Inch units are given in parentheses.)

On other machines the size variations of all tools are determined in relation to a fixed point on the machine, such as the corner of a tool post, as illustrated in Figure 8.50. In this particular example the variations are entered in a tool data file, there being a second file for programmer-devised offsets that are, through appropriate program data, paired with the tool data file entries.

Tool radius and diameter entries are less complex, being simply a case of ascertaining the correct value, by actually measuring the tool if need be, and entering the numerical value as required by the control system of the machine being used.

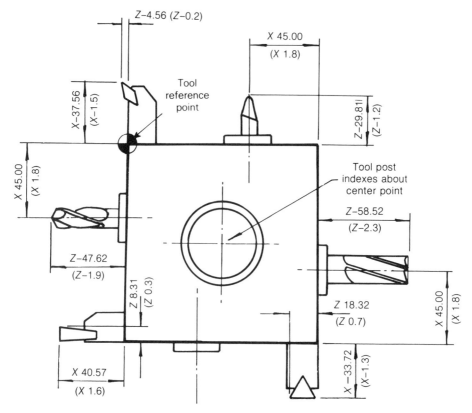

Figure 8.50 Tool offset data related to a fixed point on the toolpost. (Inch units are given in parentheses.)

Since tool data can be entered, modified, or erased by the machine operator at will the facility can be used to

(a) accommodate replacement tooling that varies from the original;
(b) make variations to the component size;
(c) initiate a series of cuts, say roughing and finishing, using the same dimensional programmed data.

If the machine operator varies the tool offset values for whatever reason, the effect is temporary. It has no permanent effect on the original program. However, the programmer can utilize the offset facility within the part program, and this creates a situation where accurate communication between the programmer and the shop floor personnel is essential if the programming objectives are to be clearly understood.

Two situations involving tool offsets that are particularly useful from a programming point of view are when variations in the sizes of components are to be made from the same basic program and when a series of cuts are to be initiated along a profile using the same programmed dimensional data.

The ability to use offsets in this manner is based on pairing offset values with specific tools. Just as tools are allocated a numerical identity, so are offsets. Two digits are commonly used, just as in the case of tool identity. The offset digits are paired with the tool digits and are included in the program as part of the tool call. Thus, tool number three with offset number six would be entered in the program as T0306. Older word address programming systems may have special letter codes for calling the tool offset active, such as "H" for length and "D" for diameter.

Control systems usually provide for more offset entry capacity than there will be tools available, so it is possible to call any offset with any tool. The ability of programming any offset with any tool also allows programming more than one offset per tool. An example when to use this feature is when one tool is used to create more than one critical dimension.

The technique of using a number of offsets to make a series of cuts along a profile is illustrated in Figure 8.51. (A similar technique can be used when milling profiles and this is discussed later in the text.)

While the use of offsets as described previously is a very useful programming facility, it should be remembered that the prime objective of an offset facility is to make zero-gage-length programming a possibility and to allow for variation in cutter size during replacement simplifying the programming process. The preceding text has dealt only with tool lengths. It is now necessary to consider the way in which a variety of cutter diameters and tip radii can be accommodated.

To facilitate zero diameter programming with a variety of cutters of varying radii, the control should move the cutter away from the work profile a distance equal to its radius. This facility is referred to as "cutter radius compensation" or "cutter diameter compensation." This compensation also allows for variation in size do to cutter sharpening or deflection.

The distance the cutter will actually move away from or toward the profile—the offset—will be related to the data entry made by the machine setup person or operator. The offset is activated via the appropriate program entry.

The offset can be programmed to occur to the right or left of the required profile, commonly by the use of G41 or G42 when programming in word address mode. To determine which offset code should be programmed, the technique is to imagine being the tool and facing the direction of tool travel. The tool can then be visualized as being either to the right or left of the profile. It is very important to ensure that the correct offset is programmed since a move in the wrong direction may have disastrous results, particularly when large diameter cutters are being used. Tool radius to the right and left of a profile is shown in Figure 8.52.

When activating cutter radius compensation, it must be ensured that the slides will first make a noncutting move, to enable the correct tool and workpiece relationship to be established. A similar move is necessary prior to cancellation of the radius compensation. These noncutting moves are referred to as "ramp on" and "ramp off," respectively.

It is now possible to return to the technique referred to earlier, of using offsets to make a series of passes along a milled profile. It is achieved by simply entering a bogus value for the cutter diameter into the control system. By making an entry that is greater than the size of the cutter being used, the actual offset activated via the program will be greater. Thus, the final profile will remain oversize as illustrated in Figure 8.53. The technique can also be used progressively to remove surplus material before making a final cut.

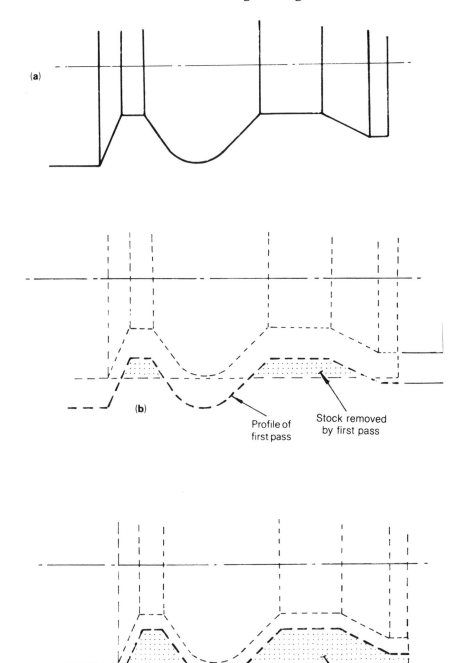

Figure 8.51 Use of tool offsets for progressive stock removal to a set profile: **(a)** profile detail; **(b)** first cut; **(c)** second cut.

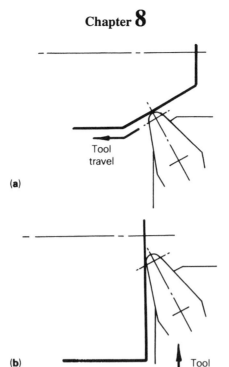

Figure 8.52 Tool nose radius compensation (TNRC): (**a**) radius compensation left; (**b**) radius compensation right.

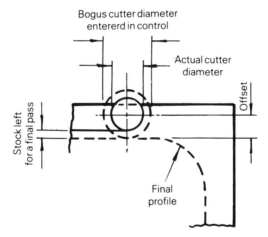

Figure 8.53 Using an offset to create an oversize milled profile.

The reverse application of this technique, that is, entering a value smaller than the actual cutter size, will result in a smaller offset and, in the case illustrated, an undersize component profile. Thus, it is possible to produce components of varying dimensions from the same program when milling, just as it is possible to do so when turning.

Block Delete

Production engineering often involves machining a range of components that have slight variations from each other. For example, a hole that has to be drilled in one component is not required in a second component, although all the other details remain the same. Thus, one program would serve for both components providing that some means exists for not drilling the hole when it is not required. The way this is achieved is by use of a "block delete" facility.

Blocks relating to machining features that may not always be required incorporate the symbol /, which is referred to as a slash. The exact position of the slash within the block may vary from one system to another, but it is usually at the start before the sequence number (/N0245).

The machine operator will need to be instructed as to whether the data are to be retained or deleted from the current machining task. If the data are to be retained, the operator takes no action. If the data are to be deleted, the operator has to activate the block delete button on the control panel before running the program. Activation of the button is usually indicated by a light.

If the slash delete button is not activated, the control will respond to all the data contained in the program. If the slash delete button is activated, then all the blocks containing a slash will be ignored.

On some control systems if the slash delete button is not activated, the program will automatically stop when the first slash is reached and the operator then has to make a positive response, either to activate the data contained within the slashes or delete them.

The block delete facility is also useful when machining castings or forgings, where stock removal requirements may vary. The operator is given the option to include an extra cut or not as necessary.

The use of the block delete facility relies on a clear and concise relay of instructions between the part programmer and the machine operator. The machine operator must be left in no doubt as to what is required.

Program Stops

Apart from the program stop that is automatically effected when the end of a program is reached, and which arrests all slide and spindle motions, there are two other situations where a halt in proceedings may need to be included in the part program.

The first of these is the point at which the operator is required to carry out some specific task directly associated with the machining program, such as resetting the work or replacing a tool. With word address programming this is normally achieved by programming M00. When such a stop is effected, it is essential that the operator knows exactly what has to be done before the program is reactivated. Some controls will allow for a man readable message to be read from the program and placed on the screen.

The second type of program stop is used when a halt in activity is not quite so critical, and the operator decides whether a stop is actually made. This type of stop is referred to as "optional" and will only take place if the operator has activated the optional stop button on the control console. The programmer may include an optional stop in the program whenever he or she considers it may be of value to the machine operator, such as when a dimensional check or an inspection of the tooling condition is appropriate. But quite often it is the operator who will edit into the program, via the control console, stops that will permit the solving of particular problems that have presented themselves during the machining process. The optional stop in a word address program is normally effected via a programmed M01.

In addition to the stops included in the part program, the operator has, of course, recourse to an emergency stop should the need arise.

Calculations

It could be argued that, in a well-organized CNC machining environment, the people responsible for the production of the detail drawings of the components to be machined should appreciate the needs of the part programmer and ensure that the drawings are dimensioned accordingly. For example, it is of considerable help when positional slide movements are to be programmed in absolute mode if all dimensions on the drawing are given in relation to a suitable datum. This is especially valuable when the programming technique involves conversational or manual data input, since the last thing a programmer wants to do is to interrupt his thought process in order to calculate unspecified dimensions.

However, whatever the ideal situation may be, it is almost certain that eventually the part programmer will be confronted with a detail drawing that does not cater to his or her requirements. He or she will then find it necessary to make calculations and add dimensions, and perhaps in some cases to completely redimension the drawing.

(The reader should differentiate between poor industrial practice and situations with which he or she may be deliberately confronted in a learning situation, where the objective will be to provide an understanding of the problems likely to be encountered in practice.)

Mention has already been made of the need for dimensions to be given in relation to a set datum when absolute programming is to be used. The opposite situation could also arise, whereby the dimensions are stated in relation to a datum but the programmer needs to program incremental slide moves. In this case the stated dimensions will need to be subdivided. The programmer should exercise caution in this particular situation, and ensure that such an approach is acceptable from a design point of view; minor errors on each of a series of incremental moves could, due to inaccuracies in calculations or round off, accumulate into a larger error that would be unacceptable.

There are other situations that are more complex than simply converting absolute dimensions to incremental and vice versa. Two of these in particular are the need to determine:

(a) profile intersection points;
(b) the location of arc centers.

However complex the profile or shape of a machined surface may appear to be, it can be broken down and defined geometrically as a number of intersecting straight lines or arcs or a combination of the two. To program appropriate machine slide movements, the programmer is required to determine this geometry, and translate production of the profile into a series of linear or circular movements.

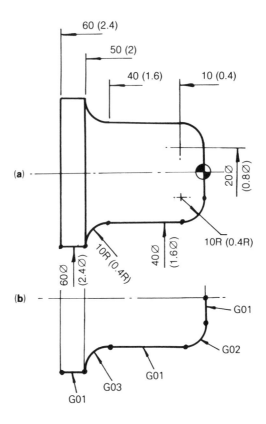

Figure 8.54 Geometric elements of a profile: **(a)** component detail; **(b)** profile definition. (Inch units are given in parentheses.)

Thus, to finish machine the profile shown in Figure 8.54 the following movements will be necessary:

        Move 1   Linear
        Move 2   Circular, clockwise
        Move 3   Linear
        Move 4   Circular, counterclockwise
        Move 5   Linear

If word address programming is being used, these moves can be described using the appropriate G code: G01, G02, G01, G03, and G01. It may be helpful to mark the drawing accordingly, as in the illustration.

The reader will already appreciate that when programming positional moves, whether they are linear or circular, the target position has to be numerically defined. In this particular example, because the component is dimensioned correctly and the arcs are conveniently 90°, the target position, that is, the intersection points of the geometrical elements of the profile, are readily discerned. No further calculations are necessary.

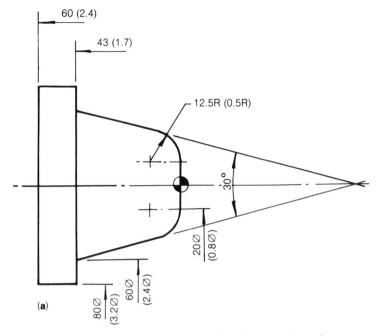

Figure 8.55 Component detail. (Inch units are given in parentheses.)

Consider now the component shown in Figure 8.55(a). Although it is a relatively simple profile, from a programming point of view the drawing is not as helpful as it might be. The target position of the arc, that is, the point at which the circular move ends and the linear move commences, is not defined. Calculations are required as follows in order to determine the target position in the X and Z axes. (Only the metric unit calculation is given.)

In Figure 8.56:

$$\varnothing X_1 = 2(CB + 10) \text{ and } Z_1 = CD$$

In triangle ABC:

$$\angle ABC = 15° \text{ and } AB = 12.5$$

1. To calculate CB:

$$\cos \angle ABC = \frac{CB}{AB}$$

$$
\begin{aligned}
CB &= \cos \angle ABC \times AB \\
&= \cos 15 \times 12.5 \\
&= 0.966 \times 12.5 \\
&= 12.074 \\
\varnothing X_1 &= 2(12.074 + 10) = 44.148
\end{aligned}
$$

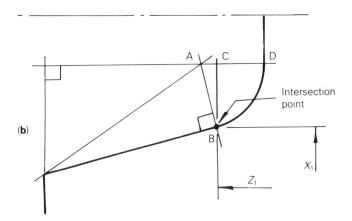

Figure 8.56 Profile intersection calculation.

2. To calculate AC:

$$\sin \angle ABC = \frac{AC}{AB}$$

$$
\begin{aligned}
AC &= \sin \angle ABC \times AB \\
&= \sin 15 \times 12.5 \\
&= 0.259 \times 12.5 \\
&= 3.235
\end{aligned}
$$

$$
\begin{aligned}
\text{Since } Z_1 = CD, \text{ then } Z_1 &= AD - AC \\
&= 12.5 - 3.235 \\
&= 9.265
\end{aligned}
$$

Thus, the target position, with the X value being programmed as a diameter, is X44.148 Z − 9.265. These values would need to be included in the part program.

This particular calculation is fairly typical of the situations the part programmer has to deal with. A similar situation presents itself in the profile shown in Figure 8.57(a) where one radius blends with another. The problem is: where does one radius end and the second one start? Calculations are necessary to determine the location of point P in the X and Y axes as indicated in Figure 8.57(b). The reader may like to consider the solution to the problem. (Answers: 47.81 mm and 71.25 mm, respectively.)

This type of profile also presents the second type of calculation referred to earlier, namely, determining the location of arc centers.

From the previous information the reader will recall that when circular arcs are programmed using word address programming one of three techniques may be involved. All require the target positions to be identified, but the radius definition varies. The first involves defining the arc center in relation to the program datum, and the second requires the arc center to be defined in relation to the arc starting position.

Using the first method, the center of the 30 mm radius arc is easily determined from the dimensions already on the drawing. But the location of the center of the 50 mm radius is not so straightforward and a calculation is required.

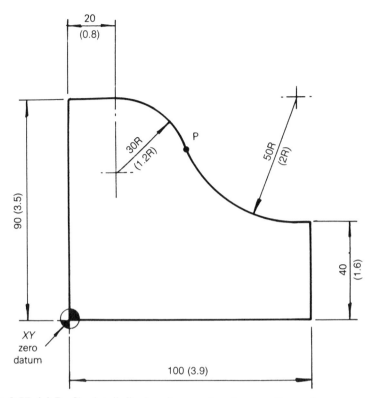

Figure 8.57 (a) Profile detail. (Inch units are given in parentheses.)

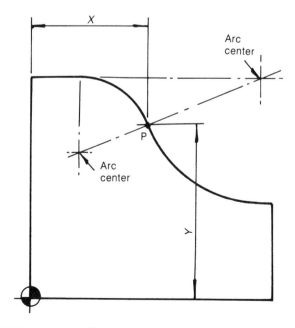

Figure 8.57 (b) Required profile intersection dimensions.

Using the second method of circular interpolation the definition of the arc centers in relation to the start points again presents a problem as far as the 50 mm radius is concerned, and a calculation will be necessary before the program can be written.

Exercises involving the calculation of profile intersection points and arc centers are included in this chapter's section titled "Part Programming Calculations."

Tool Paths

A prime objective of the part programmer should be to ensure that a component is machined in the shortest possible time. Earlier in the text reference was made to the way a well-planned sequence of machining operations can contribute to this objective. But often within each individual machining sequence there is room for further efficiency, which results in time saving.

Consider the drilling of the series of five holes in the component shown in Figure 8.58. Two sequences in which the holes might be drilled are indicated. Which sequence would be the quicker?

The actual operation of drilling the holes, that is, movement in the Z axis, would be identical in both cases. Therefore, any saving that can be achieved must be by reducing the total length of the positioning moves, and therefore the time taken.

Providing the detail drawing is reasonably accurately drawn a simple rule measurement check may suffice to determine the shorter route. Applying this technique to this particular example will reveal that the second sequence is quicker than the first.

The need to give careful consideration to tool paths is also important during stock removal operations. This is particularly so when there are no stock removal canned cycles available within the control system, or if they cannot be utilized in a particular situation.

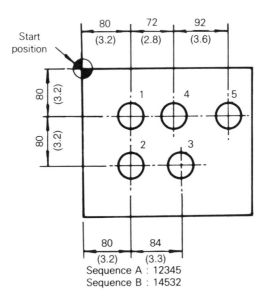

Figure 8.58 Alternative drilling sequences. (Inch units are given in parentheses.)

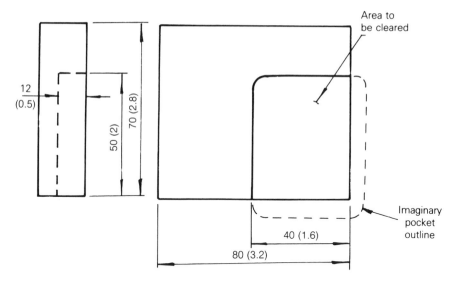

Figure 8.59 "Pocket" detail. (Inch units are given in parentheses.)

Consider the removal of stock, or area clearance as it is also known, in order to machine the step shown in Figure 8.59.

If a pocket milling cycle is available on the control system of the machine, this could be used, the missing sides of the "pocket" being indicated by the dotted line. Use of the cycle would ensure that efficient tool paths are employed.

If such a cycle is not available, then the matter becomes a little more complex. The process of producing the step will involve programming a series of linear moves, with careful attention being given to providing an appropriate cutter overlap to ensure a clean face. The lengths of relative cutter travel will also have to ensure a uniform amount of metal is left for a finish pass along the profile. The programmer should also ensure that the cutter paths used are the shortest and therefore the quickest.

Similar problems often present themselves during turning operations. Figure 8.60 shows a typical example.

There is no short cut when solving this type of problem. After a little experience of dealing with situations of this nature, the trainee programmer soon comes to appreciate the value of canned cycles, which reduce the amount of machining dealt with in this manner to a minimum.

If the part programmer is confronted with machining situations such as these, he or she will have to resort to drawing the profile, preferably to an enlarged scale, and then imposing appropriate tool paths on the drawing. In the case of milling examples it may be necessary to draw circles indicating the cutter diameter. The milled step referred to above, when dealt with in this way, is shown in Figure 8.61. Having decided on the most suitable tool paths (which may take a number of attempts), the slide movements may be dimensionally determined by carefully scaling the drawing or through mathematical calculation.

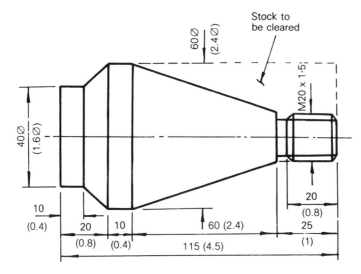

Material: medium carbon steel 60Ø (2.4Ø)

Figure 8.60 Component requiring excess stock removal. (Inch units are given in parentheses.)

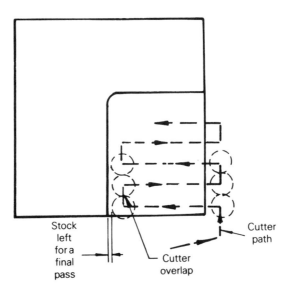

Figure 8.61 Determination of cutter path to mill a step.

An alternative approach is to reproduce the profile on graph paper, as shown in Figure 8.62, in which case the graduated lines on the graph paper can be used to determine the dimensional value of the necessary moves.

Exercises involving the determination of cutter paths are included in subsequent examples.

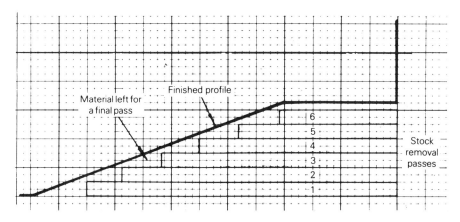

Figure 8.62 Determination of tool paths when turning.

Program Listing and Proving

Before starting to create a part program listing, all the various facets of competent part programming discussed so far should have received due attention.

The sequence of operations, together with the tooling and work-holding techniques to be employed, should be documented. Appropriate speeds and feed rates should have been determined and all the necessary calculations affecting slide movements must be complete.

Having reached this stage the way is clear to list the program, and this requires the programmer to be conversant with the machine programming language.

To become fully proficient with a particular programming system takes time and practice. As with most things it is a case of starting with relatively simple tasks and gradually progressing to more complex examples. If you are a student, or perhaps undergoing training in an industrial establishment, it is almost certain that your course work will be structured in this way.

Competent part programming demands a logical approach and a high degree of concentration and care when actually listing the program. Mistakes are easily made and can have disastrous results, although fortunately most mistakes can be discovered and rectified before machining takes place.

Programs may be listed on appropriate forms, or on plain paper or they can be entered into a computer and listed on the display screen. Programs initially handwritten can, of course, also be entered into a computer and visually displayed.

The use of a computer for program listing is often coupled with the facility to prove the program using animated computer graphics. This involves, in effect, "machining" the component on the screen.

The effectiveness of proving programs in this way will depend on the sophistication of the software available. The simplest software will usually highlight major errors such as movement occurring in the wrong direction or a lathe tool crashing into a chuck, while the more complex will also indicate errors relating to speeds and feeds and even the absence of a coolant supply.

Ultimately, the part program will be entered into the machine control unit, but this may also involve computer graphics. Figure 8.63 shows a controller that includes a

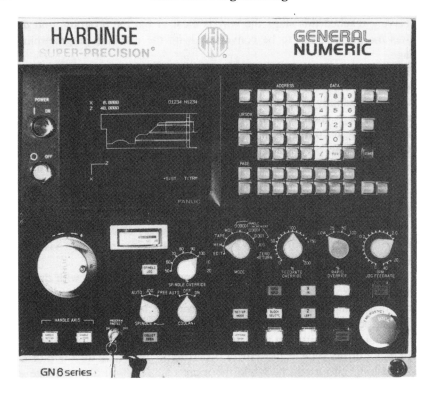

Figure 8.63 A machine controller with built-in CRT to facilitate program proving.

built-in visual display. As the program is entered the CRT screen will display the geometric profile of the part and the programmed cutter paths and thus confirm, or otherwise, the validity of the data input. The illustration relates to a program written for the part detailed in Figure 8.64. An enlargement of the CRT display is shown in Figure 8.65 where the component profile can be more readily defined.

A large number of machines currently in use do not have the benefit of built-in computer graphics, and if off-line computer graphics proving facilities are not available, then the proving of the part program must take the form of a test run or a dry run or both.

The test run is basically a check that the data input is valid, that is, that the machine is capable of responding to the data entries included in the program. Data errors are usually indicated by a displayed message. No slide movement takes place during the test run.

The dry run procedure also excludes metal cutting, but, with this checking procedure, slide movements occur at a rapid rate of traverse. This test ensures that the intended machine movements are occurring, and that they will result in the machined features required.

The most common test available, even on the simplest of machines, is to run the program through one block at a time with reduced programmed feed rates, but without the job material being in position so that no machining actually takes place—block by block prove out. This prove out method is usually followed by a block by block run with part material and reduced feed rates before an automatic run is attempted.

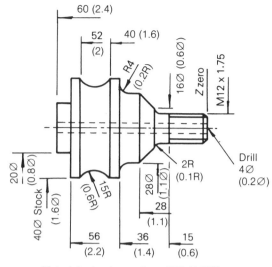

Material: aluminum allow 40∅ (1.6∅)

Figure 8.64 Component detail. (Inch units are given in parentheses.)

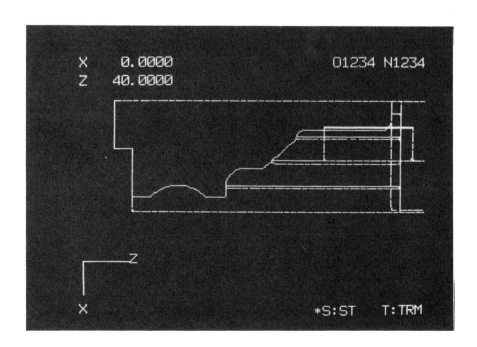

Figure 8.65 An enlargement of the CRT display shown in Figure 8.63.

Tests of this nature carried out on the machine may or may not be the responsibility of the programmer, although he or she will soon be involved if any errors are indicated.

Finally, there is the need, particularly in industrial situations, to record the program for future use. In its simplest form, storage can be a handwritten version of the proved program. Normally, it will be in the form of a computer disk or a file in computer memory.

Whatever the storage medium, it must be remembered that people looking to reuse the program at a later date will also need information relating to tooling and workholding. This information is as critical as the part program and must also be carefully filed for future reference.

Manual Part Programming Examples

The programming examples that follow were prepared to show the calculation and writing of generic manual part programs. Examples follow for both a lathe and mill in inch and metric calculations. The intent of the author is to give you the realization of putting an entire program document together. We must realize though that most machines program slightly different and programmers take various approaches to how they process, fixture, tool, and program.

Finally, note that it is common practice to number blocks of information by increments of five or ten: N0010, N0020, N0030, and so on. The reason for adopting this approach is that if, on completion of the program, it is found that something has been omitted, it will be possible to insert additional blocks. It also provides space that will facilitate general editing of the program at the machine control should this be found to be necessary.

Example 1: Lathe Inch Programming

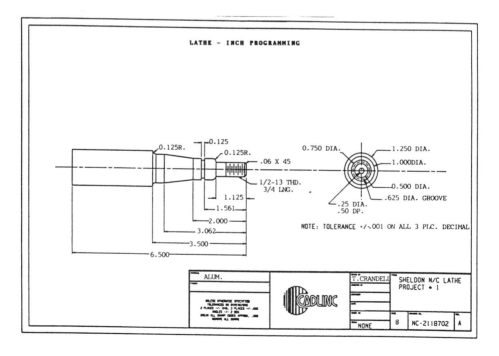

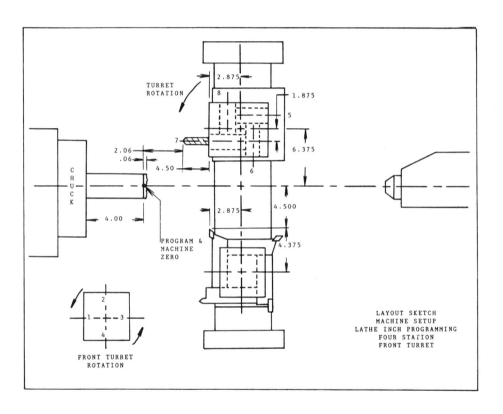

TURRET
ROTATION

2.875

8

1.875

5

7

2.06
.06

4.50

6.375

6

C
H
U
C
K

PROGRAM &
MACHINE
ZERO

4.00

2.875

4.500

4.375

2
1 — 3
4

FRONT TURRET
ROTATION

LAYOUT SKETCH
MACHINE SETUP
LATHE INCH PROGRAMMING
FOUR STATION
FRONT TURRET

TOOL SHEET
LATHE INCH PROGRAMMING

PART NO. NC-2118702		MATERIAL ALUM.	OPERATION 20	PROGRAMMED BY T. CRANDELL
PART NAME PROJECT 1		B/P CHANGE DATE 9-21-87		DATE 5-5-89 SHEET 1 OF 1

SEQ.	NUMBER	TOOL DESCRIPTION	TOOL LENGTH X PROG.	ACT.	#	TOOL LENGTH Z PROG.	ACT.	#	OPERATION DESCRIPTION	SPEED R P M	CODE	FEED IN/MIN	CODE
	T01	55 DEG. DIAMOND TURNING TOOL (RGH) .031 TOOL NOSE RADIUS Valenite Holder MDJNR-13-4 Insert DNMP432E VN5	4.375			2.875			RGH. FACE & RGH. TURN	960 to 2000		.010 IPR	
	T02	55 DEG. DIAMOND TURNING TOOL (FIN) .031 TOOL NOSE RADIUS Valenite Holder MDJNR-13-4 Insert DNMP432E VN5	4.375			2.875			FIN. FACE & FIN. TURN	2000		.005 IPR	
	T03	.125 GROOVE TOOL Valenite Holder SD-IMR-16-3 Insert TNMC32NG VN5	4.375			2.875			.125 GROOVE	1000		.005 IPR	
	T04	60 DEG. THREAD TOOL Valenite Holder SD-IMR-16-3 Insert TNMC32NV VC7	4.375			2.875			½-13 THREAD	2000		.077 IPR	
	T07	.250 DIA. HSS DRILL	1.875			4.500			DRILL .250 DIA.	2000		.006 IPR	

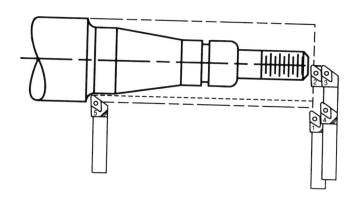

COORDINATE CALCULATIONS
LATHE INCH PROGRAMMING

ROUGH FACE & FIRST ROUGH TURN

POINT CODE	X COORDINATE	Z COORDINATE	CALCULATION
P1	X .725	Z .030	X .625 Stock Radius + .100 Clearance Z .030 Finish Stock
P2	X-.050	Z .030	X-.030 Tool Radius - .020 Cut Past Center Z .030 Finish Stock
P3	X-.050	Z .050	X-.030 - .020 Z .030 Finish Stock + .020 Clearance
P4	X. 525	Z .050	X .500 Part Radius + .025 Stock
P5	X .525	Z-3.406	Z-3.375 - $\sqrt{.069^2 - .069^2}$ - .031 Formula #1 Appendix E

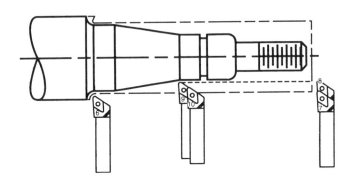

SECOND ROUGH TURN

POINT CODE	X COORDINATE	Z COORDINATE	CALCULATION
P6	X .575	Z-3.356	X .525 Radius + .050 Clearance Z-3.406 Pos."5" + .050 Clearance
P7	X .575	Z .050	Z .030 Finish Stock + .020 Clearance
P8	X .400	Z .050	X .375 Part Radius + .025 Stock
P9	X .400	Z-2.0277	$Z\text{-}2.0 - [.031 - (\text{Tan.}\frac{6.7129^{O}}{2} \ X \ (.031 + .025))]$ Formula #2 Appendix E
P10	X .450	Z-1.9777	X .400 Radius + .050 Clearance Z-2.0277 Pos."9" + .050 Clearance

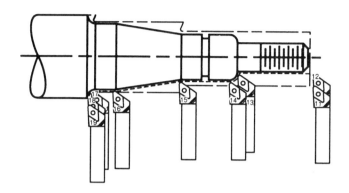

SEMI FINISH TURN

POINT CODE	X COORDINATE	Z COORDINATE	CALCULATION
P11	X .450	Z .050	Z .030 Finish Stock + .020 Clearance
P12	X .265	Z .050	X .250 Part Radius + .015 Finish Stock
P13	X .265	Z-1.1164	Z-1.125 - .125 + .1646 - .031 Formula #3 Appendix E
P14	X .390 I.046	Z-1.281 K.1646	X .375 Part Radius + .015 Finish Stock Z-1.250 Radius Center - .031 Tool Radius
P15	X .390	Z-2.0283	Z-2.0 -[.031-(Tan.$\frac{6.7129°}{2}$ X (.031+.015))] Formula #2 Appendix E
P16	X .515	Z-3.0903	X .500 Part Radius + .015 Finish Stock Z-2.0283 Pos. 15 - 1.062 Taper Length
P17	X .515	Z-3.406	Z-3.500 Part Dim. + .125 Radius - .031 Tool Radius
P18	X .594 I.079	Z-3.485 KO	X .625 Part Radius - .031 Tool Radius Z-3.500 Part Dim. + .015 Finish Stock
P19	X .750	Z-3.485	X .625 Part Radius + .125 Clearance

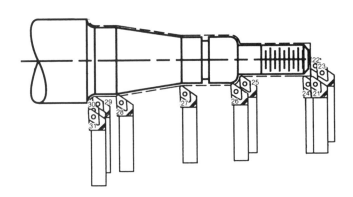

FINISH FACE AND FINISH TURN

POINT CODE	X COORDINATE	Z COORDINATE	CALCULATION
P20	TOOL	CHANGE	POSITION
P21	X .365	Z O	X .250 Part Radius + .015 Stock + .100 Clearance Z O Finish Datum
P22	X-.050	Z O	X O Datum - .031 Tool Radius - .019 Past Center
P23	X .0718	Z .100	X .250 Part Radius - .06 Cham. - .10 Clearance +.0128 Formula #4 Appendix E -.031 Tool Radius Z O Datum + .100 Clearance
P24	X .250	Z .0782	X .250 Part Radius Z-.060 Chamfer + .0128(formula 4) -.031 Tool Radius
P25	X .250	Z-1.1281	Z-1.125 - .125 + .1529 - .031 Formula #3 No Stock Appendix E
P26	X .375 I.031	Z-1.281 K.1529	X .375 Part Radius Z-1.125 - .125 radius - .031 Tool Radius
P27	X .375	Z-2.0292	Z-2.0 -[.031-(Tan.$\frac{6.7129^\circ}{2}$ X.031)] Formula #2 No Stock Appendix E
P28	X .500	Z-3.0912	X .500 Part Radius Z-2.0292 Pos. 27 - 1.062 Taper Length

POINT
CODE   X COORDINATE   Z COORDINATE   CALCULATION

P29	X.500	Z-3.406	Z-3.500 Part Dim. + .125 Radius - .031 Tool Radius
P30	X .594 I.094	Z-3.500 K0	X .625 Part Radius - .031 Tool Radius Z-3.500 Part Dim.
P31	X .750	Z-3.500	X .625 Part Radius + .125 Clearance
P32	TOOL	CHANGE	POSITION

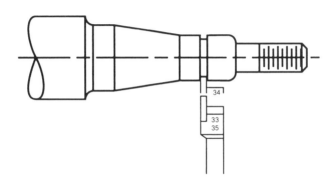

CUT GROOVE

POINT
CODE   X COORDINATE   Z COORDINATE   CALCULATION

P33	X .475	Z-1.687	X .375 Part Radius + .100 Clearance Z-1.561 Part Dim. - .125 Groove Width
P34	X .3125	Z-1.687	X .3125 Groove Radius
P35	X .475	Z-1.687	X .375 Part Radius + .100 Clearance
P36	TOOL	CHANGE	POSITION

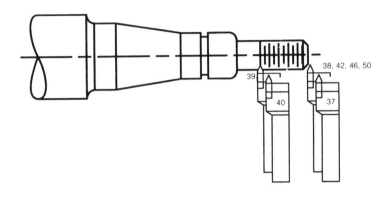

```
                        THREAD CUTTING
POINT
CODE    X COORDINATE   Z COORDINATE    CALCULATION
```

POINT CODE	X COORDINATE	Z COORDINATE	CALCULATION
P37	X .350	Z .100	X .250 Part Radius + .100 Clearance Z O Finish Datum + .100 clearance
P38	X .2284	Z .0876 K.0769	X .250 Part Radius − .0216 Thread In Feed Z .100 Clearance − .0124 Thread In Feed K 1 ÷ 13 (Thread Pitch)
P39	X .2284	Z−.750	Z−.750 Thread Length Dim.
P40	X .350	Z−.750	X .250 Part Radius + .100 Clearance
P42	X .2166	Z .0808	X .250 Part Radius − .0334 Thread In Feed Z .100 Clearance − .0192 Thread In Feed
P46	X .2076	Z .0756	X .250 Part Radius − .0424 Thread In Feed Z .100 Clearance − .0244 Thread In Feed
P50	X .200	Z .0714	X .250 Part Radius − .050 Thread In Feed Z .100 Clearance − .0286 Thread In Feed
	TOOL	CHANGE	POSITION

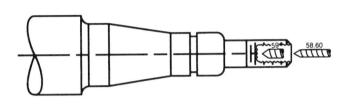

DRILL .250 DIAMETER HOLE

POINT CODE	X COORDINATE	Z COORDINATE	CALCULATION
P58	X O	Z .100	X O Datum Z O Datum + .100 Clearance
P59	X O	Z-.575	Z-.500 Hole Depth - .075 Drill Point .3 X Dia. Drill Point Allowance
P60	X O	Z .100	X O Datum Z O Datum + .100 Clearance
P61	TOOL	CHANGE	POSITION

Lathe—Inch Program (Example 1)

%   *Rewind stop code*
N0010 G70   *Inch programming*
N0020 G97   *rpm spindle speed programming*
N0030 G95   *ipr feedrate programming*
N0040 G90   *Absolute coordinate programming*
N0050 G00 T00   *Clear tool offsets*
N0060 T0600   *Index rear turret to empty station*
N0070 T0101 S960 M03   *Index tool 1 to cutting position (rough face & turn),*
                                        start spindle
N0080 G92 X4.5 Z6.56   *Preset X & Z axes*
N0090 G00 X.725 Z.03 M08   *Position tool to rough face, turn coolant on (P1)*
N0100 G01 X-.05 F.01   *Rough face part leaving 0.030 (P2)*
N0110 G00 Z.050   *Retract from face (P3)*
N0120 X.525   *Position X for first rough turn (P4)*
N0130 G01 Z-3.406 F.01   *Feed for first rough turn (P5)*
N0140 G00 X.575 Z-3.356   *Retract X & Z axes (P6)*
N0150 Z.05 S1132   *Rapid to face of part (P7)*
N0160 X.4   *Position X for second rough turn (P8)*
N0170 G01 Z-2.0277 F.01   *Feed for second rough turn (P9)*
N0180 G00 X.450 Z-1.9777   *Retract X & Z axes (P10)*
N0190 Z.05 S2000   *Rapid to face of part (P11)*
N0200 X.265   *Position X for semifinish pass (P12)*
N0210 G01 Z-1.1164   *Feed tangent to convex radius (P13)*
N0220 S1538   *Change rpm*
N0230 G03 X.39 Z-1.281 1.046 K.1647   *Contour convex radius (P14)*
N0240 G01 Z-2.0283   *Feed tangent to taper (P15)*
N0250 S1200   *Change rpm*
N0260 X.515 Z-3.0903   *Feed up taper (P16)*
N0270 Z-3.406   *Feed tangent to concave radius (P17)*
N0280 S1010   *Change rpm*
N0290 G02 X.594 Z-3.485 1.079 K0   *Contour concave radius (P18)*
N0300 G01 X.750   *Feed off part (P19)*
N0310 G00 X4.5 Z6.56 T0000   *Rapid to tool change position—cancelling tool*
                                        offset (P20)
N0320 G92 X0 Z0   *Cancel axis presets*
N0330 G00 T0202   *Index finish facing and turning tool into cutting position*
N0340 G90 S2000 M03   *Set finishing rpm*
N0350 G92 X4.5 Z6.56   *Axis presets*
N0360 G00 X.365 Z0   *Rapid position to start finish face (P21)*
N0370 G01 X-.05 F.005   *Finish face part (P22)*
N0380 G00 X.0718 Z.100   *Retract in Z and position for chamfer (P23)*
N0390 G01 X.25 Z.0782   *Turn chamfer (P24)*
N0400 Z-1.1281   *Finish turn to convex radius (P25)*
N0410 S1600   *Change rpm*
N0420 G03 X.375 Z-1.281 1.031 K.1529   *Contour convex radius (P26)*
N0430 G01 Z-2.0292   *Finish turn tangent to taper (P27)*
N0440 S1200   *Change rpm*
N0450 X.5 Z-3.0912   *Finish turn taper (P28)*

N0460 Z-3.406   *Finish turn tangent to concave radius (P29)*
N0470 S1010   *Change rpm*
N0480 G02 X.594 Z-3.51.094 K0   *Contour concave radius (P30)*
N0490 G01 X.750   *Feed away from part (P31)*
N0500 G00 X4.5 Z6.56 T0000 M09   *Rapid to tool change position cancelling tool*
                                    offsets and turning off coolant (P32)

N0510 G92 X0 Z0   *Cancel axis presets*
N0520 G00 T0303   *Index grooving tool into cutting position*
N0530 G90 S1000 M03   *Start spindle*
N0540 G92 X4.5 Z6.56   *Preset axes*
N0550 G00 X.475 Z-1.687 M08   *Position in X & Z to cut groove (P33)*
N0560 G01 X.3125 F.005   *Cut groove to depth (P34)*
N0570 G04 F05   *Dwell for 5 seconds*
N0580 G00 X.475 M09   *Retract from groove, turning coolant off (P35)*
N0590 X4.5 Z6.56 T0000   *Rapid to tool change position cancelling tool offset (P36)*
N0600 G92 X0 Z0   *Cancel axis presets*
N0610 G00 T0404   *Index threading tool into cutting position*
N0620 G90 S2000 M03   *Start spindle*
N0630 G92 X4.5 Z6.56   *Preset axes*
N0640 G00 X.35 Z.1 M08   *Position in X & Z to cut thread (P37)*
N0650 X.2284 Z.0876   *First thread in feed (P38)*
N0660 G33 Z-.75 K.0769   *Cut first thread pass (P39)*
N0670 G00 X.35   *Retract X (P40)*
N0680 Z.1   *Rapid to end of part (P41)*
N0690 X.2166 Z.0808   *Thread in feed for second pass (P42)*
N0700 G33 Z-.75 K.0769   *Cut second pass (P43)*
N0710 G00 X.35   *Retract X (P44)*
N0720 Z.1   *Rapid to end of part (P45)*
N0730 X.2076 Z.0756   *Thread in feed for third pass (P46)*
N0740 G33 Z-.75 K.0769   *Cut third pass (P47)*
N0750 G00 X.35   *Retract X (P48)*
N0760 Z.1   *Rapid to end of part (P49)*
N0770 X.2 Z.0714   *Thread in feed for finish pass (P50)*
N0780 G33 Z-.75 K.0769   *Cut finish pass (P51)*
N0790 G00 X.35   *Retract X (P52)*
N0800 Z.1   *Rapid to end of part (P53)*
N0810 X.2 Z.0714   *Thread in feed for tool pressure pass (P54)*
N0820 G33 Z-.75 K.0769   *Cut tool pressure pass (P55)*
N0830 G00 X.35 M09   *Retract X (P56)*
N0840 X4.5 Z6.56 T0000   *Rapid to tool change cancelling tool offsets (P57)*
N0850 G92 X0 Z0   *Cancel axis preset*
N0860 G00 T0707   *Index 0.250 diameter drill into cutting position*
N0870 G90 S2000 M03   *Start spindle*
N0880 G92 X-4.5 Z2.06   *Preset axes*
N0890 G00 X0 Z.1 M08   *Position to drill (P58)*
N0900 G01 Z-.575 F.006   *Drill to depth (P59)*
N0910 G00 Z.1 M09   *Retract drill (P60)*
N0920 X-4.5 Z2.06 T0000   *Rapid to tool change cancelling tool offsets (P61)*
N0930 G92 X0 Z0   *Cancel axis presets*
N0940 M02   *End of program*

Example 2: Lathe Metric Programming

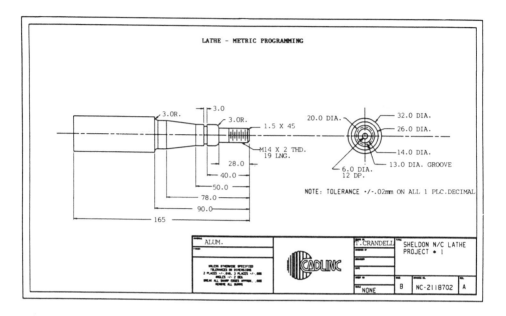

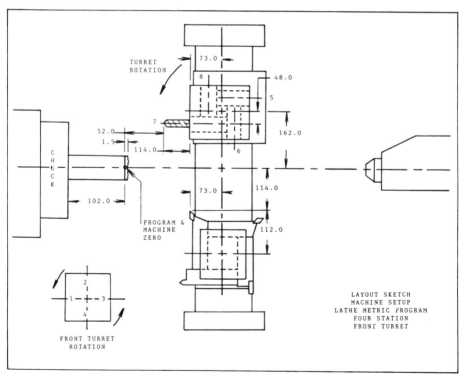

TOOL SHEET
LATHE METRIC PROGRAMMING

PART NO. NC-2118702	MATERIAL ALUM.	OPERATION 20
PART NAME PROJECT 1	B/P CHANGE DATE	PROGRAMMED BY T. CRANDELL
	DATE	SHEET 1 OF 1

TOOL		TOOL LENGTH X		TOOL LENGTH Z			OPERATION		SPEED		FEED	
SEQ. NUMBER	DESCRIPTION	PROG.	ACT.	#	PROG.	ACT.	#	DESCRIPTION	R.P.M.	CODE	IN/MM	CODE
T01	55 DEG. DIAMOND TURNING TOOL (RGH) 0.8 mm TOOL NOSE RADIUS / Valenite Holder / MDJNR-13-4 Insert / DNMP432E VN5	112.0			73.0			RGH. FACE & RGH. TURN	960 to 2000		.25 MMPR	
T02	55 DEG. DIAMOND TURNING TOOL (FIN) 0.8 mm TOOL NOSE RADIUS / Valenite Holder / MDJNR-13-4 Insert / DNMP432E VN5	112.0			73.0			FIN. FACE & FIN. TURN	2000		.12 MMPR	
T03	3.0 GROOVE TOOL / Valenite Holder / SD-TMR-16-3 / Insert TNMC32NG VN5	112.0			73.0			3.0 GROOVE	1000		.12 MMPR	
T04	60 DEG. THREAD TOOL / Valenite Holder / SD-IMR-16-3 / Insert TNMC32NV VC7	112.0			73.0			M14X2 THREAD	1000		2.0 MMPR	
T07	6.0mm DIA. HSS DRILL	48.0			114.0			DRILL 6.0mm DIA.	2000		.15 MMPR	

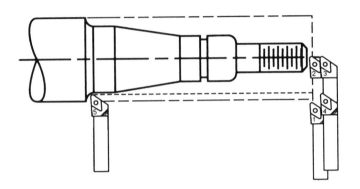

COORDINATE CALCULATIONS
LATHE METRIC PROGRAMMING

ROUGH FACE & FIRST ROUGH TURN

POINT CODE	X COORDINATE	Z COORDINATE	CALCULATION
P1	X 18.5	Z .75	X 16.0 Stock Radius + 2.5 Clearance Z .75 Finish Stock
P2	X-1.3	Z .75	X-.8 Tool Radius - .5 Cut Past Center Z .75 Finish Stock
P3	X-1.3	Z 3.25	X-.8 - .5 Z .75 Finish Stock + 2.5 Clearance
P4	X 13.6	Z 3.25	X 13.0 Part radius + .6 Stock
P5	X 13.6	Z-87.8	$Z-87.0 - \sqrt{1.6^2 - 1.6^2} - .8$ Formula #1 Appendix E

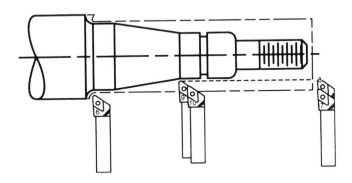

SECOND ROUGH TURN

POINT CODE	X COORDINATE	Z COORDINATE	CALCULATION
P6	X 14.8	Z-86.6	X 13.6 Radius + 1.2 Clearance Z-87.8 Pos."5" + 1.2 Clearance
P7	X 14.8	Z 1.25	Z .75 Finish Stock + .5 Clearance
P8	X 10.6	Z 1.25	X 10.0 Part Radius + .6 Stock
P9	X 10.6	Z-50.72	$Z-50.0 -[.8-(Tan.\frac{6.7129°}{2}X(.3+.6))]$ Formula #2 Appendix E
P10	X 11.8	Z-49.52	X 10.6 Radius + 1.2 Clearance Z-50.72 Pos."9" + 1.2 Clearance

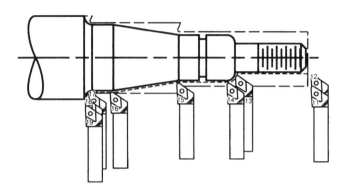

SEMI FINISH TURN

POINT CODE	X COORDINATE	Z COORDINATE	CALCULATION
P11	X 11.8	Z 1.25	Z .75 Finish Stock + .5 Clearance
P12	X 7.4	Z 1.25	X 7.0 Part Radius + .4 Finish Stock
P13	X 7.4	Z-27.78	Z-28.0 - 3.0 + 4.02 - .8 Formula #3 Appendix E
P14	X 10.4 I1.2	Z-31.8 K4.02	X 10.0 Part Radius + .4 Finish Stock Z-31.0 Radius Center - .8 Tool Radius
P15	X 10.4	Z-50.73	Z-50 -[.8-(Tan.$\frac{6.7129°}{2}$ X (.8+.4))] Formula #2 Appendix E
P16	X 13.4	Z-78.73	X 13.0 Part Radius + .4 Finish Stock Z-50.73 Pos. 15 - 28.0 Taper Length
P17	X 13.4	Z-87.8	Z-90 Part Dim. + 3.0 Radius - .8 Tool Radius
P18	X 15.2 I1.8	Z-89.6 K0	X 16.0 Part Radius - .8 Tool Radius Z-90 Part Dim. + .4 Finish Stock
P19	X 18.5	Z-89.6	X 16.0 Part Radius + 2.5 Clearance

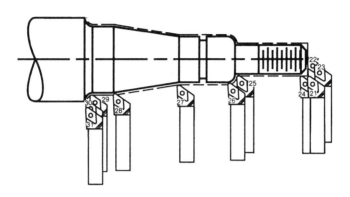

FINISH FACE AND FINISH TURN

POINT CODE	X COORDINATE	Z COORDINATE	CALCULATION
P20	TOOL	CHANGE	POSITION
P21	X 9.9	Z 0	X 7.0 Part Radius + .4 Stock + 2.5 Clearance Z 0 Finish Datum
P22	X-1.3	Z 0	X 0 Datum - .8 Tool Radius - .5 Past Center
P23	X 2.53	Z 2.5	X 7.0 Part Radius - 1.5 Cham. - 2.5 Clear + .33 Formula #4 Appendix E - .8 Tool Radius Z 0 Datum + 2.5 Clearance
P24	X 7.0	Z-1.97	X 7.0 Part Radius Z-1.5 Chamfer + .33 (formula 4) - .8 Tool Radius
P25	X 7.0	Z-25.39	Z-28.0 - .3 + 3.71 - .8 Formula #3 No Stock Appendix E
P26	X 10.0 I.8	Z-31.8 K3.71	X 10.0 Part Radius Z-28.0 - 3.0 Radius - .8 Tool Radius
P27	X 10.0	Z-50.75	Z-50.0 -[.8-(Tan.$\frac{6.7129°}{2}$X .8)] Formula #2 No Stock Appendix E
P28	X 13.0	Z-78.75	X 13.0 Part Radius Z-50.75 Pos. 27 - 28.0 Taper Length

POINT CODE	X COORDINATE	Z COORDINATE	CALCULATION
P29	X 13.0	Z-87.8	Z-90.0 Part Dim. + 3.0 Radius - .8 Tool Radius
P30	X 15.2 I 2.2	Z-90.0 K 0	X 16.0 Part Radius- .8 Tool Radius Z-90.0 Part Dim.
P31	X 18.5	Z-90.0	X 16.0 Part Radius + 2.5 Clearance
P32	TOOL	CHANGE	POSITION

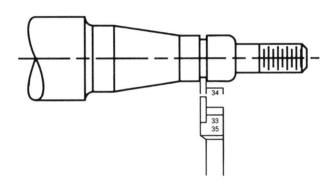

CUT GROOVE

POINT CODE	X COORDINATE	Z COORDINATE	CALCULATION
P33	X 12.5	Z-43.0	X 10.0 Part Radius + 2.5 Clearance Z-40.0 Part Dim. - 3.0 Groove Width
P34	X 6.5	Z-43.0	X 6.5 Groove Radius
P35	X 12.5	Z-43.0	X 10.0 Part Radius + 2.5 Clearance
P36	TOOL	CHANGE	POSITION

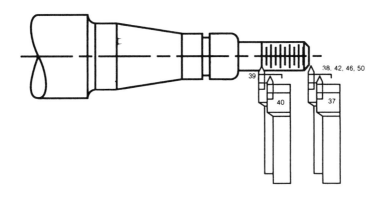

THREAD CUTTING

POINT CODE	X COORDINATE	Z COORDINATE	CALCULATION
P37	X 9.5	Z 2.5	X 7.0 Part Radius + 2.5 Clearance Z O Finish Datum + 2.5 Clearance
P38	X 6.1	Z 1.98	X 7.0 Part Radius - .9 Thread In Feed Z 2.5 Clearance - .52 Thread In Feed K (Thread Pitch)
P39	X 6.1	Z-19	Z-19 Thread Length Dim.
P40	X 9.5	Z-19	X 7.0 Part Radius + 2.5 Clearance
P42	X 5.4	Z 1.58	X 7.0 Part Radius - 1.6 Thread In Feed Z 2.5 Clearance - .92 Thread In Feed
P46	X 4.9	Z 1.29	X 7.0 Part Radius - 2.1 Thread In Feed Z 2.5 Clearance - 1.21 Thread In Feed
P50	X 4.546	Z 1.09	X 7.0 Part Radius - 2.454 Thread In Feed Z 2.5 Clearance - 1.41 Thread In Feed
	TOOL	CHANGE	POSITION

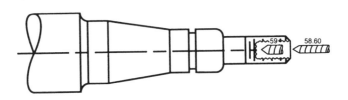

DRILL 6MM DIAMETER HOLE

POINT CODE	X COORDINATE	Z COORDINATE	CALCULATION
P58	X 0	Z 2.5	X 0 Datum Z 0 Datum + 2.5 Clearance
P59	X 0	Z-13.8	Z-12 Hole Depth - 1.8 Drill Point .3 X Dia. Drill Point Allowance
P60	X 0	Z 2.5	X 0 Datum Z 0 Datum + 2.5 Clearance
P61	TOOL	CHANGE	POSITION

Lathe—Metric Program

%   *Rewind stop code*
N0010 G71   *Metric programming*
N0020 G97   *rpm spindle speed programming*
N0030 G95   *mmpr feedrate programming*
N0040 G90   *Absolute coordinate programming*
N0050 G00 T00   *Clear tool offsets*
N0060 T0600   *Index rear turret to empty station*
N0070 T0101 S960 M03   *Index tool 1 to cutting position (rough face and turn),*
                            start spindle
N0080 G92 X114.0 Z166.0   *Preset X & Z axes*
N0090 G00 X18.5 Z.75 M08   *Position tool to rough face, turn coolant on (P1)*
N0100 G01 X-1.3 F.25   *Rough face part leaving 0.5 stock (P2)*
N0110 G00 Z3.25   *Retract from face (P3)*
N0120 X13.6   *Position X for first rough turn (P4)*
N0130 G01 Z-87.8 F.25   *Feed for first rough turn (P5)*
N0140 G00 X14.8 Z-86.6   *Retract X & Z axes (P6)*
N0150 Z1.25 S1132   *Rapid to face of part (P7)*
N0160 X10.6   *Position X for second rough turn (P8)*
N0170 G01 Z-50.72 F.25   *Feed for second rough turn (P9)*
N0180 G00 X11.8 Z-49.52   *Retract X & Z axes (P10)*
N0190 Z1.25 S2000   *Rapid to face of part (P11)*
N0200 X7.4   *Position X for semifinish pass (P12)*
N0210 G01 Z-27.78   *Feed tangent to convex radius (P13)*
N0220 S1538   *Change rpm*
N0230 G03 X10.4 Z-31.8 I1.2 K4.02   *Contour convex radius (P14)*
N0240 G01 Z-50.73   *Feed tangent to taper (P15)*
N0250 S1200   *Change rpm*
N0260 X13.4 Z-78.73   *Feed up taper (P16)*
N0270 Z-87.8   *Feed tangent to concave radius (P17)*
N0280 S1010   *Change rpm*
N0290 G02 X15.2 Z-89.6 I1.8 K0   *Contour concave radius (P18)*
N0300 G01 X18.5   *Feed off part (P19)*
N0310 G00 X114.0 Z166.0 T0000   *Rapid to tool change position—cancelling tool*
                                       offset (P20)
N0320 G92 X0 Z0   *Cancel axis presets*
N0330 G00 T0202   *Index finish facing and turning tool into cutting position*
N0340 G90 S2000 M03   *Set finishing rpm*
N0350 G92 X114.0 Z166.0   *Axis presets*
N0360 G00 X9.9 Z0   *Rapid to start finish face (P21)*
N0370 G01 X-1.3 F.12   *Finish face part (P22)*
N0380 G00 X2.53 Z2.5   *Retract in Z and position for chamfer (P23)*
N0390 G01 X7.0 Z-1.97   *Turn chamfer (P24)*
N0400 Z-25.39   *Finish turn to convex radius (P25)*
N0410 S1600   *Change rpm*
N0420 G03 X10.0 Z-31.8 I.8 K3.71   *Contour convex radius (P26)*
N0430 G01 Z-50.75   *Finish turn tangent to taper (P27)*
N0440 S1200   *Change rpm*
N0450 X13.0 Z-78.75   *Finish turn taper (P28)*
N0460 Z-87.8   *Finish turn tangent to concave radius (P29)*
N0470 S1010   *Change rpm*

N0480 G02 X15.2 Z-90.0 12.2 K0   *Contour concave radius (P30)*
N0490 G01 X18.5   *Feed away from part (P31)*
N0500 G00 X114.0 Z166.0 T0000 M09   *Rapid to tool change position cancelling*
                                      tool offsets and turning off coolant
                                      (P32)
N0510 G92 X0 Z0   *Cancel axis presets*
N0520 G00 T0303   *Index grooving tool into cutting position*
N0530 G90 S1000 M03   *Start spindle*
N0540 G92 X114.0 Z166.0   *Preset axes*
N0550 G00 X12.5 Z-43.0 M08   *Position in X & Z to cut groove (P33)*
N0560 G01 X6.5 F.12   *Cut groove to depth (P34)*
N0570 G04 F05   *Dwell for 5 sec*
N0580 G00 X12.5 M09   *Retract from groove turning coolant* off *(P35)*
N0590 G00 X114.0 Z166.0 T0000   *Rapid to tool change position cancelling tool*
                                  offsets (P36)
N0600 G92 X0 Z0   *Cancel axis presets*
N0610 G00 T0404   *Index threading tool into cutting position*
N0620 G90 S1000 M03   *Start spindle*
N0630 G92 X114.0 Z166.0   *Preset axes*
N0640 G00 X9.5 Z2.5 M08   *Position in X & Z to cut thread (P37)*
N0650 X6.1 Z1.98   *First thread in feed (P38)*
N0660 G33 Z-19.0 K2.0   *Cut first thread pass (P39)*
N0670 G00 X9.5   *Retract X (P40)*
N0680 Z2.5   *Rapid to end of part (P41)*
N0690 X5.4 Z1.58   *Thread in feed for second pass (P42)*
N0700 G33 Z-19.0 K2.0   *Cut second pass (P43)*
N0710 G00 X9.5   *Retract X (P44)*
N0720 Z2.5   *Rapid to end of part (P45)*
N0730 X4.9 Z1.29   *Thread in feed for third pass (P46)*
N0740 G33 Z-19.0 K2.0   *Cut third pass (P47)*
N0750 G00 X9.5   *Retract X (P48)*
N0760 Z2.5   *Rapid to end of part (P49)*
N0770 X4.546 Z1.09   *Thread in feed for finish pass (P50)*
N0780 G33 Z-19.0 K2.0   *Cut finish pass (P51)*
N0790 G00 X9.5   *Retract X (P52)*
N0800 Z2.5   *Rapid to end of part (P53)*
N0810 X4.546 Z1.09   *Thread in feed for tool pressure pass (P54)*
N0820 G33 Z-19.0 K2.0   *Cut tool pressure pass (P55)*
N0830 G00 X9.5 M09   *Retract X (P56)*
N0840 X114.0 Z166.0 T0000   *Rapid to tool change cancelling tool offsets (P57)*
N0850 G92 X0 Z0   *Cancel axis preset*
N0860 G00 T0707   *Index 6.0 mm drill into cutting position*
N0870 G90 S2000 M03   *Start spindle*
N0880 G92 X-114.0 Z52.0   *Preset axes*
N0890 G00 X0 Z2.5 M08   *Position to drill (P58)*
N0900 G01 Z-13.8 F.15   *Drill to depth (P59)*
N0910 G00 Z2.5 M09   *Retract drill (P60)*
N0920 X-114.0 Z166.0 T0000   *Rapid to tool change cancelling tool offsets (P61)*
N0930 G92 X0 Z0   *Cancel axis presets*
N0940 M02   *End of program*

Example 3: Milling, Inch

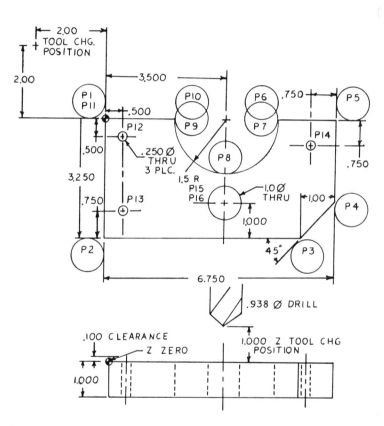

MILL EXAMPLE INCH

⊕ DENOTES PROGRAM
   ZERO

MACHINING CENTER -- INCH PROGRAMMING

TOOL SHEET

PART NO. NC-2118906	MATERIAL 1018 M.S.	OPERATION 20	PROGRAMMED BY T. CRANDELL
PART NAME MILL EXAMPLE	B/P CHANGE DATE	DATE	SHEET 1 OF 1

SEQ	TOOL NUMBER	TOOL DESCRIPTION	TOOL DIAMETER PROG.	ACT.	#	TOOL LENGTH PROG.	ACT.	#	OPERATION DESCRIPTION	SPEED R.P.M.	CODE	FEED IN/MIN	CODE
	01	1.0 DIA. FOUR FLUTE ENDMILL #56779 HSS National Twist HOLDER # QC40-EM100-338 Kennametal	1.000			5.500 PROJECTION 2.00 MIN.			MILL PERIPHERY OF PART LOC. 1 THRU 10	400 RPM		11.2	IPM
	02	.250 DIA. DRILL HSS #49016 National Twist HOLDER # QC40-DA300-163 Kennametal COLLE T # 300DA-0250	.250			4.500 PROJECTION 2.5 MIN.			DRILL .(3) .250 DIA. HOLES THRU LOC. 11 THRU 13	1600 RPM		9.6	IPM
	03	15/16 DIA. DRILL HSS #10472 National Twist HOLDER #2-60-209-303 Kennametal	.938			7.000 PROJECTION 3.5 MIN.			DRILL .937 DIA. HOLE THRU LOC. 14	425 RPM		8.5	IPM
	04	1.000 DIA. BORING TOOL CARB. BORING BAR # 2-80-076-026 Kennametal Insert #E32ACP HOLDER # QC40-TG150-450 Kennametal	1.000			6.000 PROJECTION 2.5 MIN.			FIN. BORE 1.0 DIA. HOLE THRU LOC. 15	1200 RPM		7.2	IPM

INCH
MACHINING CENTER
COORDINATE SHEET

COMPANY FERRIS STATE UNIVERSITY   **PART NAME** MILL EXAMPLE   **OPERATION NO.** 20   **BY** CRANDELL   **SHEET** 1 **OF** 5   **DATE**

PART NO. NC-2118906

POINT CODE	X ABSOLUTE COORDINATE	Y ABSOLUTE COORDINATE	TABLE DEG. ABS.	TOOL DESCRIPTION	T SETTING LENGTH	D DEPTH BELOW WORK SUR.	S WORK SUR.	Z TOOL CHG. SET TOOL - PRESENT + TOOL CHG. CLEARANCE	Z CLEAR POS. WORK SUR. + CLEARANCE	Z DEPTH POS. WORK SUR. - FEATURE DP. - TOOL POINT
TOOL CHG.	-2.000	+2.000		T01 1.0 END MILL	7.000	0	0	1.000	1.000	-
	X 0 Datum - 2.000 Cutter Center Position				Tool Chg. 7.000 - 7.000 + 1.000 = 1.000					
	Y 0 Datum + 2.000 Cutter Center Position				Clear Pos. 0 + 1.000 = 1.00					
P1	-.500	+.500			5.500	1.100	0	2.500	.100	-1.100
	X 0 Datum - .500 Cutter Radius				Tool Chg. 7.000 - 5.500 + 1.000 = 2.500					
	Y 0 Datum + .500 Cutter Radius				Clear Pos. 0 + .100 = .100					
					Z Depth 0-1.0 Part Thickness-.100 Clear=-1.100					
P2	-.500	-3.750								
		Y 0 Datum - 3.750 Part Width - .500 Cutter Radius								
P3	5.9413	-3.750								
	X 0 + 6.75 Part Length - 1.00 Angle Length + COTAN 67.5° * .5 Cutter Center = 5.75 +.2071 = 5.9571									
P4	7.250	-2.4571								
	X 0 Datum + 6.75 Part Length + .500 Cutter Radius = 7.250									
	Y 0 Datum - 3.25 Part Width + 1.00 Angle Width Length - COTAN 67.5° * .5 Cutter Center = -2.25 - .2071 = -2.4571 Continued									

67.5°

INCH
MACHINING CENTER
COORDINATE SHEET

COMPANY FERRIS STATE UNIVERSITY	PART NAME MILL EXAMPLE	OPERATION NO. 20	BY CRANDELL	SHEET 2 OF 5	DATE

PART NO. NC-2118906

POINT CODE	X ABSOLUTE COORDINATE	Y ABSOLUTE COORDINATE	TABLE DEG. ABS.	TOOL DESCRIPTION	T SETTING LENGTH	D DEPTH BELOW WORK SUR.	S WORK SUR.	Z TOOL CHG.	Z CLEAR POS.	Z DEPTH POS.
	67.5°			Note: The longest tool (.938 dia. drill 7.00 gage length) is used for setting the Z tool chg.				SET TOOL – PRESENT + TOOL CHG. CLEARANCE	WORK SUR. + CLEARANCE	WORK SUR. – FEATURE DP. – TOOL POINT
P5	7.250	.500		X 0 Datum + 6.750 Part Length + .500 Cutter Radius / Y 0 Datum + .500 Cutter Radius						
P6	4.500	.500		X 0 Datum + 3.500 Part Radius Center + 1.500 Part Radius – .500 Cutter Radius						
P7	4.500	0		I 0 J1.0 / Y 0 Datum						
P8	3.500	-1.000		I 1.0 J0 / X 0 Datum + 3.500 Part Radius Center / Y 0 – 1.500 Part Radius + .500 Cutter Radius	I 1.500 Part radius – .500 Cutter Radius					
P9	2.500	0		I 0 J1.0 / X 0 Datum + 3.500 Part Radius Center – 1.500 Tool Radius + .500 Tool Radius / Y 0 Datum	I 1.500 Part Radius – .500 Cutter Radius / J 1.500 Part Radius – .500 Cutter Radius					

INCH
MACHINING CENTER
COORDINATE SHEET

COMPANY FERRIS STATE UNIVERSITY   PART NAME MILL EXAMPLE   OPERATION NO. 20   BY C.RANDELL   SHEET 3 OF 5   DATE

PART NO. NC-2118906

POINT CODE	X ABSOLUTE COORDINATE	Y ABSOLUTE COORDINATE	TABLE DEG. ABS.	TOOL DESCRIPTION	T SETTING LENGTH	D DEPTH BELOW WORK SUR.	S WORK SUR.	Z TOOL CHG. SET TOOL - PRESENT + TOOL CHG. CLEAR-ANCE	Z CLEAR POS. WORK SUR. + CLEAR-ANCE	Z DEPTH POS. WORK SUR. - FEATURE DP. - TOOL POINT
P10	2.500	.500								
	Y 0 Datum + .500 Cutter Radius									
P11	-.500	.500								
	X 0 Datum - .500 Cutter Radius									
	Y 0 Datum + .500 Cutter Radius									
TOOL CHG.	-2.000	2.000		T02 .250 DIA. DRILL	5.500 TL.#1	0	0	2.500		
	X 0 Datum - 2.000 Tool Change Position									
	Y 0 Datum + 2.000 Tool Change Position									
	Z 7.000 Set Tl. - 5.500 Present Tl.#1 + 1.000									
	Clearance = 2.500									
P12	.500	-.500			4.500 TL.#2	1.175	0	3.500	.100	
	X 0 Datum + .500 Hole Center Dim.									
	Y 0 Datum - .500 Hole Center Dim.									
	Tool Chg. 7.000 - 4.500 + 1.000 = 3.500									
	Clear Pos. 0 + .100 = .100									
	Z Depth 0 - 1.00 - .175 = -1.175									
P13	.500	-2.500								-1.175
	Y 0 Datum - 3.250 Part Width + .750 Hole Center Dim.									

INCH
MACHINING CENTER
COORDINATE SHEET

COMPANY FERRIS STATE UNIVERSITY   PART NAME MILL EXAMPLE   OPERATION NO. 20   BY CRANDELL   SHEET 4 OF 5   DATE

PART NO. NC-2118906

POINT CODE	X ABSOLUTE COORDINATE	Y ABSOLUTE COORDINATE	TABLE DEG. ABS.	TOOL DESCRIPTION	T SETTING LENGTH	D DEPTH BELOW WORK SUR.	S WORK SUR.	Z TOOL CHG. SET TOOL - PRESENT + TOOL CHG. CLEARANCE	Z CLEAR POS. WORK SUR. + CLEARANCE	Z DEPTH POS. WORK SUR. - FEATURE Dp. - TOOL POINT
P14	6.000	-.750								
	X 0 Datum + 6.750 Part Length - .75 Hole Center Dim. Y 0 Datum - .750 Hole Center Dim.									
TOOL CHG.	-2.000	2.000		T03 .938 DIA. DRILL	4.500 TL.#2	0	0	3.500		
	X 0 Datum - 2.000 Tool Change Position Y 0 Datum + 2.000 Tool Change Position					Z 7.000 Set TL. - 4.500 Present Tl.#2 + 1.000 Clearance = 3.500				
P15	3.500	-2.250			7.000 TL.#3	1.3814	0	1.000	.100	-1.3814
	X 0 Datum + 3.500 Hole Center Dim. Y 0 Datum - 3.250 Part Width + 1.000 Hole Center Dim.					Tool Chg. 7.00 - 7.00 + 1.00 = 1.000 Clear Pos. 0 + .100 = .100 Z Depth 0 - 1.00 - .2814 - .100 = -1.3814				
TOOL CHG.	-2.000	2.000		T04 1.000 DIA. BORING BAR	7.000 TL.#3	0	0	1.000		
	X 0 Datum - 2.000 Tool Change Position Y 0 Datum 2.000 Tool Change Position					Z 7.000 Set TL. -7.000 Present TL.#3 + 1.000 Clearance = 1.000				
P16	3.500	-2.250			6.000 TL.#4	1.100	0	2.000	.100	-1.100
	X 0 Datum + 3.500 Hole Center Dim. Y 0 Datum - 3.250 Part Width + 1.000 Hole Center Dim.					Tool Chg. 7.00 - 6.00 + 1.00 = 2.000 Clear Pos. 0 + .100 = .100 Z Depth 0 - 1.00 - .100 = -1.100				

INCH

MACHINING CENTER

COORDINATE SHEET

COMPANY FERRIS STATE UNIVERSITY   PART NAME MILL EXAMPLE   OPERATION NO. 20   BY CRANDELL   DATE

PART NO. NC-2118906   SHEET 5 OF 5

POINT CODE	X ABSOLUTE COORDINATE	Y ABSOLUTE COORDINATE	TABLE DEG. ABS.	TOOL DESCRIPTION	T SETTING LENGTH	D DEPTH BELOW WORK SUR.	S WORK SUR.	Z TOOL CHG.	Z CLEAR POS.	Z DEPTH POS.
								SET TOOL - PRESENT + TOOL CHG. CLEAR- ANCE	WORK SUR. + CLEAR- ANCE	WORK SUR. - FEATURE DP. - TOOL POINT
TOOL CHG.	-2.000	2.000			6.000 TL#4	0	0	2.000		

X 0 Datum - 2.000 Tool Change Position
Y 0 Datum - 2.000 Tool Change Position

Z 7.000 Set Tl. - 6.000 Present Tl.#4 + 1.000
Clearance = 2.000

Inch Machining Center Example Program

N0010 G90   *Absolute programming*
N0020 G70   *Inch programming*
N0030 G94   *Inch per minute feedrate*
N0040 G17   *X-Y circular interpolation plane*
N0050 G40 T00   *Cancel cutter diameter compensation and tool length*
                       compensation
N0060 G80 Z1.0   *Retract Z axis*
N0070 G00 X-2.0 Y2.0 T01 M06   *Tool change "1.0 end mill"*
N0080 X-.5 Y.5 Z.1 S400 M03   *Rapid to position 1, start spindle*
N0090 Z-1.1 M08   *Rapid to Z depth, turn coolant on*
N0100 G01 Y-3.75 F11.2   *Feed to position 2*
N0110 X5.9413   *Feed to position 3*
N0120 X7.25 Y-2.4571   *Feed to position 4*
N0130 Y.5   *Feed to position 5*
N0140 X4.5   *Feed to position 6*
N0150 Y0   *Feed to position 7*
N0160 G02 X3.5 Y-1.0 I1.0 J0   *Circular interpolate to position 8*
N0170 X2.5 Y0 I0 J1.0   *Circular interpolate to position 9*
N0180 G01 Y.5   *Feed to position 10*
N0190 X-.5   *Feed to position 11*
N0200 G00 Z.1 M09   *Clear part*
N0210 G80 X-2.0 Y2.0 Z2.5 T02 M06   *Tool change ".250 dia. drill"*
N0220 X.5 Y-.5 Z.1 S1600 M03   *Rapid to position 12 turn, spindle on*
N0230 G81 Z-1.175 R.1 F9.6 M08   *Drill position 12, turn coolant on*
N0240 Y-2.5   *Drill position 13*
N0250 X6.0 Y-.75 M09   *Drill position 14, turn coolant off*
N0260 G80 X-2.0 Y2.0 Z3.5 T03 M06   *Tool change ".938 dia drill"*
N0270 X3.5 Y-2.25 Z.1 S425 M03   *Rapid to position 15, turn spindle on*
N0280 G81 Z-1.3814 R.1 F8.5 M08   *Drill position 15, turn coolant on*
N0290 M09   *Turn coolant off*
N0300 G80 X-2.0 Y2.0 Z1.0 T04 M06   *Tool change "1.0 dia. boring bar"*
N0310 X3.5 Y-2.25 Z.1 S1200 M03   *Rapid to position 16, turn spindle on*
N0320 G81 Z-1.1 R.1 F7.2 M08   *Bore position 16, turn coolant on*
N0330 M09   *Turn coolant off*
N0340 G80 X-2.0 Y2.0 Z2.0 M02   *Rapid to tool change position and end program*

Example 4: Milling, Metric

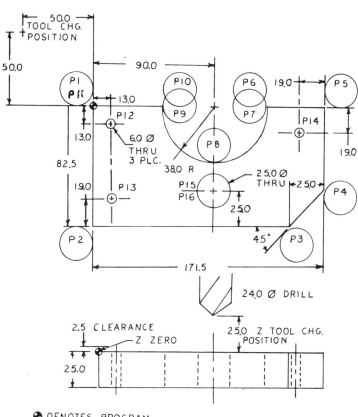

MILL EXAMPLE METRIC

MACHINING CENTER – METRIC PROGRAMMING

TOOL SHEET

PART NO. NC-2118906 | MATERIAL 1018 M.S. | OPERATION 20 | PROGRAMMED BY T. CRANDELL
PART NAME MILL EXAMPLE | B/P CHANGE DATE | | DATE | SHEET 1 OF 1

SEQ. NUMBER	TOOL NUMBER	TOOL DESCRIPTION	TOOL DIAMETER PROG.	TOOL DIAMETER ACT.	#	TOOL LENGTH PROG.	TOOL LENGTH ACT.	#	OPERATION DESCRIPTION	SPEED R.P.M.	SPEED CODE	FEED IN/MIN CODE	FEED
	01	24.0 DIA. FOUR FLUTE ENDMILL # D3242-EDP244449 HSS Vern Wheeler Co. HOLDER # QC40-EM100-338 Kennametal	24.0MM			140.0MM PROJECTION 50.0MM MIN.			MILL PERIPHERY OF PART LOC. 1 THRU 10	400 RPM			284 MM/MIN.
	02	6.0 DIA. DRILL HSS #12695 National Twist HOLDER # QC40-DA300-163 Kennametal COLLE T #300DA-0250	6.0MM			114.0MM PROJECTION 64MM MIN.			DRILL (3) 6.0 DIA. HOLES THRU LOC. 11 THRU 13	1600 RPM			244 MM/MIN.
	03	24.0 DIA. DRILL HSS # HOLDER #	24.0MM			178.0MM PROJECTION 90MM MIN.			DRILL 24.0 DIA. HOLE LOC. 14	425 RPM			216 MM/MIN.
	04	25.0 DIA BORING TOOL CARB. BORING BAR # 2-80-076-026 Kennametal INSERT #E32ACP HOLDER # QC40-TG150-450 Kennametal	25.0MM			152.0MM PROJECTION 64MM MIN.			FIN. BORE 25.0 DIA. HOLE THRU LOC. 15	1200 RPM			183 MM/MIN.

METRIC
MACHINING CENTER
COORDINATE SHEET

COMPANY FERRIS STATE UNIVERSITY   **PART NAME** MILL EXAMPLE   **OPERATION NO.** 20   **BY** CRANDELL   **SHEET** 1 **OF** 5   **DATE**

PART NO. NC-2118906

POINT CODE	X ABSOLUTE COORDINATE	Y ABSOLUTE COORDINATE	TABLE DEG. ABS.	TOOL DESCRIPTION	T SETTING LENGTH	D DEPTH BELOW WORK SUR.	S WORK SUR.	TOOL CHG. SET TOOL - PRESENT + TOOL CHG. - CLEAR-ANCE	Z CLEAR POS. WORK SUR. + CLEAR-ANCE	Z DEPTH POS. WORK SUR. FEATURE DP. - TOOL POINT
TOOL CHG.	-50.0	+50.0		TO1 25.0 ENDMILL	178.0 SET TOOL	0	0	25.0	25.0	
	X 0 Datum - 50.0 Cutter Center Position				Tool Chg. 178.0 - 178.0 + 25.0 = 25.0					
	Y 0 Datum + 50.0 Cutter Center Position				Clear Pos. 0 + 25.0 = 25.0					
P1	-12.5	+12.5			140.0	27.5	0	63.0	2.5	-27.5
	X 0 Datum - 12.5 Cutter Radius				Tool Chg. 178 - 140 + 25.0 = 63.0					
	Y 0 Datum + 12.5 Cutter Radius				Clear Pos. 0 + 2.5 = 2.5					
					Z Depth 0 - 25.0 Part Thickness -2.5 Clear=-27.5					
P2	-12.5	-95.0								
		Y 0 Datum - 95.0								
P3	151.68	-95.0								
		Y 0 Datum - 82.5 Part Width - 12.5 Cutter Radius								
67.5°	X 0 + 171.5 Part Length - 25.0 Angle Length + COTAN 67.5° * 12.5 Cutter Center = 146.5 + 5.18 = 151.68									
P4	184.0	-62.68								
	X 0 + 171.5 Part Length + 12.5 Cutter Radius = 184.0									
	Y 0 Datum - 82.5 Part Width + 25.0 Angle Length - COTAN 67.5° * 12.5 Cutter Center = -57.5 - 5.18 = -62.68									
	Continued									

METRIC
MACHINING CENTER
COORDINATE SHEET

COMPANY FERRIS STATE UNIVERSITY	PART NAME MILL EXAMPLE	OPERATION NO. 20	BY CRANDELL	SHEET 2 OF 5
PART NO. NC-2118906				DATE

POINT CODE	X ABSOLUTE COORDINATE	Y ABSOLUTE COORDINATE	TABLE DEG. ABS.	TOOL DESCRIPTION	T SETTING LENGTH	D DEPTH BELOW WORK SUR.	S WORK SUR.	TOOL CHG.	Z CLEAR POS.	Z DEPTH POS.
			67.5°	Note: The longest tool (24.0 dia. drill 178.0 gage length) is used for setting the Z tool chg.				SET TOOL CHG. = PRESENT TOOL CHG. + TOOL CLEARANCE	WORK SUR. + CLEARANCE	WORK SUR. - FEATURE DP. - TOOL POINT
P5	184.0	12.5								
	X O Datum + 171.5 Part Length + 12.5 Cutter Radius	Y O Datum + 12.5 Cutter Radius								
P6	115.5	12.5								
	X O Datum + 90.0 Part Radius Center + 38.0 Part Radius - 12.5 Cutter Radius									
P7	115.5	0								
		Y O Datum								
P8	90.0	-25.5		I 25.5 J0						
	X O Datum + 90.0 Part Radius Center	Y O Datum - 38.0 Part Radius + 12.5 Cutter Radius				I 38.0 Part Radius - 12.5 Cutter Radius				
P9	64.5	0		I0 J 25.5						
	X O Datum + 90.0 Part Radius Center - 38.0 Part Radius + 12.5 Cutter Radius	Y O Datum				J 38.0 Part Radius - 12.5 Cutter Radius				

METRIC
MACHINING CENTER
COORDINATE SHEET

COMPANY FERRIS STATE UNIVERSITY | PART NAME MILL EXAMPLE | OPERATION NO. 20 | BY CRANDELL SHEET 3 OF 5 DATE

PART NO. NC-2118906

POINT CODE	X ABSOLUTE COORDINATE	Y ABSOLUTE COORDINATE	TABLE DEG. ABS.	TOOL DESCRIPTION	T SETTING LENGTH	D DEPTH BELOW WORK SUR.	S WORK SUR.	Z TOOL CHG. SET TOOL − PRESENT + TOOL CHG. CLEARANCE	Z CLEAR POS. WORK SUR. + CLEARANCE	Z DEPTH POS. WORK SUR. − FEATURE DP. − TOOL POINT
P10	64.5	12.5								
	Y 0 Datum + 12.5 Cutter Radius									
P11	-12.5	12.5								
	X 0 Datum − 12.5 Cutter Radius Y 0 Datum + 12.5 Cutter Radius									
TOOL CHG.	-50.0	50.0		T02 6.0 DIA. DRILL	140.0 TL.#1	0	0	63.0		
	X 0 Datum − 50.0 Tool Chg. Position Y 0 Datum + 50.0 Tool Chg. Position					Z 178.0 Set TL. − 140.0 Present TL.#1 + 25.0 Clearance = 63.0				
P12	13.0	-13.0			114.0 TL.#2	29.3	0	89.0	2.5	-29.3
	X 0 Datum + 13.0 Hole Center Dim. Y 0 Datum + 13.0 Hole Center Dim.					Tool Chg. 178.0 − 114.0 + 25.0 = 89.0 Clear Pos. 0 + 2.5 = 2.5 Z Depth 0 − 25 − 4.3 = −29.3				
P13	13.0	-63.5.								
	Y 0 Datum − 82.5 Part Width + 19.0 Hole Center Dim.									

METRIC
MACHINING CENTER
COORDINATE SHEET

COMPANY FERRIS STATE UNIVERSITY   **PART NAME** MILL EXAMPLE   **OPERATION NO.** 20   **BY** CRANDELL   **SHEET** 4 **OF** 5

PART NO. NC-2118906   **DATE**

POINT CODE	X ABSOLUTE COORDINATE	Y ABSOLUTE COORDINATE	TABLE DEG. ABS.	TOOL DESCRIPTION	T SETTING LENGTH	D DEPTH BELOW WORK SUR.	S WORK SUR.	Z TOOL CHG. SET TOOL - PRESENT + TOOL CHG. CLEARANCE	Z CLEAR POS. WORK SUR. + CLEARANCE	Z DEPTH POS. WORK SUR. - FEATURE DP. - TOOL POINT
P14	152.5	-19.0								
	X O Datum + 171.5 Part Length - 19.0 Hole Center Dim. Y O Datum - 19.0 Hole Center Dim.									
TOOL CHG.	-50.0	50.0		T03 24.0 DIA. DRILL	114.0 TL.#2	0	0	89.0		
	X O Datum - 50.0 Tool Chg. Position Y O Datum + 50.0 Tool Chg. Position							Z 178.0 Set TL. - 114.0 Present TL. #2 + 25.0 Clearance = 89.0		
P15	90.0	-57.5			178.0 TL.#3	34.7	0	25.0	2.5	-34.7
	X O Datum + 90.0 Hole Center Dim. Y O Datum - 82.5 Part Width + 25.0 Hole Center Dim.							Tool Chg. 178.0 - 178.0 + 25.0 = 25.0 Clear Pos. 0 + 2.5 = 2.5 Z Depth 0 - 25.0 - 7.2 - 2.5 = -34.7		
TOOL CHG.	-50.0	50.0		T04 25.0 DIA. BORING BAR	178.0 TL.#3	0	0	25.0		
	X O Datum - 50.0 Tool Change Position Y O Datum+50.0 Tool Change Position							Z 178.0 Set TL. -178.0 Present TL.#3 + 25.0 Clearance = 25.0		
P16	90.0	-57.5			152.0 TL.#4	27.5	0	51.0	2.5	-27.5
	X O Datum + 90.0 Hole Center Dim. Y O Datum - 82.5 Part Width + 25.0 Hole Center Dim.							Tool Chg. 178.0 - 152.0 + 25.0 =51.0 Clear Pos. 0 + 2.5 = 2.5 Z Depth 0 - 25.0 - 2.5 = -27.5		

METRIC
MACHINING CENTER

COORDINATE SHEET

COMPANY FERRIS STATE UNIVERSITY   PART NAME MILL EXAMPLE   OPERATION NO. 20   BY CRANDELL   SHEET 5 OF 5   DATE

PART NO. NC-2118906

POINT CODE	X ABSOLUTE COORDINATE	Y ABSOLUTE COORDINATE	TABLE DEG. ABS.	TOOL DESCRIPTION	T SETTING LENGTH	D DEPTH BELOW WORK SUR.	S WORK SUR.	Z TOOL CHG. SET TOOL - PRESENT + TOOL CHG. CLEAR- ANCE	Z CLEAR POS. WORK SUR. + CLEAR- ANCE	Z DEPTH POS. WORK SUR. FEATURE - DP. - TOOL POINT
TOOL CHG.	-50.0	50.0			152.0 TL.#4	0	0	51.0		

X O Datum - 50.0 Tool Change Position
Y O Datum+50.0 Tool Change Position

Z 178.0 Set TL. - 152.0 Present TL.#4 + 25.0
Clearance = 51.0

Metric Machining Center Example Program

N0010 G90   *Absolute programming*
N0020 G71   *Metric programming*
N0030 G94   *Millimeter per minute feedrate*
N0040 G17   *X-Y circular interpolation plane*
N0050 G40 T00   *Cancel cutter diameter compensation and tool length*
                   compensation
N0060 G80 Z25.0   *Retract Z axis*
N0070 G00 X-50.0 Y50.0 T01 M06   *Tool change "25.0 endmill"*
N0080 X-12.5 Y12.5 Z2.5 S400 M03   *Rapid to position 1, start spindle*
N0090 Z-27.5 M08   *Rapid to Z depth turn coolant on*
N0100 G01 Y-95.0 F284   *Feed to position 2*
N0110 X151.68   *Feed to position 3*
N0120 X184.0 Y-62.68   *Feed to position 4*
N0130 Y12.5   *Feed to position 5*
N0140 X115.5   *Feed to position 6*
N0150 Y0   *Feed to position 7*
N0160 G02 X90.0 Y-25.5 I25.5 J0   *Circular interpolate to position 8*
N0170 X64.5 Y0 I0 J25.5   *Circular interpolate to position 9*
N0180 G01 Y12.5   *Feed to position 10*
N0190 X-12.5   *Feed to position 11*
N0200 G00 Z2.5 M09   *Clear part*
N0210 G80 X-50.0 Y50.0 Z63.0 T02 M06   *Tool change "6.0 dia. drill"*
N0220 X13.0 Y-13.0 Z2.5 S1600 M03   *Rapid to position 12, turn spindle on*
N0230 G81 Z-29.3 R2.5 F244 M08   *Drill position 12, turn coolant on*
N0240 Y-63.5   *Drill position 13*
N0250 X152.0 Y-19.0   *Drill position 14, turn coolant off*
N0260 G80 X-50.0 Y50.0 Z89.0 T03 M06   *Tool change "24.0 dia drill"*
N0270 X90.0 Y-57.5 Z2.5 S425 M03   *Rapid to position 15, turn spindle on*
N0280 G81 Z-34.7 R2.5 F216 M08   *Drill position 15, turn coolant on*
N0290 M09   *Turn coolant off*
N0300 G80 X-50.0 Y50.0 Z25.0 T04 M06   *Tool change, "25.0 dia boring bar"*
N0310 X90.0 Y-57.5 Z2.5 S1200 M03   *Rapid to position 16, turn spindle on*
N0320 G81 Z-27.5 R2.5 F183 M08   *Bore position 16, turn coolant on*
N0330 M09   *Turn coolant off*
N0340 G80 X-50.0 Y50.0 Z51.0 M02   *Rapid to tool change position and*
                                end program

Conversational Part Programming

Conversational part programming requires the programmer/operator to respond to a set of questions or inquires that are a built-in feature of the machine control system and displayed on the CRT screen or dual screens of the control unit, Figure 8.66. As each response is made through the keyboard or touch screen further options/operator inputs are presented and responses made until that particular group, or "block" of related program data, is complete. The programmer then moves on to the next block of program information. Options are provided at the completion of programming to store the part program to computer disk or back to a host computer for storage. Offline software is also available so that programs can be created on a personal computer and then down loaded to the machine control later.

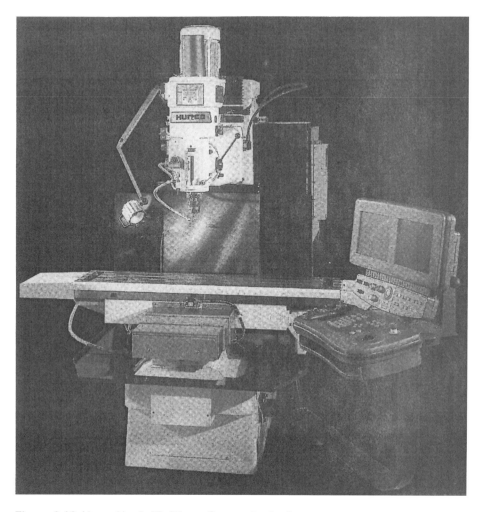

Figure 8.66 Hurco Hawk 4D. (Hurco Companies Inc.)

As in other pieces of CNC equipment the control console can be divided or grouped into function areas. Figure 8.67 shows a Hurco Ultimax 4 dual screen control console and its various function groups. The programming keyboard and graphics trackball allow the operator to move through the displayed graphics and screen inputs while the keyboard provides for entry of numerical data. The axis, spindle and machine control is provided to override programmed spindle speeds and feedrates during the machining operations. The remote jog unit is used to make manual/non programmed machine movements especially during setup. Machine operation allows for machine mode selection, such as manual, automatic and etc., as well as spindle and coolant on and off. The dual screens allow for the display of program and system data as well as program graphics, Figure 8.68. Dual screen display also provides the ability to manually input program data for the next job while running the current program. The auto run screen in Figure 8.68 shows positional X, Y, and Z axis data as well as spindle speed, feedrate and block number data. The graphics screen shows not only part geometry, but also maps out the actual tool path generated by the program. The tool path graphics is an extremely important option and assistance in

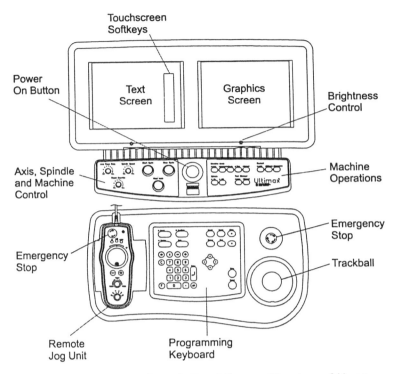

Figure 8.67 Ultimax 4 Dual Screen Console Panel Groups. (Courtesy of Hurco Machine Tool Products.)

proving part programs before actual machining takes place. Screen options will allow for view selection, zooming in and out, and parameter selection to assist the programmer.

In conversational programming as in other forms of programming there are major steps that must be performed. In the case of the Ultimax control the programmer will go through five major steps to create the program.

1. Planning the machining setup and sequence of operations performed.
2. Physically setting up the cutting tools, fixturing, and the machine tool.
3. Entering of the part setup information into the control unit.
4. Entering the tooling information into the control unit.
5. Creating or entering the part programming information into the control unit.

Let's take a look at the control programming screens used to go through these five steps. Upon powering up the control the programmer comes to the text screen shown in Figure 8.69 and can select from any of the options on the right side of the screen by simply touching the desired selection.

Upon entering the programming mode and clearing any existing program information you will enter a new program name. Upon program name entry the system will prompt for whether the program will be entered in inch or metric units of measure. This will be done by selecting the proper location on the system touch screen display, Figure 8.69(1).

After completing the units of measure screen the system will request the axis configuration of the machine. The options as shown in the screen display Figure 8.69(2) are

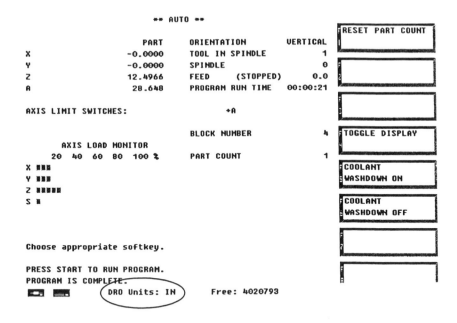

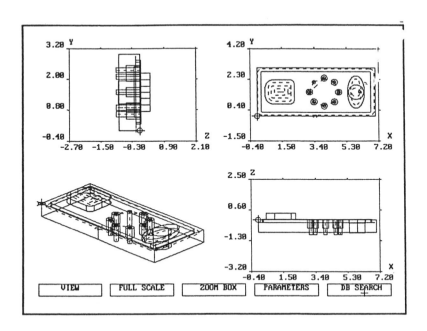

Figure 8.68 Sample Graphics Screen with Menu Options. (Courtesy of Hurco Machine Tool Products.)

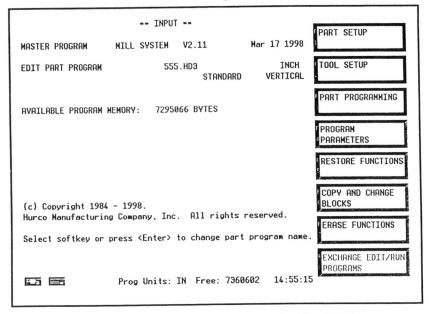

Figure 8.69 Input Screen. (Courtesy of Hurco Machine Tool Products.)

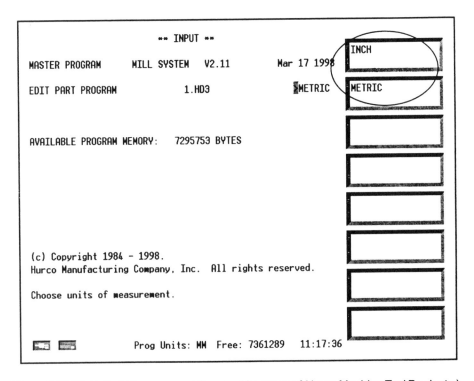

Figure 8.69(1) Unit of Measurement Screen. (Courtesy of Hurco Machine Tool Products.)

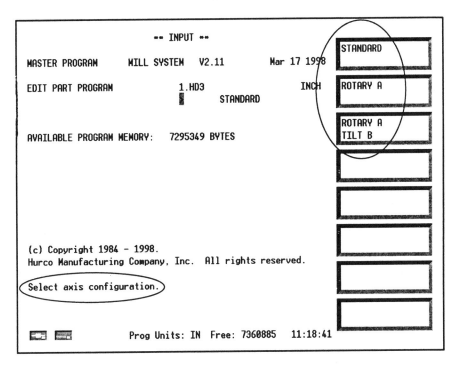

Figure 8.69(2) Input screen with Select Axis prompt. (Courtesy of Hurco Machine Tool Products.)

standard X Y Z three axis selections, additional rotary "A" axis, or rotary "A" axis with tilt "B" axis are available.

The next step in establishing a program is to enter part fixturing and cutting tool setup data. Before doing this screen though the fixture and part will be attached to the machine table and a tool will be placed in the machine spindle for use in locating the X Y Z part zero from the X Y Z machine zero, Figure 8.69(3). The operator will use the machine manual positioning mode to locate the part program zero from the machine absolute zero. By entering the offset information from machine zero to the part zero in the control the programmer/operator can input dimensions from the part print without having to calculate in the zero offset of the machine. The zero offset, once entered, is automatically calculated into positioning data by the controller.

The zero offset operation is accomplished by selecting "Part Setup" off the input screen Figure 8.69 and entering the required fields of information in the Part Setup screen and pushing enter, Figure 8.69(4). Note that the "Z" axis offset is setup so that there will be a safety clearance above the work-piece for the longest tool used.

Next the "Tool Setup" data will be entered after selecting the Tool Setup option from the input screen Figure 8.69. The programmer will enter tool number, tool length, diameter, offset, spindle speed, feedrate, and coolant condition inputs into the screen shown in Figure 8.69(5). Data will be entered this way for each tool used in the program. Note in actual programming the machine operator's manual will give specifics in all these areas presented.

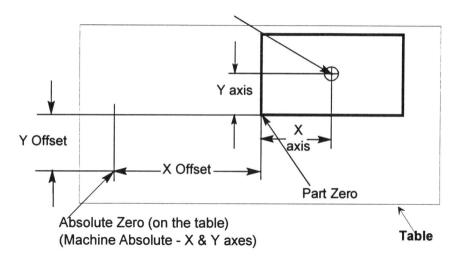

Y axis

Y Offset

X Offset

X axis

Part Zero

Absolute Zero (on the table)
(Machine Absolute - X & Y axes)

Table

Figure 8.69(3a) Part Zero Relationship to Machine Absolute Zero. (Courtesy of Hurco Machine Tool Products.)

Head Zero
(Machine Absolute - Z axis)

Tool Zero
Calibration Plane
(typical)

Part (Workpiece)

Table

Figure 8.69(3b) Tool Zero Calibration Plane and Part Zero in Z. (Courtesy of Hurco Machine Tool Products.)

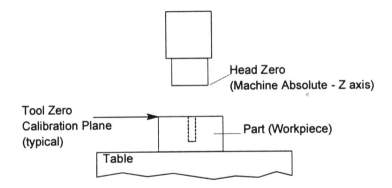

Calibrate all tools here

Reference Gauge Block

Offset Z

Work Piece

Table

Figure 8.69(3c) Offset Z. (Courtesy of Hurco Machine Tool Products.)

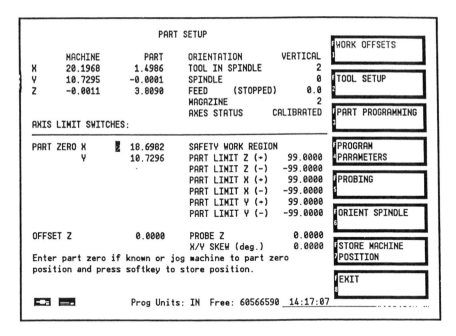

Figure 8.69(4) Part setup screen. (Courtesy of Hurco Machine Tool Products.)

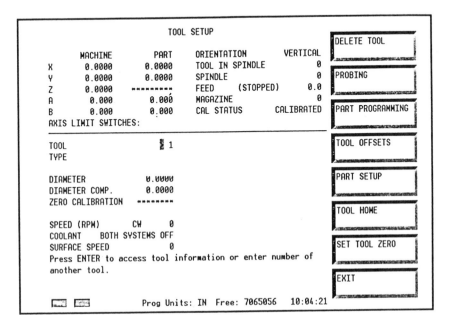

Figure 8.69(5) Tool Setup screen. (Courtesy of Hurco Machine Tool Products.)

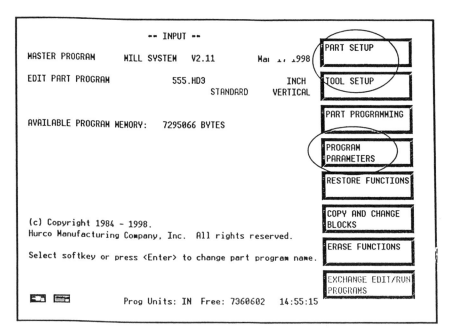

Figure 8.69(6) Input Screen—Part Setup, Tool Setup, Program Parameters Softkeys. (Courtesy of Hurco Machine Tool Products.)

Following the tool setup screens the programmer can select the "Program Parameters" entry from the input screen Figure 8.69. Here the programmer can setup machine parameters during Hole Making, Milling, Program Conditions, and General Conditions for use throughout the program. Typical conditions/parameters that can be set are as follows: Figure 8.69(6)

Holes—bore orient retract, drill dwell, and bore dwell.

Milling—blend offset, blend overlap, finish feed, finish speed, finish material XY, finish material Z, milling direction, pocket overlap, and cutter compensation parameters.

Program—override lockout, tool change position, and surface finish quality.

General—retract clearance, rapid traverse rate, peck drill cycle clearance plane, chord error (deviation from true arcs), depletion retract (Z axes retract above part surface), and interrupt cycle Z retract (Z retract during console cycle interrupt by operator).

After tool setup the programmer/operator goes to the "Part Programming" selection on the input screen Figure 8.69. The new block screen appears and one can obtain a number of different cycles by selecting options as *holes* or *milling*. The number of different options that are available are illustrated in the decision trees indicated in Figures 8.69(7) and 8.69(8).

As indicated on the hole operation hierarchy chart standard programming selections have been made available to assist the programmer. One widely used function is referred to as the "bolt hole circle" Figure 8.69(9a). This is for drilling a series of equally spaced holes on a pitch circle diameter. Given that the cutter has been brought to the

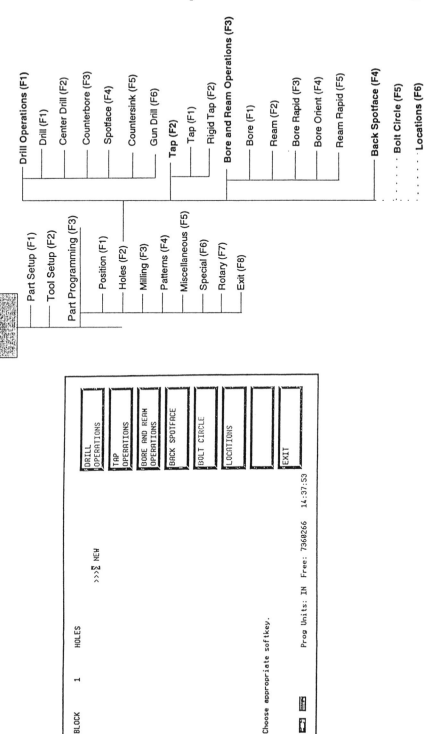
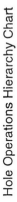

Figure 8.69(7) Holes Screen with Option Softkeys. (Courtesy of Hurco Machine Tool Products.)

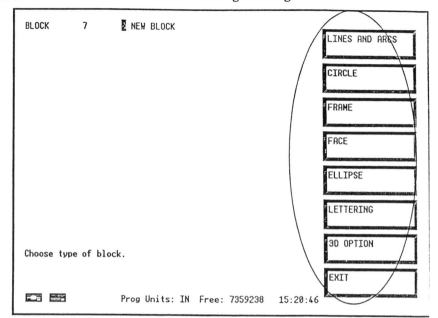

Figure 8.69(8) New Block Screen with the Milling Softkeys. (Courtesy of Hurco Machine Tool Products.)

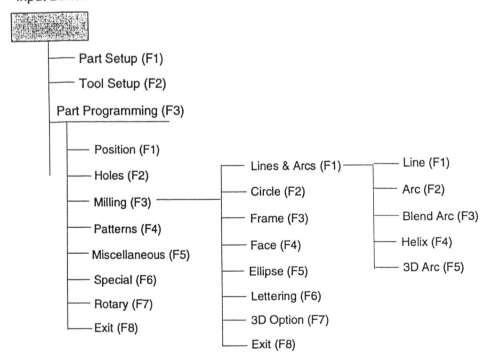

Figure 8.69(8) (Contd.) Milling Options Chart. (Courtesy of Hurco Machine Tool Products.)

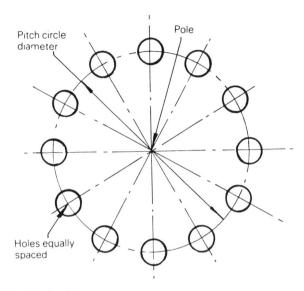

Figure 8.69(9a) *Bolt hole circle.*

pole (circle center) position indicated, the other dimensional data required are the position of the first hole, the Z axis movement, the pitch diameter or radius depending on the control system, and the number of holes required. The control will make all the necessary calculations to convert the polar coordinates to linear coordinates and will effect slide movements accordingly.

A variation of the bolt circle cycle will cater to just two or three holes positioned in an angular relationship to each other. An example of a partial bolt circle is detailed in Figure 8.69(9b). Again the pole position is programmed and the cutter will be in this position when the cycle commences. The additional data that will be required are the Z axis movement, the polar radius and polar angle(s). The controller will convert this information to slide movement in the relative axes. These program features and others for rectangular patterns are found in the Hurco menu options.

As in the drilling hierarchy chart the milling also contains special cycles. A common cycle found on most equipment is a provision for face milling such as illustrated in Figure 8.69(10a). In face milling data input specifies the dimensions of the face to be milled. From this information and tool data the control will determine the number of passes required while taking into consideration a stated cutter overlap that will ensure the face is evenly machined.

Figure 8.69(10b) illustrates the tool path found in slot milling cycles incorporated in most controls. Here again the overall dimensions are programmed. The first machining pass made by the cutting tool goes through the slot center and then returns to the start. Further passes are made until the correct depth is achieved, the number of passes necessary being determined from the programmed movement to be made in the Z axis before each cut commences. When the correct depth is reached, the cutter path will be a series of loops increasing in size with each pass. As with the face milling cycle, the control unit will determine the number of loops necessary to machine the slot to size, again taking into

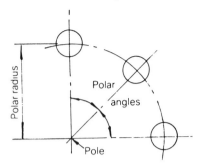

Figure 8.69(9b) Positioning using polar coordinates.

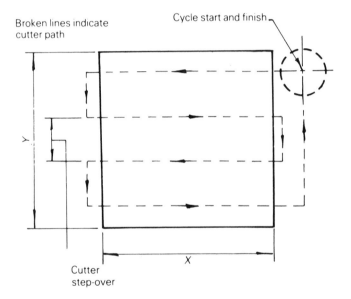

Figure 8.69(10a) Face milling cycle.

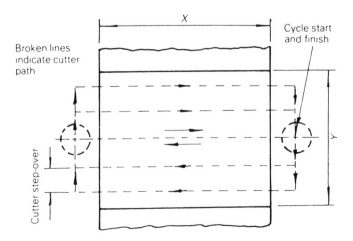

Figure 8.69(10b) Slotting cycle.

consideration the need for each cutter pass to provide a completely clean surface. Another variation of this cycle will complete the looping sequence before dropping to the next Z depth.

Similar to the slot milling cycle is the pocket milling cycle. This cycle commences at the center of the pocket, the cutter feeding in the Z axis to a programmed depth. Once to depth the cutter follows a series of loops until the programmed X and Y dimensions of the pocket are reached, again with a cutter overlap on each pass. If the pocket depth is such that more than one increment in the Z axis is necessary, the cutter is returned to the center of the pocket, Z increments down, and the cycle is repeated. Some systems provide for a cycle that roughs out the main pocket and then machines it to size with a small finishing cut. A pocket milling cycle is illustrated in Figure 8.69(10c).

Special routines in conversational controls are not unique just to milling, turning centers have their own cycles. Such special routines for turning were also created in order to make part material removal and respective operations easier. Figure 8.69(10d) shows a very useful turning stock removal cycle. From one data block, plus blocks defining the component profile, the controller will automatically determine the number of passes necessary to remove the excess material. The cycle can constantly vary the length of travel in the Z axis with each pass if need be, and finally take a finishing cut to reduce the component profile precisely to size. The definition of the component profile in program data is added at the end of the program and is automatically activated via the stock removal cycle call. The profile definition can be achieved by the inclusion of appropriate minor cycles such as those described above. This stock removal cycle is for application along the Z axis. Similar cycles exist that cater to stock removal along the face or X axis of a work-piece as well.

Figures 8.69(10e) and 8.69(10f) illustrate cycles that may be used for reducing the diameter at any position along the length of a part and for grooving. Figure 8.69(10g)

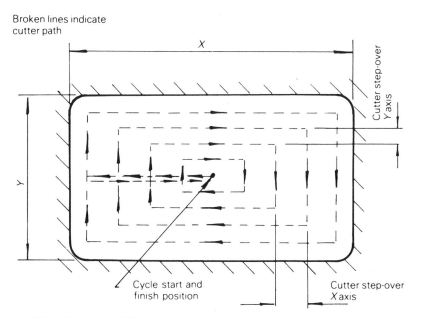

Figure 8.69(10c) Pocket milling cycle.

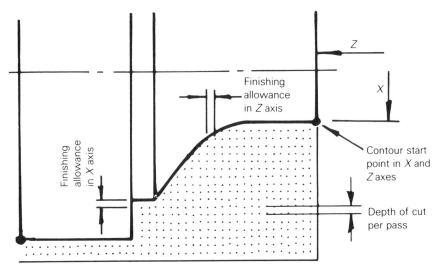

Further data required:

(1) Profile data (added at end of program);

(2) Profile data start block number;

(3) Profile data end block number.

A final profile trace is optional.

Figure 8.69(10d) Stock removal to a defined contour cycle. (Refer to your programming manual for specific examples.)

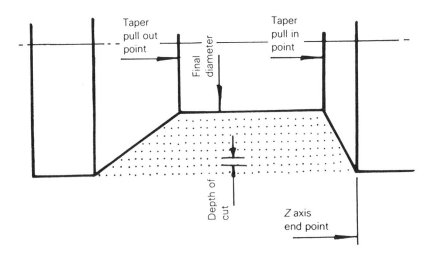

Figure 8.69(10e) Stock removal cycle with optional tapered entry and exit.

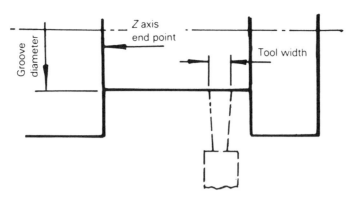

Figure 8.69(10f) Stock removal or grooving cycle.

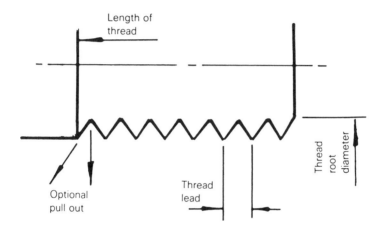

Data example: G84X8.168Z-20P₁ IP₂ I.5

Figure 8.69(10g) Automatic threading cycle (millimeter example).

illustrates a thread cutting cycle, an essential feature of any control system devoted to turning. This particular version of a thread cutting cycle is particularly easy to use. From just one block of data the control automatically determines the number of passes necessary to achieve the required thread depth. In the block of data shown G84 is the cycle code, X specifies the thread root diameter, Z specifies the thread length, the P1 value is the depth of the first pass, and P2 is the thread lead. The control automatically effects a progressive reduction in the depth of cut of each pass that results in improved surface finish and prolonged tool life.

On less sophisticated thread cutting cycles the X diameter for each pass along the thread length has to be predetermined by the part programmer. Each predetermined depth pass is than programmed in a separate data block.

Additional cycles that could be found on milling or turning machines include those for boring, threading (various forms), elliptical profiles, and even those for the machining of helical arcs. Helical arc programming requires data defining an arc in two axes along with a linear move in a third axis between the start and finish points of the arc. A moment's thought about the complexity of programming a cutter path such as this should be more than sufficient to emphasize how valuable canned cycles are. Canned cycles are an aid to simplifying part programming procedures. It should be noted that specialized cycles are normally meant for uniform or symmetrical shapes and as programming becomes more complex it is usually necessary to return to "G" code programming. Many conversational controls now have the ability to be programmed in two or three dimensional modes and conversational or "G" code mode.

Conversational Control Sample Drilling Program for Hurco Machine Tool

Programming continues by selecting proper soft key options presented followed by filling in the appropriate machine axis and conditions information. The data blocks entered will contain machining information on the operation type (position, holes, milling, patterns), tool number, coordinate dimensions (X, Y, Z, etc.), feedrate and location of operations on the part. Lets now take a look at a sample program for drilling. Note that the Hurco system is equipped with a built in calculator, and speed/feed selector to assist the programmer/operator. The system also allows for editing (copy, move, delete) of program data blocks much like a word processor on a personal computer. As in G code programming previously discussed in this text conversational programming systems also have various drill cycles selected from soft key selections as illustrated in Figure 8.69(11).

Drilling Operations

Fields of information used to describe any of the drilling operations used are as follows: tool number, Z axis start point, Z bottom, plunge feedrate, spindle speed, peck depth and type. See Figures 8.70 and 8.70(1) for diagrams of two different drill cycles and their parameters. Note that complete instructions for all parameters and their entry into the control system will be covered in machine programming manuals provided by the machine tool manufacturer.

When the cursor is positioned at the *Peck Type* field, the softkeys change to provide a choice of Standard and Chip Breaker functions.

- **Standard (F1)**—the tool retracts to the Z Start and then rapidly plunges to the peck clearance plane selected in Program Parameters or Change Parameters.

- **Chip Breaker (F2)**—the tool dwells at each peck level before continuing to feed to the next peck level. (Drill dwell is the time selected in Program Parameters or Change Holes Parameters.)

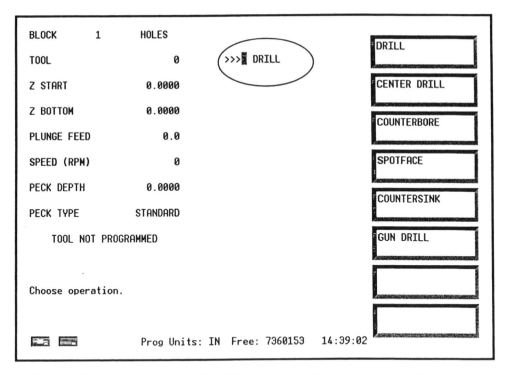

BLOCK	1	HOLES	
TOOL		0	>>> DRILL
Z START		0.0000	
Z BOTTOM		0.0000	
PLUNGE FEED		0.0	
SPEED (RPM)		0	
PECK DEPTH		0.0000	
PECK TYPE		STANDARD	

TOOL NOT PROGRAMMED

Choose operation.

Prog Units: IN   Free: 7360153   14:39:02

DRILL

CENTER DRILL

COUNTERBORE

SPOTFACE

COUNTERSINK

GUN DRILL

Figure 8.69(11) Holes Screen with Drill Operations Softkeys (Courtesy of Hurco Machine Tool Products.)

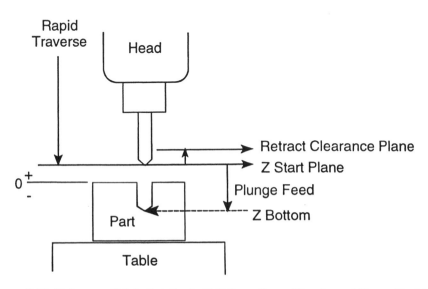

Figure 8.70 Reference Points Relative to Drill Operations. (Courtesy of Hurco Machine Tool Products.)

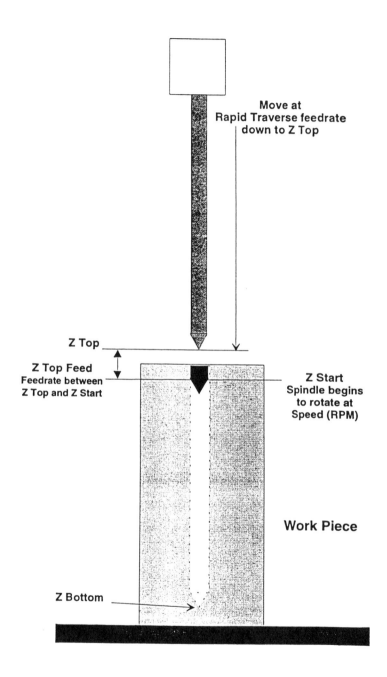

Figure 8.70(1) Gun Drill Positions. (Courtesy of Hurco Machine Tool Products.)

Figure 8.70(1) shows the Gun Drill program fields as they relate to a part and the drilling tool.

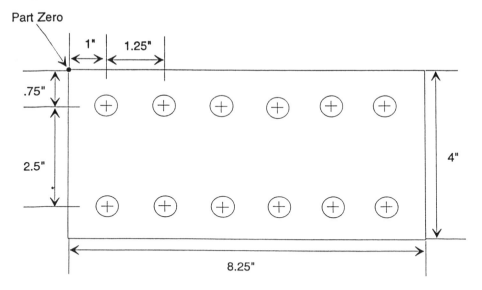

Material: Alloy Steel
8.25" x 4" x .25"

Tools		Feeds	Speeds
1/8" Center Drill	HSS	4.2	2800
3/8" Drill	HSS	5.6	930

Figure 8.70(2) Hole Drilling Example. (Courtesy of Hurco Machine Tool Products).

Sample Drilling Program

The following example demonstrates some basic Ultimax hole drilling capabilities. The job calls for drilling twelve holes with a 3/8" drill through a rectangular piece of alloy steel as shown in the diagram: Figure 8.70(2).

The program presented on the following pages is a copy of the printed part program developed for this drawing. This program is presented in the same format as an Ultimax part program that was printed on a printer from the control. Therefore, the program data may be presented in a different order than it is on the Ultimax screens.

In the sample program, the operator added a tool setup for tool #99 to use only to draw the *part outline block*. Since the speed and feed information is missing from the tool description, the control will not execute any block using this tool. To prevent an error during running, the operator will delete that tool and the outline block before running the program.

Since Ultimax allows considerable flexibility in developing part programs, this sample program does not represent the only way the part can be programmed. Watch for inserted explanations of the special features of this sample program.

Part Setup

			Safety Work Region		
Part Zero X		5.0000			
	Y	10.0000	Z Top	(+)	99.0000
Offset	Z	0.0000	Z Bottom	(−)	−0.4010
			X Left	(−)	0.0000
			X Right	(+)	8.2500
			Y Front	(−)	−4.0000
			Y Back	(+)	0.0000
			Fixture Offset		1

General Parameters

Retract Clearance	0.2500	IN
Rapid Traverse	400.0	IPM
Peck Clearance Plane	0.0500	IN
Chord Error	0.0001	IN
Depletion Retract	0.0050	IN

Holes Parameters

Bore Orient Retract	0.0200	IN
Drill Dwell	0.5	SEC
Bore Dwell	1.0	SEC

Milling Parameters

Blend Offset	0.1250	IN
Blend Overlap	0.1250	IN
Finish Feed	100	%
Finish Speed	100	%
Finish XY	0.0100	IN
Finish Z	0.0050	IN
Milling Direction	Climb	
Pocket Overlap	10	%
Cutter Comp Parameter	Insert	Arc

Program Parameters

Override Lockout	Off
Program Protect	Partial
Tool Change Position	Yes

Tool Setup

The number to the left of the type field is the tool number, so this setup section lists three tools: 1, 2, and 99. Since tool 99 is not going to be used in the program, the tool type was not identified in setup. Zero calibration values will, of course, vary for different work pieces and tools.

1	Type	Drill
	Diameter	0.1250
	Zero Calibration	−10000.
	Speed (RPM)	CW 2800
	Coolant	Flood
	Gear range	1
	Tool Number	1
	Diameter Offset	1
	Length Offset	1
2	Type	Drill
	Diameter	0.3750
	Zero Calibration	−10000.
	Speed (RPM)	CW 930
	Coolant	Flood
	Gear range	1
	Tool Number	2
	Diameter Offset	2
	Length Offset	2
99	Diameter	0.0000
	Zero Calibration	−10000.
	Speed (RPM)	CW 0
	Coolant	Off
	Gear range	1
	Tool Number	99
	Diameter Offset	99
	Length Offset	99

Hurco Ultimax Part Program   **3**   **Inch**
Holes.HD3   **Standard**

The number to the left of the following data block name is the block number in the part program.

Data Blocks

1	Mill Frame			
	Tool	99	Z Start	0.0000
	Type	Out/Tan	Z Bottom	−0.2500
	Finish Tool	0	Plunge Feed	0.0
	X Corner	0.0000	Mill Feed	0.0
	Y Corner	0.0000	Speed (RPM)	0
	X Length	8.2500	Peck Depth	0.0000
	Y Length	−4.0000		
	Corner Radius	0.0000		

Block #1 creates an outline of the part for the graphics display. Tool 99 is an imaginary tool and does not perform any cutting. You can use this outline during programming to check the location of the programmed holes and delete the block before running the program. The Z Start parameter draws the surface of the part, and the Z Bottom draws the bottom. Block #2 performs all of the hole drilling operations. The tools are entered into the program in the order in which they are used.

2	Holes	
	Center Drill	
	Tool	1
	Finish Tool	0
	Z Start	0.0500
	Z Bottom	−0.0125
	Plunge Feed	4.2
	Speed (RPM)	2800
	Peck Depth	0.0000
	Peck Type	Standard
	Drill	
	Tool	2
	Finish Tool	0
	Z Start	0.0500
	Z Bottom	−0.3000
	Plunge Feed	5.6
	Speed (RPM)	930
	Peck Depth	0.1500
	Peck Type	Standard

Hurco Ultimax Part Program   4   **Inch**
Holes.HD3   **Standard**

Locations

	X	Y
1	1.0000	−0.7500
2	2.2500	−0.7500
3	3.5000	−0.7500
4	4.7500	−0.7500
5	6.0000	−0.7500
6	7.2500	−0.7500
7	7.2500	−3.2500
8	6.0000	−3.2500
9	4.7500	−3.2500
10	3.5000	−3.2500
11	2.2500	−3.2500
12	1.0000	−3.2500

These hole locations are also a portion of Block #2. They are programmed in the order that they will be cut. The operator used the Ultimax No-Calc feature to enter the location data.

First, the operator entered the X and Y coordinates for hole #1 from the drawing. To calculate the X values for holes 2 through 6, the operator typed "1.25" and pressed the console plus (+) key and Enter for each of these values. The operator pressed the Enter key for each of the Y values since those values are all the same as the first hole.

For hole #7, the operator pressed Enter on the X value to keep it the same as the previous value. Then the operator typed "−2.5" and pressed the console plus (+) key and Enter key to add −2.5 to the previous Y value and pressed Enter for each of the subsequent Y values. For the X value of holes 8 through 12, the operator typed "1.25" and pressed the console minus ($-$) key and Enter to subtract 1.25 for each new position.

Milling Programs

In conversational programming milling programs are created in a similar way to drilling or other program content. The programmer/operator selects modes of operation and setup commands from a menu and then enters from the keyboard pertinent digital information. In the Hurco Ultimax system there are many more options than just milling and drilling as can be seen on the input hierarchy chart Figure 8.70(3).

Let's look at some of the advanced features that the Ultimax control is capable of. Figures 8.70(4) and 8.70(5) show the hierarchy chart and pattern entry screen of the control. Figures 8.70(6) and 8.70(6a) describe the pattern loop rectangular option and show the screen inputs required.

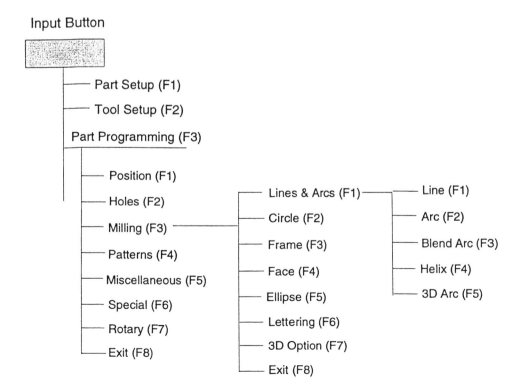

Figure 8.70(3) Milling Options Chart. (Courtesy of Hurco Machine Tool Products.)

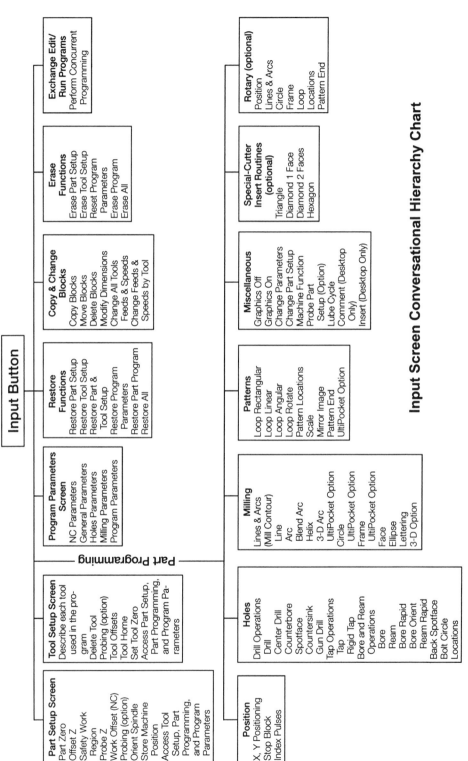

Figure 8.70(4) Conversational Hierarchy Chart. (Courtesy of Hurco Machine Tool Products.)

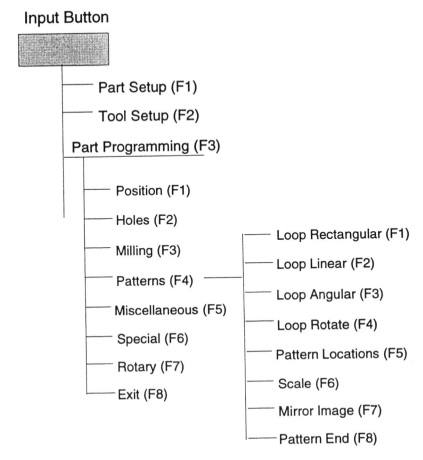

Figure 8.70(5) Pattern Options Hierarchy Chart. (Courtesy of Hurco Machine Tool Products.)

Pattern Operations

This section presents detailed descriptions of the Ultimax Pattern options. Use Pattern operations to save programming time by duplicating part geometry to complete a part program or create multiple parts from one program. Pattern operations repeat or modify a sequence of data blocks.

The chart in Figure 8.70(5) shows the relationship of the pattern options to the Input button and its subsequent menu selections. Pattern operations repeat or modify a sequence of data blocks.

The available softkey options are shown in Figure 8.70(5a).

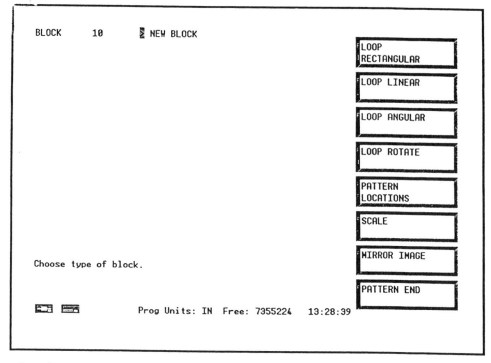

- **Loop Rectangular (F1)**—repeat a pattern along lines parallel to the X and Y axes.

- **Loop Linear (F2)**—repeat a pattern along a line defined in the XY plane.

- **Loop Angular (F3)**—repeat a pattern along a circular path. Right-side up is preserved as in a clock-face.

- **Loop Rotate (F4)**—repeat a pattern along a circular path. The part rotates as the pattern is repeated around its center point.

- **Pattern Locations (F5)**—List the locations where a pattern will be repeated. Up to 999 different locations may be entered.

- **Scale (F6)**—Reduce or increase the size of a pattern by a factor ranging from 10% to 1000%.

- **Mirror Image (F7)**—Copy an existing part as a mirror image.

- **Pattern End (F8)**—Identifies the pattern operation's last block.

Figure 8.70(5a) Pattern Softkeys. (Courtesy of Hurco Machine Tool Products.)

Loop Rectangular

The loop rectangular routine allows a given pattern to be repeated a specified number of times along lines parallel to the X and Y axes. The original pattern is always milled at its programmed location. This feature is also referred to as translation were a machining sequence or pattern is datum shifted alone one or more axes. Figures 8.70(6) and 8.70(6a).

The other advanced control options of loop angular, loop rotate, pattern locations, scaling, and mirror image are explained in the following Figures 8.70(7), 8.70(8), 8.71, 8.71(a), 8.71(1), and 8.71(1a).

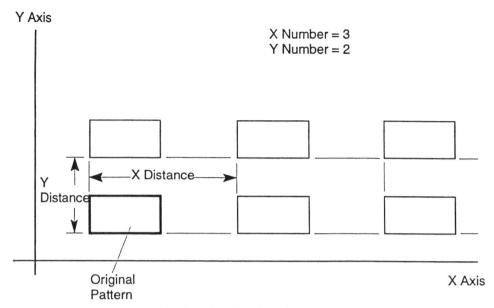

The fields on this screen hold this information about the pattern:

Fields	Definitions
X Number	Number of times the programmed routine will be repeated along a line parallel to the X-axis.
Y Number	Number of times the programmed routine will be repeated along a line parallel to the Y-axis.
X Distance	Distance between the patterns along the X-axis lines. (Negative values indicate direction.)
Y Distance	Distance between the patterns along the Y-axis lines. (Negative values indicate direction.)

Figure 8.70(6) Sample Loop Rectangular Operation. (Courtesy of Hurco Machine Tool Products.)

Loop Linear

The loop linear routine allows a given pattern to be repeated a specified number of times along a line defined in the X-Y plane.

Even though the defined line of this pattern is not parallel to the X or Y axes, the original pattern is always milled at its programmed location and orientation does not change with respect to the X and Y axes. An example of this type of routine is shown in Figure 8.70(7).

Loop Angular

This routine allows a programmed pattern to be repeated a specified number of times along a circular path.

Pattern orientation does not change with respect to the X and Y axes. The original programmed pattern is not executed at its original position, unless the routine places it at that location. The pattern is only shown in the locations specified by the routine. Figure 8.70(8).

Scale

The scaling facility enables components that are geometrically identical, but uniformly variable dimensionally to be produced from the same program data. This routine allows a programmed pattern to be scaled-down or scaled-up to a programmed factor ranging from 0.100 to 10.000 (10% to 1000% respectively). Scaling is executed around the specified X, Y, and Z coordinates for the pattern where scaling occurs Figure 8.71.

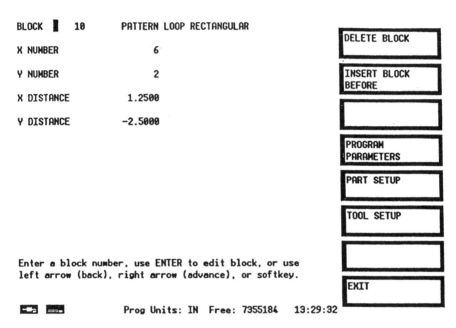

```
BLOCK   ▌  10        PATTERN LOOP RECTANGULAR

X NUMBER              6

Y NUMBER              2

X DISTANCE         1.2500

Y DISTANCE        -2.5000
```

```
┌──────────────────┐
│ DELETE BLOCK     │
└──────────────────┘
┌──────────────────┐
│ INSERT BLOCK     │
│ BEFORE           │
└──────────────────┘
┌──────────────────┐
│                  │
└──────────────────┘
┌──────────────────┐
│ PROGRAM          │
│ PARAMETERS       │
└──────────────────┘
┌──────────────────┐
│ PART SETUP       │
└──────────────────┘
┌──────────────────┐
│ TOOL SETUP       │
└──────────────────┘
┌──────────────────┐
│                  │
└──────────────────┘
┌──────────────────┐
│ EXIT             │
└──────────────────┘
```

Enter a block number, use ENTER to edit block, or use left arrow (back), right arrow (advance), or softkey.

Prog Units: IN   Free: 7355184   13:29:32

Figure 8.70(6a) Pattern Loop Rectangular Screen. (Courtesy of Hurco Machine Tool Products.)

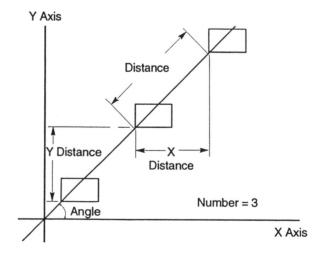

Figure 8.70(7) Sample Loop Linear Operation. (Courtesy of Hurco Machine Tool Products.)

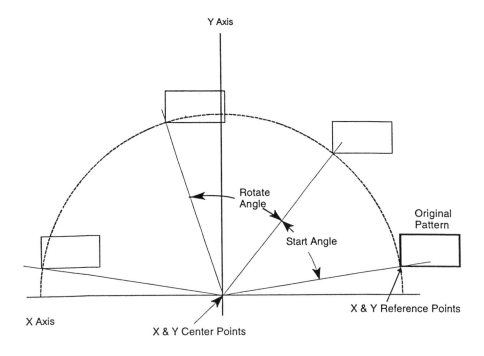

Figure 8.70(8) Sample Loop Angular Operation. (Courtesy of Hurco Machine Tool Products.)

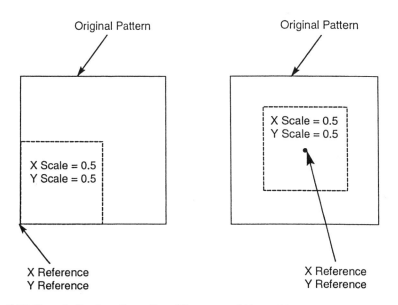

Figure 8.71 Sample Scaling Operation. (Courtesy of Hurco Machine Tool Products.)

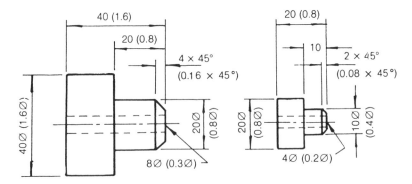

Figure 8.71(a) Geometrically identical components suitable for production by scaling. (Inch units are given in parentheses.)

Figure 8.71(a) illustrates two components, the production of which could be accommodated by scaling. Scaling can be applied to complete components or to one feature of a component. Some feel it is proper to use the lower end of a scaling factor range to minutely increase or decrease the machined size in one or more axes to maintain a dimensional tolerance that may vary out of tolerance. An example may be to allow for the effects of distortion in the work-piece caused by clamping pressures. This practice is not normally done though and is usually the task of the tool or fixture compensation option to be discussed subsequently.

Mirror Image

Mirror image is the term used to describe a programming facility used to machine components, or features of components, that are dimensionally identical, but geometrically opposite either in two axes or one axis. By using the mirror image facility, such components can be machined from just one set of data.

In Figure 8.71(1) an original component feature is indicated in the bottom left hand corner of the diagram. A complete mirror image of that feature is shown in the top right hand corner, while mirror images in the X axis and Y axis are shown respectively, in the bottom right and top left hand corners of the diagram. To produce a complete mirror image both the X axis and Y axis dimensional values will change from negative to positive. For half mirror images the dimensional values will change from negative to positive in one axis only.

This pattern routine allows a part to be programmed as a mirror image of an existing programmed part. The routine can be programmed to execute either the mirror image only, or the original part and the mirror image.

The mirror image about a line defined in the routine is shown in the example operation shown in Figure 8.71(1a)

In this example, the X coordinate is 2.00, and the Y coordinate can be any value because the angle is 90° and the mirror line travels in the Y axis indefinitely. The mirror line

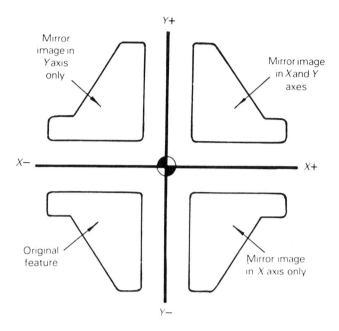

Figure 8.71(1)

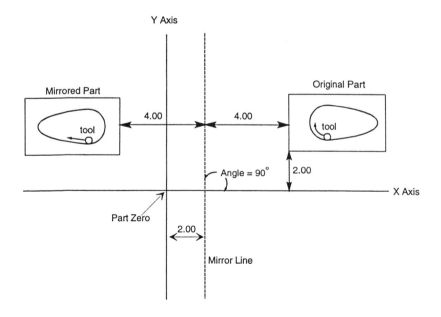

Figure 8.71(1a) Mirror Image Example. (Courtesy of Hurco Machine Tool Products.)

is identified by a point and an angle because a single point identified on the axis cannot define a line. The mirror line shown above is parallel to the Y axis, so the angle is 90°.

As with all patterns, you must also program a Pattern End data block for the sequence that is repeated in the Mirror Image block.

If the original part is programmed to use *conventional milling* in Program Parameters or Change Parameters, the mirror image part is also executed with conventional milling. If *climb milling* produced the original part, climb milling executes the mirror image part.

Enhanced Machine Capabilities

From the advanced control features we than move to the enhanced features of the machine. Here you will be introduced to the pocket milling, three dimensional milling, tool probing, and part probing capabilities that can be found on conversationally programmed machine tools.

Pocket Milling

The UltiPocket™ programming option adds special milling routines for machining pocket boundaries with islands Figure 8.71(2). This option provides complete clean out of odd-shaped pockets without cutting the islands programmed inside the boundary. The

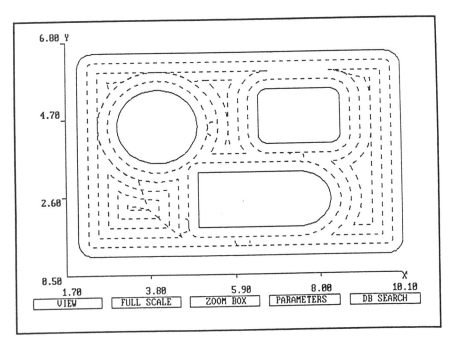

Figure 8.71(2) Pocket Boundary with Inward Spiral Islands. (Courtesy of Hurco Machine Tool Products.)

software automatically calculates the tool path around islands eliminating the long task of plotting these shapes. Islands may also be rotated, scaled, and repeated.

These two drawings show different views of an inward spiral boundary with three differently shaped islands. Figures 8.71(2) and 8.71(3) you may select from the following pocket features when creating the standard ultimax program data blocks: Mill Contour, Mill Frame, Mill Circle, or Pattern.

Types of 3-D Contours

The Hurco Ultimax conversational control allows for four types of 3-D surfaces (male and female) to be created from a single 2-D contour. The examples shown in this section use a *2-D contour* (Figure 8.71(4)) as the basis for the 3-D figures (Figure 8.71(5) and (6)).

XY Revolved about X

The original 2-D contour is shown in Figure 8.71(4) as a two-dimensional profile composed of arc segments defined in the XY plane. The contour is then revolved about a centerline Figure 8.71(5) on the X axis to produce this finished 3-D contour (Figure 8.71(6)).

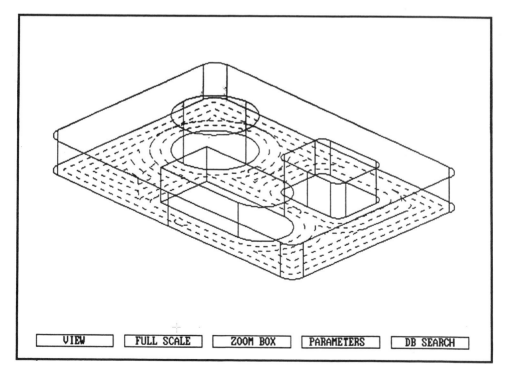

Figure 8.71(3) Isometric View of Inward Spiral Islands. (Courtesy of Hurco Machine Tool Products.)

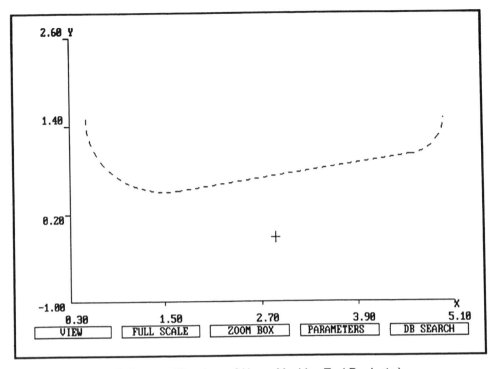

Figure 8.71(4) 2-D Contour. (Courtesy of Hurco Machine Tool Products.)

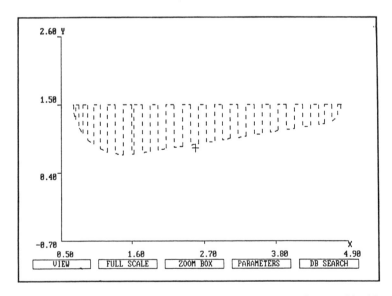

Figure 8.71(5) 3-D Contour XY Revolved About X. (Courtesy of Hurco Machine Tool Products.)

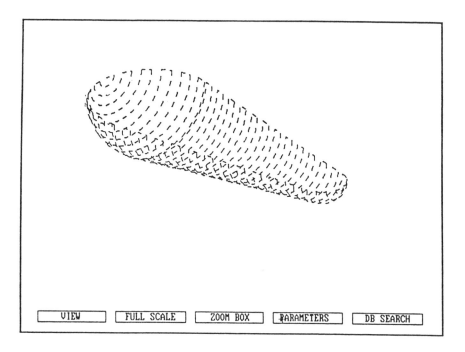

| VIEW | FULL SCALE | ZOOM BOX | PARAMETERS | DB SEARCH |

Figure 8.71(6) Isometric View of 3-D Contour Cutter Path XY Revolved About X. (Courtesy of Hurco Machine Tool Products.)

XZ Provile Revolved about Z

The next set of screen graphics are of the starting 2-D profile Figure 8.71(7) which is then XZ revolved around the Z axis to create cutter paths Figure 8.71(8). So from simply defined two dimensional shapes and the rotate feature of the control three dimensional cutter paths can be created.

Probing Options

The next enhanced control features to be reviewed are the probing options. There are two probing features available, tool and / or part both assist with machine setup. Tool and part probing may be used independently or in conjunction with one another. Each probing type includes additional hardware and software.

Tool Monitoring/Probing

Probe tool monitoring is available to automatically monitor calibrated tools to detect breakage or wear. The software compares the current tool dimensions, length and diameter, to the calibrated dimensions stored in tool setup for the programmed tool. If the current dimensions deviate from the defined tolerance programmed the tool is defective. Defective tool detection will cause axis motion to stop and a operator message to appear unless spare tools have been programmed and loaded into the machine. If spare tools are available the machine can be programmed to pick them up and continue its machining sequence.

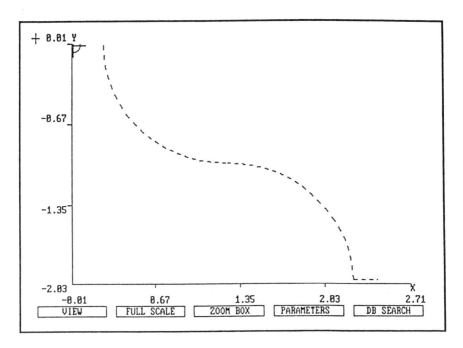

Figure 8.71(7) Graphics Display of XY 2-D Contour. (Courtesy of Hurco Machine Tool Products.)

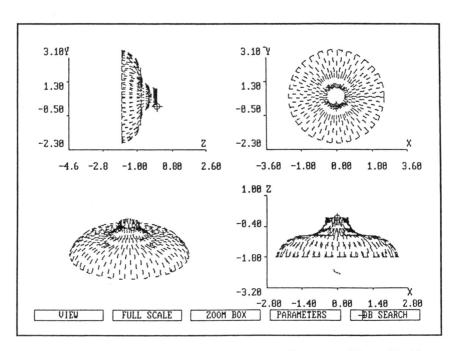

Figure 8.71(8) All Views of the XZ Revolved About Z. (Courtesy of Hurco Machine Tool Products.)

Tool Probing Equipment

There are two types of tool probes: touch tool probe and laser tool probe as shown in Figures 8.71(9) and 8.72. Either type of tool probe is connected to the Ultimax hardware and monitored by the software. The tool probe is mounted to the table, usually in an out-of-the-way corner. Tool probing can be performed with individual tools or with a select group of tools.

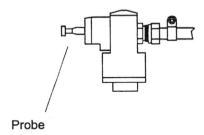

Probe

Figure 8.71(9) Typical Touch Tool Probe. (Courtesy of Hurco Machine Tool Products.)

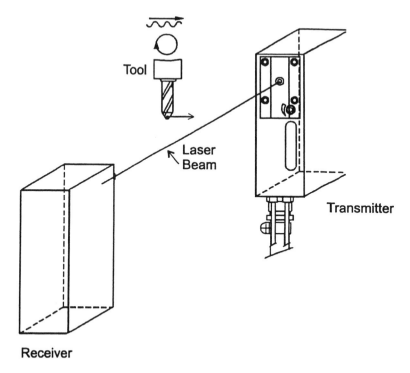

Figure 8.72 Typical Laser Tool Probe. (Courtesy of Hurco Machine Tool Products.)

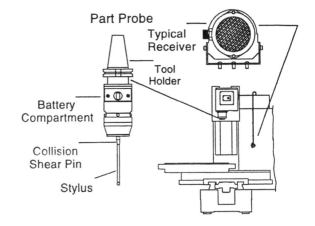

Figure 8.72(1) Part Probing Equipment. (Courtesy of Hurco Machine Tool Products.)

Touch Tool Probe   The touch tool probe is figure 8.71(9). The probe is attached to a cable that has the signal-conditioning module built in. Power is supplied from the 24-volt supply already present in the control. A single output is used to indicate when the probe has been deflected.

Laser Tool Probe   The laser tool probe is shown in figure 8.72. The laser probe is located on the table and consists of a transmitter from which a laser light beam travels to a receiver. The laser tool probe measures the tool's length and diameter. The software monitors when the tool interrupts the laser beam during probe calibration and stores the information.

Part Probing   Part probing uses the touch probe illustrated, Figure 8.72(1) to check the part location before machining occurs. X Y Z locations can then be automatically compensated to match the machine tool movements to the current part location. The Ultimax system can also compensate for skewed parts as well. The other use for this part probe option is part dimensional verification or inspection after machining occurs. A standard inspection report can then be generated for each part machined if necessary. Programming for the enhanced options are fully described in the programming manual provided with the machine tool.

Conversational Program Example

Example This conversational control program example is for a Hurco CNC mill with the Ultimax control. This machine has dual CRT screens so that positional and program data can be reviewed on one and tool path graphics on the other.

The part example to be used for the Hurco program is the base component of a drill vise (Figure 8.73). The operations to be performed are the milling of a 1.375 × 3.837 pocket with a .500 endmill, the milling of a .500 slot with a .432 endmill, and the milling of eleven .125 radius adjusting notches with a .250 ball nose end mill. See tool graphics for tool change position and program zero location.

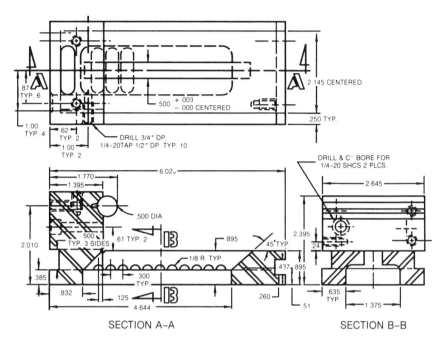

Figure 8.73 Base component drill vise.

Hurco Example of Program Inputs

Operation to be Performed	Message on CRT	Operator Key Strokes
With machine powered up, define tool to be used (Figure 8.74).		Push tool setup soft key
	Upper screen displays machine status	
	Lower screen display reads tool setup display figure	
	Cursor at tool	Key in 1 and enter.
	Cursor at Type	Push End Mill key
	Cursor at Diameter	Key in 0.500
	Cursor at zero calibration	Jog tool down against reference point and push SET TOOL ZERO
		Push TOOL UP key to retract spindle
	Cursor at speed	Push CLOCKWISE key and then enter 0 speed to get control speed calculation
	Cursor at coolant	Push MIST key
	Cursor at material	Push HSS key
	Cursor at flutes	Enter number of flutes in cutter

Operation to be Performed	Message on CRT	Operator Key Strokes
Repeat process for tools 2 and 3		
Position tool away from part (Figure 8.75).	Block 1	Push POSITION soft key
	Cursor at TOOL	Enter the tool number followed by the X and Y coordinates for the position
	Cursor at STOP	Enter NO by pushing button so machine does not stop at this position
	Cursor at INDEX PULSES	Enter 0 no index table is involved.
Create MILL FRAME (Figures 8.76 and 8.77)	Block 2	Press MILLING soft key to get main milling menu
	Choose type of block	Press FRAME soft key Enter 1—using key pad
	Cursor at TOOL	Press POCKET
	Cursor at TYPE	Press YES soft key
	Cursor at FINISH PASS	Enter − .563—to establish lower left hand corner of pocket in X axis
	Cursor at X CORNER	
	Cursor at Y CORNER	Enter − .687—to establish lower left hand corner of pocket in Y axis
	Cursor at X LENGTH	Enter 3.837—the "X" length of the pocket to be cut
	Cursor at Y LENGTH	Enter 1.375—the "Y" length of the pocket to be cut
	Cursor at CORNER RADIUS	Enter .250—the cutter radius
	Cursor at Z START	Enter .05—the starting depth of cut
	Cursor at Z BOTTOM	Enter −.950—the final depth of pocket
	Cursor at PLUNGE FEED	Enter 1.5—feed in IPM for plunging to depth
	Cursor at MILL FEED	Enter 8.0—feed in IPM for X and Y cutting moves
	Cursor at SPEED (RPM)	Enter 500—cutter rpm
	Cursor at PECK DEPTH	Enter .100—Z axis in feed increment for each pass.

This type of program entry process is continued until the entire program is complete.

TOOL SET UP

	MACHINE	PART		
X	0.0000	0.0000	TOOL IN SPINDLE	0
Y	0.0000	0.0000	SPINDLE	0
Z	0.0000	0.0000	FEED	0.0
			MAGAZINE	0

DELETE TOOL

TOOL		>1
TYPE		
PITCH		0.000
DIAMETER		0.0000
ZERO CALIBRATION		0.0000
SPEED (RPM)	CW	0
COOLANT		OFF
MATERIAL		
FLUTES		2

PART SETUP

PART
PROGRAMMING

TOOL UP

SET TOOL ZERO

Figure 8.74 Tool setup screen.

BLOCK	1	POSITION
TOOL		>0
X		0.0000
Y		0.0000
STOP		NO
INDEX PULSES		0

Figure 8.75 Positioning.

		1)	ON

BLOCK 2   MILL FRAME

				2)	INSIDE

TOOL		1	Z START	0.0000		
TYPE	>	ON	Z BOTTOM	0.0000		
FINISH PASS		NO	PLUNGE FEED	0.0	3)	OUTSIDE
X CORNER		0.0000	MILL FEED	0.0		
Y CORNER		0.0000	SPEED (RPM)	200		
X LENGTH		0.0000	PECK DEPTH	0.0000	4)	INSIDE TANGENT
Y LENGTH		0.0000	(TOOL DIAMETER	0.2500)		
CORNER RADIUS		0.0000				

	5)	OUTSIDE TANGENT

	6)	POCKET

Enter cutter placement

Figure 8.76 Mill frame.

BLOCK 2   MILL FRAME

TOOL		1	Z START	0.0500	1)	ON
TYPE	>	ON	Z BOTTOM	−0.9500		
FINISH PASS		YES	PLUNGE FEED	1.5	2)	INSIDE
X CORNER		−0.5630	MILL FEED	8.0		
Y CORNER		−0.6870	SPEED (RPM)	500	3)	OUTSIDE
X LENGTH		3.8370	PECK DEPTH	0.1000		
Y LENGTH		1.3750	(TOOL DIAMETER)	0.2500	4)	INSIDE TANGENT
CORNER RADIUS		0.2500				

	5)	OUTSIDE TANGENT

	6)	POCKET

Enter cutter placement

Figure 8.77 Mill frame.

Hurco Example Program Readout

HURCO ULTIMAX PART PROGRAM	INCH	STANDARD

PART SETUP

PART ZERO X	7.0481	SAFETY WORK REGION	
Y	5.9507	Z TOP (+)	999.0000
		Z BOTTOM (−)	−999.0000
		X LEFT (−)	−999.0000
		X RIGHT (+)	999.0000
		Y FRONT (−)	−999.0000
		Y BACK (+)	999.0000
		MATERIAL	CARBON STEEL

PROGRAM PARAMETERS

GENERAL	OVERRIDE LOCKOUT	OFF
	PROGRAM PROTECT	PARTIAL
	RETRACT CLEARANCE	99.0000 IN
	RAPID TRAVERSE	250.0 IPM
HOLES	BORE ORIENT RETRACT	0.0200 IN
	DRILL DWELL	0.5 SEC
	BORE DWELL	1.0 SEC
MILLING	BLEND OFFSET	0.1250 IN
	BLEND OVERLAP	0.1250 IN
	FINISH FEED	100%
	FINISH SPEED	100%
	FINISH XY	0.0050 IN
	FINISH Z	0.0050 IN
	MILLING DIRECTION	CONV
	POCKET OVERLAP	10%

TOOL SETUP

						(Tool Definitions)
1	TYPE	END MILL	COOLANT		MIST	(Tool #1
	DIAMETER	0.5000	MATERIAL		HSS	.500 End
	ZERO CALIBRATION	1.2032	FLUTES		2	Mill)
	SPEED (RPM) CW	0				
2	TYPE	END MILL	COOLANT		MIST	(Tool #2 .432
	DIAMETER	0.4320	MATERIAL		HSS	end mill)
	ZERO CALIBRATION	1.4859	FLUTES		2	
	SPEED (RPM) CW	0				
3	TYPE	END MILL	COOLANT		MIST	(Tool #3
	DIAMETER	0.2500	MATERIAL		HSS	.250 ball
	ZERO CALIBRATION	1.6097	FLUTES		2	nose end
	SPEED (RPM) CW	0				mill)

DATA BLOCKS

1 POSITION
TOOL	1	STOP	NO	(Tool change
X	−2.0000	INDEX PULSES	0	.5 end
Y	−2.0000			mill)

2 MILL FRAME
TOOL	1	Z START	0.0500	(Milling of
TYPE	POCKET	Z BOTTOM	−0.3850	1.375 ×
FINISH PASS	YES	PLUNGE FEED	1.5	3.837
X CORNER	−0.5630	MILL FEED	8.0	pocket)
Y CORNER	−0.6870	SPEED (RPM)	500	(See
X LENGTH	3.8370	PECK DEPTH	0.1000	graphics
Y LENGTH	1.3750			of tool
CORNER RADIUS	0.2500			path,
				Fig-
				ure 8.78)

3 POSITION
TOOL	1	STOP	NO	(Tool #2
X	−2.0000	INDEX PULSES	0	change
Y	−2.0000			position)

4 MILL CONTOUR
                                              (Mill .500
                                              slot)

SEGMENT 0	START		
TOOL	2	Z START	−0.3500
CUTTER COMP.	LEFT	Z BOTTOM	−0.9500
FINISH PASS	YES	PLUNGE FEED	1.5
X START	0.0000	SPEED (RPM)	500
Y START	0.0000	PECK DEPTH	0.0750
SEGMENT 1	LINE		
X END	0.0000	XY LENGTH CAL	0.2510
Y END	−0.2510	XY ANGLE CAL	−90.000
Z END	−0.9500	FEED	8.0
SEGMENT 2	LINE		
X END	3.2490	XY LENGTH CAL	3.2490
Y END	−0.2510	XY ANGLE CAL	0.000
Z END	−0.9500	FEED	8.0
SEGMENT 3	LINE		
X END	3.2490	XY LENGTH CAL	0.5020
Y END	0.2510	XY ANGLE CAL	90.000
Z END	−0.9500	FEED	8.0
SEGMENT 4	LINE		
X END	0.0000	XY LENGTH CAL	0.3.2490
Y END	0.2510	XY ANGLE CAL	180.000
Z END	−0.9500	FEED	8.0
SEGMENT 5	LINE		
X END	0.0000	XY LENGTH CAL	0.2510
Y END	0.0000	XY ANGLE CAL	−90.000
Z END	−0.9500	FEED	8.0

5	POSITION					
	TOOL	2	STOP	YES	(Tool #3
	X	−2.0000	INDEX PULSES	0	change,
	Y	−2.0000			.250 End Mill)
6	PATTERN LOOP LINEAR				
	NUMBER	11	ANGLE	0.000	(Pattern loop
	X DISTANCE	0.3000	DISTANCE	0.3000	definition
	Y DISTANCE	0.0000			for .250
					notches)

7	MILL CONTOUR				
	SEGMENT 0	START		−0.370	
	TOOL	3	Z START	−0.5100	(Machining
	CUTTER COMP.	NO	Z BOTTOM	1.5	moves
	FINISH PASS	YES	PLUNGE FEED		for top
	X START	−0.1250	SPEED (RPM)	1200	notches)
	Y START	0.5370	PECK DEPTH	0.0300	
	SEGMENT 1	LINE			
	X END	−0.1250	XY LENGTH CAL	1.0740	(Machining
	Y END	−0.5370	XY ANGLE CAL	−90.000	moves for
	Z END	−0.5100	FEED	4.0	bottom
					notches)

8	PATTERN END		(End of
			pattern
			and
			program)

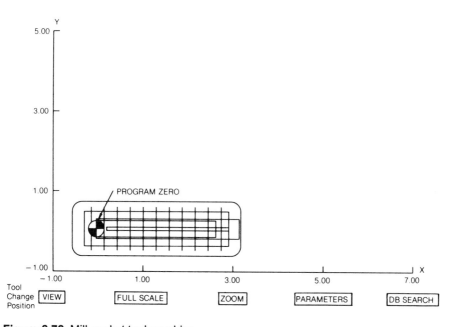

Figure 8.78 Mill pocket tool graphics.

QUESTIONS*

1 Devise a simple diagram to illustrate the axes of movement of a vertical machining center and explain why it is necessary to redefine some of these movements as an aid to part programming.

2 Make a simple sketch to show the difference between absolute and incremental dimensional data.

3 How is the difference between an incremental and absolute value indicated on word address control systems that permit the use of either in the same part program?

4 What value should be programmed when a drawing states an upper and lower limit to a toleranced dimension?

5 Briefly explain the difference in data required by the three methods of circular interpolation which use I, J and K values.

6 Explain when the use of a programmer-devised sub-routine would be justified.

7 How does a 'macro' differ from other types of programmer-devised routines?

8 Describe the concept of 'parametric' programming and suggest when its use would be advantageous.

9 Describe the programming technique of 'point definition' and describe the type of situation where it could be used to advantage.

10 What is the advantage of using a datum shift within a program?

11 What is the purpose of the: Operation Schedule? Tool Sheet? Coordinate Sheet?

12 What are the five responsibilities of a part programmer related to tooling?

13 What is meant by the term word address programming?

14 What is meant by the term conversational programming?

15 Write a definition for the following terms: Point to Point; Linear Interpolation; Circular Interpolation.

16 What is the difference between datum shift and the program datum point.

17 Explain what a canned cycle is.

18 What is the major purpose of tool offsets?

19 Describe the difference between translation and rotation of program segments.

20 Describe two basic planning considerations which facilitate producing a part in the shortest possible time.

21 Explain what is meant by a 'floating zero' and state the advantages of such a facility.

22 With the aid of a simple sketch, or sketches, describe a situation where two programmed zero shifts would be required during the production of a turned part.

23 Assuming a situation where the part programmer is not in close contact with the machine shop, what documentation should be prepared to facilitate the transfer of essential information between the two activities of programming and production?

24 Explain how the tool offset facility can be used to program a series of cuts along a turned profile using the same programmed slide movements for each pass.

25 Suggest one method each for keeping (i) tool indexing time, and (ii) slide movement to a minimum and state why this should be a programming objective.

26 With the aid of a simple sketch describe what is meant by 'tool nose radius compensation' and describe a practical approach that can be employed to determine whether the required compensation is to the right or left of a profile.

27 Describe in detail the methods that can be used to prove a part program.

*For additional programming exercises that can be completed by students refer to Appendix C.

PART PROGRAMMING CALCULATIONS

Having read the previous chapters the reader should now be aware that the application of CNC technology to the production of machined parts requires considerable knowledge and ability.

In the first instance there is the practical expertise associated with process planning, work-holding, tooling, and so on. In this respect there is continuity between what was expected of the traditional machine shop craftsman and what is required of the machine shop technician involved with new technology. The advent of CNC has had a considerable effect on the way machining tasks are tackled, but the need for practical expertise remains much the same. Furthermore, this expertise can only be obtained by shop floor experience. It is assumed that students involved with CNC part programming will have acquired, or will be in the process of acquiring, this essential knowledge.

Second, the machine shop technician using modern technology is required to become familiar with the programming languages employed by the control units fitted to the machines he or she will be using. In addition, if computer-aided part programming facilities are to be used, then the technician must also become proficient in the application of these techniques. In the last few years those who have been involved in the education and training of others in the use of CNC technology have found that students, in general, rapidly master the use of programming systems. The most advanced aspect of the technology seems to be the one which is most quickly mastered and applied, but unfortunately its application is often marred by a lack of practical expertise and mathematical ability.

It is the mathematical ability of workshop technicians that is the third area of expertise that has to be considered. Mention was made earlier of the need for the part programmer to be able to carry out calculations associated with speeds and feeds, profile intersection points, arc centers, and so on. Competent manual part programming is not possible without a fairly well-developed mathematical ability and a sound understanding of geometric construction.

The mathematics involved in part programming are essentially practical in nature. It is assumed that readers of this text will have already developed these particular skills, and that they will be capable of carrying out the necessary calculations.

Thus it is not the purpose here to provide a text for the student who wishes to learn mathematical concepts, but rather to provide a means of revising certain areas that are of particular interest to the CNC part programmer, and to supply the student with examples that will develop the ability to deal with the mathematical elements of programming tasks. Reference to the geometry data contained below may be helpful in some cases.

While the following exercises are intended primarily for manual solution, a number of them will serve to introduce the facilities afforded by computer-aided part programming before the student attempts more comprehensive problems.

Geometry Data

The following information is provided for reference purposes.

Pythagoras' Theorem

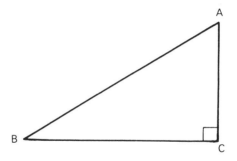

$$AB^2 = AC^2 + BC^2$$
$$AB = \sqrt{AC^2 + BC^2}$$

Similarly,

$$AC = \sqrt{AB^2 - BC^2} \quad \text{and} \quad BC = \sqrt{AB^2 - AC^2}$$

Example Figure 9.1 shows the detail of a milled component that has been dimensioned without regard to part programming needs. Dimension X is required. Using Pythagoras' theorem, calculate its value.

$$D^2 = 50.84^2 + 63.58^2$$
$$D = \sqrt{50.84^2 + 63.58^2}$$
$$= \sqrt{6627.2}$$
$$= 81.41$$
$$X = 81.41 + 10. = 91.41 \text{ mm}$$

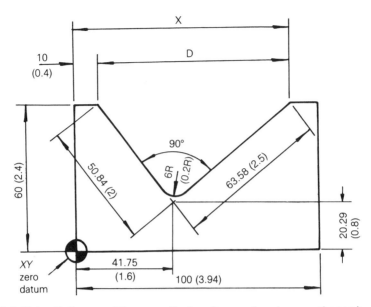

Figure 9.1 Using Pythagoras' theorem. (Inch units are given in parentheses.)

Trigonometrical Ratios

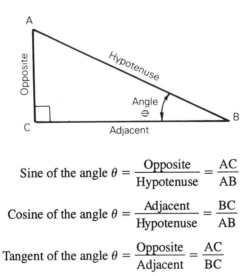

$$\text{Sine of the angle } \theta = \frac{\text{Opposite}}{\text{Hypotenuse}} = \frac{AC}{AB}$$

$$\text{Cosine of the angle } \theta = \frac{\text{Adjacent}}{\text{Hypotenuse}} = \frac{BC}{AB}$$

$$\text{Tangent of the angle } \theta = \frac{\text{Opposite}}{\text{Adjacent}} = \frac{AC}{BC}$$

Example Figure 9.2 shows the part detail of a component that is to be programmed with dimensional values being expressed in incremental mode. Thus the target position B has to be defined in relation to the end of the previous move A. Calculate the dimensions X and Y.

To calculate Y

$$Y = 60. - 30.16 = 29.84 \text{ mm}$$

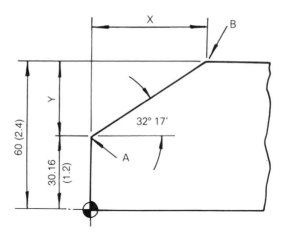

Figure 9.2 Using trigonometrical ratios. (Inch units are given in parentheses.)

To calculate X:

$$\tan 32°17' = \frac{OPP}{ADJ} = \frac{Y}{X}$$

$$X = \frac{Y}{\tan 32°17'}$$

$$= \frac{29.84}{0.6317}$$

$$= 47.23 \text{ mm}$$

The Sine Rule

For use with triangles that are not right-angled.

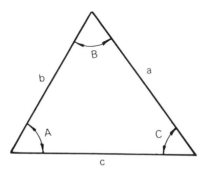

$$\frac{a}{\sin A} = \frac{b}{\sin B} = \frac{c}{\sin C}$$

Example   Figure 9.3 shows a drawing detail of a machined feature. To facilitate part programming, calculate the dimensions X and Y.

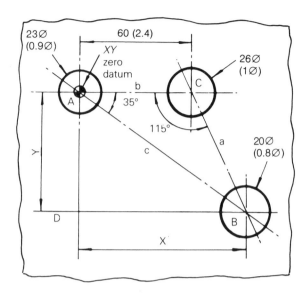

Figure 9.3 Using the sine rule. (Inch units are given in parentheses.)

To calculate the dimensions X and Y it is first necessary to determine $A\hat{B}D$ and the length AB from the information given. Note that AB = c.

$$A\hat{B}D = B\hat{A}C = 35°$$

$$A\hat{C}B = 180 - (115 + 35) = 30°$$

Using the sine rule to calculate AB:

$$\frac{b}{\sin B} = \frac{c}{\sin C}$$

$$\frac{b \times \sin C}{\sin B} = c$$

$$c = \frac{60. \times \sin 115°}{\sin 30°}$$

$$= \frac{60. \times 0.906}{0.5}$$

$$= 108.72$$

To calculate dimensions X and Y using trigonometry:

$$\cos 35° = \frac{ADJ}{HYP} = \frac{X}{AB} \qquad \sin 35° = \frac{OPP}{ADJ} = \frac{Y}{AB}$$

$$\cos 35° \times AB = X \qquad \sin 35° \times AB = Y$$

$$X = 0.819 \times 108.72 \qquad Y = 0.574 \times 108.72$$

$$= 89.042 \text{ mm} \qquad Y = 62.405 \text{ mm}$$

Exercises

1. Figure 9.4 shows details of a turned component dimensioned in a manner that does not accord with the part programmer's wish to locate the prepared billet against the backface of the chuck, this being the Z axis zero for the machine to be used, and to use absolute dimensional definition.

    Make a half profile sketch of the component, and dimension it so that the process of preparing the part program will be simplified.

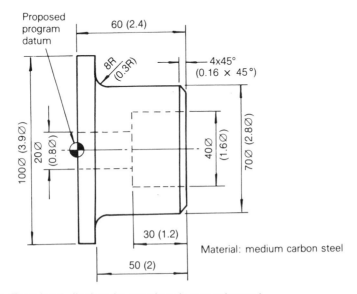

Figure 9.4 Exercise 1. (Inch units are given in parentheses.)

2. Figure 9.5 shows details of a component that is to be milled and drilled on a vertical machining center. The programmer has decided to use the corner of the

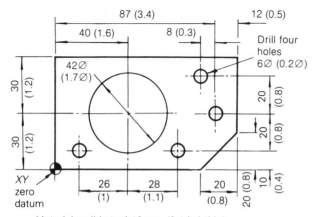

Figure 9.5 Exercise 2. (Inch units are given in parentheses.)

component as the program zero in both the X and Y axes. Make a sketch of the component and dimension it in a manner that will be more convenient from a programming point of view, assuming that the programmer intends to use incremental positioning data.

3. There is no obvious sequence in which to program the drilling of the six holes in the component shown in Figure 9.6. The programmer has initially chosen to adopt the sequence ABCDEF as indicated on the drawing. Since the time taken to actually drill the holes will be the same whatever sequence is used, the only time saving that can be made is by using the shortest possible positioning route.

Using graph paper, draw the component accurately to scale, and check by measuring whether the proposed route is in fact the most efficient. If it proves not to be the shortest possible, state an alternative.

Given that the rapid feedrate for the machine is 2500 mm/min (100 in./min), estimate the total time saving that could be made by using this different positioning route, during a production run of 5000 components.

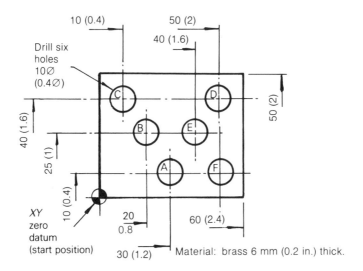

Figure 9.6 Exercise 3. (Inch units are given in parentheses.)

4. Figure 9.7 shows a component having a number of drilled holes. Assume that the starting point for the drilling operation is from a clearance plane 4 mm (0.2 in.) above the work surface and immediately above the XY zero datum indicated.

Accurately redraw the component on graph paper, and by scaling the drawing determine the most economical drilling sequence, taking account of the time taken in positioning.

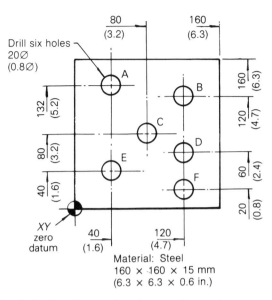

Figure 9.7 Exercise 4. (Inch units are given in parentheses.)

5. The milled impression shown in Figure 9.8 is to be machined on a vertical machining center.

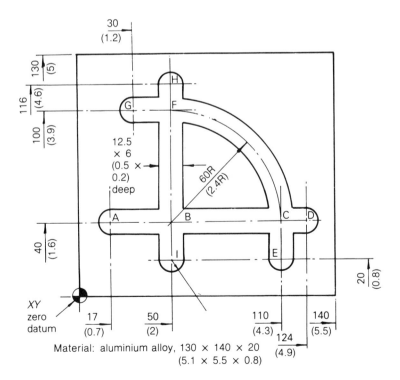

Figure 9.8 Exercise 5. (Inch units are given in parentheses.)

Determine the shortest continuous tool path possible to machine the impression, assuming a start and finish position at zero in the *X* and *Y* axes. (Ignore movement in the *Z* axis as this is likely to be identical regardless of the route chosen in the *X* and *Y* axes.)

Calculate the time taken to complete the operation given that the rapid traverse rate for the machine is 4000 mm/min (158 in./min), the feed rate for the metal cutting operation is 0.3 mm/rev (0.01 in./rev), the spindle speed is 3000 rev/min and the *Z* up position is 200 mm (8 in.) from the *Z* axis zero which is set at the top face of the work. Assume the tool change position is immediately above the *XY* axes zero. Normal *Z* axis clearance is 0.1 inch or 2 mm above the part face.

6. Assume that the feature shown in Figure 9.9, the machining of which involves a certain amount of stock removal prior to a finishing pass along the profile, is to be produced on a machine with a control system which does not possess a suitable canned cycle. Thus the programmer has no alternative but to determine, manually, the most efficient way of clearing the step. He or she may choose to program a series of cuts, with a small amount of cutter overlap to ensure a clean face, with the bulk of the stock being removed as the cutter travels along the *X* axis or, alternatively, along the *Y* axis.

Reproduce the pocket accurately to scale on graph paper and determine which, if any, of the two cutting directions would remove the stock in the shortest time. Assume a cutter diameter of 12 mm (0.5 in.).

Express the movements required to remove the stock in terms of *X* and *Y* values, which could be incorporated as data in a part program.

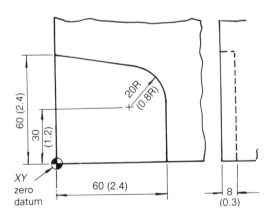

Figure 9.9 Exercise 6. (Inch units are given in parentheses.)

7. On a piece of graph paper, accurately reproduce the component shown in Figure 9.10 to a scale of twice full size and indicate on the drawing a series of roughing cuts, each having a depth of 4 mm (0.2 in.), that would reduce the bar sufficiently to leave approximately 1 mm (0.03 in.) along the profile for the final finishing cut.

Express the roughing cuts in terms of *X* and *Z*, that would enable them to be incorporated in the part program.

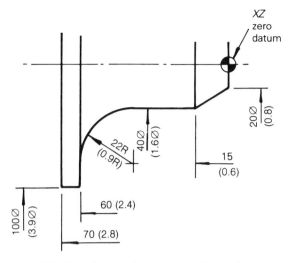

Figure 9.10 Exercise 7. (Inch units are given in parentheses.)

8. The angular feature of the component shown in Figure 9.11 is to be machined on a CNC-controlled machine, the control system of which does not include the cutter radius compensation facility. Calculate the incremental linear moves that will need to be included in the part program, assuming movement starts from and returns to the indicated datum. The diameter of the cutter to be used is 50 mm (2 in.), and there is to be approach and overrun distances of 4 mm (0.2 in.) as indicated.

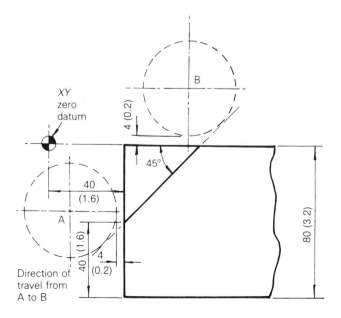

Figure 9.11 Exercise 8. (Inch units are given in parentheses.)

9. Calculate the incremental linear movements in the X and Z axes that will be required to finish machine the taper shown in Figure 9.12.

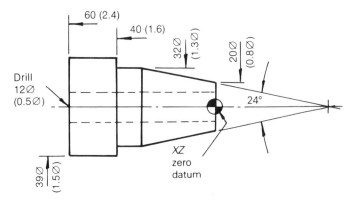

Figure 9.12 Exercise 9. (Inch units are given in parentheses.)

10. Figure 9.13 shows a feature of a turned component. Two of the dimensions necessary to complete a part program are not given.
    Determine which dimensions are missing and calculate their values.

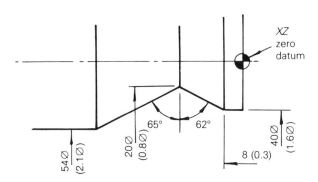

Figure 9.13 Exercise 10. (Inch units are given in parentheses.)

11. Figure 9.14 shows a feature of a component, namely, two parallel slots positioned at an angle of 52° to the X axis. The programmer intends to specify the numerical data for the required slide movements in absolute terms from the XY zero datum indicated on the drawing. To do this a number of calculations will have to be made and the drawing must be redimensioned.
    Carry out the necessary calculations and produce a second drawing of the component dimensioned in a manner that will be more appropriate.

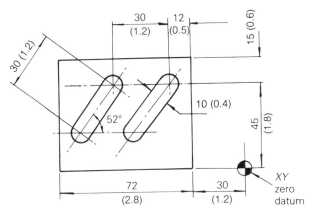

Figure 9.14 Exercise 11. (Inch units are given in parentheses.)

12. The component shown in Figure 9.15 is to have two holes drilled in the positions indicated. The programmer has opted to program slide movements in absolute mode from the *XY* zero datum. In order to program in this way it will be necessary to calculate the linear coordinates for one of the holes.

   Sketch the component, carry out the required calculations, and dimension your drawing accordingly.

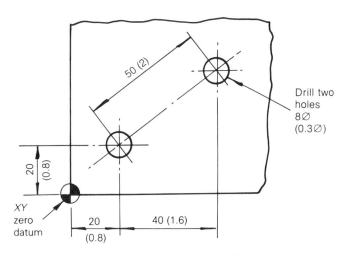

Figure 9.15 Exercise 12. (Inch units are given in parentheses.)

13. Calculate and list in programmable form the absolute coordinate dimensions in the *XY* axes necessary to drill the four holes shown in Figure 9.16 in the sequence ABCD, starting and returning to the program datum. Assume that a drill cycle controlling the depth to be drilled is already operative, and may be cancelled by programming G80.

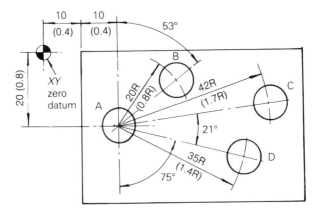

Figure 9.16 Exercise 13. (Inch units are given in parentheses.)

14. Figure 9.17(a) shows the position of three holes dimensioned in such a way that is not particularly helpful to the person preparing a part program, since the

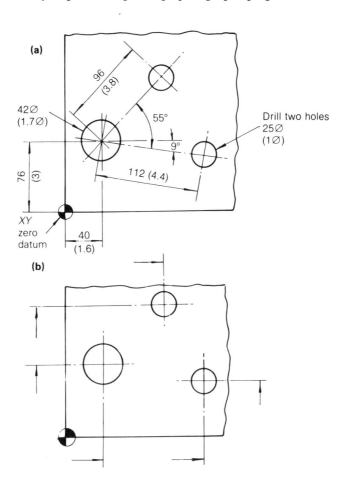

Figure 9.17 Exercise 14. (Inch units are given in parentheses.)

facility to program polar coordinates is not available. The preferred method of dimensioning is indicated in Figure 9.17(b). From the information provided, calculate the missing dimensions.

15. The four holes shown in Figure 9.18 are to be drilled in the sequence ABCD with the necessary slide movements expressed in absolute terms. Assuming a *Z* up travel of 200 mm (8 in.) immediately above the program datum to accommodate a manual tool change, and that a G81 drill cycle (cancelled by a programmed G80) is available, carry out the following:

   From the data stated on the drawing determine the dimensional value of the required slide movements.
   List the data, in word address format, that would be required to complete the machining, assuming that all speeds, feeds etc. are already operative.

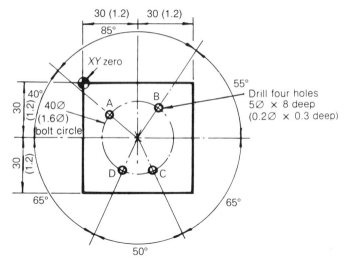

Figure 9.18 Exercise 15. (Inch units are given in parentheses.)

16. Eight holes are to be drilled on a bolt circle diameter as shown in Figure 9.19. The holes are to be drilled in the sequence A to H immediately after the central hole has been drilled. Taking the position of the central hole as the zero datum in both the *X* and *Y* axes carry out the following:

   Calculate the dimensional value of the required slide movements, to facilitate programming in incremental mode.
   List the data as they would be presented in a word address program, assuming a *Z* datum clearance of 2 mm (0.1 in.) and an excess travel of 5 mm (0.2 in.) on breakthrough. Assume that a spindle speed and feed rate have already been programmed and that a G81 drilling cycle is to be used.

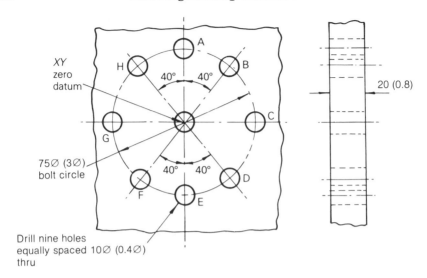

Figure 9.19 Exercise 16. (Inch units are given in parentheses.)

17. The positions of three holes are given on a drawing as shown in Figure 9.20. The holes are to be drilled in the sequence ABC and the previous program data have brought the machine spindle into vertical alignment with hole A. Calculate the linear values of the incremental moves to be included in the part program to control slide movement in the X and Y axes.

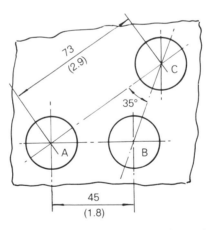

Figure 9.20 Exercise 17. (Inch units are given in parentheses.)

18. Complete the program data given below (for metric values only) for achieving relative cutter movement from P1 to P2 on the profile illustrated in Figure 9.21. The circular arcs are to be programmed by defining the target positions using X and Y values, and the arc centers are defined in relation to the starting point of the arc using I and J values.

N60 G01 Y–25
N70 G03
N80 G01 X20
N90
N100 G02
N110 G01 X10
N120
N130 G03
N140 G01

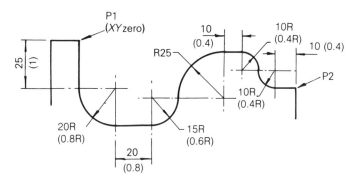

Figure 9.21 Exercise 18. (Inch units are given in parentheses.)

19. The turned component shown in Figure 9.22 is to be produced on a turning
center where arc centers are defined in relation to the program datum using the
address letters I and K. Complete the program block below in incremental
terms (in metric units only):

N 025 G02 X– – Z– – I– – K– –

Repeat the above exercise with the data expressed in absolute terms.

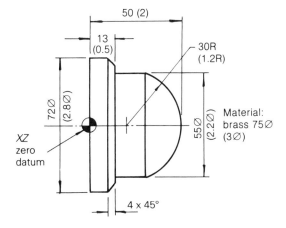

Figure 9.22 Exercise 19. (Inch units are given in parentheses.)

20. The concave arc of the turned component shown in Figure 9.23 is to be produced on a lathe where the control system will simply require a data input stating the radius of the arc, the direction of rotation, and the target position defined by X and Z values. Assume that the 8 mm (0.3 in.) diameter hole has already been drilled, and that the curve is to be produced by making a cutting pass starting from the center of the component and working outward. Complete the data necessary to machine the feature, with the tool starting and finishing in the positions indicated. Assume that a suitable cutting speed and feed rate, and also cutter radius compensation, are already active.

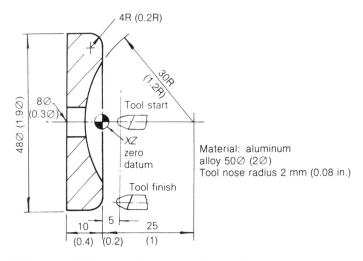

Figure 9.23 Exercise 20. (Inch units are given in parentheses.)

21. A cutout of 30 mm (1.2 in.) radius is to be machined in a 40 mm (1.6 in.) diameter disk as shown in Figure 9.24. The cutter start and finish positions giving a suitable approach and runout are indicated. Assume that cutter radius

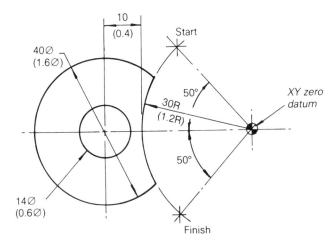

Figure 9.24 Exercise 21. (Inch units are given in parentheses.)

compensation mode will be operative and that the circular interpolation will involve two separate data blocks, one for each quadrant. Determine the two data blocks that will be required, defining the arc start point in relation to the center using I and J values. Express the positional data in absolute terms.

22. Figure 9.25 shows a radial slot that is to be machined using a relative cutter movement from the start point to the finish point as indicated.

    Calculate the target position in relation to the indicated program datum.

    If the start position is to be defined in relation to the arc center using I and J definition, state their numerical values.

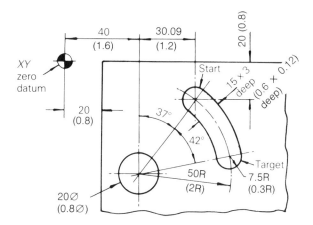

Figure 9.25 Exercise 22. (Inch units are given in parentheses.)

23. The two radial slots shown in Figure 9.26 are to be produced on a vertical machining center, with the starting points as indicated and the relative cutter

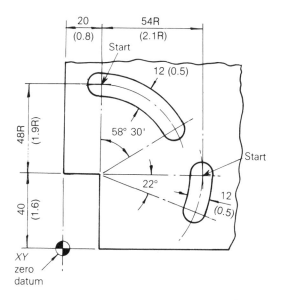

Figure 9.26 Exercise 23. (Inch units are given in parentheses.)

movement being in a clockwise direction. The control system requires arc centers to be defined in relation to the arc starting point.

Determine the additional dimensional data, in absolute terms, that will be necessary for programming purposes in order to machine the slots.

24. The turned component in Figure 9.27 is to be produced on a machine fitted with a control system that requires the circular interpolation data entries to be programmed as follows:

   (a) The target position using X and Z numerical values.
   (b) The arc center in relation to the program datum using I and K numerical values.

   Assuming that the program is to be compiled using absolute dimensions, complete the following N125 G02 X– – Z– – I– – K– – program entry for machining the arc.

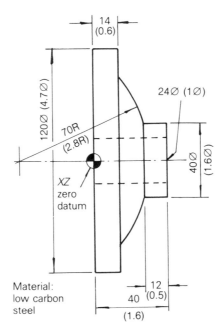

Figure 9.27 Exercise 24. (Inch units are given in parentheses.)

25. Figure 9.28(a) gives the details of part of a turned component. Figure 9.28(b) shows the same feature but with an indication of the dimensioning method that would be more appropriate since the machine to be used does not cater to multiquadrant programming.

   Calculate the alternative dimensions required and make a redimensioned sketch of the component feature.

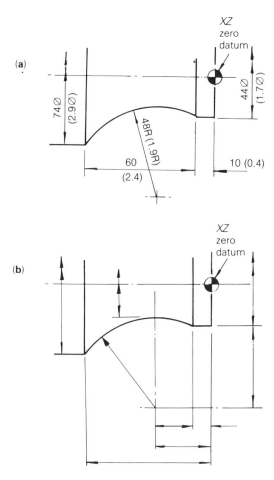

Figure 9.28 Exercise 25. (Inch units are given in parentheses.)

26. Figure 9.29 shows part of the profile of a milled component. The profile consists of four blending arcs of varying dimensions. In order to program the necessary circular moves the programmer will need to know the exact points at which the curves intersect with each other.

   Construct accurately on graph paper the given profile and locate on your drawing the points of intersection.

   Calculate and define numerically each intersection point.

   Given the following programming information, list the program data necessary to achieve a cutter path that would machine the profile, commencing with linear movement from the *XY* zero datum and ending at point B.

   Programming information:

G01   Linear interpolation, programmed feed rate.
G02   Circular interpolation, clockwise.
G03   Circular interpolation, counterclockwise.

Define all target positions incrementally and the arc centers in relation to the arc starting points using I and J values. Assume spindle control data, feed rates, etc., have already been programmed and that cutter radius compensation is active.

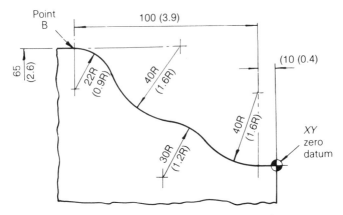

Figure 9.29 Exercise 26. (Inch units are given in parentheses.)

27. The milled profile shown in Figure 9.30 is to be produced on a machine with a control system that requires numerical definition of the target positions of all slide movements using the address letters X and Y, and arc centers to be defined in relation to the start of the arc using address letters I and J. Also, the system is not capable of multiquadrant programming, so movement in each quadrant must be programmed separately even when the same radius passes from one quadrant into a second.

Accurately construct the profile and indicate in absolute terms in relation to the program zero all intersection points and also arc start positions in relation to the arc centers.

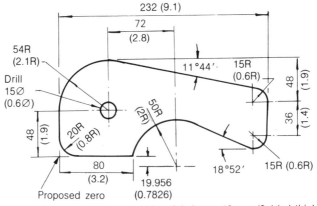

Material: brass 10 mm (0.4 in.) thick

Figure 9.30 Exercise 27. (Inch units are given in parentheses.)

28. The internal profile of the component shown in Figure 9.31 is to be produced on a vertical machining center. Calculate and indicate on an appropriate sketch the additional dimensions that will be required to define the profile intersection points.

State which common programming facility would be suited to facilitate machining the profile.

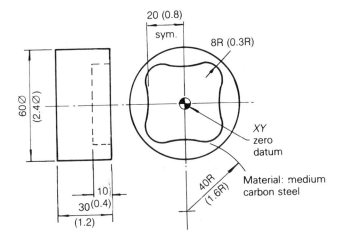

Figure 9.31 Exercise 28. (Inch units are given in parentheses.)

29. Figure 9.32 shows details of a milled component.

Draw the raised profile accurately to size and indicate on your drawing the arc centers and the intersecting points of the profile.

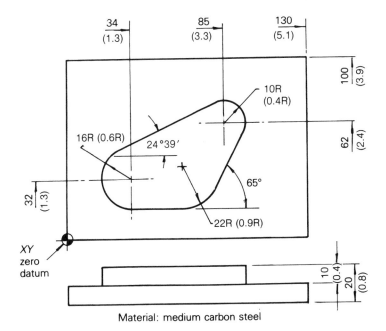

Material: medium carbon steel

Figure 9.32 Exercise 29. (Inch units are given in parentheses.)

Calculate all the profile intersecting points required to complete a part program and dimension your drawing accordingly. Assume that arcs can only be programmed for one quadrant in any one block, with the arc centers being specified in relation to the program zero using I and J values.

Refer to the cutting speeds and feeds given in the Appendices for appropriate data to complete the following questions.

30. Calculate a suitable spindle speed for drilling 6 mm (0.2 in.) diameter holes in a medium carbon steel using a high speed steel drill.
31. Determine a suitable spindle speed for face cutting T6 aluminum using a shell end mill of 40 mm (1.6 in.) diameter with cemented carbide insert teeth.
32. What increase in spindle speed would be appropriate if, when drilling a low carbon steel, a 20 mm (0.8 in.) diameter high speed steel drill is replaced with another having cemented carbide brazed tips?
33. Select a suitable cutting speed for turning a complex profile from brass using a cemented carbide insert turning tool. Given that the component is of variable diameter along its length, why would it be preferable to program a constant surface cutting speed rather than a set spindle speed?
34. Calculate the spindle speed to be used when milling grey cast iron using a 20 mm (0.8 in.) diameter cemented carbide insert end mill. If the speed calculated eventually proved to be too high, what action should be taken by the machine operator to rectify the situation?
35. Calculate suitable spindle speeds for roughing and finishing cuts when turning T6 aluminum, using cemented carbide tooling on a component having a nominal diameter of 38 mm (1.5 in.).
36. Select a suitable feedrate in mm/rev for turning medium carbon steel, using cemented carbide insert tooling.
37. Calculate a suitable feedrate in mm/min or in./min for a light turning operation on a stainless steel component having a diameter of 75 mm (3 in.), and when using cemented carbide tooling.
38. Given that an appropriate feedrate per tooth for face milling a low carbon steel is 0.3 mm (0.01 in.) per tooth when using cemented carbide tooling, what would be a suitable program entry in mm/min or in./min when using a 75 mm (3 in.) diameter cutter having six teeth.
39. The profile shown in Figure 9.33 is of part of a component that is to be machined from brass. The feed rate is to be programmed in mm/rev (in./rev)

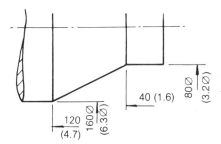

Figure 9.33 Exercise 39. (Inch units are given in parentheses.)

and the spindle speed controlled by programming a constant surface cutting speed in m/min (ft/min).

Select appropriate values for cutting speed and feed to be included in the part program, when using cemented carbide insert tooling.

Using the above combination of data, would the resulting surface finish be identical for both the parallel surfaces and the taper? If not, and assuming that a variation is not acceptable, how could the program be modified?

40. A face milling operation on aluminum alloy is to be carried out using a nine-cartridge cutter of 100 mm (4 in.) diameter and having cemented carbide inserts. Determine a suitable spindle speed and feed rate in mm/rev (in./rev) for inclusion in the part program.

Chapter 10

COMPUTER-AIDED PART PROGRAMMING

The Application and Advantages of Computer-Aided Part Programming

When NC, as opposed to CNC, was first introduced, the only way a curve could be produced was by approximation, making a series of angular moves using slide movements in two axes that, when blended together, approximated to the curve required. The larger the number of small angular movements made, the more precise the final curve.

On the face of it this would appear to be a very reasonable solution to the problem of producing a curve until the work involved in making the necessary calculations is considered, not to mention the mathematical ability required. It was the sort of situation where a little computer help with the calculations was much appreciated. The more complex the profile—imagine an elliptical path, for instance—the more essential computer help became.

Today, thanks to the inclusion of a microcomputer as an integral part of even the most basic CNC control systems, the programming of a constant radius curve is a very simple matter indeed, often requiring nothing more than dimensional definition of the target position and the value of the radius. Even the more complex elliptical profiles can be programmed on some control systems simply by defining the major and minor axes.

The reader will recall that the programming of radial cutter paths is referred to as "circular interpolation," while the facility used to program an elliptical profile is known as a special canned or program cycle.

There is a wide variety of canned cycles currently available with modern machine controllers. A number of these were described in Chapter 8. All of these canned cycles were designed and included in the control system with one objective in mind, that is, to simplify programming.

Canned cycles cater to sequences that are likely to recur regularly. But not all complex profiles regularly recur and when such a profile does occur, it can present problems as difficult, and possibly more so, as the problems associated with curves in the early days of NC.

In particular, the machining of complex profiles, or rather the preparation of the part program to achieve the machining, means that fairly complex calculations have to be performed to determine the geometry intersection points. There is also the problem of determining efficient cutter paths to remove stock, and that can also be a laborious business.

It is to meet these requirements that special computer-based programming systems have been developed. The process of using these systems is referred to as Computer-Aided Part Programming, generally referred to as CAPP or more commonly Computer Aided Machining (CAM). (Note: the initials CAPP are also used in production engineering to denote Computer-Aided Process Planning, which is concerned with the total organization of a production operation of which Computer-Aided Part Programming may be an included activity.) (CAM is the more widely used term in use today so it will be used throughout the remainder of the text.)

CAM provides for a simpler, quicker, and more accurate approach to preparing a CNC part program. But at the same time it represents a considerable capital outlay that has to be justified by an eventual increase in efficiency and productivity.

The CAM process involves preparing a program using a specially developed language or graphical means, entering the resulting data into a computer and receiving back from the computer a program presented in a format acceptable to the machine controller. During the process the computer will have processed the data to verify their validity and, where necessary, performed computing tasks (many that would have been mathematically difficult and/or time-consuming if attempted manually), and then processed the results into machine language.

CAM can, in the hands of experienced users, provide rapid programming solutions for the most difficult of work. Even for very simple work, where manually prepared programs could be produced fairly quickly, the use of CAM is still a viable proposition.

A trend among engineering contractors on small parts is to ask the potential customer for a drawing or electronic data file of the component to be produced and then quickly program, using CAM, and manufacture a component. The result is then returned to the customer with the quotation, indicating very effectively the speed and quality of the service they offer. At the same time the contractor is able to cost the contract precisely, since it will be known exactly how long it took to machine the sample. This process is normally referred to as a customer bench mark.

A further advantage of CAM is that the program is prepared and initially proven "off-line," that is, away from the machine. Data transfer electronically to the machine is available and rapid so there is no delay in getting a machine back into production following job changes.

Computer Installations

CAM systems are available for use on all types of computer installations from mainframe to personal computers.

The large mainframe computers possess the greatest computing power and their use is indispensable for very complex programming requirements. Unfortunately they are extremely costly and their installation is only economically viable in large organizations where the computing needs—not only for CAM but for a whole range of industrial and commercial activities—are considerable.

A mainframe computer will cater to a large number of networked work-stations or terminals that, provided the distance between the two is not excessive, can be permanently cable-linked. Where the distance is considerable, they can be linked via telephone modem, fiber optic cable, satellite or micro wave dish devices. This also makes it possible to cross international frontiers and even link continents for transfer of data.

Small industrial and commercial organizations can gain access to a mainframe computer, and the required software, on a "time-share" basis. The computer, which may be many miles distant, is accessed via the public telephone network. The facility is available to numerous subscribers and each pays for the actual computing time used; but to this cost it is necessary to add the normal telephone charges which can be considerable.

Subscription to such a system also provides access to a range of back-up services such as the use of the latest software and professional advice regarding its application. Help is also available to solve problems encountered when using the system generally.

In addition, time-share subscribers do not have to concern themselves with maintenance or servicing of the system, as is the case with an in-house installation when a service contract with the manufacturer or supplier would be another costly but essential requirement.

One drawback to time-sharing, assuming that the financial considerations are acceptable, is that access to the computer may not always be conveniently available because too many subscribers are trying to "log on," or connect into the system, at any one time. Another is that the data security may be inadequate if the work concerned is of a sensitive nature.

Many organizations have requirements that do not justify the installation of a mainframe, but at the same time could not be satisfactorily allowed for by time-sharing. They often install their own large to medium-sized systems. The available capacity and computing power will be less extensive than that available from a mainframe computer, but still capable of servicing a very large organization.

A feature of these installations is the permanent linking of work stations, or terminals, to the host computer. When terminals are linked in this way, they are said to be "networked." By this means the complete system may become fully interactive, making it possible for data to be originated and accessed by a number of users. It may be possible for a programmer to utilize data originated by a designer, thus providing a link between design and manufacture, referred to as CAD/CAM (Computer-Aided Design/Computer-Aided Manufacturing), which will be presented subsequently. There may also be direct connections to the machine tools on the shop floor, a facility referred to as Direct Numerical Control (DNC).

A variation of this approach is to transfer the completed part program to a temporary data storage facility on the shop floor, which is situated alongside and connected to the machine that is to manufacture the part. The production controller can download the data into the machine control unit as and when required. Programs can also be downloaded from the machine into the storage unit. With the advent of embedded personal computers as machine controllers this storage of programs may take place internal to the shop floor controller. The computer systems can also be configured to deliver program data to floppy disk, zip disk or CD units.

The networking of user terminals described above is also available on even smaller computer installations, but the number of terminals and, of course, the computing power available is proportionally reduced. However, a "mini", "supermini" computer or engineering work station, small enough to fit under a desk, is still capable of handling a comprehensive 3D CAD/CAM system, providing control of both the design and manufacturing elements of engineering and often including other functions such as costing, invoicing, etc.

Finally, there are the installations involving personal computers. Stand-alone CAM systems that operate on personal computers (PC) are now capable of handling very complex programming requirements and are widely used. This type of installation is relatively inexpensive, which makes their installation by smaller companies a feasible proposition.

PC based systems can be networked and linked to peripheral equipment such as printers, storage, and file transfer devices. Provided the distance is not too great, they can also be cable-linked to machine tools.

Because of restrictions on expenditure, most educational establishments have found it necessary to install PC based CAM systems, and it is this type of installation which students are most likely to use when first being introduced to computer-aided part programming.

Figure 10.1 shows a general arrangement of a CAM work station utilizing a microcomputer.

It is possible that a company may not become involved in any of the arrangements outlined above, since there are many consulting offices that offer a program preparation and proving service. The use of a consultant can sometimes be attractive to companies that do not have sufficient programming work to sustain a part programmer working full time, and which may prefer to retain a lower, and therefore less expensive, level of skill on the shop floor. Even when the skill levels on the shop floor are such that part programming could satisfactorily be undertaken, the use of a consultant, providing an already proved program, means that no time is lost between ending one production run and beginning the next.

Figure 10.1 General arrangement of a CAM work station.

The staff of programming consultant offices will work in close cooperation with the client company, so that the machining is processed in a way acceptable to all concerned. In some cases they also offer supporting services associated with the selection of tooling and the design of special work-holding arrangements if required.

Hardware Configurations

Whatever the computer installation used, it is possible to establish, in a general way, the hardware configurations associated with CAM.

The diagram 10.2 shows a very basic computer-aided part programming system: a computer, a data recording facility in the form of a floppy disk drive, a data transfer facility in the form of a controller disk drive attached to the machine tool, and the machine tool itself.

In Figure 10.3 this basic arrangement is extended and includes, instead of the floppy and controller disk drives, a direct cable link to the machine tool, which is a much quicker and more convenient method of transferring data. When the computer and machine are linked by cable, the arrangement is referred to as Direct Numerical Control (DNC).

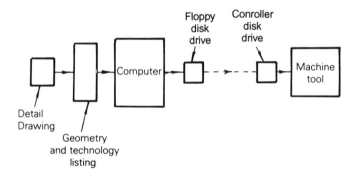

Figure 10.2 Basic CAM system.

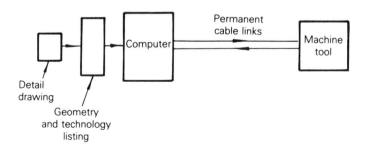

Figure 10.3 Simple direct numerical control.

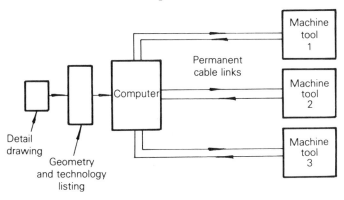

Figure 10.4 Direct numerical control of a machine group.

Figure 10.4 shows the concept extended still further, this time to include cable links to a number of machine tools which may be of different types. These machines may be arranged in a particular way, possibly associated with robot work-handling devices, to form a machining cell.

Taking an even broader view, there may even be a number of programming stations and a number of machines, or machining cells, all linked to the same computer. In this situation the part programming function could be but a small element of a totally integrated computer-controlled manufacturing environment including design, marketing, accounting, materials handling, personnel control, and so on. Complex systems such as this are referred to as Computer Integrated Manufacturing, CIM. Of course, the greater the demands on the system the more extensive will be the required computing and data storage facilities.

From the foregoing the reader will appreciate that it is possible for the CAM system with which he or she is concerned to be a relatively simple stand-alone system, the purpose of which is solely to produce CNC part-programs for a particular machine or a limited number of machines, or it may be an integral part of a much more complex installation.

Even if the overall computing arrangement is complex, it is still possible to consider the CAM element in isolation and return to the basic objective: preparing a part program with computer assistance and then transferring the resulting data to the machine tool. The main elements in this process are shown in Figure 10.5. Also indicated is the range of peripheral equipment that can be used to support the activity.

The CAM system available for use by the reader may include all or only some of the items indicated. Systems are structured according to the funds available at the time of purchase, and limited finance can have a restricting effect.

However, it is essential that a part programmer is fully conversant with any system he or she is going to use. Time spent in getting to understand the system before making any attempt to prepare a part program is time well spent, since it can do much to eliminate the time-consuming and often frustrating need to ask for help every time an unfamiliar feature of the system is encountered.

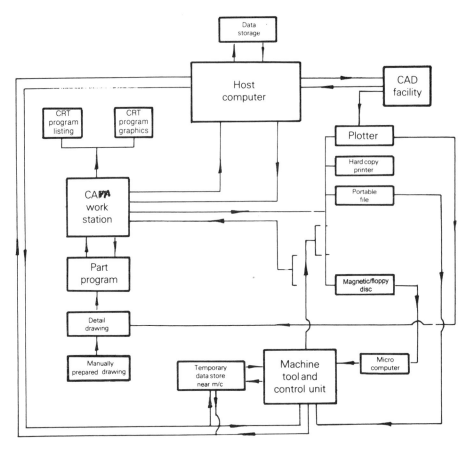

Figure 10.5 CAM station incorporated in a system.

Input and Control Devices

There are a number of ways by which data can be entered into a computer during the CAM process.

Input via the familiar alphanumeric keyboard is laborious and rather slow. But since many of the data entries associated with CAM are repetitive, it is possible to speed up the process by using various supplementary devices and techniques.

Selection from a menu, that is, a list of options, is one such facility. The menu may be included as an overlay on a digitizing tablet or be displayed on the CRT screen.

A digitizing tablet (Figure 10.6(a)) is a device like a small rectangular board that is positioned alongside the computer keyboard and is cable-linked to the computer. The tablet is capable of detecting the position of a puck, light pen, or stylus when any of these devices is placed on it.

An overlay is like a plan that divides the surface of the tablet into a number of small areas. Each area is allocated to a specific function such as representing an item from the menu.

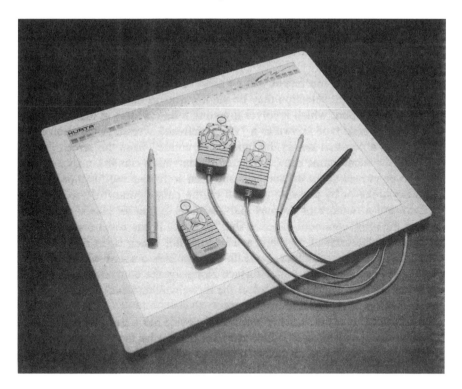

Figure 10.6(a) Digitizing tablet. (Photograph of IS/ONE courtesy of Kurta Corp., 3007 E. Chambers, Phoenix, AZ 85040.)

A puck is a device with cross-hairs mounted in a small block. It is traversed by hand over the tablet until the cross-hairs are located over the function to be selected. The selection is then confirmed either by an appropriate keystroke or by pressing a button on the puck as you would with a PC mouse. A light pen or stylus is rather like a pen. It is used to identify the menu item required and the choice is then activated by pushing a button or applying slight pressure to the tablet or CRT screen position.

A digitizing tablet is a feature of the programming station illustrated in Figure 10.1, which also shows the puck used for menu selection.

Screen menus can either occupy a complete CRT screen, in which case the graphic image which is an important feature of the CAM process is temporarily lost, or it can occupy part of the screen so that the graphic image is retained. On small CRTs, the second arrangement can mean that the graphic display is rather cramped. A hardware configuration that will eliminate the disadvantages inherent in both arrangements is to have a two-screen display, one for the menu and program listing and one for the graphic display, but this does add to the cost of the installation.

Selection from screen menus can be achieved in several ways. If the menu items are numbered, selection may be via a keyboard input. A second method is to use a light pen, which involves directing a light source at the CRT screen that is of a special type known as a "vector refresh" screen. A variation of this approach is a pen that senses the light being emitted from the screen itself.

Third, the menu items can be selected by moving a cursor—a spot or cross that can be moved about the screen—and then activating the function by making a keystroke or by pressing a button on the cursor control device (mouse).

There are a number of devices that are used to control cursor movement. One of the most commonly used is the "mouse." It has some resemblance to a real mouse because of its shape and its long tail which is, in fact, the cable connecting it to the computer. Beneath the mouse is a set of wheels/balls; as the mouse is moved about a flat surface alongside the computer—a table top, for instance—the wheels/balls detect the movement and cause the screen cursor to make a corresponding movement.

Another device is the "tracker ball." This device has a partially exposed ball mounted in a small box. The ball is rolled around by the palm of the hand. The movement of the ball is detected and, as with the mouse, a corresponding cursor movement appears on the screen.

A third method of cursor control is by the use of a "joystick." As this is moved around in all directions, the screen cursor moves in unison. A joystick is shown in the illustration of the CAM work station in Figure 10.6(b).

It is possible that an area of a digitizing tablet can be allocated to represent the CRT screen. The stylus or the puck referred to earlier can then be used to pass over the screen area and effect a corresponding movement on the screen.

Figure 10.6(b) Part programming station showing use of computer graphics for program proving.

Apart from menu selection, a cursor is also used within the CAM process to identify geometric elements such as points, lines and circles that have been constructed on the screen. For example, to construct a line at 90° to a base line will first need a menu selection to identify the type of construction required, followed by identification of the point on the base line at which the second line is to be constructed. The cursor will be moved to identify the point, and the function activated by making a keystroke or pressing a button on the cursor control device. Similarly, a line may need to be deleted, in which case it is first identified by positioning the cursor and then removed by making a keystroke or by pressing a delete button on the cursor control.

The foregoing description has, of necessity, been general in nature. Cursor controllers, even of one particular type, are very variable in design. The way in which cursors are used varies from one CAM system to another. The essential thing to appreciate is that a part programmer is not required to be familiar with all the possibilities; nevertheless, it will be necessary to become competent in the application of the particular devices associated with the program system he or she will be using, and this can only be achieved by using the equipment.

Computer-Assisted Programming Activities

In Chapter 8 the procedure for manual part programming, taking the detail drawing as a starting point, was listed. That list is reproduced below, but this time the programming activities that will be assisted by the use of CAM are shown in bold type.

1. Select a machine capable of handling the required work.
2. Prepare a schedule of machining operations.
3. Determine work holding and location techniques.
4. Determine tooling requirements and their identity.
5. Document, or otherwise record, instructions relating to work holding, work location, and tooling.
6. **Calculate suitable cutting speeds and feedrates.**
7. **Calculate profile intersecting points, arc centers, etc.**
8. **Determine appropriate tool paths including the use of canned cycles and subroutines.**
9. **Prepare the part program.**
10. **Prove the part program and edit as necessary.**
11. **Record the part program for future use.**

Before proceeding further it is necessary to make the point that the more practical elements of the list, that is, those numbered from 1 to 5, are as necessary for CAM as they are for manual part programming. CAM does not eliminate the need for the programmer to have a good working knowledge in the practicalities of metal cutting. The reader is referred to the fuller consideration given to these aspects of CNC machining which is included in previous chapters.

To return to the CAM process. It will be assumed that consideration has been duly given to the practicalities of a particular machining task, and the computer-aided element of preparing the part program can begin.

It is not possible to list precisely the stages in the CAM process since there is some variation in approach according to the type of system being used. But in general terms the stages may be itemized as follows:

1. Define the geometric detail of the component. This will involve a series of individually constructed elements or the loading of an electronic file that embraces the final component detail.
2. Use the geometric detail to define appropriate machining sequences.
3. Supplement the proposed machining sequences with technology data relating to tooling, feedrates, spindle speeds, etc.
4. Process these data to determine tool paths and to produce a cutter location data file.
5. Produce a CRT screen or paper tool path plot for initial program prove out.
6. Postprocess these data into a form or language that is acceptable to the machine to be used.
7. Transmit these data direct to the machine tool. Alternatively, a floppy disc or electronic file for transfer will be produced, or the program otherwise electronically stored for future use.

CAM Systems

Before a CAM system can be used to prepare a program, time will have to be spent in becoming familiar with the techniques or language/program to be used—just as it is necessary to study the language of a machine control system before programs for a particular machine can be prepared manually. But the use of CAM does have a major advantage in this respect: it is probable that the programmer will be required to become familiar with only one technique, since it is possible to postprocess or translate the data into whatever machine control language is to be used.

It is not possible in a text of this nature to give a comprehensive review of every CAM system, since there are far too many currently in use. Neither would it be of value to consider a particular system in detail. Later in the text, however, programming examples are included in an attempt to give at least a general impression of some of the variations that exist. To start examples will be given in the Compact II language by Manufacturing Data Systems Incorporated and APT (Automatically Programmed Tools). Compact II and APT were selected as examples for their leading roles in the development of CAM and their major influences in CAD/CAM evolution.

In reality, a part programmer will find it necessary to devote as much time as possible to becoming proficient in the application of the particular system he or she will be required to use. Some of the techniques and skills developed in the use of one system are likely to be transferable to another if the need arises.

Although the number of CAM systems available are many and varied they may be generally defined as being either language or graphics based. The basic difference between the two concepts is the way in which the appropriate tool paths for the machining sequences are ascertained. The following text deals with language-based programming. Graphics-based programming will be discussed further later in the chapter.

Language-Based Systems

Early CAM systems were entirely language-based, the geometry of the part being described by a series of statements constructed from letters of the alphabet, numbers, and a few other symbols. The systems were not interactive, there was no indication if errors had been made in the data, and therefore no correction was possible during the computer input process. Confirmation of the validity of data could only be ascertained by processing it. If necessary, the program could then be edited. The only visual confirmation of the program data was via a diagram produced on an interfaced pen plotter after the data entry was completed.

As language-based CAM systems improved alphanumeric input was supplemented by certain symbols, but were considerably improved by the incorporation of computer graphics. As data are entered, there is an instant corresponding graphic display giving an indication of the validity of the input. The systems are fully interactive: if data are not acceptable, the fact will be indicated, often with messages to indicate why this is so, and the programmer can then act on this information and modify the input as programming proceeds.

Having defined the component by the use of a series of geometric statements, the programmer then selects elements from the overall construction and includes these in what is, in effect, a composite statement that will form the basis of a particular machining operation. The composite statement, which may represent, for example, a profile or a series of holes, will be expressed in language form.

The composite statements are now supplemented by data relating to speeds and feeds, tooling, etc. These are referred to as tool change data statements, and will be discussed further.

At this stage these data are processed to determine tool paths and to generate a cutter location data file, referred to as CL Data. Finally, the data are postprocessed to generate a program in machine tool code for the particular machine to be used. Each of these stages is explained further in the following text.

Geometric Definition

It is assumed that a person making a study of CAM will already be familiar with manual part programming techniques, and will therefore appreciate that any machined feature or profile can be geometrically defined. He or she will already be familiar with defining tool movements in relation to the workpiece as being linear, circular, and point-to-point. An appreciation of how one geometric feature can intersect with another and the need to define dimensionally such intersection points should also be well understood.

In manual part programming the profile is, in effect, split up into its geometric elements. This is also the case with CAM, in which the shape or feature to be machined is expressed in terms of directions, distances, lines, points, and circles.

The way in which these geometric elements are generally defined when using CAM systems is listed below. The lists should not be considered to be definitive since the approach to geometric construction differs between programming systems, and there are also variations in the words used to describe what is essentially the same feature. A further complication is that some of the definitions used, while perfectly logical and therefore acceptable when applied to geometric construction involving computer graphics, do not conform to true mathematical expression. However, the reader is assured that the descriptions that follow are typical of those likely to be encountered.

Directions are defined in the usual way, that is by the use of the letters X, Y and Z which relate to the axes of movement of the machine tools. Distances are given a dimensional value in millimeters or inches and angles are stated in degrees.

A point may be defined in a number of ways as follows:

(a) As a zero;
(b) as a point with known Cartesian coordinates;
(c) as a point with known polar coordinates;
(d) as an intersection of two straight lines;
(e) as an intersection of a straight line and a curve;
(f) as an intersection of two curves.

Examples of the above definitions are illustrated in Figure 10.7(a) to (f), respectively.

Straight lines may also be defined in a number of ways and the following descriptions correspond to the illustrations in Figures 10.8(a) to (h).

(a) As being parallel to a stated axis;
(b) as being at a known distance from a previously defined point and at a known angle to a previously defined straight line;
(c) as being between two known points;

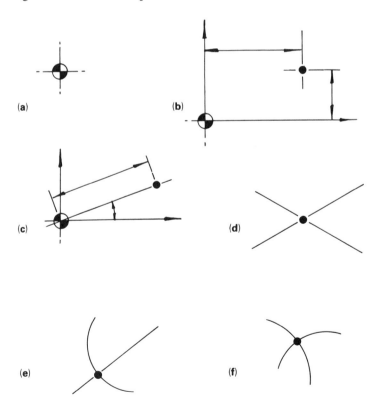

Figure 10.7 Point definition.

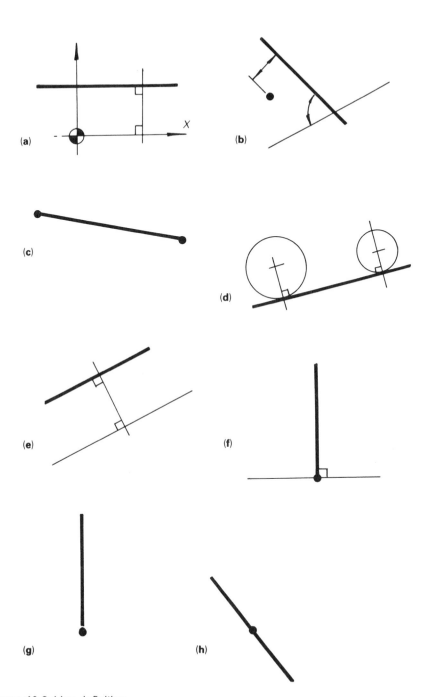

Figure 10.8 Line definition.

(d) as being tangential to two known circles;
(e) as being parallel to a defined straight line;
(f) as being perpendicular to a defined straight line;
(g) as being perpendicular to a defined point;
(h) as passing through a defined point, at an angle.

Circles may be defined as follows, and as illustrated in Figures 10.9(a) to (g).

(a) As a known radius passing through two defined points;
(b) as an unknown radius passing through three defined points;

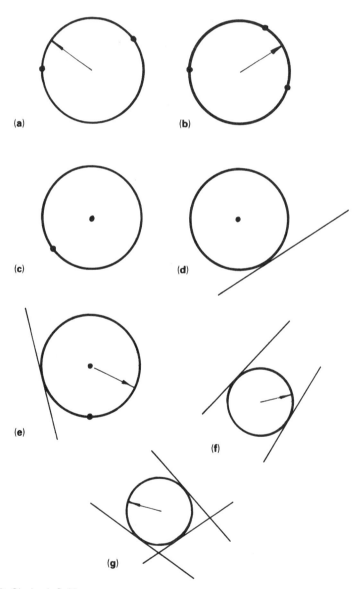

Figure 10.9 Circle definition.

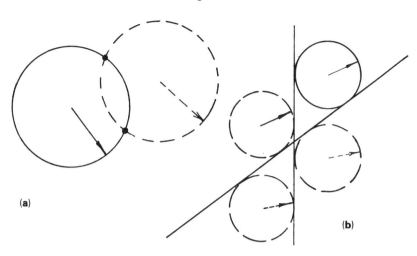

Figure 10.10 Alternative constructions.

(c) as a center point and passing through a defined point;
(d) as a center point and tangential to a defined straight line;
(e) as being tangential to a defined line, passing through a defined point and with a known radius;
(f) as being tangential to two defined lines and with a known radius;
(g) as being tangential to three lines and with a known radius.

A further complication with some constructions is that two versions are sometimes possible. Consider Figure 10.10(a), a radius passing through two defined points. One construction is shown in full line and an alternative construction is shown in broken line. Similarly, the construction shown in Figure 10.10(b), of a circle of given radius tangential to two defined lines, has four possible versions as indicated.

Clearly there is a need to clarify the situation by providing the new element with a sense of orientation or direction in relation to the existing geometry. The way this is achieved differs between one system and another and the student will require specific instructions relating to the system he or she will be using.

Geometry File Construction

The programmer begins the process of geometric definition by first studying the profile or feature to be machined and then giving each element an identity. He or she may do this by marking a drawing prior to entering data into the computer or, if sufficiently competent in the use of the system, the programmer may allocate identities as the entries are made. The student is likely to benefit, at least in the early stages of using a particular CAM system, by adopting the first approach. As with all methods of programming a logical approach is essential to avoid making frustrating mistakes.

The precise method used to identify elements varies from one system to another, but it is common practice to give each element a numerical identity, which is then followed by the appropriate definition. Thus a line identified as line number 7 that is to be constructed from point number 1 at an angle of 90° may be programmed simply as L7, P1, A90. A complete profile consisting of a series of lines, circles, and points previously defined may be listed as follows: PF, P1, L1, L2, L3, L4, C1, L5, L6, P2. The initials PF identify the statement as being a profile.

It should be possible to gain a general appreciation of the techniques used by studying the two examples of geometry statements listed below. Both lists relate to the milled component illustrated in Figure 10.11. For the sake of simplicity the problems associated with holding such a component while the profile is machined have been ignored. Normally, clamping arrangements and work-holding devices have to be accommodated within the part program if collisions are to be avoided. Areas they will occupy, which in effect become "no go" areas for the tool, have to be identified dimensionally and may be displayed graphically as part of the general geometry.

The program definition lists which follow were prepared by two different language based CAM systems for comparison. The result is two different approaches to the

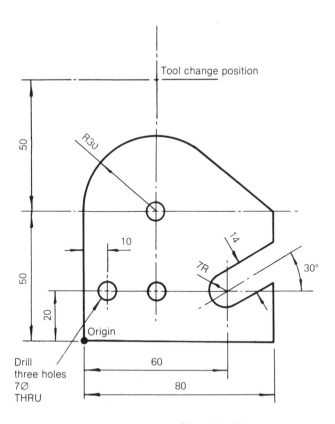

Figure 10.11 Component detail.

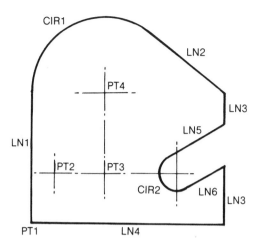

Figure 10.12 Profile definition—MDSI Compact II (Manufacturing Data Systems Inc.).

geometry definition. Reference to Figures 10.12 and 10.13 will indicate how each definition refers to the part geometry and start to show you how computers work with and use the program.

The reader will note the common use of P or PT to indicate a point, L or LN to indicate a line, and C or CIR to indicate a circle. But there, apart from the numerical identity referred to above, the similarities end. Further study of the lists will show that the variations become even more pronounced when the individual elements are compared.

Example No. 1 Software: Compact II (Figure 10.12)

MACHIN, MILL	Statement identifies machine used
IDENT	Program identifier
SETUP, 30LX, 100LY, 100LZ	Machine setup information
BASE, 0XB, 0YB, 20ZB	Absolute zero location
DPT1, 0XB, 0YB, 0ZB	
DPT2, PT1, 10X, 20Y	
DPT3, PT2, 30XB	Definition of point locations
DPT4, PT3, 50YB	
DCIR1, PT4, 30R	
DCIR2, 60XB, 20YB, 0ZB, 7R	Definition of circles
DLN1, XB	
DLN2, 80XB, 50YB, 0ZB, CIR1, YL	
DLN3, 80XB	
DLN4, YB	Definition of lines
DLN5, 30CCW, CIR2, YL	
DLN6, PARLN5, CIR2, YS	

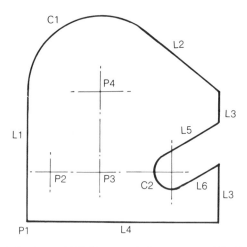

Figure 10.13 Profile definition—APT (Automatic Programmed Toolpath).

Example No. 2 Software: APT (Figure 10.13)

PARTNO PROFILE DEFINITION EXAMPLE	Program identification
CUTTER/0	Cutter call up
MACHIN/MILL	Statement identifies machine used
P1 = POINT/0,0,20	
P2 = POINT/10,20,20	
P3 = POINT/30,20,20	Definition of point locations
P4 = POINT/30,50,20	
C1 = CIRCLE/CENTER,P4,RADIUS,30	Definition of circles
C2 = CIRCLE/60,20,20,7	
L1 = LINE/P1,PARLEL,LY	
L2 = LINE/80,50,20,RIGHT,TANTO,C1	
L3 = LINE/PARLEL,L1,XLARGE,80	
L4 = LINE/P1,PARLEL,LX	Definitions of lines
L5 = LINE/LEFT, TANTO,C2,ATANGL,30,YLARGE	
L6 = LINE/PARLEL,L5,YSMALL,14	
SETPT = POINT/30,100,100	Machine setup point

Now that we have looked at two examples of geometry statements from popular computer-assisted languages let us review an entire program in Compact II. It is noted that programs of this type can be broken down into five major areas of initialization, geometry, tool change, tool motion, and termination as can be seen in Figures 10.14 through 18. The programming process starts from a part print such as Figure 10.14, from which the programmer decides on the machine, tools, and process to use. In this example the programmer has decided to use three tools, the first for rough turning leaving 0.020 in. finish stock on the diameter and 0.005 in. stock on the length for finish. The second tool selected is for finish turning, while the third and final tool is for a single-point threading operation.

The second step the programmer has taken is to determine what the machine setup should be for this program. Figure 10.15 shows the machine layout decided upon. The machine zero is located at the chuck end stop end of the part and the machine tool turret reference point will be established by the operator 10.5 in. from this point in the Z axis. The X axis turret reference point will be established 8.0 in. from the center of the workpiece.

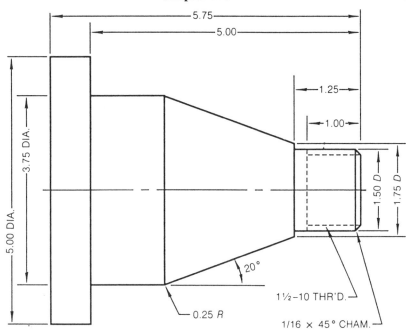

Figure 10.14 Spindle bolt part print. (From Numerical Control Technology Workbook, courtesy of Schlumberger Technologies Inc., Ann Arbor, MI.)

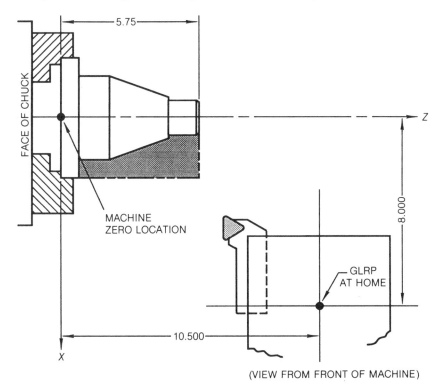

(VIEW FROM FRONT OF MACHINE)

(GLRP = TOOL GAGE LENGTH REFERENCE POINT)

Figure 10.15 Machine setup layout. (From Numerical Control Technology Workbook, courtesy of Schlumberger Technologies Inc., Ann Arbor, MI.)

Section I Initialization

Once the machine setup has been determined, the program initialization statements can be written for the computer program. Figure 10.16 shows the five initialization statements for a Compact II program. Starting with the MACHINe statement the computer is told what specific type of machine tool it is creating a program for. Since this is a demonstration program, just a generic post or machine file is used. For each specific type of machine and control there will be a special command. Next is the IDENTification statement, which assigns the title to be output on the various files generated by the computer. The third line is a INITialization statement to indicate whether input will be inch or metric and whether output is wanted in inch or metric. The fourth statement SETUP informs the computer as to where the machine tool turret reference point is in relation to the machine absolute zero point location. The fifth and final initialization statement is BASE. The base statement informs the computer of the location of the program zero location, used for defining part geometry, in relation to the machine absolute zero.

Section II Geometry

The second major section of a computer program involves the description of the part's geometry to be machined. The programmer first marks up the part print as to the geometry required to machine the part. The geometry labels are normally placed on the part print as in Figure 10.17 as a record for future reference. In the example in Figure 10.17 the programmer has defined two lines and two part boundaries. Line LN1 represents the $1/16 \times 45°$ chamfer, while Line LN2 is the 20° part angle. Part boundary PB1 is defined as the finish part outline, while PB2 is the outline of the rough stock.

The amount of geometric definitions required and their complexity will vary with the skill of the programmer and the capability of the language to handle complex statements. Computer systems will handle geometry verifications in different ways. Some systems process all statements in a batch mode together for statement validity and then allow the system to plot the results on paper or a CRT screen. Other language-based systems are fully interactive: the correctness of data input is verified as programming proceeds and error messages are displayed if appropriate. This ensures that the data input is acceptable to the system, but it does not necessarily ensure that the programmer has not made other mistakes, so it makes sense to reprocess the input in its entirety as a final check.

When the geometry statements have been verified as being correct, it is possible to obtain a printout from an interfaced printer of the data listing. This may be required for filing for future reference, forming part of the general documentation file relating to that particular job.

It is also possible to obtain printed copies of the graphic construction developed during the programming process. Figure 10.18 illustrates the graphics that appeared on the plotter/CRT when, using the Compact II software, the geometry statements were entered for the lathe exercise in Figure 10.17.

From the graphics screen or printout the programmer can easily see the various pieces of geometry defined and can visualize the outline of the rough and finish piece part. Geometry relationships and gross errors can be determined in this type of output.

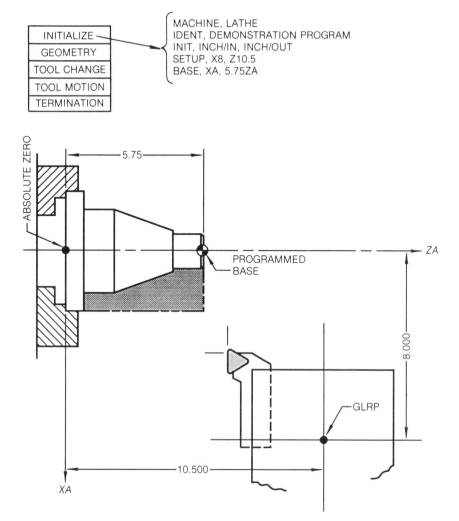

INITIALIZE ──────┐
GEOMETRY   │
TOOL CHANGE   │
TOOL MOTION   │
TERMINATION   │

MACHINE, LATHE
IDENT, DEMONSTRATION PROGRAM
INIT, INCH/IN, INCH/OUT
SETUP, X8, Z10.5
BASE, XA, 5.75ZA

Figure 10.16 Initialization statements. (From Numerical Control Technology Workbook, courtesy of Schlumberger Technologies Inc., Ann Arbor, MI.)

Tool Change Data

After the geometry of the component has been defined, the programmer has to consider the more practical aspects of producing a machined component, such as the sequence of operations, the cutting tools to be used, and the choice of appropriate cutting speeds and feeds. If the programming task has been approached in a logical manner, most of these aspects will have been considered before the CAM process was started. Now data defining these factors have to be added to the part program to supplement the geometric data previously entered. It is possible that some computer assistance may be available.

Tool Change Data statements are included in the Compact II and APT program examples that follow. See Figure 10.19. The tool change statement will be found in various

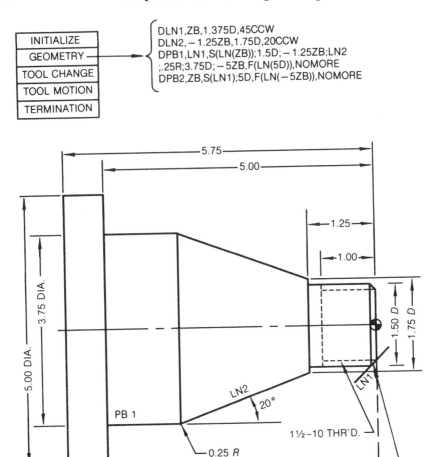

```
                          ⎧ DLN1,ZB,1.375D,45CCW
    INITIALIZE            │ DLN2,−1.25ZB,1.75D,20CCW
    GEOMETRY ───────────→ │ DPB1,LN1,S(LN(ZB));1.5D;−1.25ZB;LN2
    TOOL CHANGE           │ ;.25R;3.75D;−5ZB,F(LN(5D)),NOMORE
    TOOL MOTION           │ DPB2,ZB,S(LN1);5D,F(LN(−5ZB)),NOMORE
    TERMINATION           ⎩
```

Figure 10.17 Part geometry definition. (From Numerical Control Technology Workbook, courtesy of Schlumberger Technologies Inc., Ann Arbor, MI.)

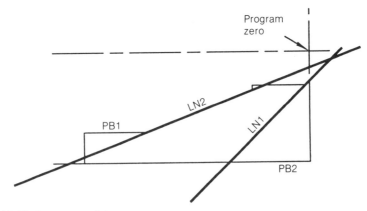

Figure 10.18 Geometry plot.

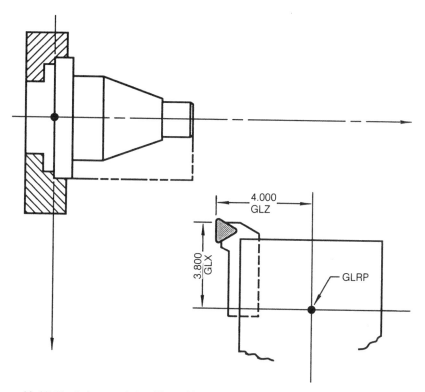

Figure 10.19 Tool change data. (From Numerical Control Technology Handbook, courtesy of Schlumberger Technologies Inc., Ann Arbor, MI.)

locations of the machining body of the program, wherever a tool selection is required, and will be followed by its tool motion statements. Tool statements normally will include information on tool number, gage lengths and diameters, cutting speeds, and feed rates.

On some systems the tooling available for a particular machine will be listed and contained on file within the programming system. Such a data file is referred to as a "tool library" and can be displayed on the screen. All the data relevant to a particular tool, such as the material from which it is made, its shape, and its dimensions, will be indicated together with an identity code for use within the part program. The dimensions of the tool, in particular its radius or diameter, are of particular importance since they will have a direct effect on the cutter paths automatically generated at the next stage of the CAM process.

Cutting speeds and feeds can be determined without computer assistance, and entered into the program in much the same way as when preparing a manual CNC part program.

On the other hand, there may be assistance via the system in response to data input identifying the cutting tool and the part material. The correct speeds and feeds will then be determined automatically and included in the program.

Tool Motion Data

The fourth major section of a CAM program is Tool Motion statements, which are grouped with the corresponding tool change statement. These statements will determine how the part will be cut. Machining cycles and feed/rapid traverse moves will be established. Knowledge of the particular language used is important here because there are many options from which to choose. Figures 10.20, 10.21, and 10.22 give only a few examples of tool motion statements for lathe work.

When defining the sequence and types of machining operations to be carried out, the programmer will be required to take into consideration the special cycles that are an inbuilt feature of the programming system. All the normal machining sequences—drilling, screw cutting, face milling, boring, etc.—are likely to be catered for. It will also be possible to generate subroutines. To use these facilities effectively the programmer will need to be fully conversant with the particular system being used, and this is only achieved by experience.

(One statement will produce all the roughing passes indicated.)
This statement causes the rough cutting of material between part boundary 1 and material boundary 2. A finish stock of 0.02 in. will be left in the X axis, while 0.005 in. will be left in the Z axis.

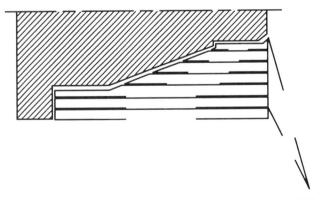

Figure 10.20 Roughing cutting cycle in Compact II. (From Numerical Control Technology Workbook, courtesy of Schlumberger Technologies Inc., Ann Arbor, MI.)

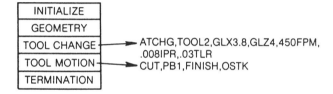

The first statement calls for a tool change to the finish turning tool. The second statement calls for the finish profile of the part to be cut.

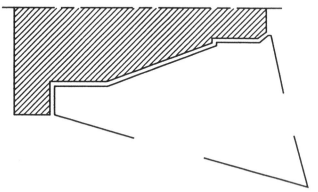

Figure 10.21 Finishing turning—Compact II. (From Numerical Control Technology Workbook, courtesy of Schlumberger Technologies Inc., Ann Arbor, MI.)

Termination

The fifth major section of most CAM programs is the termination of the program. Many systems use a single statement of END or FINISH to indicate that the program is complete. This single statement will normally cause the generation of machine "CNC" program steps to return the tool to its home position and complete an orderly machine shut down. The complete Compact II program can be reviewed in Figure 10.23.

Cutter Location Data

When the computer is programmed with all the data defining the part geometry, the machining sequence, tooling, etc., the process of determining the cutter location data, referred to as the CL Data, can begin. In simple terms, the CL Data can be described as the dimensional definition of the cutter path from a defined datum point.

In determining the CL Data the computer automatically calculates the movements necessary to achieve the geometric features previously defined. In doing so, account will be taken of cutter sizes; where appropriate, compensation for the cutter radius will be made. Where area clearance is required, and excess stock material has to be removed, the computer will determine the appropriate tool paths.

CL Data can be viewed on some CRT screens and a printout can be obtained if required.

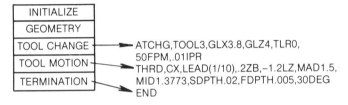

INITIALIZE
GEOMETRY
TOOL CHANGE → ATCHG,TOOL3,GLX3.8,GLZ4,TLR0,
50FPM,.01IPR
TOOL MOTION → THRD,CX,LEAD(1/10),.2ZB,−1.2LZ,MAD1.5,
TERMINATION → MID1.3773,SDPTH.02,FDPTH.005,30DEG
END

The first statement calls for a tool change to the threading tool. The
second statement calls for a multiple threading cycle to be
generated. The third statement calls for termination of the computer
program and commands the tool back to its home position.

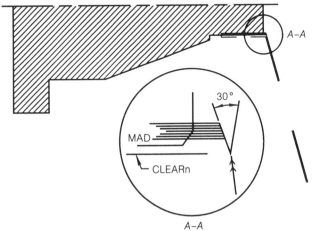

Figure 10.22 Threading cycle—Compact II. (From Numerical Control Technology Workbook, courtesy of Schlumberger Technologies Inc., Ann Arbor, MI.)

Tool paths can be displayed graphically, in some cases with a three-dimensional or pictorial effect. It is also possible to produce, via a pen plotter or a printer, a diagrammatic representation of the part geometry and the cutter paths in relation to that geometry. Both the graphical display on the CRT screen and the plotter output are usually enhanced by the use of different colors to indicate different features: one color for the geometric shape of the component and a different color indicating the paths of each tool to be used, for instance.

In Figures 10.20 through 10.22 the printouts of the cutter paths for programming the component shown in Figure 10.14 is illustrated.

When the CL Data are considered to be correct, the final stage in the CAM process, that of postprocessing, can be undertaken.

With the CL Data file compiled, it is also possible, on some systems, to determine the time that will be taken to machine the part. The computer calculation is based on the cutting speeds and feeds entered as part of the technology data.

It should be noted that computer languages may be interactive or batch processed. If interactive, the system may check each individual statement for validity, then create its CL Data, postprocess it to machine language, and plot/display the results or error before proceeding to the next statement. Batch processing systems, on the other hand, takes the

Compact II Part Program

MACHIN,LATHE	Identifies machine used
IDENT,DEMONSTRATION PROGRAM	Program file identification
INIT,INCH/IN,INCH/OUT	Set up data format in and out
SETUP,X8,Z10.5	Machine setup
BASE,XA,5.75ZA	Program zero location
DLN1,ZB,1.375D,45CCW	Define Line 1
DLN2,−1.25ZB,1.75D,20CCW	Define Line 2
DPB1,LN1,S(LN(ZB));1.5D;−1.25ZB;LN2;.25R;	Define finish
3.75D;−5ZB,F(LN(5D)),NOMORE	part boundary
DPB2,ZB,S(LN1);5D,F(LN(−5ZB)),	
NOMORE	Define material boundary
ATCHG,TOOL1,GLX3.8,GLZ4,350FPM,	
.015IPR,.03TLR	Define roughing tool
CUT,PB1,MB2,MAXDP.255,XSTK.02,	
ZSTK.005	Create roughing cuts
ATCHG,TOOL2,GLX3.8,GLZ4,450FPM,	
.008IPR,.03TLR	Define finish turning tool
CUT,PB1,FINISH,0STK	Create finish turning pass
ATCHG,TOOL3,GLX3.8,GLZ4,TLR0,	
50FPM,.01IPR	Define threading tool
THRD,CX,LEAD(1/10),.2ZB,−1.2LZ,MAD1.5,	Create
MID1.3773,SDPTH.02,FDPTH.005,30DEG	threading pass
END	Terminate program

Figure 10.23 Compact II program. (From Numerical Control Technology Workbook, courtesy of Schlumberger Technologies Inc., Ann Arbor, MI.)

entire program through each step of processing (statement validity, CL Data, postprocessing, and display) before going on to the next step. In batch processing the computer processing is normally stopped at the end of the step reporting errors with an error statement print out. Interactive program systems will allow error correction "on the fly."

Postprocessing

Postprocessing is the stage in the CAM process where the CL Data and other information relevant to the machining of the component is assembled into a form that will be accepted and meaningful to the control system of the particular machine to be used. Features such as G and M codes, previously not part of the program data, are now automatically incorporated.

Because there are many variations in the control systems fitted to machine tools, it is necessary to have a postprocessor to suit each control system for which part programs are to be prepared. The manufacturers of CAM systems will supply specific postprocessors to order, these being immediately available for the more widely used machine controls. It is also possible with some systems to purchase a "writing kit/generic post," which permits users to compile their own postprocessor, for it is actually a relatively simple computer program. In this way, if a new machine is acquired, it can be readily as-similated into the CAM system.

The postprocessing of data into a machine control language is achieved very rapidly, being simply a case of making a few key strokes. The resulting program can now be recorded for future use in whatever form is deemed to be appropriate.

Examples of postprocessed programs follow in Figures 10.24 and 10.25. Figure 10.24 shows a combination program output that is good for programmer use during machine tryout. This output shows the computer statement followed by the CL Data or the machine information it generates. It is good for tryout because when an error is found in the machine program you know right away what computer statement generated it. Figure 10.25, on the other hand, is a machine tool operator's program read out. On the machine tool program output no other information is included to cloud the issue.

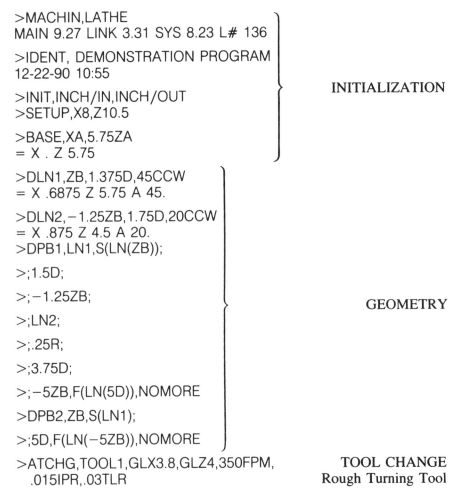

```
>MACHIN,LATHE
MAIN 9.27 LINK 3.31 SYS 8.23 L# 136

>IDENT, DEMONSTRATION PROGRAM
12-22-90 10:55                                    INITIALIZATION

>INIT,INCH/IN,INCH/OUT
>SETUP,X8,Z10.5

>BASE,XA,5.75ZA
= X . Z 5.75

>DLN1,ZB,1.375D,45CCW
= X .6875 Z 5.75 A 45.

>DLN2,−1.25ZB,1.75D,20CCW
= X .875 Z 4.5 A 20.
>DPB1,LN1,S(LN(ZB));

>;1.5D;

>;−1.25ZB;                                         GEOMETRY

>;LN2;

>;.25R;

>;3.75D;

>;−5ZB,F(LN(5D)),NOMORE

>DPB2,ZB,S(LN1);

>;5D,F(LN(−5ZB)),NOMORE

>ATCHG,TOOL1,GLX3.8,GLZ4,350FPM,           TOOL CHANGE
   .015IPR,.03TLR                         Rough Turning Tool
```

Figure 10.24 Combination file output of part in Figure 10.14. (*Note:* Programmer-generated statements are indicated by the ">" symbol. All other information is generated by the computer.)

```
>CUT,PB1,MB2,MAXDP.255,XSTK.02,ZSTK.005
N001 X-01.825 Z-00.6352 F200.00 S0298 T0001 M03
N002 X-00.1 Z-00.0348 F010.00
N003 Z-05.045 F004.47
N004 X 00.255 F004.04 S0269
N005 Z 04.945 F200.00
N006 Z 00.1 F010.00
N007 X-00.41 F200.00 S0336
N008 X-00.1 F010.00
N009 Z-05.045 F005.04
N010 X 00.255 F004.49 S0299
N011 Z 04.945 F200.00
N012 Z 00.1 F010.00
N013 X-00.41 F200.00 S0386
N014 X-00.1 F010.00
N015 Z-03.6317 F005.79
N016 X 00.1428 Z-00.3924 F005.37 S0358
N017 G02 X 00.0172 Z-00.0974 I00.2678
     K00.0974 F005.33 S0355
N018 Z-00.9235 F005.30 S0353
N019 X 00.095 F005.07 S0338
N020 Z 04.945 F200.00
N021 Z 00.1 F010.00
N022 X-00.41 F200.00 S0453
N023 X-00.1 F010.00
N024 Z-02.9311 F006.80
N025 X 00.255 Z-00.7006 F005.82 S0388
N026 Z 03.5317 F200.00
N027 Z 00.1 F010.00
N028 X-00.41 F200.00 S0547
N029 X-00.1 F010.00
N030 Z-02.2305 F008.21
N031 X 00.255 Z-00.7006 F006.84 S0456
N032 Z 02.8311 F200.00
N033 Z 00.1 F010.00
N034 X-00.41 F200.00 S0692
N035 X-00.1 F010.00
N036 Z-01.5298 F010.38
N037 X 00.255 Z-00.7006 F008.28 S0552
N038 Z 02.1304 F200.00
N039 Z 00.1 F010.00
```

TOOL
MOTION
Rough
Turning Tool

Figure 10.24 (Continued)

```
N040 X-00.41 F200.00 S0941
N041 X-00.1 F010.00
N042 Z-00.073 F014.12
N043 X 00.055 Z-00.055 F013.28 S0885
N044 Z-01.167 F013.10 S0873
N045 X 00.1145 F011.52 S0768
N046 X 00.0855 Z-00.2348 F010.50 S0700
N047 Z 01.4298 F200.00
N048 Z 00.1 F010.00
N049 X-00.2125 F200.00 S1024
N050 X-00.1 F010.00
N051 Z-00.0155 F015.36
N052 X 00.0575 Z-00.0575 F014.33 S0955
N053 X 03.355 Z 00.7215 F200.00
N054 X 00.1 Z 00.0215 F010.00
ABS D 8.4 ZB .75
```

> ATCHG,TOOL2,GLX3.8,GLZ4,450FPM,
>   .008IPR,.03TLR

TOOL CHANGE
Finish Turning Tool

```
>CUT,PB1,FINISH,0STK
N055 X-03.4125 Z-00.6509 F200.00 S1307 T0002
N056 X-00.1 Z-00.0191 F010.00
N057 Z-00.0375 F010.46
N058 X 00.0925 Z-00.0925 F009.29 S1161
N059 Z-01.17 F009.16 S1145
N060 X 00.116 F008.03 S1004
N061 X 00.2754 Z-00.7545 F006.02 S0753
N062 X 00.3798 Z-01.0447 F004.52 S0565
N063 X 00.3369 Z-00.9266 F003.72 S0465
N064 G02 X 00.0169 Z-00.0957 I00.2631
     K00.0957 F003.68 S0460
N065 Z-00.9285 F003.66 S0458
N066 X 00.625 F002.76 S0345
N067 X 01.6408 Z 05.62 F200.00
N068 X 00.0292 Z 00.1 F010.00
ABS D 8.4 ZB .75
```

TOOL MOTION
Finishing
Turning Tool

> ATCHG,TOOL3,GLX3.8,GLZ4,TLR0, 50FPM,.01IPR

**TOOL
CHANGE**
Threading Tool

Figure 10.24 (Continued)

```
>THRD,CX,LEAD(1/10),.2ZB,-1.2LZ,MAD1.5,
  MID1.3773,SDPTH.02, FDPTH.005, 30DEG
N069 X-03.4 Z-00.55 F200.00 S0250 T0003
N070 X-00.0695 Z-00.0401 F002.50
N071 G33 Z-01.1599 K0.1
N072 X00.0695 F200.00
N073 Z 01.2
N074 X-00.0854 Z-00.0493 F002.50
N075 G33 Z-01.1507 K0.1
N076 X 00.0854 F200.00
N077 Z 01.2
N078 X-00.0976 Z-00.0564 F002.50
N079 G33 Z-01.1436 K0.1
N080 X 00.0976 F200.00
N081 Z 01.2
N082 X-00.1063 Z-00.0614 F002.50
N083 G33 Z-01.1386 K0.1
N084 X 00.1063 F200.00
N085 Z 01.2
N086 X-00.1113 Z-00.0642 F002.50
N087 G33 Z-01.1358 K0.1
N088 X 00.1113 F200.00
N089 Z 01.2
ABS D 1.6 ZB .2
```

TOOL MOTION
Threading Operation

```
>END
```

PROGRAM TERMINATION

```
N090 X 03.4 Z 00.55
N091 M05
ABS D 8.4 ZB .75
N092 M30
END MIN: .8 FT: 20.9 MTR: 6.3
```

TOOL MOTION
Return to Home Position

Figure 10.24 (Continued)

```
N001 X-01.825 Z-00.6352 F200.00 S0298 T0001 M03
```

Rough
Turning Tool

```
N002 X-00.1 Z-00.0348 F010.00
N003 Z-05.045 F004.47
N004 X 00.255 F004.04 S0269
N005 Z 04.945 F200.00
N006 Z 00.1 F010.00
N007 X-00.41 F200.00 S0336
N008 X-00.1 F010.00
N009 Z-05.045 F00
```

Figure 10.25 Machine tool output from Compact II program.

N010 X 00.255 F004.49 S0299
N011 Z 04.945 F200.00
N012 Z 00.1 F010.00
N013 X-00.41 F200.00 S0386
N014 X-00.1 F010.00
N015 Z-03.6317 F005.79
N016 X 00.1428 Z-00.3924 F005.37 S0358
N017 G02 X 00.0172 Z-00.0974 I00.2678 K00.0974 F005.33 S0355
N018 Z-00.9235 F005.30 S0353
N019 X 00.095 F005.07 S0338
N020 Z 04.945 F200.00
N021 Z 00.1 F010.00
N022 X-00.41 F200.00 S0453
N023 X-00.1 F010.00
N024 Z-02.9311 F006.80
N025 X 00.255 Z-00.7006 F005.82 S0388
N026 Z 03.5317 F200.00
N027 Z 00.1 F010.00
N028 X-00.41 F200.00 S0547
N029 X-00.1 F010.00
N030 Z-02.2305 F008.21
N031 X 00.255 Z-00.7006 F006.84 S0456
N032 Z 02.8311 F200.00
N033 Z 00.1 F010.00
N034 X-00.41 F200.00 S0692
N035 X-00.1 F010.00
N036 Z-01.5298 F010.38
N037 X 00.255 Z-00.7006 F008.28 S0552
N038 Z 02.1304 F200.00
N039 Z 00.1 F010.00
N040 X-00.41 F200.00 S0941
N041 X-00.1 F010.00
N042 Z-00.073 F014.12
N043 X 00.055 Z-00.055 F013.28 S0885
N044 Z-01.167 F013.10 S0873
N045 X 00.1145 F011.52 S0768
N046 X 00.0855 Z-00.2348 F010.50 S0700
N047 Z 01.4298 F200.00
N048 Z 00.1 F010.00
N049 X-00.2125 F200.00 S1024
N050 X-00.1 F010.00
N051 Z-00.0155 F015.36
N052 X 00.0575 Z-00.0575 F014.33 S0955

Figure 10.25 (Continued)

N053 X 03.355 Z 00.7215 F200.00
N054 X 00.1 Z 00.0215 F010.00
N055 X-03.4125 Z-00.6509 F200.00 S1307 T0002   Finish Turning
                                                        Tool

N056 X-00.1 Z-00.0191 F010.00
N057 Z-00.0375 F010.46
N058 X 00.0925 Z-00.0925 F009.29 S1161
N059 Z-01.17 F009.16 S1145
N060 X 00.116 F008.03 S1004
N061 X 00.2754 Z-00.7545 F006.02 S0753
N062 X 00.3798 Z-01.0447 F004.52 S0565
N063 X 00.3369 Z-00.9266 F003.72 S0465
N064 G02 X 00.0169 Z-00.0957 I00.2631 K00.0957 F003.68 S0460
N065 Z-00.9285 F003.66 S0458
N066 X 00.625 F002.76 S0345
N067 X 01.6408 Z 05.62 F200.00
N068 X 00.0292 Z 00.1 F010.00
N069 X-03.4 Z-00.55 F200.00 S0250 T0003   Threading Tool
N070 X-00.0695 Z-00.0401 F002.50
N071 G33 Z-01.1599 K0.1
N072 X 00.0695 F200.00
N073 Z 01.2
N074 X-00.0854 Z-00.0493 F002.50
N075 G33 Z-01.1507 K0.1
N076 X 00.0854 F200.00
N077 Z 01.2
N078 X-00.0976 Z-00.0564 F002.58
N079 G33 Z-01.1436 K0.1
N080 X 00.0976 F200.00
N081 Z 01.2
N082 X-00.1063 Z-00.0614 F002.50
N083 G33 Z-01.1386 K0.1
N084 X 00.1063 F200.00
N085 Z 01.2
N086 X-00.1113 Z-00.0642 F002.50
N087 G33 Z-01.1358 K0.1
N088 X 00.1113 F200.00
N089 Z 01.2
N090 X 03.4 Z 00.55
N091 M05
N092 M30   End of Program Rewind

Figure 10.25 (Continued)

APT Program

As a past leader of the many computer languages besides Compact II, APT (Automatically Programmed Tools) was selected. APT was selected because it is found in many similar forms such as ADAPT, UNIAPT, and AUTOSPOT. APT has played a large role in the computer-assisted programming language market. Many other languages and CAD/CAM systems grew out of this language. This language was developed and was heavily used in the aerospace industry due to its ability to handle multiaxis contour programming to the fifth and seventh axis level. Other languages like Compact II were only developed to do contouring moves to three axes deep, after which additional axes became positional only. It is because of this that the author feels many CAD/CAM systems have patterned themselves after the APT language. A comparison of actual computer statements generated on a CAD/CAM system will easily show this. As the APT program is reviewed, refer to the Compact II program to see the minor differences in program statements and structures.

The part to be reviewed is a simple milled part in which the periphery and a pass around the top of the part will be machined (see Figure 10.26). As in the Compact II program the part print must be reviewed, a machine selected, and setup determined before programming can start.

The machine zero is indicated on Figure 10.26 to be 2.0 in. to the left of the finish part profile on the X axis. The Y axis zero is 2.0 in. below the profile and Z zero is 1.0 in. beneath the part. To keep the process simple, it has been decided to machine one path around the periphery at full depth, and then to take one pass around the top surface. The programmer has selected a 1.0 in. diameter cutter with a 0.250 in. corner radius.

The next step in the process is to mark the geometry on the part print that needs to be defined by the programmer. Figure 10.26 shows the indicated points "P," lines "L," circles "C," and planes "PL" necessary to describe the piece part.

Once the needed geometry is determined, programming can begin. Figure 10.27 shows one programmer's solution to this particular problem. For easy reference, the

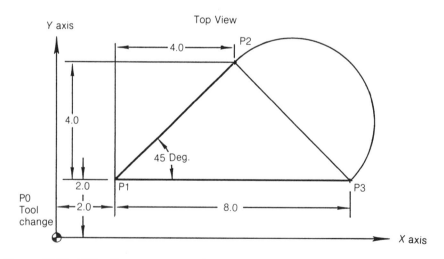

Figure 10.26 APT mill program example.

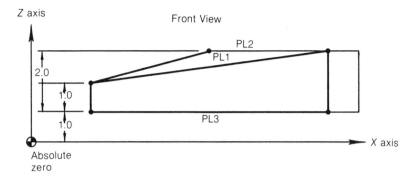

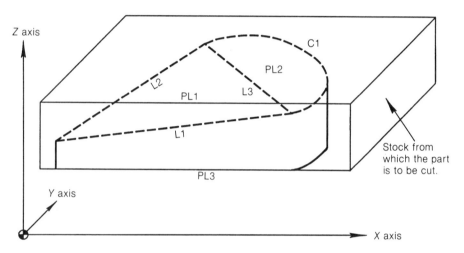

Figure 10.26 (Continued)

program has been marked up to show its major sections. The following pages give a line by line description of the various commands in the UNIAPT program.

001 PARTNO UNIAPT SAMPLE PROGRAM PART

Identifies the part and serves as a title for the program listing as well as identification for the CNC control tape.

002 $$ GEOMETRY

The double dollar sign indicates a comment line.

003 CLPRNT

Specifies that the cutter location input data to the postprocessor is to be printed. This statement caused the X, Y, Z outputs in the following cutter location data file "CL Data" from program line numbers 24 through 51.

```
2466 ↑ LU,
     OPT=4
001 PARTNO   UNIAPT SAMPLE PART PROGRAM
002 $$  GEOMETRY
003     CLPRNT
004     PRINT/ON

005 P0=POINT/0,0
006 P1=POINT/2,2,2
007 P3=POINT/10,2,3
010 L1=LINE/P1,P3
011 L2=LINE/P1,ATANGL,45
012 L3=LINE/(P2=POINT/6,6,3),P3
013 PL1=PLANE/P1,P2,P3   $$ CANTED PLANE ON TOP
014 PL2=PLANE/0,0,1,3   $$ PLANE  Z=3
015 PL3=PLANE/PARLEL,PL2,ZSMALL,2   $$ Z=1
016 R  =(LNTHF(VECTOR/P2,P3))/2
017 C1 =CIRCLE/TANTO,L2,XSMALL, P3,RADIUS,R
020 $$
021 $$    MAKE PASS AROUND PERIPHERY
022 $$
023     CUTTER    /1,.25 $$DIA.=1,CORNER RADIUS=.25
024     FROM      /P0
025     DNTCUT
```

Identification statement*
Program statement
Printer statements

Point definition

Line definition

Plane definitions

Circle definition

Program statement

Cutter definition

INITIALIZATION Statements

GEOMETRY Statements

TOOL CHANGE Statements

Figure 10.27 Source program listing—UNIAPT Milling Example. (*Note*: 001 becomes a MACHIN/statement when programming for a specific machine tool.)

```
TOOL         026    GOTO         /-.75,.75,1 $$ MOVE CLEAR OF PART      ⎫
MOTION       027    GO           /L2,PL3,ON,L1,10 $$10 IPM FEEDRATE     ⎬ Tool motion for
Statements   030    CUT                                                ⎭ periphery cut
             031    TLLFT,GOLFT  /L2
             032    GOFWD        /C1,PAST,L1
             033    GORGT        /L1,PAST,L2
             034    GOTO         /P0
             035 $$
             036 $$  MAKE A PASS AROUND TOP OF PART                       Program statement
             037 $$
             040    GODLTA       /0,0,2                                 ⎫
             041    GO           /ON,L2,PL1,L1,20 $$ FEEDRATE=20 IPM    ⎪
             042    TLON,GOFWD   /L2,PAST,PL2                           ⎪
             043    PSIS         /PL2 $$ AUTOPS WOULD BE THE SAME       ⎪
             044    GOFWD        /L2,TANTO,C1                           ⎬ Tool motion for
             045    GOFWD        /C1,ON,L1                              ⎪   top edge
             046    GO           /ON,L1,PL1,ON,L3 $$GET BACK ON PL1     ⎪
             047    INDIRV       /-1,0,0 $$ESTABLISH DIRECTION          ⎪
             050    GOFWD        /L1,PAST,L2                            ⎪
             051    GOTO         /P0                                    ⎭
TERMINATION  052    STOP
Statements   053    END
             054    FINI
```

Figure 10.27 (Continued)

004 PRINT/ON

Causes surface data to be printed in its canonical form. This statement caused the output from program line numbers 005 through 17 in the CL Data file.

005 P0 = POINT/0,0

Assigns the name P0 to the point whose coordinates are $x = 0$, $y = 0$. The processor assumes $z = 0$ if only two points are given and no ZSURF statement has been given.

006 P1 = POINT/2,2,2

Assigns the name P1 to the point whose coordinates are $x = 2$, $y = 2$, $z = 2$.

007 P3 = POINT/10,2,2

Assigns the name P3 to the point whose coordinates are $x = 10$, $y = 2$, $z = 2$.

*010 L1 = LINE/P1,P3

Defines a line through the two points P1 and P3.

011 L2 = LINE/P1, ATANGL, 45

Defines a line through the point P1 and at an angle of 45° to the X axis.

012 L3 = LINE/(P2 = POINT/6,6,3), P3

Define a line through two points P2 and P3. P2 is an example of a nested definition, i.e., it defines P2 in terms of its coordinates ($x = 6$, $y = 6$, $z = 3$) within the line statement. P2 could have been written as a separate statement in which case the preceding statement would have appeared simply as L3 = LINE/P2, P3.

013 PL1 = PLANE/P1,P2,P3 $$ CANTED PLANE ON TOP

Defines a canted plane (which is the top of the part) in terms of three points: P1,P2,P3. The words following the double dollar sign are not processed by the program. They are for programmer documentation only.

014 PL2 = PLANE/0,0,1,3 $$ PLANE, $Z = 3$

Defines a plane in terms of the coefficients of the plane equation $ax + by + cz - d = 0$, where $a = 0$, $b = 0$, $c = 1$, $d = 3$.

015 PL3 = PLANE/PARLEL,PL2,ZSMALL,2 $$ $Z = 1$

Defines a plane parallel (PARLEL) to plane (PL2) 2 units away from PL2. Two planes can meet this definition—one above and one below PL2. The modifier ZSMALL removes the ambiguity by specifying the plane with the smaller Z value: below PL2.

---

*Although called a line these are actually surfaces with an infinite plane perpendicular to the X–Y plane of the paper. They are called lines for convenience. It is always understood that a line in UNIAPT is really a plane. The same is true for a circle. It is actually an infinite cylinder whose sides are perpendicular to the XY, YZ, or XZ plane.

016 R = (LNTHF(VECTOR/P2,P3))/2

Defines the radius (R) by computing the length (LNTHF) of the vector (VECTOR) which connects points P2 and P3 and taking one-half of the resulting value.

017 C1 = CIRCLE/TANTO,L2,XSMALL,P3,RADIUS,R

Defines the circle (C1) in terms of line (L2) that it (C1) is tangent to and the point P3 that it passes through with a radius R. As shown in the following schematic, two circles can meet these requirements. The modifier XSMALL indicates to the system to use the one with the smallest X value.

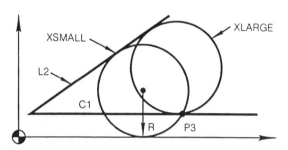

020 $$

Causes a line to be skipped.

021 $$ MAKE A PASS AROUND PERIPHERY

A comment.

022 $$

Causes a line to be skipped.

023 CUTTER/1,.25 $$ DIA. = 1, CORNER RADIUS = .25

Defines cutter diameter (1 in.) and corner radius (0.25 in.).

024 FROM/P0

Defines cutting tool beginning position as being at point (P0). To see tool path generated by computer statement refer to Figure 10.28.

025 DNTCUT

Indicates that tool center information for motion statements is not to be passed on to the postprocessor.

026 GOTO/-.75,.75,1 $$ MOVE CLEAR OF PART

Move cutter (clear of part) tool to $x = -0.75$, $y = 0.75$, and $z = 1$.

027 GO/L2,PL3,ON,L1,10 $$ 10 IPM FEEDRATE

Move cutting tool to the position where L2, PL3, and L1 intersect. PL3 is established as the part surface (the second surface in the command) for all subsequent motion commands. This command also sets the feedrate to 10 ipm.

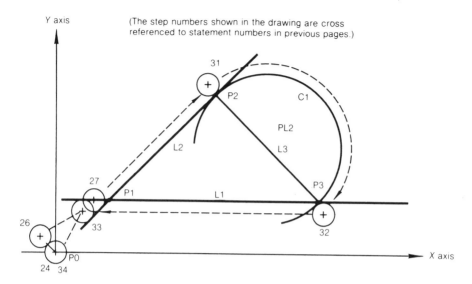

Figure 10.28 Top view showing path of cutter, which makes a pass around periphery. (The step numbers shown in the drawing are cross referenced to statement numbers in previous pages.)

030 CUT

Indicates that tool center information for motion statements is to be passed on to the postprocessor. It causes cutter location data output to begin with preceding statement.

031 TLLFT, GOLFT/L2

Position the tool to left (TLLFT) of L2 and move it along the intersection of surfaces L2 and PL3 to C1. A check surface is implied, which means to use the drive surface from the next command for the check surface for this command. Also a TANTO condition is indirectly specified since the next command is a GOFWD. (*drive surface:* surface which tool is moved along; *check surface:* surface which tool will stop at.)

032 GOFWD/C1,PAST,L1

Move tool along intersection of surfaces C1 and PL3 until past the plane L1.

033 GORGT/L1,PAST,L2

Turn right and move tool along intersection of L1 and PL3 past the plane L2.

034 GOTO/P0

Move tool from its present position to P0 ($x = 0, y = 0, z = 0$).

035 $$

A remark—causes a line space.

036 $$ MAKE A PASS AROUND TOP OF PART

A remark. Notes that the next group of statements will begin machining the part surface top.

037 $$

A line space.

040   GODLTA/0,0,2

Adds the indicated increments to the tool position. Since x and y are zero, tool is moved straight up 2 in. To see tool path generated by computer statement, refer to Figure 10.29.

041   GO/ON,L2,PL1,L1,20 $$ FEEDRATE = 20 IPM

Position the tool at the intersection of drive surface L2, part surface PL1, and check surface L1. Tool end is centered on the L2 surface and to the PL1 and L1 surfaces. Feedrate is set at 20 ipm. PL1, since it is the second surface in the GO/ command, is established as the modal part surface.

042   TLON, GOFWD/L2,PL2

Tool is centered on (TLON) the drive surface which is L2 in this statement example. Go forward (GOFWD) along the intersection of L2 and PL1, which is the part surface. Stop at PL2, which is the check surface.

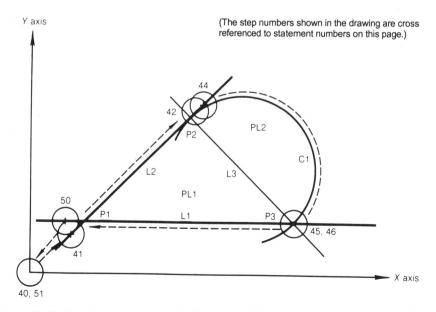

Figure 10.29 Top view showing path of cutter, which makes a pass around top of part. (The step numbers shown in the drawing are cross referenced to statement numbers on this page.)

043   PSIS/PL2 $$ AUTOPS WOULD BE THE SAME

Causes part surface to be changed to PL2. PSIS means "part surface is." The comment refers to the command AUTOPS, which can be used to establish a plane at the cutters current z height.

044   GOFWD/L2,TANTO,C1

Move tool along the intersection of L2 and PL2 until tangent to circle C1.

045   GOFWD/C1,ON,L1

Move tool along the intersection of C1 and PL2. Stop on surface L1.

046   GO/ON,L1,PL1,ON,L3 $$ GET BACK ON PL1

Move tool to the position where L1, PL1, and L3 intersect. The "ON" modifier means the tool center is to be positioned "on" L1 and "on" L3.

047   INDIRV/–1,0,0 $$ ESTABLISH DIRECTION

This command, in the direction of vector, establishes a tool direction as being in the minus x direction ($x = -1, y = 0, z = 0$).

050   GOFWD/L1,PAST,L2

Go forward along the intersection of L1 and PL1 and stop just past the surface L2.

051   GOTO/P0

A point to point command. Position tool from where it is to point P0.

052   STOP

A postprocessor command that stops the machine tool and machine tool controller input reader. Feedrate is reduced to zero and spindle and coolant are turned off.

053   END

A postprocessor command that signals the end of a logical section of a part program.

054   FINI

The end of the complete part program.

In an APT program's processing, after the programmer creates the computer source program, it is submitted to the computer. The computer upon receipt of source information checks to see if it is a valid statement. Once validity is established, the computer creates the cutter location file data either by interaction or through batch processing. The CL Data file consists of all the geometry and cutter location information required to machine the part in coordinate numerical form. This information can then be transformed into the correct numerical control format for the particular machine tool and CNC control unit. The information in Figure 10.30 is a printout of the CL Data from the UNIAPT sample program. Note: For the readers benefit, the axis designators are shown in parentheses.

Source Program Line #
REC0005 SURFACE=POINT   P0
(X) .000000   (Y) .000000   (Z) .000000
REC0006 SURFACE=POINT   P1
(X) 2.000000   (Y) 2.000000   (Z)2.000000
REC0007 SURFACE=POINT   P3
(X)10.000000   (Y) 2.000000   (Z)3.000000
REC0010 SURFACE=LINE   L1
(X) .000000   (Y) 1.000000   (X) .000000   (Y)2.000000
REC0011 SURFACE=LINE   L2
(X) .707106   (Y)−.707106   (X) .000000   (Y) .000000
REC0012 SURFACE=POINT   P2
(X) 6.000000   (Y) 6.000000   (Z)3.000000
REC0012 SURFACE=LINE   L3
(X) .707106   (Y) .707106   (X) .000000   (Y)8.485282
REC0013 SURFACE=PLANE   PL1
(X) −.123091   (Y)−.123091   (Z) .984731   1.477097
(X, Y, Z values of unit vector perpendicular to plane, fourth value is
minimum distance of plane from origin.)
REC0014 SURFACE=PLANE   PL2
(X) .000000   (Y) .000000   (Z)1.000000   (Z)3.000000
(First three values establish plane vector.)
REC0015 SURFACE=PLANE   PL3
(X) .000000   (Y) .000000   (Z)1.000000   (Z)1.000000
REC0016 SURFACE=VECTOR
    4.000000   −4.000000   .000000
REC0016 SURFACE=SCALAR   R
    2.828427
REC0017 SURFACE=CIRCLE   C1
(X) 8.000000   (Y) 3.999999   (Z) .000000   (X$_1$) .000000
(Y$_1$) .000000   (Z$_1$) 1.000000   (Radius) 2.828427
(X$_1$, Y$_1$, Z$_1$ form unit vector of cylinder passing through circle.)
REC0024
(X) .000000   (Y) .000000   (Z) .000000
REC0030
(X) 1.292893   (Y) 2.000000   (Z)1.000000
REC0031
(X) 5.646446   (Y) 6.353553   (Z)1.000000
REC0032
(X) 5.687013   (Y) 6.394128   (Z) 1.000000
    5.770902   6.472423   1.000000
    5.857440   6.547782   1.000000

Figure 10.30 Program output; surface data in canonical form and cutter location data.
(*Note:* Axis call labels will not be printed on computer generated readouts.)

5.946523	6.620113	1.000000
6.038047	6.689330	1.000000
6.131902	6.755352	1.000000
6.227977	6.818100	1.000000
6.326156	6.877500	1.000000
6.426326	6.933480	1.000000
6.528365	6.985975	1.000000
6.632152	7.034921	1.000000
6.737565	7.080262	1.000000
6.844478	7.121942	1.000000
6.952764	7.159913	1.000000
7.062294	7.194129	1.000000
7.172939	7.224550	1.000000
7.284566	7.251140	1.000000
7.397043	7.273866	1.000000
7.510238	7.292701	1.000000
7.624013	7.307626	1.000000
7.738235	7.318619	1.000000
7.852769	7.325669	1.000000
7.967477	7.328768	1.000000
8.082225	7.327911	1.000000
8.196873	7.323100	1.000000
8.311290	7.314340	1.000000
8.425335	7.301643	1.000000
8.538875	7.285022	1.000000
8.651775	7.264497	1.000000
8.763900	7.240094	1.000000
8.875118	7.211841	1.000000
8.985297	7.179771	1.000000
9.094303	7.143923	1.000000
9.202010	7.104339	1.000000
9.308289	7.061067	1.000000
9.413013	7.014158	1.000000
9.516059	6.963666	1.000000
9.617302	6.909654	1.000000
9.716624	6.852184	1.000000
9.813907	6.791326	1.000000
9.909034	6.727149	1.000000
10.001891	6.659734	1.000000
10.092372	6.589157	1.000000
10.180365	6.515504	1.000000
10.265769	6.438862	1.000000
10.348479	6.359323	1.000000

Note: Amount of output will depend on path tolerance setup in computer.

Figure 10.30 (Continued)

10.428398	6.276979	1.000000
10.505432	6.191930	1.000000
10.579490	6.104276	1.000000
10.650482	6.014123	1.000000
10.718326	5.921575	1.000000
10.782939	5.826745	1.000000
10.844246	5.729745	1.000000
10.902172	5.630689	1.000000
10.956650	5.529695	1.000000
11.007617	5.426883	1.000000
11.055007	5.322376	1.000000
11.098769	5.216298	1.000000
11.138848	5.108775	1.000000
11.175198	4.999934	1.000000
11.207775	4.889905	1.000000
11.236541	4.778819	1.000000
11.261459	4.666807	1.000000
11.282504	4.554002	1.000000
11.299648	4.440540	1.000000
11.312870	4.326555	1.000000
11.322158	4.212180	1.000000
11.327496	4.097554	1.000000
11.328883	3.982812	1.000000
11.326312	3.868091	1.000000
11.319790	3.753526	1.000000
11.309322	3.639254	1.000000
11.294922	3.525411	1.000000
11.276608	3.412132	1.000000
11.254401	3.299551	1.000000
11.228325	3.187802	1.000000
11.198414	3.077018	1.000000
11.164703	2.967332	1.000000
11.127232	2.858872	1.000000
11.086044	2.751768	1.000000
11.041190	2.646148	1.000000
10.992722	2.542136	1.000000
10.940697	2.439856	1.000000
10.885180	2.339430	1.000000
10.826233	2.240978	1.000000
10.763928	2.144615	1.000000
10.698340	2.050457	1.000000
10.629544	1.958615	1.000000
10.557624	1.869199	1.000000

Figure 10.30 (Continued)

10.482666	1.782316	1.000000
10.404758	1.698067	1.000000
10.323992	1.616553	1.000000
10.240463	1.537871	1.000000
10.197368	1.500000	1.000000

REC0033
  (X) .792893   (Y) 1.500000   (Z) 1.000000
REC0034
  (X) .000000   (Y) .000000   (Z) .000000
REC0040
  (X) .000000   (Y) .000000   (Z) 2.000000
REC0041
  (X) 1.500000   (Y) 1.500000   (Z) 1.923070
REC0042
  (X)5.807718   (Y)5.807718   (Z)2.999999
REC0044
  (X)6.000000   (Y)5.999999   (Z)2.999999
REC0045

(X)6.037401	(Y)6.037408	(Z)2.999999
6.114954	6.109367	2.999999
6.195144	6.178376	2.999999
6.277858	6.244339	2.999999
6.362981	6.307162	2.999999
6.450393	6.366759	2.999999
6.539973	6.423045	2.999999
6.631595	6.475944	2.999999
6.725130	6.525378	2.999999
6.820449	6.571281	2.999999
6.917417	6.613588	2.999999
7.015899	6.652239	2.999999
7.115758	6.687181	2.999999
7.216853	6.718365	2.999999
7.319044	6.745746	2.999999
7.422187	6.769288	2.999999
7.526138	6.788957	2.999999
7.630752	6.804725	2.999999
7.735883	6.816570	2.999999
7.841382	6.824476	2.999999
7.947103	6.828432	2.999999
8.052899	6.828432	2.999999
8.158621	6.824476	2.999999
8.264121	6.816570	2.999999
8.369251	6.804725	2.999999

Figure 10.30 (Continued)

8.473865	6.788957	2.999999
8.577816	6.769288	2.999999
8.680958	6.745746	2.999999
8.783149	6.718364	2.999999
8.884245	6.687180	2.999999
8.984103	6.652238	2.999999
9.082585	6.613586	2.999999
9.179553	6.571279	2.999999
9.274872	6.525377	2.999999
9.368407	6.475942	2.999999
9.460029	6.423044	2.999999
9.549609	6.366757	2.999999
9.637020	6.307160	2.999999
9.722144	6.244336	2.999999
9.804858	6.178374	2.999999
9.885048	6.109365	2.999999
9.962601	6.037406	2.999999
10.037410	5.962597	2.999999
10.109370	5.885043	2.999999
10.178378	5.804853	2.999999
10.244339	5.722139	2.999999
10.307163	5.637016	2.999999
10.366760	5.549604	2.999999
10.423046	5.460023	2.999999
10.475944	5.368402	2.999999
10.525379	5.274866	2.999999
10.571282	5.179548	2.999999
10.613589	5.082580	2.999999
10.652240	4.984098	2.999999
10.687182	4.884239	2.999999
10.718365	4.783143	2.999999
10.745747	4.680953	2.999999
10.769290	4.577810	2.999999
10.788958	4.473859	2.999999
10.804725	4.369245	2.999999
10.816570	4.264114	2.999999
10.824477	4.158614	2.999999
10.828433	4.052892	2.999999
10.828433	3.947097	2.999999
10.824477	3.841376	2.999999
10.816570	3.735876	2.999999
10.804725	3.630746	2.999999
10.788956	3.526132	2.999999

Figure 10.30 (Continued)

10.769287	3.422181	2.999999
10.745746	3.319038	2.999999
10.718364	3.216847	2.999999
10.687179	3.115752	2.999999
10.652237	3.015893	2.999999
10.613586	2.917411	2.999999
10.571278	2.820443	2.999999
10.525375	2.725125	2.999999
10.475940	2.631589	2.999999
10.423042	2.539968	2.999999
10:366756	2.450388	2.999999
10.307159	2.362976	2.999999
10.244335	2.277853	2.999999
10.178372	2.195139	2.999999
10.109363	2.114950	2.999999
10.037403	2.037396	2.999999
10.000000	2.000000	2.999999

```
REC0046
  (X)10.000000   (Y)2.000000   (Z)3.048070
REC0050
  (X)1.292893    (Y)2.000000   (Z)1.959681
REC0051
  (X).000000     (Y).000000    (Z).000000
OPT=
```

Figure 10.30 (Concluded)

After computer processing has occurred to the point of the CL Data file just reviewed, the programmer can then request tool path graphics from the system. Graphics such as those in Figures 10.28 and 10.29 will either be drawn on a plotter or displayed on a CRT screen depending on the system. Note though that the computer system does not normally indicate cross reference numbers of the program statements.

The next computer processing step will be for the CL Data to be postprocessed into a machine control program file. During postprocessing the computer converts the CL Data into the proper format to be understood by the machine tool control unit. At this time the postprocessor also adds additional function codes to specify types of motion, speeds, and feeds and auxiliary codes for turning program options on and off. Figure 10.31 shows a typical machine tool output or tape file generated by the postprocessor for our UNIAPT sample program.

Graphics-Based Systems

Graphics-based systems are referred to as Graphical Numerical Control (GNC). They differ from language-based systems in the following manner.

N010 G00 X0 Y0 Z10 S400 M03	Check home position P0
	start spindle
N020 X-.75 Y.75 Z1 M08	Move clear of part, set Z depth
N030 G01 X1.2929 Y2.000 F10.0	Feed to Ref. 27, Figure 10.10
N040 X5.6464 Y6.3536	Feed to Ref. 31
N050 G02 X8.0 Y7.3284 I2.3536 J.9748	Cut circle 1
N060 X11.3284 Y4.00 I0 J3.3284	
N070 X10.1974 Y1.5 I3.3284 J0	Cut circle to Ref. 32
N080 G01 X.7929	Feed to Ref. 33
N090 G00 Z3.1 M09	Retract Z, turn coolant off
N100 X0 Y0 Z10	Rapid to P0 Ref. 34
N110 Z2.0	Rapid position Z Ref. 40
N120 G01 X1.5 Y1.5 Z1.9231 F20 M08	Feed to Ref. 41
	turn coolant on
N130 X5.8077 Y5.8077 Z3.0	Feed to Ref. 42
N140 X6.0 Y6.0	Feed to Ref. 44
N150 G02 X8.00 Y6.8284 I2.0 J.8284	Cut circle 1 top
N160 X10.8284 Y4.0 I0 J2.8284	Cut circle 1
N170 X10.0 Y2.0 I2.8284 J0	Cut circle 1 Ref. 45
N180 G01 Z3.0481	Position Z axis Ref. 46
N190 X1.2929 Z1.9597	Feed to position Ref. 50
N200 G00 Z3.1 M09	Retract Z position Ref. 50, turn coolant off
N210 X0 Y0 Z10 M05	Rapid to home position P0, turn spindle off
N220 M30	End of program

Figure 10.31 Postprocessor output UNIAPT sample program.

When the geometric detail of the component has been constructed on the CRT screen, the outline shape of the cutting tool, or tools, to be used are superimposed on the component image and can be freely moved around using the cursor control device. Thus the programmer can, in effect, select appropriate tool paths to facilitate machining of the component or component detail. A better impression of the process may be obtained by considering the following example.

Figure 10.32 illustrates a component detail as it might be "drawn" on the computer screen. Also shown are two different-sized circles representing the superimposed cutters required to machine the outside profile and clear the inner shape, which represents a pocket.

Consider the large-diameter cutter first. This cutter is to be used to machine the outside profile. The size and type of cutter will have been established already and entered into the data file, possibly via a keyboard entry. The programmer now has free control to move the cutter to any position he or she chooses.

The cutter is first positioned in a suitable starting position. If cutter radius compensation is required, then the starting position will be a suitable distance away from the profile so that the cutter can attain the correct position before contacting the work surface. This start position is then entered into the data file either via the cursor control or the keyboard.

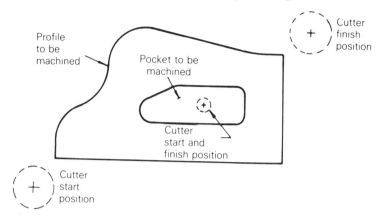

Figure 10.32 A graphical numerical control display.

Having established the start position the programmer moves the cutter image to the finish position, and this too is entered into the file.

Using this very simple data entry the computer is able to compute the complete cutter route, indicating it on the screen alongside the component. It will also list, in numerical form, the cutter location in relation to a previously established datum at each stage in the machining process; the list appears on a second CRT screen or an interfaced printer.

Now consider the machining of the pocket. To achieve this the programmer simply has to move the cutter to the start position at the center of the pocket as indicated. All that is now needed are keyboard data entries to establish that a pocket clearance routine is required. From this data entry the computer will establish all the moves necessary to clear the pocket and machine the final profile. Again, the cutter paths will be shown graphically and also presented in numerical form, the dimensional values being in relation to a predetermined datum.

Note that in this simple description no mention has been made of movement in the third, that is, Z axis. Clearance in the Z axis, and the depth to which the cutter is required to go, will be entered via the keyboard as the program is constructed. Data relating to speeds and feeds will be entered in the same way.

In addition to the component image displayed on the screen, it is possible to include any workholding or tool-holding arrangements that may influence the choice of tool paths. An example of such a display for a turning operation is shown in Figure 10.33. By including such detail it is possible for the programmer to be reasonably confident that all programmed moves will be collision-free.

As with language-based systems, it will be possible to obtain copies of the data entered via an interfaced printer.

Data can also be reprocessed to verify its accuracy prior to postprocessing into machine control language. Graphics-based systems, such as language based systems, have also given way to the more powerful CAD/CAM systems that can generate commands through graphics for all axes.

Figure 10.33 Part programming station showing use of computer graphics for program proving.

CAD/CAM: Computer-Aided Design and Manufacture

The expression "computer-aided design," or more commonly the abbreviation CAD, is the term used to describe the process by which engineering designers use the computer as a creative tool allowing them to produce, evaluate, modify, and finalize their designs. The computer becomes a terminal at which the designer sits to analyze data, make calculations, and use the computer graphics to build up quickly and efficiently a three-dimensional image of a projected design. The image can be rotated and viewed from different angles, sectioned through various planes, stretched, condensed, and generally assessed. Modifications can be made instantly. As each stage of the design process proceeds, the resulting data can be stored and retrieved at will.

When the designer is satisfied, the details of the design can be transferred electronically to the drafting department. Here the draftsman or draftswoman transforms the original designs into a series of engineering drawings which he or she creates on the computer screen, and again at this stage each individual component can be rotated, sectioned, scaled up or down and so on in a further process of evaluation which may or may not result in modifications to the original design. When this task is finished, fully dimensioned drawings can be printed from an interfaced printer or plotter, or alternatively the information can be stored in computer files as numerical data for later retrieval. The use of computers as an aid to manufacturing processes is referred to as Computer-Aided Manufacturing (CAM). The CAPP process is part of that general definition. Together CAD and CAM form the basis of Computer-Aided Engineering (CAE).

From the foregoing text the reader will now appreciate that an important element of the CAM process is the geometric definition of the component detail. It is, of course, also central to any computer-aided drafting process. It is logical therefore that the two processes should be linked. Most CAD/CAM software currently in use provides this facility.

The transfer involves reducing the detail drawing (Figure 10.39) to its basic geometry by removing all dimensions, notes, leader lines etc. This is easily and instantly achieved, since the part's computer file will have been compiled by the use of overlays or layers, with one layer containing the basic part geometry and subsequent layers containing dimensions and other data. Each layer is capable of being displayed independently of the others.

With the part file reduced to its basic form, the geometry created as part of the drafting process can be used for part programming purposes, thus eliminating the geometry construction stage of the CAPP/CAM process, and speeding part programming activity considerably.

Computer-aided manufacturing (CAM) is the term generally used to describe manufacturing processes that are computer controlled. One very important manufacturing process is metal cutting, and the computer involvement in this area of activity has been the subject of this text. Metal cutting is, however, just one type of manufacturing process that is computer controlled. There are many others: welding, flame cutting, presswork, electrodischarge machining, parts assembly, and so on.

All the processes listed previously are truly manufacturing processes, that is, the end result is a component or an assembly of components. But there are a host of other essential functions that play a part in the overall setup. The supply of materials and tooling, part programming, process control, and inspection/quality control, are some functions that are workshop-related. Spreading the net further, there are the financial aspects—marketing, stock control, and distribution, for example—and of course there is the design and drafting process discussed earlier. It is possible for all these functions to be interrelated via computer control into a total computerized manufacturing system referred to as CIM (Computer-Integrated Manufacturing).

Since it is the practical aspects of the system that are most likely to be of interest to the reader, that is, the design and making of the product, the relationships between these two areas are worthy of further comment and are perhaps the key elements in the system. In the past, CAD and CAM, that is the production element of CAM, have developed as two separate activities, with the application of computers to the production process being somewhat ahead of CAD. Increasingly, even in small companies, they are now being seen not as two related functions but as one integrated function. Already the more sophisticated design/drafting systems are linked to the manufacturing process via part-programming facilities. Manufacturing aspects are fully considered at the design stage, and machine-control programs are produced direct from design data rather than from a separate, and therefore error prone, analysis of an already finalized engineering drawing. The process may also, ultimately, eliminate the need for conventional drawings. Totally computerized engineering has arrived, and the rate at which it is implemented, especially in large companies, is likely to be rapid.

CAD/CAM systems like computer-assisted programming systems can be found with many different capabilities running on a multitude of platforms. Capabilities run from low-level two-dimensional to high-level three-dimensional systems. The hardware used ranges from small personal computers through minis and mainframes. All systems, though, will have a keyboard for operator commands, a user interface device (mouse, joystick, puck and tablet, or light pen), graphics screen, and central processing unit (CPU) with an information storage media device like a floppy disk, zip disk, or CD-ROM (Figure 10.34). For discussion purposes in this book we will be looking at a mini-based system that uses a mouse-actived command system displayed on a CRT screen. Figure 10.35 shows the area of the screen where various information will be displayed.

User Interface

CAD/CAM systems normally use some form of standard user interface, which essentially replaces direct keyboard input to an applications program with six types of interactive input:

- interactive headline
- graphic icons
- pop-up menus

- single keyboard input
- pointer strokes
- text macro processor

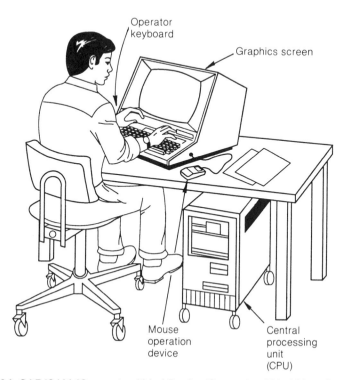

Figure 10.34 CAD/CAM (Computer-Aided Design/Computer-Aided Manufacturing) workstation.

CIM CAD USER ENVIRONMENT

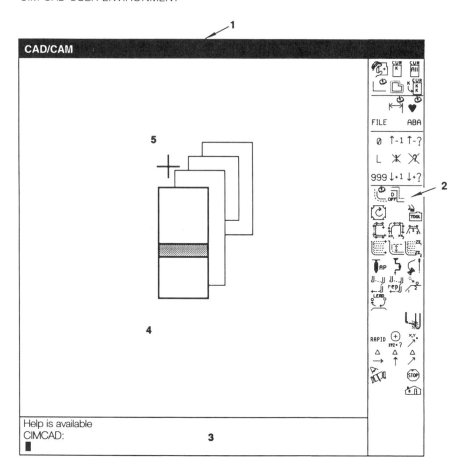

1. HEADLINE

2. GRAPHIC ICONS

3. SCROLL AREA

4. GRAPHICS AREA

5. POP-UP MENUS

Figure 10.35 CAD/CAM work station screen display. (Courtesy of CIMLINC Inc.)

Graphic icons are always visible and reside in a fixed location at the side, top or bottom of the user CRT screen and are activated through the use of the mouse instead of keying in information. Other systems may use electronic pucks, joysticks, or light pens to select commands from the CRT screen or a tablet. Pop-up menus are a method of command input by which text or symbols representing commands are selected, rather than typing in the command itself. When the *middle mouse button* (MMB) (Fig. 10.37)

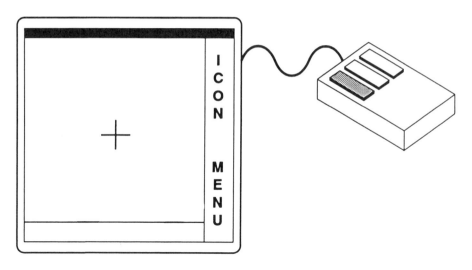

Figure 10.36 Left Mouse Button (LMB) GRAPHICS (Working) Cursor.

is pressed, pop-up menus appear on the screen near the screen pointer position. Both menus and icons are userdefinable and may be modified at any time during a session. By providing both graphic icons and pop-up menus, the user's focus remains on the screen.

The mouse-controlled screen pointer is used to select items from the pop-up menus and graphic icons, and for input of coordinating information. The information is added by pressing the *left mouse button* (LMB) (Figure 10.36).

Single keystrokes by keyboard input can be used to invoke a particular effect, such as inputting a new geometric point at exactly the same location as an existing point near the screen pointer.

As in all application programs that use various forms of user interface, all menu selections and single-keystroke commands are converted into long computer commands for execution. It is these long commands that form the basis of the applications program and out of which any new user menus or single-keystroke commands are built.

Cursor and Mouse Concepts

A cursor is a symbol displayed on the CRT screen. Cursors vary in style depending on which mouse (or activation device) button is pressed and the menu being used. The style of the cursor has a specific meaning. It functions as a pointing device and is positioned by moving the mouse or activation device. Sometimes you use it to point to a location where you wish to start a line or specify the next position on a line. Other times you use it to make a selection from a menu. In many cases you use it to indicate which entity is used to preform a specific function, which is related to the entity near the cursor, by a command chosen from one of the many available menus. *The position of the cursor is very important in these conditions.* The following defines how a system might work which employs a three button mouse.

Left Mouse Button (LMB)—GRAPHICS (Working) Cursor   The graphics cursor (normally a plus sign) is used as a pointing device to create and modify the entities (lines, text, machining paths, etc.), which define the graphics. It has other uses also, which are addressed further on in this section. The style of the graphic cursor may be changed by the user.

Middle Mouse Button (MMB)—Pop-Up Cursor   Pop Up cursors are used to make a selection from the Pop Up menus. Pressing the MMB activates and displays the various Pop Up menus, *only for as long as the MMB is held down.* They appear near the graphics cursor position at the time the MMB is pressed. When it is released, the pop up menus disappear.

On the once popular CIMLINC system shown the TITLES are displayed in inverse video (white letters black background).

As the mouse is moved within the menus, the selection the cursor is on turns to inverse video. When the cursor is positioned on a menu that is underneath another, it instantly pops to the top as shown in Figure 10.37. In cases where the menu is small, position the cursor in the title area to pop it to the top, then on the desired selection of the menu. Releasing the button on a highlighted command will activate the command without typing.

Right Mouse Button (RMB)—Static Menu (ICON) Cursor   The static icons are graphic representations of various computer commands, either CAD or CAM, that can be cursor-selected to keep typing to a minimum. By placing the commands on the computer screen instead of a desk tablet device, the operator's eyes do not have to leave the screen.

The icon cursor is an inverse video of a specific icon (see Figure 10.38). It is used to make selections from the static menu.

When the RMB is pressed, the cursor is displayed instantly in the static menu (icon menu), for as long as pressure is applied. When the RMB is released, the command or

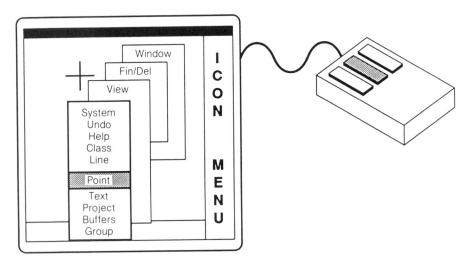

Figure 10.37 Middle Mouse Button (MMB) Pop Up Cursor.

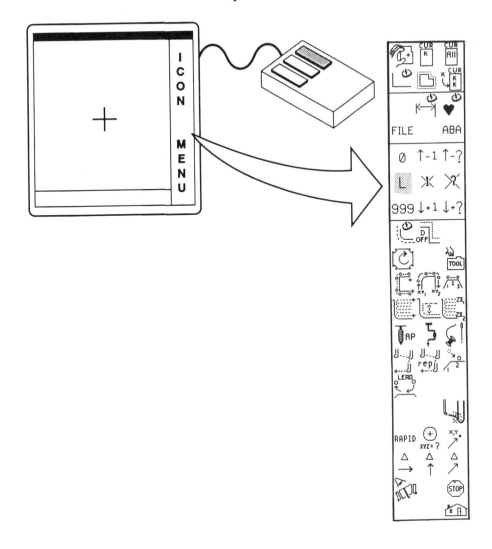

Figure 10.38 Right Mouse Button (RMB) Static Menu (ICON) Cursor.

action associated to the icon is issued to the CAD/CAM control processor unit and the actual printed command appears at the bottom of the screen.

Now that we have established a general definition of a CAD/CAM system, let us follow the complete process through of generating a program for a part on a CNC lathe. The first step is to generate a CAD design of the part to be manufactured. Figure 10.39 shows a screen display of the screw jack part once it is completed.

After the part creation in the CAD system is complete, the programmer must process the part for its machining operations deciding on the tools to be used. For the screw jack the following tools were decided upon.

- 80° diamond-shaped-insert right-hand turning tool for rough facing and turning

- 0.500 in.-diameter drill for hole

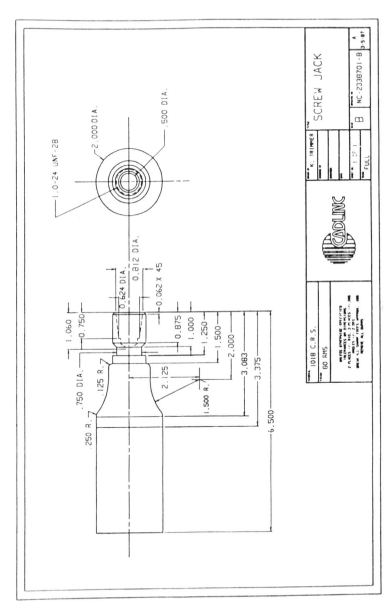

Figure 10.39 CAD screen displaying headline, graphic icons, and part print in graphics area.

- 0.125-in.-width parting tool for grooves or thread relief

- 30° diamond-shaped-insert right-hand turning tool for finish facing and turning

- Brazed carbide-tipped boring bar for rough and finish boring of tapered bore

- 60° threading tool for 1-24 UNF-2B thread

- 0.125-in.-width parting tool for part cutoff.

Once processing is complete, the programmer will check the tool library generated on the computer system to see if additional tools need to be generated. Figure 10.40 illustrates the necessary geometry and origin point that need to be created in CAD so tool information can be transferred into the tool library in CAM. Having this information stored in the CAM system allows programmers to create and display a variety of tooling packages for use on various part programs.

It has been shown that tools can be drawn up in CAD and its computer definition transferred to a tool library for later use in CAM. It should be noted, though, that tools can also be defined in the CAM system through the use of special icons and pop up menus such as those that appear in Figure 10.41.

Now that the tooling is complete, the programmer will reduce the part computer file to only the machining curves/geometry that are required to produce the part program. The programmer reduces the file, as shown in Figure 10.42, to its basic profile and then the system will convert them to machining curves with some basic entered commands. Figure 10.42 shows the labeled machining curves that appear as a profile of half the part.

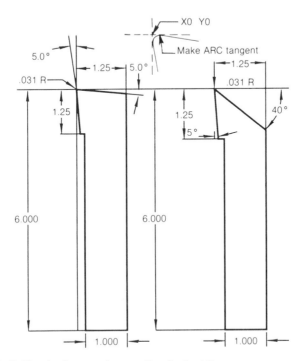

Figure 10.40 Cutting tool geometry creation for tool library.

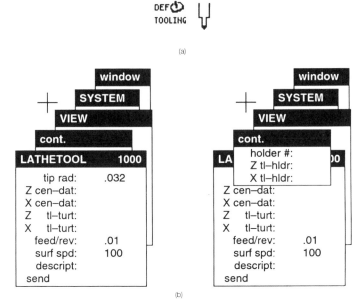

Figure 10.41 CAM (a) tool definition icons and (b) pop up menus.

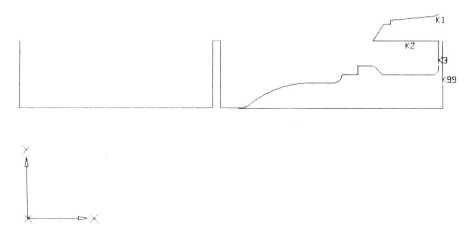

Figure 10.42 CAD part drawing/computer file reduced to required CAM profile curves.

Curve $K1$ is the internal bore, $K2$ is the part center, $K3$ is the outside profile, and $K99$ is the original part stock outline.

Figure 10.43 shows us that the machining curves are made up of straight and circular line segments called spans. The CAM system gives us the freedom to machine all spans or any percentage of a given span. This kind of freedom allows for any type of machining pass to be created.

Now that the CAD data are generated, the programmer can enter the CAM system to start the creation of machining paths. The machining system is entered in this case by typing in the command CIMCAM. The computer system responses by asking for part data and tool library input files and a name for the output file. The CRT will then display

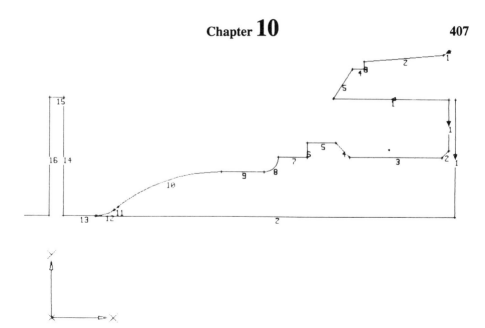

Figure 10.43 CAM profile curves displayed in spans or segments form.

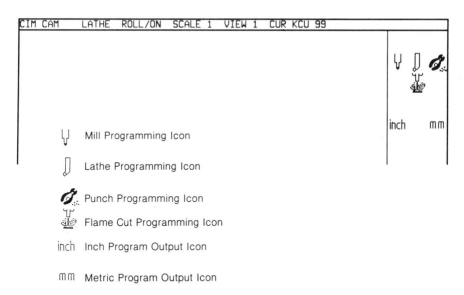

Figure 10.44 CRT display entering CAM for machining option and inch/metric output, a—mill programming icon; b—lathe programming icon; c—punch programming icon; d—flame cut programming icon; e—inch program output icon: f—metric program output icon.

the screen in Figure 10.44 so the type of machining to be performed (milling, lathe work, punching, or flame cutting), and inch or metric output for the machine tool can be selected. The majority of CAD/CAM systems today will allow options as to inch or metric output, and at least milling and lathe work selections. The selections on this system are completed by selecting icons with the mouse or typing the command.

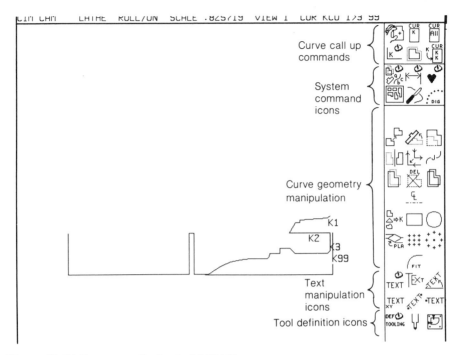

Figure 10.45 Part curve display in CIMCAM.

Once CIMCAM is entered, the programmer can then display the machining curves or the machine's tool curves or both as in Figures 10.45 and 10.46. Using the top six icons the programmer can show and close-up on just one curve or show all curves at once. Figure 10.47 indicates the programmer's next task of properly orienting the part and machine tool turrets of tools. Figure 10.47 shows this operation completed. The programmer could then use the system to dimension Figure 10.48 and give it to the machine operator as setup instructions.

The task to perform now is to create the machining paths that you would like the computer to create for you in the machine tools language. In order to do this, the program must enter the machining sequence mode by activating the geometry index icon to switch to the sequence or operation mode index icon display, Figure 10.49. With the sequence mode icons active, the programmer selects a new operation and enters a operation number, automatically going into the machining mode.

With tool path generation icons active, the programmer then goes step by step through the process allowing the computer system to generate the needed tool path. Figures 10.50–10.61 and computer program (Fig. 10.62) show the computer commands and program statements generated and the graphics commands used to do so.

The machining path commands when finished are placed in one master file by filing out of the sequence mode of operation (see Figure 10.63). The programmer now has a file of computer commands, like those found in language based programs but created from computer graphics and icon commands, that will generate a CNC machine program. The machine program is created by running the computer program

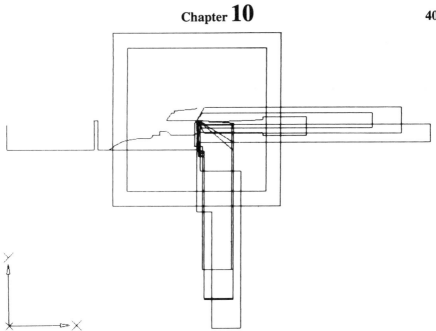

Figure 10.46 CRT display of part, turret, and tool data indicating common datum point.

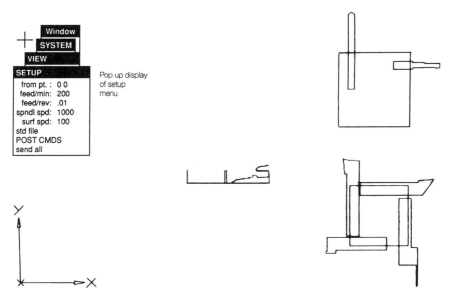

Figure 10.47 CRT display of part, turret, and tool data after completion of computer setup statement. The setup statement is completed by using the indicated pop-up menu.

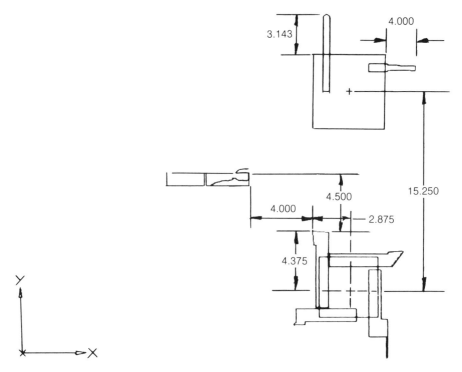

Figure 10.48 CRT display of part, turret, and tool setup dimensions.

through a postprocessor program in the computer. The postprocessor program is a translator that converts the computer program to a CNC program for the particular machine you will be using just as was done in language-based programming. There is normally a postprocessor file for each different machine you have. This process is very simply completed by activating first the program to convert and then the postprocessor required, through typed in commands. The output of our example program for the screw jack can be seen in Figure 10.64. It is also indicated on the CNC program what computer statements generated what machine statements. By using a few more commands to the CAD/CAM system, we could transfer the information to the machine tool by electronic means or create disks or CDs and take it to the machine control.

You have now seen the basic powers of a CAD/CAM system, but they are far beyond what you have seen. The PC (personal computer) based CAD/CAM systems have grown tremendously over the past few years. The PC broke into the CAD/CAM market as early as 1983 and became full three dimensional modeling capable by 1991. By 1993 specialized programming tools for programmers where part nesting volumes could be calculated automatically, surface modeling appeared, as well as special options for mold cavity programming. Systems can have the capability of creating complex three-dimensional programs for three- to five-axes CNC machining. Three-dimensional programming is common in both the toolmaking (sheet metal forming dies and plastic/rubber molds) and aircraft manufacturing industries. In these industries the three-dimensional shapes must be cut from solid blocks of material. Around 1994 PC

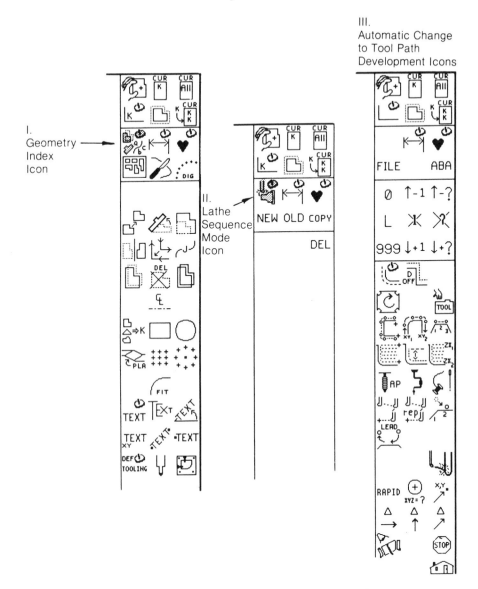

Figure 10.49 Icon commands for entering tool path generation mode.

based CAD/CAM systems became Windows Based. In 1995 we saw the beginning of solids based programming with 3-D tool path verification providing time and dollar savings in program prove-out.

In surface or 3 to 5 axis programming, as in machine controls there are various systems that can be used and different levels of complexity. Surfacing programs started out with the surface to be manufactured defined by what is referred to as wire frame. A wire frame is a part surface defined by a mesh of many points or nerbs. These points can be collected from a model using a coordinate measuring machine (CMM), defined

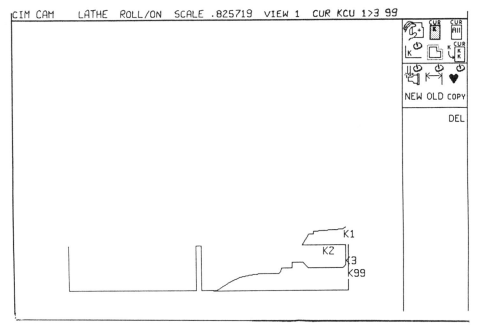

Figure 10.50 Screen display showing part curves activated by operator.

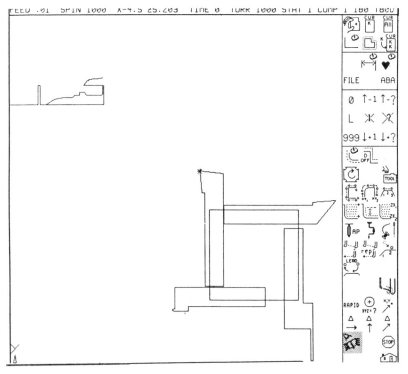

Figure 10.51 Screen display after the setup statement (Fig. 10.47) in pop-up menu has been completed. Turret display icon has been activated.

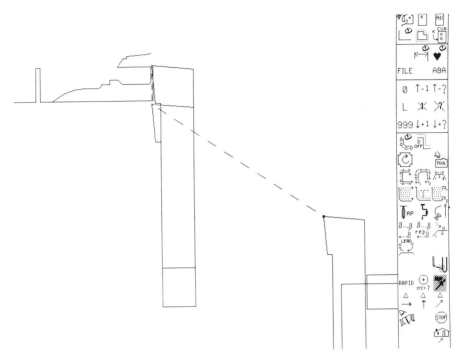

Figure 10.52 Interactive CRT display of facing operation and computer icons. (See Figure 10.62 for computer statements generated, GOTO commands—sequence 10, lines 11 and 13.)

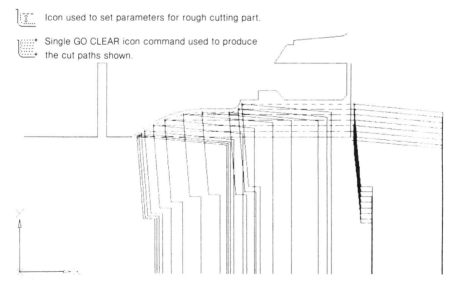

Icon used to set parameters for rough cutting part.

Single GO CLEAR icon command used to produce the cut paths shown.

Figure 10.53 Interactive CRT display of computer-generated roughing passes. (See Figure 10.62 for computer statements generated by GO CLEAR command—sequence 10, line 23.)

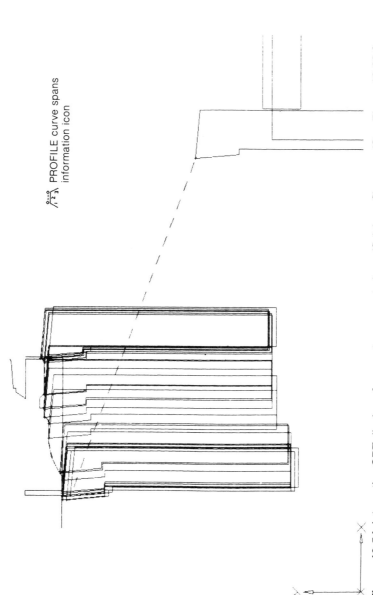

PROFILE curve spans
information icon

Figure 10.54 Interactive CRT display of computer-generated semifinish profile pass. (See Figure 10.62 for computer statements generated by profile command—sequence 10, lines 26, 27, and 28.)

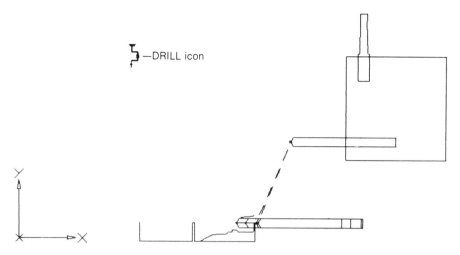

Figure 10.55 Interactive CRT display of computer-generated drilling cycle. (See Figure 10.62 for computer statements generated by the drilling command—sequence 20, line 11.)

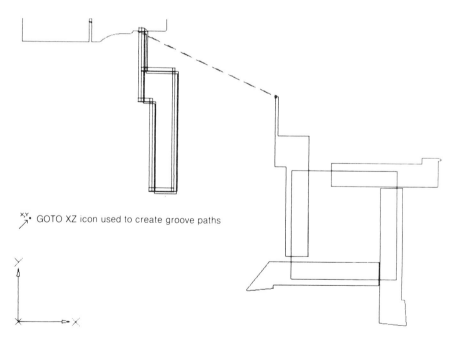

Figure 10.56 Interactive CRT display of computer-generated grooving operation. (See Figure 10.62 for computer statements generated by the GOTO command—sequence 30, lines 12, 17, and 22.)

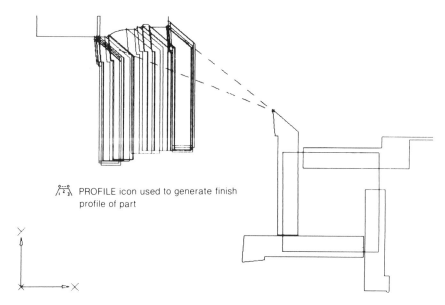

PROFILE icon used to generate finish
profile of part

Figure 10.57 Interactive display of computer-generated finish profile pass on part.
(See Figure 10.62 for computer statements generated by the PROFILE command—
sequence 40, lines 15, 16, and 17.)

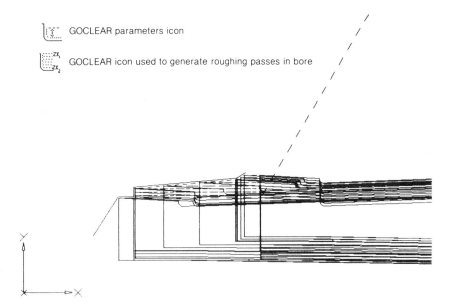

GOCLEAR parameters icon

GOCLEAR icon used to generate roughing passes in bore

Figure 10.58 Close-up interactive display of computer-generated rough boring of
tapered hole. (See Figure 10.62 for computer statements generated by the GOCLEAR
command—sequence 50, lines 11 and 12.)

PROFILE icon used to generate finish bore

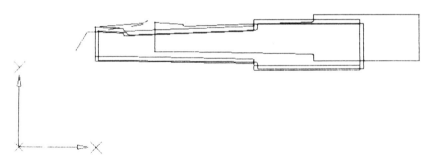

Figure 10.59 Close-up interactive display of computer-generated finish profile cut on bore. (See Figure 10.62 for computer statement generated by the PROFILE command— sequence 50, line 21.)

THREADING icon used to generate outside diameter of threads

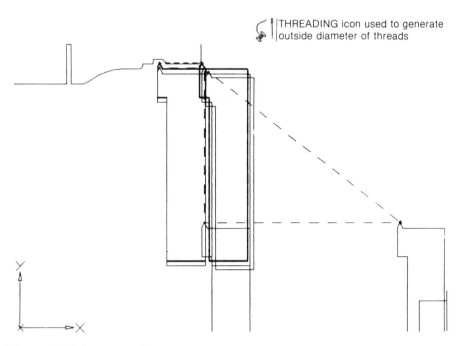

Figure 10.60 Interactive CRT display of computer-generated threading operation. (See Figure 10.62 for computer statement generated by THREADING command— sequence 60, line 12.)

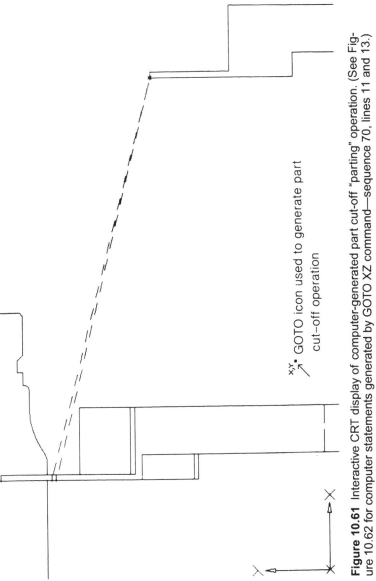

Figure 10.61 Interactive CRT display of computer-generated part cut-off "parting" operation. (See Figure 10.62 for computer statements generated by GOTO XZ command—sequence 70, lines 11 and 13.)

x,y. GOTO icon used to generate part cut-off operation

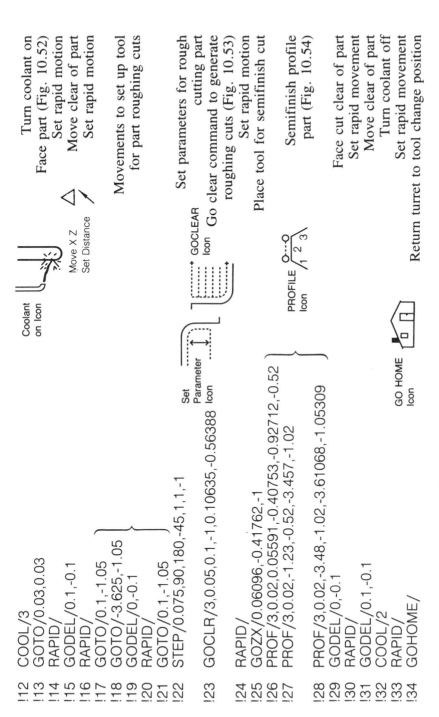

!12 COOL/3   Turn coolant on
!13 GOTO/0.03,0.03   Face part (Fig. 10.52)
!14 RAPID/   Set rapid motion
!15 GODEL/0.1,-0.1   Move clear of part
!16 RAPID/   Set rapid motion
!17 GOTO/0.1,-1.05
!18 GOTO/-3.625,-1.05   Movements to set up tool
!19 GODEL/0,-0.1   for part roughing cuts
!20 RAPID/
!21 GOTO/0.1,-1.05
!22 STEP/0.075,90,180,-45,1,1,-1   Set parameters for rough
                                                                               cutting part
!23 GOCLR/3,0.05,0.1,-1,0.10635,-0.56388   Go clear command to generate
                                                                 roughing cuts (Fig. 10.53)
!24 RAPID/   Set rapid motion
!25 GOZX/0.06096,-0.41762,-1   Place tool for semifinish cut
!26 PROF/3,0.02,0.05591,-0.40753,-0.92712,-0.52
!27 PROF/3,0.02,-1.23,-0.52,-3.457,-1.02
                                                                               Semifinish profile
!28 PROF/3,0.02,-3.48,-1.02,-3.61068,-1.05309   part (Fig. 10.54)
!29 GODEL/0,-0.1   Face cut clear of part
!30 RAPID/   Set rapid movement
!31 GODEL/0.1,-0.1   Move clear of part
!32 COOL/2   Turn coolant off
!33 RAPID/   Set rapid movement
!34 GOHOME/   Return turret to tool change position

Figure 10.62 Computer statements generated by the CAD/CAM system from which the CNC program will be created.

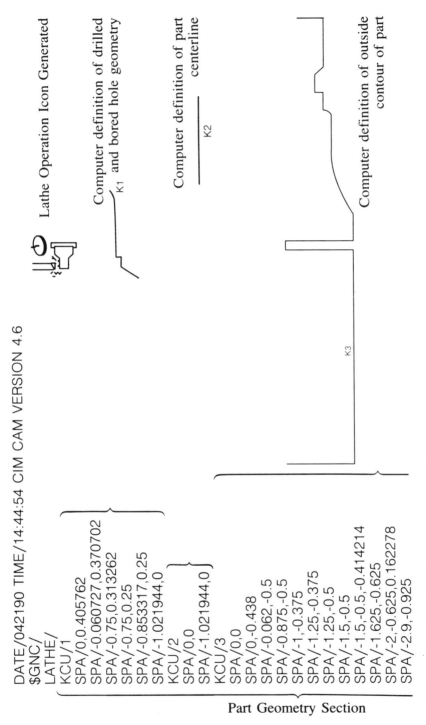

DATE/042190 TIME/14:44:54 CIM CAM VERSION 4.6
$GNC/
LATHE/
KCU/1
SPA/0,0.405762
SPA/-0.060727,0.370702
SPA/-0.75,0.313262
SPA/-0.75,0.25
SPA/-0.853317,0.25
SPA/-1.021944,0
KCU/2
SPA/0,0
SPA/-1.021944,0
KCU/3
SPA/0,0
SPA/0,-0.438
SPA/-0.062,-0.5
SPA/-0.875,-0.5
SPA/-1,-0.375
SPA/-1.25,-0.375
SPA/-1.25,-0.5
SPA/-1.5,-0.5
SPA/-1.5,-0.5,-0.414214
SPA/-1.625,-0.625
SPA/-2,-0.625,0.162278
SPA/-2.9,-0.925

Part Geometry Section

Lathe Operation Icon Generated

Computer definition of drilled
and bored hole geometry

K1

Computer definition of part
centerline

K2

Computer definition of outside
contour of part

K3

Figure 10.62 Computer statements generated by the CAD/CAM system from which the CNC program will be created.

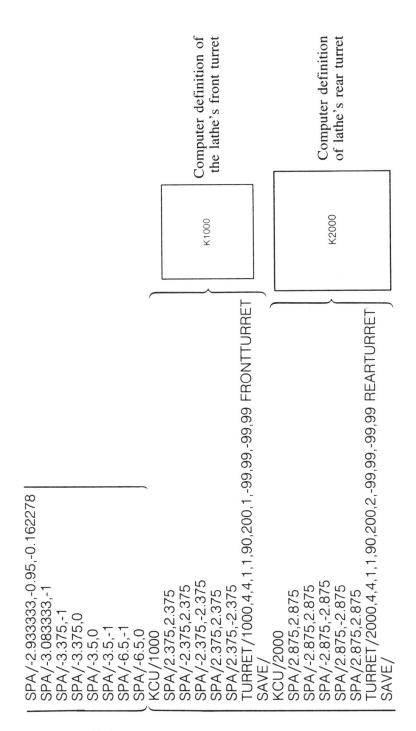

```
SPA/-2.933333,-0.95,-0.162278
SPA/-3.083333,-1
SPA/-3.375,-1
SPA/-3.375,0
SPA/-3.5,0
SPA/-3.5,-1
SPA/-6.5,-1
SPA/-6.5,0
KCU/1000
SPA/2.375,2.375
SPA/-2.375,2.375
SPA/-2.375,-2.375
SPA/2.375,2.375
SPA/2.375,-2.375
TURRET/1000,4,4,1,1,90,200,1,-99,99,-99,99 FRONTTURRET
SAVE/
KCU/2000
SPA/2.875,2.875
SPA/-2.875,2.875
SPA/-2.875,-2.875
SPA/2.875,-2.875
SPA/2.875,2.875
TURRET/2000,4,4,1,1,90,200,2,-99,99,-99,99 REARTURRET
SAVE/
```

K1000

Computer definition of the lathe's front turret

K2000

Computer definition of lathe's rear turret

Figure 10.62 (Continued)

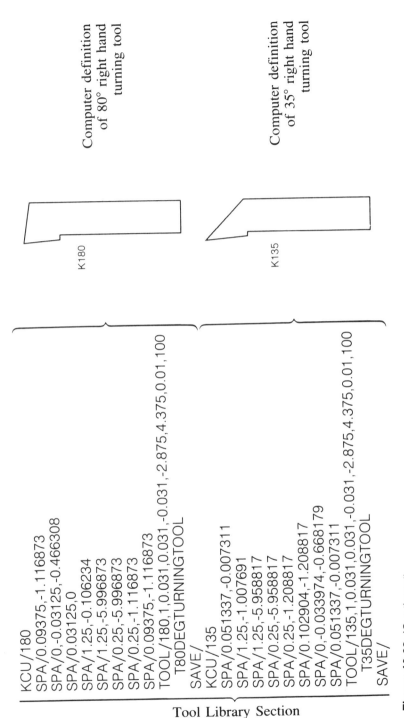

Computer definition of 80° right hand turning tool

K180

Computer definition of 35° right hand turning tool

K135

KCU/180
SPA/0.09375,-1.116873
SPA/0,-0.03125,-0.466308
SPA/0.03125,0
SPA/1.25,-0.106234
SPA/1.25,-5.996873
SPA/0.25,-5.996873
SPA/0.25,-1.116873
SPA/0.09375,-1.116873
TOOL/180,1,0.031,0.031,-0.031,-2.875,4.375,0.01,100
    T80DEGTURNINGTOOL
SAVE/
KCU/135
SPA/0.051337,-0.007311
SPA/1.25,-1.007691
SPA/1.25,-5.958817
SPA/0.25,-5.958817
SPA/0.25,-1.208817
SPA/0.102904,-1.208817
SPA/0,-0.033974,-0.668179
SPA/0.051337,-0.007311
TOOL/135,1,0.031,0.031,-0.031,-2.875,4.375,0.01,100
    T35DEGTURNINGTOOL
SAVE/

Tool Library Section

Figure 10.62 (Continued)

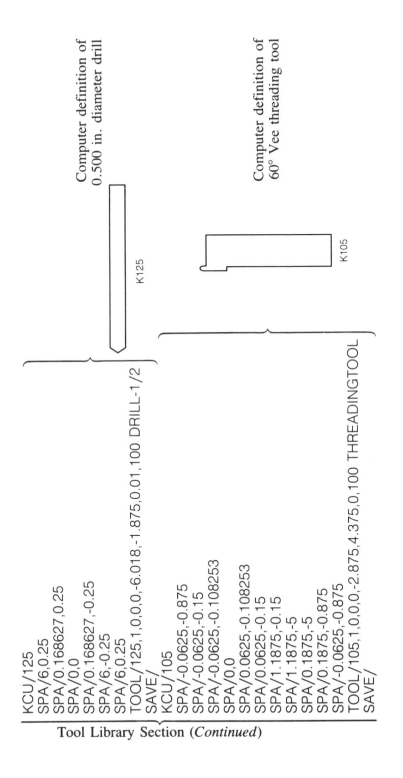

Computer definition of
0.500 in. diameter drill

K125

Computer definition of
60° Vee threading tool

K105

Tool Library Section (*Continued*)

```
KCU/125
SPA/6,0.25
SPA/0.168627,0.25
SPA/0,0
SPA/0.168627,-0.25
SPA/6,-0.25
SPA/6,0.25
TOOL/125,1,0,0,0,-6.018,-1.875,0.01,100 DRILL-1/2
SAVE/
KCU/105
SPA/-0.0625,-0.875
SPA/-0.0625,-0.15
SPA/-0.0625,-0.108253
SPA/0,0
SPA/0.0625,-0.108253
SPA/0.0625,-0.15
SPA/1.1875,-0.15
SPA/1.1875,-5
SPA/0.1875,-5
SPA/0.1875,-0.875
SPA/-0.0625,-0.875
TOOL/105,1,0,0,0,-2.875,4.375,0.100 THREADINGTOOL
SAVE/
```

Figure 10.62 (Continued)

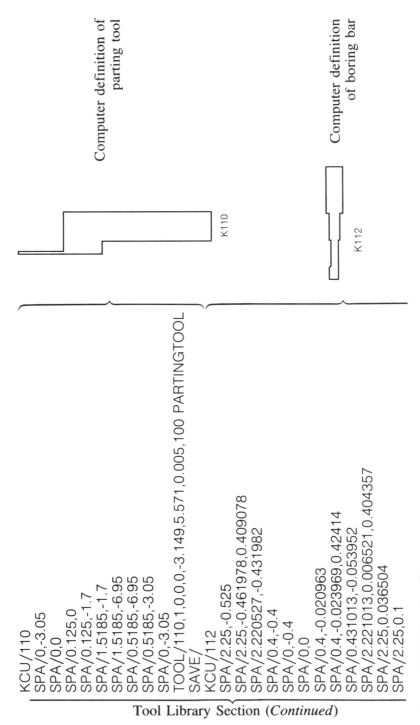

Computer definition of parting tool

Computer definition of boring bar

K110

K112

Tool Library Section (*Continued*)

```
KCU/110
SPA/0,-3.05
SPA/0,0
SPA/0.125,0
SPA/0.125,-1.7
SPA/1.5185,-1.7
SPA/1.5185,-6.95
SPA/0.5185,-6.95
SPA/0.5185,-3.05
SPA/0,-3.05
TOOL/110,1,0,0,0,-3.149,5.571,0.005,100 PARTINGTOOL
SAVE/
KCU/112
SPA/2.25,-0.525
SPA/2.25,-0.461978,0.409078
SPA/2.220527,-0.431982
SPA/0.4,-0.4
SPA/0,-0.4
SPA/0,0
SPA/0.4,-0.020963
SPA/0.4,-0.023969,0.42414
SPA/0.431013,-0.053952
SPA/2.221013,0.006521,0.404357
SPA/2.25,0.036504
SPA/2.25,0.1
```

Figure 10.62 (Continued)

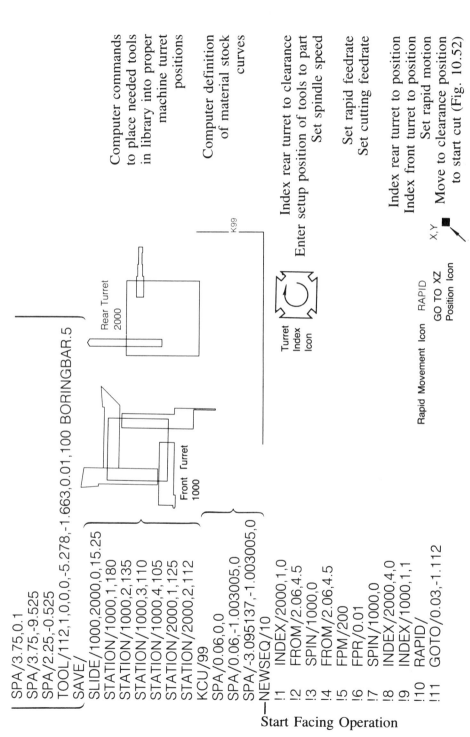

Figure 10.62 (Continued)

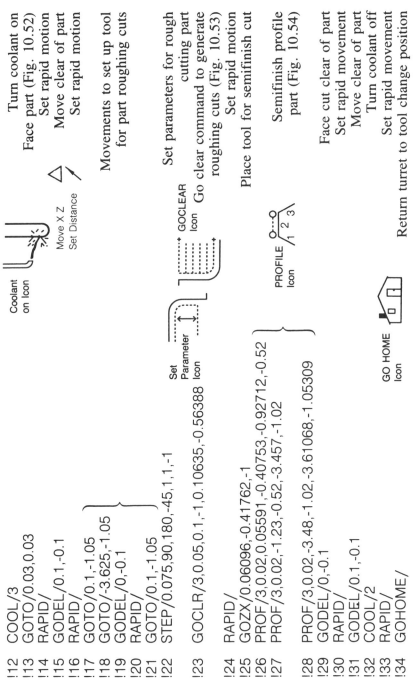

```
!12  COOL/3                                              Turn coolant on
!13  GOTO/0.03,0.03                                      Face part (Fig. 10.52)
!14  RAPID/                                              Set rapid motion
!15  GODEL/0.1,-0.1                                      Move clear of part
!16  RAPID/                                              Set rapid motion
!17  GOTO/0.1,-1.05
!18  GOTO/-3.625,-1.05                                   Movements to set up tool
!19  GODEL/0,-0.1                                        for part roughing cuts
!20  RAPID/
!21  GOTO/0.1,-1.05
!22  STEP/0.075,90,180,-45,1,1,-1                        Set parameters for rough
                                                             cutting part
!23  GOCLR/3,0.05,0.1,-1,0.10635,-0.56388               Go clear command to generate
                                                         roughing cuts (Fig. 10.53)
!24  RAPID/                                              Set rapid motion
!25  GOZX/0.06096,-0.41762,-1                            Place tool for semifinish cut
!26  PROF/3,0.02,0.05591,-0.40753,-0.92712,-0.52
!27  PROF/3,0.02,-1.23,-0.52,-3.457,-1.02                Semifinish profile
!28  PROF/3,0.02,-3.48,-1.02,-3.61068,-1.05309           part (Fig. 10.54)
!29  GODEL/0,-0.1                                        Face cut clear of part
!30  RAPID/                                              Set rapid movement
!31  GODEL/0.1,-0.1                                      Move clear of part
!32  COOL/2                                              Turn coolant off
!33  RAPID/                                              Set rapid movement
!34  GOHOME/                                             Return turret to tool change position
```

Coolant on Icon

Move X Z / Set Distance

Set Parameter Icon

GOCLEAR Icon

PROFILE Icon 1 2 3

GO HOME Icon

Figure 10.62 (Continued)

Create file of machining pathes
Machine time is 2.64 minutes

Index rear turret
Enter set-up position of tool to part
Enter machine spindle speed

Set rapid feed rate
Set cutting feed rate
Enter new spindle speed
Set rapid movement
Turn coolant on
Rapid tool to end of part
Drill part command (Fig. 10.55)
Turn coolant off
Set rapid movement
Clear tool from part
Set rapid movement
Return turret to tool change position
Create file of drilling tool pathes
Machine time for drilling operation

Enter set up tool
Enter set position of tool to part

Set up information

DRILL
Icon

Figure 10.62 (Continued)

Drilling Operation (Fig. 55)

```
FILE/
   M/C TIME 2.64
NEWSEQ/20
!1    INDEX/2000,1,5
!2    FROM/2.06,4.5
!3    SPIN/1000,0
!4    FROM/2.06,4.5
!5    FPM/200
!6    FPR/0.01
!7    SPIN/500,0
!8    RAPID/
!9    COOL/3
!10   GOTO/0.1,0
!11   DRILL/0.5,0.1,-1.022,2
!12   COOL/2
!13   RAPID/
!14   GODEL/0.1
!15   RAPID/
!16   GOHOME/
```

Grooving Operation

```
FILE/
   M/C TIME 0.29
NEWSEQ/30
!1    INDEX/2000,1,0
!2    FROM/2.06,4.5
!3    SPIN/1000,0
!4    FROM/2.06,4.5
!5    FPM/200
```

```
!6   INDEX/2000,3,0          Index rear turret to clearance position
!7   INDEX/1000,3,3          Index front turret to parting tool
!8   SPIN/300,0              Enter proper cutting rpm
!9   RAPID/                  Set rapid movement
!10  GOTO/-1.25,-0.55        Rapid to start grooving operation
!11  COOL/3                  Turn coolant on
!12  GOTO/-1.25,-0.375
!13  DWELL/2                 Dwell at end of cut
!14  GODEL/0,-0.15           Move to clear part
!15  RAPID/                  Set rapid movement
!16  GOTO/-1.125,-0.55       Rapid to next groove point
!17  GOTO/-1.125,-0.375      Cut groove area to depth
                             (Fig. 10.56) GOTO XZ
                             Position Icon
!18  DWELL/2                 Dwell at end of cut
!19  GODEL/0,-0.15           Move to clear part
!20  RAPID/                  Set rapid movement
!21  GOTO/-0.975,-0.525      Rapid to next groove point
!22  GOTO/-1.125,-0.375
!23  DWELL/2                 Dwell at end of cut
!24  GODEL/0,-0.15           Move to clear part
!25  RAPID/                  Set rapid movement
!26  GODEL/0.1,-0.1          Rapid clear of part
!27  RAPID/                  Set rapid movement
!28  COOL/2                  Turn coolant off
!29  GOHOME/                 Return turret to tool change position
```

GO TO XZ
Position Icon

X,Y

Figure 10.62 (Continued)

```
FILE/                              Create file of machining pathes
__M/C TIME 0.17                    Machine time for grooving
                                      is 0.17 minute
──NEWSEQ/40
 !1   INDEX/2000,1,0               Setup information
 !2   FROM/2.06,4.5
 !3   SPIN/1000,0
 !4   FROM/2.06,4.5
 !5   FPM/200
 !6   FPR/0.01
 !7   INDEX/2000,3,0

 !8   INDEX/1000,2,2

 !9   RAPID/
 !10  GOTO/0,-0.55
 !11  COOL/3
 !12  GOTO/0,-0.22
 !13  RAPID/
 !14  GODEL/0.1,-0.1

 !15  PROF/3,0,2,0,0,4,0,0
 !16  PROF/3,0,-1.25,-0.5,-3.437,-1
 !17  PROF/3,0,17,0,0,17,0,0.1
 !18  GODEL/0,-0.1
 !19  RAPID/
 !20  COOL/2
 !21  GODEL/0.1,-0.1
```

Finish Part Profile

Annotations:
- Index rear turret to clearance position
- Index front turret to 35° finish turning tool
- Set rapid movement
- Position tool for finish face
- Turn coolant on
- Finish face part
- Set rapid movement
- Retract clear of part to prepare for finish profile
- Finish turn outside profile of part (Fig. 10.57)
- Face cut off part surface
- Set rapid movement
- Turn coolant off
- Retract from part

PROFILE Icon

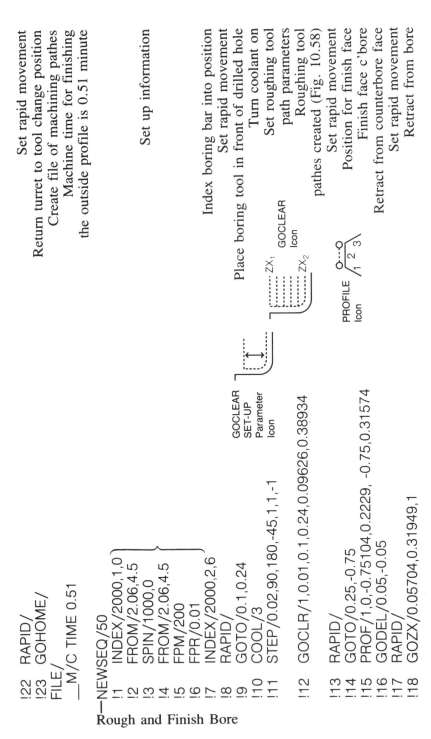

Figure 10.62 (Continued)

```
!19   RAPID/                                         Set rapid movement
!20   GOZX/0.05591,0.40951,-1                        Position tool to finish profile bore
!21   PROF/1,0,0.00043,0.40951,-0.75,031574          Finish profile bore (see Fig. 10.59)
!22   GODEL/0.05,-0.05                               Move clear of side of bore
!23   RAPID/                                         Set rapid movement
!24   GOZX/0.24252,0.21574,-1                        Retract from bore
!25   COOL/2                                         Turn coolant off
!26   RAPID/                                         Set rapid movement
!27   GOHOME/                                        Return turret to tool change position
      FILE/                                          Create file of machining pathes
      __M/C TIME 0.67                                Machine time for roughing
                                                       and finishing bore is
                                                       0.67 minute
```

PROFILE Icon

```
—NEWSEQ/60                                           Set up information
 !1   INDEX/2000,1,0
 !2   FROM/2.06,4.5
 !3   SPIN/1000,0
 !4   FROM/2.06,4.5
 !5   FPM/200
 !6   FPR/0.01
 !7   INDEX/2000,3,0                                 Index rear turret to
                                                       clearance position

 !8   INDEX/1000,4,4                                 Index front turret to
                                                       threading tool
```

Threading Operation

```
!9    SPIN/300,0                        Set spindle speed
!10   COOL/3                            Turn coolant on
!11   OPSKIP/                           Select slash delete option on
!12   THREAD/20,1,0.1,-0.5,-1.07,       Threading tool pathes
      -0.5,0.035,30,3,2,1,0.1           "O.D." (See Fig. 10.60)
!13   OPSKIP/                           Turn slash delete off
!14   COOL/2                            Turn coolant off
!15   RAPID/                            Set rapid movement
!16   GODEL/0.1,-0.1                    Retract tool clear of part
!17   RAPID/                            Set rapid movement
!18   GOHOME/                           Return turret to tool change position
FILE/                                   Crete file of machining pathes
      M/C TIME 0.12                     Machine time for producing threads
                                                       is 0.12 minute
```

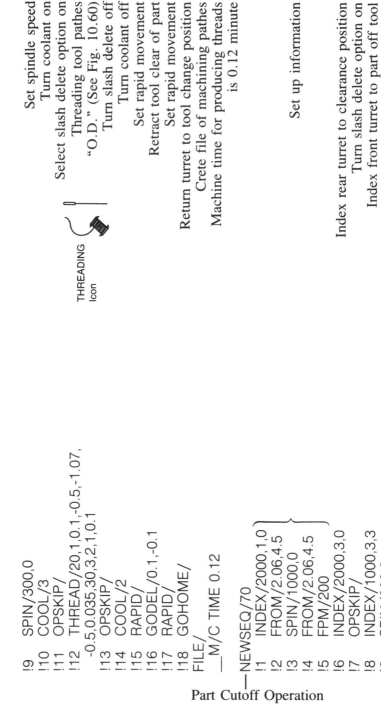

THREADING
Icon

```
NEWSEQ/70
!1    INDEX/2000,1,0  ⎫
!2    FROM/2.06,4.5   ⎬                 Set up information
!3    SPIN/1000,0     ⎭
!4    FROM/2.06,4.5
!5    FPM/200
!6    INDEX/2000,3,0                    Index rear turret to clearance position
!7    OPSKIP/                           Turn slash delete option on
!8    INDEX/1000,3,3                    Index front turret to part off tool
!9    SPIN/300,0                        Set spindle speed
!10   RAPID/                            Set rapid movement
```

Part Cutoff Operation

Figure 10.62 (Continued)

```
!11   GOTO/-3.5,-1.1        Position tool to part
                            (see Fig. 10.61)
!12   COOL/3                Turn coolant on
!13   GOTO/-3.5,0           Cut part off
!14   RAPID/                Set rapid movement
!15   GOTO/-3.5,-1.2        Retract from part
!16   RAPID/                Set rapid movement
!17   COOL/2                Turn coolant off
!18   GOHOME/               Return turret to tool change position
!19   OPSKIP/               Turn slash delete option off
FILE/                       Create file of machining pathes
   M/C TIME 0.1             Machine time for cutting part off
EOF/EOF/                    End of file
```

GOTO X,Y
Icon

Figure 10.62 (Concluded)

Figure 10.63 FILE icon command used to exit the tool path generation mode creating a master computer machining file.

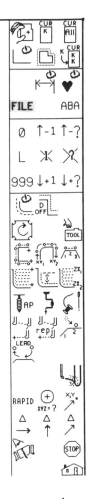

point by point, or generated by the computer by revolving or sweeping a previously defined contour. See Figures 10.65 as an example of the creation of a 3-D computer wire-frame image of a car body. Note: Figure 10.65(e) shows the tool path used to generate the 3-D shape. The CNC machine file generated will be a series of point to point moves such as those shown in Figure 10.66. The tighter the surface variation tolerance set in the computer, the more points that will be generated for machining. Many surfaces can be simple (ruled) and created through the use of nerbs or parametric programming. On the other hand they can be complex requiring lofted, revolved, swept or drafted geometry. Computer systems can now blend unlike surfaces together and project shapes or letters to be machined onto a 3-D surface. Figure 10.67 shows an example of a five-axes machining problem where a tapered boss intersects a bullet nose shaped surface. The programmers objective is to machine the side of the boss and the intersection of the boss and bullet nose at the same time. To do this the cutter axis must be tilted while moving the machine in the X, Y, and Z axes. Many machine tool statements are required to perform this operation but only a few computer statements need to be created. Now you can see the power and importance of a CAD/CAM system's geometry and tool path creation capability to industry. We are now able to make things never thought possible a few years ago.

The use of wire-frame geometry is made even more efficient through features that allow for multiple point and line creation techniques. Efficient arc, circle, and fillet functions are provided to allow for one time programming commands for each entity or occurrence in a chain of elements. There are a variety of programmer controlled functions for creating splined surfaces with projections, intersections, edge curves, slicing curves and parting lines. Programming systems also allow for quick geometry editing after creation by allowing for line length and arc radius changes. Surface trimming for multiple surfaces with complete undo capability are also available. Automatic dimensioning and dimensional changing with auto update make for easy geometric manipulation. Like options found in standard 2-D CAM systems mirror image, translation, and scaling can be completed to speed geometry creation. To allow for file management and transfer (data exchange) to other systems translators such as IGES, Parasolids, SAT, DXF, CADL, STL, VDA, ASCII and others are available. When it comes to machining of the surfaces Figures 10.65(e) and 10.67 many options are available to programmers to speed the process. Many of the added options that can be found are very similar to those found on conversational controlled machines. CAM systems are capable of volume of material removal control by changes in feed rate and can display tool path and part surfaces in 3-D for verification. Other functions may include: pocketing routines, corner cleaning, 3-D contours, automatic part facing, optimized drilling, and customizable subroutines to mention a few. The types of corporations served by 3-D programming include aerospace, automotive, consumer products, medical and surgical, mold making, prototyping, tool and die, as well as woodworking. The top reasons that these industries are involved in high levels of CAD/CAM are:

- Reliable data translators such as DXF, DWG, IGES, solids and others for communication of data to be machined.

- Powerful/easy surface molding tools in wire frame or solids to prepare geometry of parts to be machined.

- To obtain flexible up to 5 axis machining making it easy to cut curves and aerodynamic surfaces.

- Ease of tool path programming of surfaces whether using stock removal routines, pencil tracing paths, or slope cleanup yet achieve the cleanest possible part.

- Automatic feed rate optimization saving cycle time and wear on machinery.

- Associative tool path modification allows for automatic path changes with changes in geometry.

- Mold specific options can provide for automatic core and cavity separation, draft angle analysis, and shut off creation to make mold base design and programming simpler and faster.

- Reduction of CNC program size through the use of subroutine programming.

- Expandable CAD/CAM systems from 2-axis to 5-axis, with additional packages for turning, milling, EDM, flame cut, turret press, etc.

- High-speed machining for thin walled work pieces or increased production can also be allowed for.

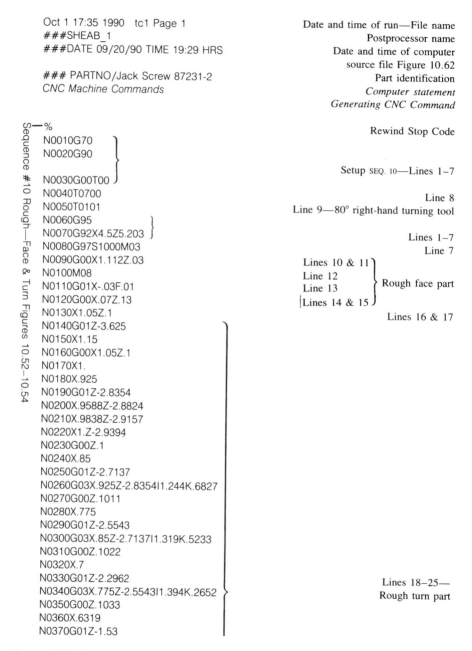

Oct 1 17:35 1990   tc1 Page 1   Date and time of run—File name
###SHEAB_1   Postprocessor name
###DATE 09/20/90 TIME 19:29 HRS   Date and time of computer
                                                                            source file Figure 10.62
PARTNO/Jack Screw 87231-2   Part identification
CNC Machine Commands   *Computer statement*
                                                                      Generating CNC Command

Sequence #10 Rough—Face & Turn Figures 10.52–10.54

%   Rewind Stop Code
N0010G70
N0020G90
                                                                        Setup SEQ. 10—Lines 1–7
N0030G00T00
N0040T0700   Line 8
N0050T0101   Line 9—80° right-hand turning tool
N0060G95
N0070G92X4.5Z5.203   Lines 1–7
N0080G97S1000M03   Line 7
N0090G00X1.112Z.03   Lines 10 & 11
N0100M08   Line 12
N0110G01X-.03F.01   Line 13   Rough face part
N0120G00X.07Z.13   Lines 14 & 15
N0130X1.05Z.1
N0140G01Z-3.625   Lines 16 & 17
N0150X1.15
N0160G00X1.05Z.1
N0170X1.
N0180X.925
N0190G01Z-2.8354
N0200X.9588Z-2.8824
N0210X.9838Z-2.9157
N0220X1.Z-2.9394
N0230G00Z.1
N0240X.85
N0250G01Z-2.7137
N0260G03X.925Z-2.8354I1.244K.6827
N0270G00Z.1011
N0280X.775
N0290G01Z-2.5543
N0300G03X.85Z-2.7137I1.319K.5233
N0310G00Z.1022
N0320X.7
N0330G01Z-2.2962   Lines 18–25—
N0340G03X.775Z-2.5543I1.394K.2652   Rough turn part
N0350G00Z.1033
N0360X.6319
N0370G01Z-1.53

Figure 10.64 Postprocessor output of CNC data for jack screw example to run on a Sheldon lathe.

N0380G02X.675Z-1.656I.1629K.126
N0390G01Z-2.031
N0400G03X.7Z-2.2962I1.419K0.
N0410G00Z.1044
N0420X.5639
N0430G01Z-1.4732
N0440G02X.6319Z-1.53I.0949K.1829
N0450G00Z.1054
N0460X.4176Z.061
N0470G01X.4073Z.02
N0480G02X.4431Z.0051I.0003K.051
N0490G01X.5051Z-.0569
N0500G02X.52Z-.093I.0361K.0361
N0510G01Z-.906
N0520G02X.5161Z-.9255I.051K0.
N0530G01X.5051Z-1.2449
N0540G02X.52Z-1.281I.0361K.0361
N0550G01Z-1.4876
N0560G02X.645Z-1.656I.051K.1684
N0570G01Z-2.031
N0580G03X.9348Z-2.9004I1.449K0.
N0590G01X.9598Z-2.9337
N0600G02X1.02Z-3.1143I.2408K.1806
N0610G01Z-3.406
N0620G02X1.0051Z-3.4421I.051K0.
N0630G01Z-3.4949
N0640G02X1.02Z-3.531I.0361K.0361
N0650G01Z-3.6107

Lines 25–28—
Semifinish part profile

N0660X1.12
N0670G00X1.22Z-3.5107
N0680M09
N0690X4.5Z5.203T0000

Line 29—Face clear of part
Lines 30 & 31—Clear part
Line 32—Turn coolant off
Lines 33 & 34—
Send turret to tool change

N0700T0505

SEQ. 20—Line 1—
Index rear turret to .500 drill

N0710G95
N0720G92X-4.5Z2.06
N0730G97S500M03

Lines 2–7—Setup information

N0740G00X0.Z.1M08

Lines 8–10—position drill to part

N0750G01Z-.4905F.01
N0760G00Z.1
N00770Z-.461
N0780G01Z-1.022
N0790G00Z.1

Line 11—Drill part—0.500 in. dia. hole

N0800M09
N0810Z.2
N0820X-4.5Z2.06T0000

Line 12—Turn coolant off
Lines 13 & 14—Clear tool from part
Lines 15 & 16—Send turret to tool change

Sequence #20 Drill Operation Figure 10.55

Figure 10.64 (Continued)

Sequence #30 Grooving Operation Figure 10.56

─N0830T0303

N0840G95
N0850G92X3.304Z4.929
N0860G97S300M03
N0870G00X.55Z-1.25
N0880M08
N0890G94
N0900G01X.375F200.
N0910G04F2.
N0920X.525
N0930G00X.55Z-1.125
N0940G01X.375
N0950G04F2.
N0960X.525
N0970G00Z-.975
N0980G01X.375Z-1.125
N0990G04F2.
N1000X.525
N1010G00X.625Z-1.025

N1020M09
N1030X3.304Z4.929T0000

SEQ. 30─
Line 7—Index front turret to parting tool

Lines 1–8—Setup information

Lines 9 & 10—Position groove
Line 11—Turn coolant on

Line 12—Cut groove
Line 13—Dwell at bottom of groove
Line 14—Clear part

Lines 15–24—Cut remaining groove area

Lines 25 & 26—Clear part

Line 28—Turn coolant off
Lines 27 & 29—Send turret
to tool change

Sequence #40 Finish Turning Operation Figure 10.57

─N1040T0202

N1050G94
N1060G92X4.5Z5.203
N1070G97S1000M03
N1080G00X.55Z0.
N1090M08
N1100G95
N1110G01X.22F.01
N1120G00X.32Z.1
N1130G01X.4289Z-.0091
N1140X.4909Z-.0711
N1150G02X.5Z-.093I.0219K.0219
N1160G01Z-.906
N1170G02X.4909Z-.9279I.031K0.
N1180G01Z-1.2591
N1190G02X.5Z-1.281I.0219K.0219
N1200G01Z-1.5031
N1210G02X.625Z-1.656I.031K.1529
N1220G01Z-2.031
N1230G03X.9188Z-2.9124I1.469K0.
N1240G01X.9438Z-2.9457
N1250G02X1.Z-3.1143I.2248K.1686

SEQ. 40—Line 8—Index front turret
to 35° finish turning tool

Lines 1–7—Setup information

Lines 9 & 10—Position for finish face

Lines 11 & 12—Finish face part

Lines 13 & 14—Move clear of part

Lines 15–17—
Finish profile part

Figure 10.64 (Continued)

N1260G01Z-3.406
N1270G02X.9909Z-3.4279I.031K0.
N1280G01X1.Z-3.531
N1290Z-3.631

N1300X1.1
N1310M09
N1320G00X1.2Z-3.531

Line 18—Face off of part
Lines 19–21—
Move clear of part/coolant off

N1330X4.5Z5.203T0000

Lines 22 & 23—
Send turret to tool change

N1340T0606

SEQ. 50—Line 7—
Index rear turret to boring bar

N1350G95
N1360G92X-4.712Z2.8
N1370G97S1000M03

Lines 1–6—Setup information

N1380G00X-.24Z.1
N1390M08

Lines 8–9—Position to drilled hole
Line 10—Coolant on

N1400X-.26
N1410G01Z-.74F.01
N1420X-.25
N1430G02X-.24Z-.75I0.K.01
N1440G01Z-.848
N1450G00Z.1
N1460X-.28
N1470G01Z-.74
N1480X-.26
N1490G00Z.0995
N1500X-.3
N1510G01Z-.74
N1520X-.28
N1530G00Z.099
N1540X-.32
N1550G01Z-.5487
N1560X-.3041Z-.74
N1570X-.3
N1580G00Z.0985
N1590X-.34
N1600G01Z-.3087
N1610X-.32Z-.5487
N1620G00Z.098
N1630X-.36
N1640G01Z-.0687
N1650X-.34Z-.3087
N1660G00Z.0975
N1670X-.3747
N1680G01Z-.0339
N1690X-.362Z-.0557

Lines 11 & 12—
Rough Bore Figure 10.58

Sequence #50 Rough and Finish Bore Figures 10.58 and 10.59

Figure 10.64 (Continued)

N1700X-.3607Z-.0599
N1710X-.36Z-.0687
N1720G00Z.097
N1730X-.3893
N1740G01Z-.0084
N1750X-.3747Z-.0339
N1760G00Z.0966
N1770X-.25Z-.751
N1780G01Z-.75
N1790X-.3133
N1800Z-.7498   Lines 14–18—
N1810X-.2633Z-.6998   Finish face counterbore
N1820G00X-.3195Z.057
N1830X-.4095Z.0559
N1840G01X-.4058Z0.
N1850X-.3707Z-.0607   Lines 19–22—Finish bore Figure 10.59
N1860X-.3133Z-.7498
N1870X-.2633Z-.6998
N1880G00X-.2157Z.2425   Lines 23 & 24—Retract from bore
N1890M09   Line 25—Coolant off
N1900X-4.712Z2.8T0000   Lines 26 & 27—
                             Return turret to tool change position

—N1910T0404   SEQ. 60—Line 8—Index front turret
                                            to threading tool

/N1920G95
/N1930G92X4.5Z5.203   Lines 1–9—Setup information
/N1940G97S300M03
/N1950G00X4.5Z.1M08
/N1960X.6
/N1970X.4907Z.0369
/N1980G33Z-1.07K0.0417
/N1990G00X.6   One thread pass
/N2000Z.1
/N2010X.4813Z.0315
/N2020G33Z-1.07K0.0417
/N2030G00X.6
/N2040Z.1
/N2050X.472Z.0261
/N2060G33Z-1.07K0.0417
/N2070G00X.6   Lines 10–13—
/N2080Z.1   Threading operation
/N2090X.4685Z.0241   with operation skip option
/N2100G33Z-1.07K0.0417
/N2110G00X.6
/N2120Z.1
/N2130X.465Z.0221
/N2140G33Z-1.07K0.0417
/N2150G00X.6
/N2160Z.1

Sequence #60 Threading Operation Figure 10.60

Figure 10.64 (Continued)

/N2170X.465Z.0221
/N2180G33Z-1.07K0.0417
/N2190G00X.6
/N2200Z.1
N2210M09
N2220G00X.7Z.2
N2230X4.5Z5.203T0000

Line 14—Coolant off
Lines 15 & 16—Move clear of part
Lines 17 & 18—
Return turret to tool change position

/N2240T0303

SEQ. 70–Line 6—Index front turret
to parting tool

/N2250G95
/N2260G92X3.304Z4.929
/N2270G97S300M03
/N2280G00X1.1Z-3.5
/N2290M08
/N2300G94
/N2310G01X0.F200.
/N2320G00X1.2
/N2330M09
/N2340X3.304Z4.929T0000
N2350M02
%

Lines 1–9—Setup information

Lines 10 & 11—Position tool to part
Line 12—Turn coolant on

Line 13—Cut part off
Lines 14 & 15—Retract clear of part
Lines 16–19—Turn coolant off return
turret to tool change position
End of program

Sequence #70 Cutoff Operation Figure 10.61

Figure 10.64 (Concluded)

Solids Modeling and Machining

The final form of CAD/CAM discussed is the newest, being Solids Modeling where parts and tool path prove-out are shown as solid images. This system like others is icon and menu driven for both part design and tool path creation. The DELCAM system shown here also has the advantage of a microsoft windows style interface for the convenience and familiarity of the operator. One of the major advantages to solids modeling is the ability to clearly see part and/or tool detail without the possibility of image reversal sometimes encountered with wireframe images such as seen in Figure 10.67. In order to help programmers learn new systems such as DELCAM's software, suppliers are including on-line tutorials and wizards to help lead one through programming steps.

Solids modeling is being used to design and view products in solid images such as the cell phone seen in Figure 10.68. The product model can then be used to develop the production tooling model required for machining, see example of camera and its injection mold tool in Figure 10.69(a) and (b). The part and/or tool models are then used to create complex machining programs as those needed on a five axes machine such as is shown in Figure 10.70. Figure 10.71(a) and (b) shows an example of a liquid product container and mold tooling samples designed using solids software. With the detailed models that can be created art work and engraving are now possible, see Figure 10.72(a) and (b) for examples. Solids programming does not stop here either, it accepts data from physical models on coordinate measuring machines to create

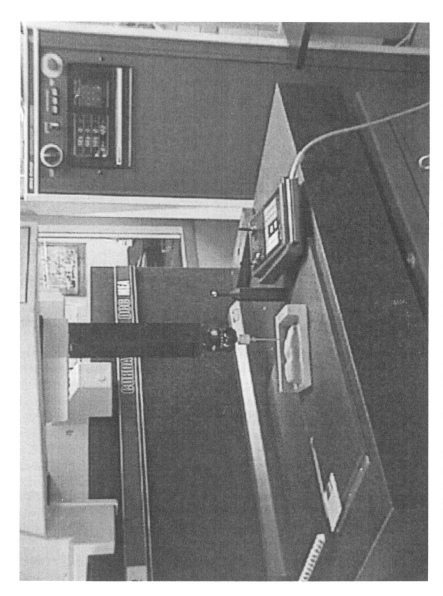

Figure 10.65(1) Collecting surface data from model of car body using coordinate measuring machine. (Courtesy of Dr. J. Gregory, Ferris State University.)

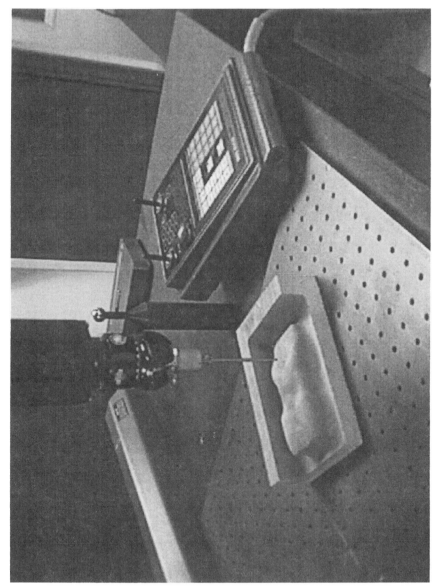

Figure 10.65(2) Close-up of surface data collection. (Courtesy of Dr. J. Gregory, Ferris State University.)

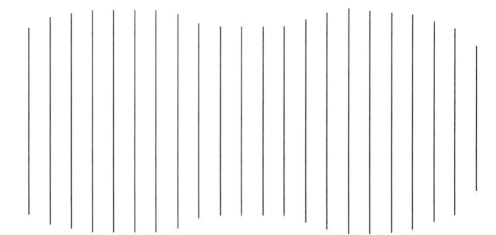

Figure 10.65(a) Plot of coordinate measuring machine data collection path (top view). (Courtesy of Dr. J. Gregory, Ferris State University.)

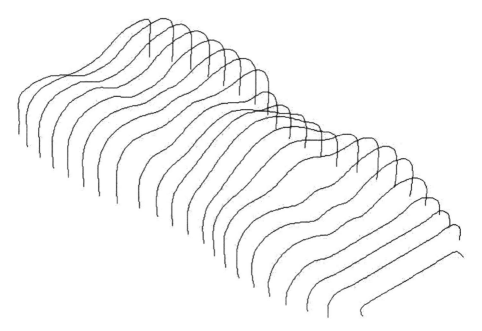

Figure 10.65(b) Isometric view of CMM data collection path. (Courtesy of Dr. J. Gregory, Ferris State University.)

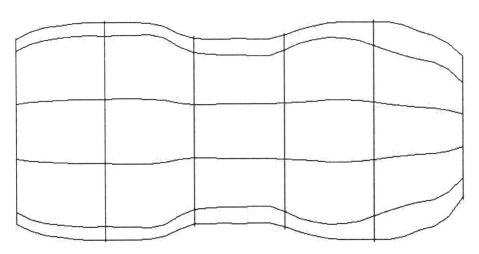

Figure 10.65(c) Top view of wireframe model from CMM data points. (Courtesy of Dr. J. Gregory, Ferris State University.)

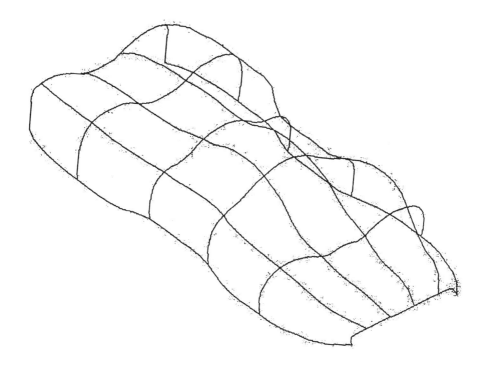

Figure 10.65(d) Isometric view of wireframe model from CMM data. (Courtesy of Dr. J. Gregory, Ferris State University.)

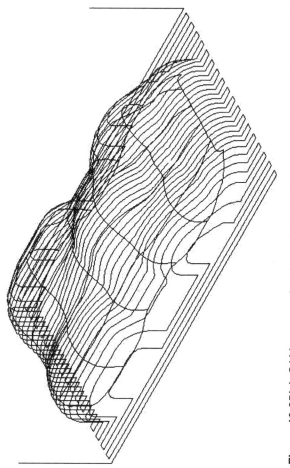

Figure 10.65(e) CAM generated tool path from wireframe car body data. (Courtesy of Dr. J. Gregory, Ferris State University.)

```
X5.2500 Y1.9256 Z-0.0100
X5.2500 Y1.8334 Z0.1056
X5.2500 Y1.7089 Z0.1267
X5.2500 Y1.5783 Z0.1278
X5.2500 Y1.4478 Z0.1272
X5.2500 Y1.3179 Z0.1262
X5.2500 Y1.1871 Z0.1254
X5.2500 Y1.0552 Z0.1250
X5.2500 Y0.9249 Z0.1254
X5.2500 Y0.7941 Z0.1262
X5.2500 Y0.6642 Z0.1272
X5.2500 Y0.5337 Z0.1278
X5.2500 Y0.4031 Z0.1267
X5.2500 Y0.2785 Z0.1069
X5.2500 Y0.3060 Z-0.0100
u
X5.0000 Y2.1210 Z0.0000
X5.0000 Y2.1144 Z0.1775
X5.0000 Y1.9667 Z0.2644
X5.0000 Y1.7871 Z0.2473
X5.0000 Y1.6066 Z0.2432
X5.0000 Y1.4247 Z0.2438
X5.0000 Y1.2446 Z0.2452
X5.0000 Y1.0636 Z0.2460
X5.0000 Y0.8834 Z0.2452
X5.0000 Y0.7011 Z0.2437
X5.0000 Y0.5214 Z0.2432
X5.0000 Y0.3397 Z0.2473
X5.0000 Y0.1595 Z0.2645
X5.0000 Y0.0127 Z0.1775
X5.0000 Y0.0060 Z0.0000
u
X4.7500 Y2.2060 Z0.0000
X4.7500 Y2.1895 Z0.1860
X4.7500 Y2.0366 Z0.3025
X4.7500 Y1.8443 Z0.2850
X4.7500 Y1.6496 Z0.2761
X4.7500 Y1.4538 Z0.2766
X4.7500 Y1.2587 Z0.2788
X4.7500 Y1.0636 Z0.2800
X4.7500 Y0.8680 Z0.2788
X4.7500 Y0.6737 Z0.2766
X4.7500 Y0.4775 Z0.2761
X4.7500 Y0.2828 Z0.2850
X4.7500 Y0.0894 Z0.3021
X4.7500 Y-0.0623 Z0.1860
X4.7500 Y-0.0790 Z0.0000
u
X4.5000 Y2.2970 Z0.0000
X4.5000 Y2.2750 Z0.1926
```

Figure 10.66 CNC machine tool point data generated from wireframe car model. (Courtesy of Dr. J. Gregory, Ferris State University.)

```
X4.5000  Y2.1128  Z0.3311
X4.5000  Y1.9099  Z0.3849
X4.5000  Y1.7019  Z0.3376
X4.5000  Y1.4916  Z0.3032
X4.5000  Y1.2774  Z0.3056
X4.5000  Y1.0635  Z0.3120
X4.5000  Y0.8503  Z0.3056
X4.5000  Y0.6370  Z0.3031
X4.5000  Y0.4264  Z0.3372
X4.5000  Y0.2190  Z0.3848
X4.5000  Y0.0154  Z0.3311
X4.5000  Y-0.1470  Z0.1926
X4.5000  Y-0.1700  Z0.0000
u
X4.2500  Y2.3150  Z0.0000
X4.2500  Y2.3309  Z0.2337
X4.2500  Y2.2123  Z0.4144
X4.2500  Y1.9905  Z0.5016
X4.2500  Y1.7534  Z0.4956
X4.2500  Y1.5219  Z0.4340
X4.2500  Y1.2922  Z0.3646
X4.2500  Y1.0633  Z0.4000
X4.2500  Y0.8344  Z0.3649
X4.2500  Y0.6057  Z0.4340
X4.2500  Y0.3737  Z0.4956
X4.2500  Y0.1365  Z0.5016
X4.2500  Y-0.0853  Z0.4144
X4.2500  Y-0.2040  Z0.2337
X4.2500  Y-0.1870  Z0.0000
u
X4.0000  Y2.3150  Z0.0000
X4.0000  Y2.3561  Z0.2564
X4.0000  Y2.2913  Z0.4982
X4.0000  Y2.0600  Z0.6038
X4.0000  Y1.8019  Z0.5882
X4.0000  Y1.5559  Z0.5078
X4.0000  Y1.3128  Z0.4210
X4.0000  Y1.0635  Z0.4620
X4.0000  Y0.8155  Z0.4207
X4.0000  Y0.5709  Z0.5078
X4.0000  Y0.3250  Z0.5882
X4.0000  Y0.0689  Z0.6040
X4.0000  Y-0.1634  Z0.4982
X4.0000  Y-0.2280  Z0.2564
X4.0000  Y-0.1870  Z0.0000
u
X3.7500  Y2.3150  Z0.0000
X3.7500  Y2.3518  Z0.2602
X3.7500  Y2.3053  Z0.5145
X3.7500  Y2.0879  Z0.6505
```

Figure 10.66 (Continued)

```
X3.7500  Y1.8266  Z0.6539
X3.7500  Y1.5715  Z0.5921
X3.7500  Y1.3172  Z0.5238
X3.7500  Y1.0645  Z0.5700
X3.7500  Y0.8111  Z0.5235
X3.7500  Y0.5571  Z0.5915
X3.7500  Y0.3022  Z0.6536
X3.7500  Y0.0395  Z0.6505
X3.7500  Y-0.1767  Z0.5155
X3.7500  Y-0.2237  Z0.2602
X3.7500  Y-0.1870  Z0.0000
u
X3.5000  Y2.2740  Z0.0000
X3.5000  Y2.3014  Z0.2576
X3.5000  Y2.2680  Z0.5111
X3.5000  Y2.0695  Z0.6633
X3.5000  Y1.8135  Z0.6816
X3.5000  Y1.5563  Z0.6935
X3.5000  Y1.3131  Z0.7819
X3.5000  Y1.0631  Z0.8440
X3.5000  Y0.8145  Z0.7819
X3.5000  Y0.5720  Z0.6938
X3.5000  Y0.3134  Z0.6816
X3.5000  Y0.0576  Z0.6633
X3.5000  Y-0.1410  Z0.5111
X3.5000  Y-0.1745  Z0.2576
X3.5000  Y-0.1470  Z0.0000
u
X3.2500  Y2.2050  Z0.0000
X3.2500  Y2.2256  Z0.2461
X3.2500  Y2.1881  Z0.4865
X3.2500  Y1.9936  Z0.6269
X3.2500  Y1.7537  Z0.6812
X3.2500  Y1.5288  Z0.7823
X3.2500  Y1.3049  Z0.8827
X3.2500  Y1.0627  Z0.9300
X3.2500  Y0.8228  Z0.8827
X3.2500  Y0.5985  Z0.7823
X3.2500  Y0.3732  Z0.6812
X3.2500  Y0.1334  Z0.6269
X3.2500  Y-0.0611  Z0.4865
X3.2500  Y-0.0986  Z0.2461
X3.2500  Y-0.0780  Z0.0000
u
X3.0000  Y2.1270  Z0.0000
X3.0000  Y2.1457  Z0.2345
X3.0000  Y2.0846  Z0.4568
X3.0000  Y1.8984  Z0.5899
X3.0000  Y1.7047  Z0.7221
X3.0000  Y1.5067  Z0.8481
```

Figure 10.66 (Continued)

```
X3.0000 Y1.2944 Z0.9441
X3.0000 Y1.0636 Z0.9850
X3.0000 Y0.8334 Z0.9441
X3.0000 Y0.6209 Z0.8481
X3.0000 Y0.4216 Z0.7215
X3.0000 Y0.2285 Z0.5899
X3.0000 Y0.0424 Z0.4568
X3.0000 Y-0.0187 Z0.2345
X3.0000 Y0.0000 Z0.0000
u
X2.7500 Y2.1270 Z0.0000
X2.7500 Y2.1449 Z0.2337
X2.7500 Y2.0808 Z0.4572
X2.7500 Y1.8956 Z0.5955
X2.7500 Y1.7055 Z0.7348
X2.7500 Y1.5083 Z0.8622
X2.7500 Y1.2943 Z0.9593
X2.7500 Y1.0636 Z1.0000
X2.7500 Y0.8336 Z0.9593
X2.7500 Y0.6192 Z0.8622
X2.7500 Y0.4217 Z0.7348
X2.7500 Y0.2315 Z0.5955
X2.7500 Y0.0457 Z0.4559
X2.7500 Y-0.0181 Z0.2337
X2.7500 Y0.0000 Z0.0000
u
X2.5000 Y2.1270 Z0.0000
X2.5000 Y2.1471 Z0.2308
X2.5000 Y2.0855 Z0.4503
X2.5000 Y1.8988 Z0.5784
X2.5000 Y1.6982 Z0.6921
X2.5000 Y1.5009 Z0.8150
X2.5000 Y1.2908 Z0.9102
X2.5000 Y1.0636 Z0.9510
X2.5000 Y0.8359 Z0.9098
X2.5000 Y0.6256 Z0.8145
X2.5000 Y0.4289 Z0.6921
X2.5000 Y0.2281 Z0.5784
X2.5000 Y0.0416 Z0.4503
X2.5000 Y-0.0202 Z0.2308
X2.5000 Y0.0000 Z0.0000
u
X2.2500 Y2.1270 Z0.0000
X2.2500 Y2.1444 Z0.2274
X2.2500 Y2.0891 Z0.4448
X2.2500 Y1.9166 Z0.5611
X2.2500 Y1.6971 Z0.6102
X2.2500 Y1.4940 Z0.7116
X2.2500 Y1.2868 Z0.8063
X2.2500 Y1.0628 Z0.8500
```

Figure 10.66 (Continued)

```
X2.2500  Y0.8410  Z0.8063
X2.2500  Y0.6333  Z0.7116
X2.2500  Y0.4298  Z0.6102
X2.2500  Y0.2104  Z0.5611
X2.2500  Y0.0379  Z0.4448
X2.2500  Y-0.0174  Z0.2274
X2.2500  Y0.0000  Z0.0000
u
X2.0000  Y2.1570  Z0.0000
X2.0000  Y2.1781  Z0.2307
X2.0000  Y2.1289  Z0.4548
X2.0000  Y1.9521  Z0.5983
X2.0000  Y1.7239  Z0.6047
X2.0000  Y1.5048  Z0.6817
X2.0000  Y1.2908  Z0.7698
X2.0000  Y1.0631  Z0.8130
X2.0000  Y0.8373  Z0.7698
X2.0000  Y0.6221  Z0.6812
X2.0000  Y0.4034  Z0.6047
X2.0000  Y0.1749  Z0.5983
X2.0000  Y-0.0019  Z0.4548
X2.0000  Y-0.0511  Z0.2307
X2.0000  Y-0.0300  Z0.0000
u
X1.7500  Y2.2740  Z0.0000
X1.7500  Y2.2868  Z0.2615
X1.7500  Y2.2682  Z0.5219
X1.7500  Y2.0980  Z0.7021
X1.7500  Y1.8382  Z0.7226
X1.7500  Y1.5813  Z0.6897
X1.7500  Y1.3203  Z0.7138
X1.7500  Y1.0635  Z0.7600
X1.7500  Y0.8060  Z0.7134
X1.7500  Y0.5474  Z0.6897
X1.7500  Y0.2887  Z0.7226
X1.7500  Y0.0279  Z0.7015
X1.7500  Y-0.1411  Z0.5219
X1.7500  Y-0.1599  Z0.2615
X1.7500  Y-0.1470  Z0.0000
u
X1.5000  Y2.3150  Z0.0000
X1.5000  Y2.3340  Z0.2687
X1.5000  Y2.3033  Z0.5347
X1.5000  Y2.1263  Z0.7285
X1.5000  Y1.8609  Z0.7684
X1.5000  Y1.5946  Z0.7336
X1.5000  Y1.3310  Z0.6783
X1.5000  Y1.0647  Z0.7080
X1.5000  Y0.7967  Z0.6783
X1.5000  Y0.5329  Z0.7336
```

Figure 10.66 (Continued)

```
X1.5000 Y0.2672 Z0.7684
X1.5000 Y0.0017 Z0.7285
X1.5000 Y-0.1753 Z0.5347
X1.5000 Y-0.2060 Z0.2687
X1.5000 Y-0.1870 Z0.0000
u
X1.2500 Y2.3150 Z0.0000
X1.2500 Y2.3343 Z0.2709
X1.2500 Y2.3024 Z0.5368
X1.2500 Y2.1218 Z0.7298
X1.2500 Y1.8571 Z0.7705
X1.2500 Y1.5912 Z0.7276
X1.2500 Y1.3329 Z0.6486
X1.2500 Y1.0630 Z0.6600
X1.2500 Y0.7961 Z0.6484
X1.2500 Y0.5364 Z0.7276
X1.2500 Y0.2710 Z0.7705
X1.2500 Y0.0062 Z0.7298
X1.2500 Y-0.1744 Z0.5368
X1.2500 Y-0.2063 Z0.2709
X1.2500 Y-0.1870 Z0.0000
u
X1.0000 Y2.3150 Z0.0000
X1.0000 Y2.3346 Z0.2748
X1.0000 YZ.2981 Z0.5476
X1.0000 Y2.1072 Z0.7359
X1.0000 Y1.8340 Z0.7679
X1.0000 Y1.5617 Z0.7265
X1.0000 Y1.3319 Z0.6032
X1.0000 Y1.0650 Z0.5620
X1.0000 Y0.7964 Z0.6026
X1.0000 Y0.5658 Z0.7265
X1.0000 Y0.2941 Z0.7679
X1.0000 Y0.0208 Z0.7359
X1.0000 Y-0.1701 Z0.5476
X1.0000 Y-0.2066 Z0.2748
X1.0000 Y-0.1870 Z0.0000
u
X0.7500 Y2.3150 Z0.0000
X0.7500 Y2.3346 Z0.2748
X0.7500 Y2.2981 Z0.5476
X0.7500 Y2.1072 Z0.7359
X0.7500 Y1.8340 Z0.7679
X0.7500 Y1.5617 Z0.7265
X0.7500 Y1.3319 Z0.6032
X0.7500 Y1.0650 Z0.5620
X0.7500 Y0.7964 Z0.6026
X0.7500 Y0.5658 Z0.7265
X0.7500 Y0.2941 Z0.7679
X0.7500 Y0.0208 Z0.7359
X0.7500 Y-0.1701 Z0.5476
```

Figure 10.66 (Continued)

```
X0.7500 Y-0.2066 Z0.2748
X0.7500 Y-0.1870 Z0.0000
u
X0.5000 Y2.2790 Z0.0000
X0.5000 Y2.2936 Z0.2655
X0.5000 Y2.2702 Z0.5301
X0.5000 Y2.0888 Z0.7076
X0.5000 Y1.8233 Z0.7302
X0.5000 Y1.5629 Z0.6822
X0.5000 Y1.3231 Z0.5648
X0.5000 Y1.0631 Z0.5270
X0.5000 Y0.8044 Z0.5648
X0.5000 Y0.5645 Z0.6822
X0.5000 Y0.3037 Z0.7302
X0.5000 Y0.0391 Z0.7076
X0.5000 Y-0.1431 Z0.5301
X0.5000 Y-0.1668 Z0.2655
X0.5000 Y-0.1520 Z0.0000
u
X0.2500 Y2.2370 Z0.0000
X0.2500 Y2.2458 Z0.2582
X0.2500 Y2.2333 Z0.5164
X0.2500 Y2.0574 Z0.6740
X0.2500 Y1.7997 Z0.6834
X0.2500 Y1.5477 Z0.6335
X0.2500 Y1.3154 Z0.5193
X0.2500 Y1.0632 Z0.4850
X0.2500 Y0.8121 Z0.5193
X0.2500 Y0.5795 Z0.6335
X0.2500 Y0.3285 Z0.6834
X0.2500 Y0.0706 Z0.6740
X0.2500 Y-0.1062 Z0.5164
X0.2500 Y-0.1190 Z0.2582
X0.2500 Y-0.1100 Z0.0000
u
X0.0000 Y2.1270 Z0.0000
X0.0000 Y2.1218 Z0.2404
X0.0000 Y2.1245 Z0.4816
X0.0000 Y1.9807 Z0.5588
X0.0000 Y1.7400 Z0.5609
X0.0000 Y1.5189 Z0.4951
X0.0000 Y1.2983 Z0.4027
X0.0000 Y1.0635 Z0.3750
X0.0000 Y0.8295 Z0.4027
X0.0000 Y0.6082 Z0.4951
X0.0000 Y0.3860 Z0.5609
X0.0000 Y0.1462 Z0.5588
X0.0000 Y0.0025 Z0.4816
X0.0000 Y0.0051 Z0.2415
X0.0000 Y0.0000 Z0.0000
u
```

Figure 10.66 (Concluded)

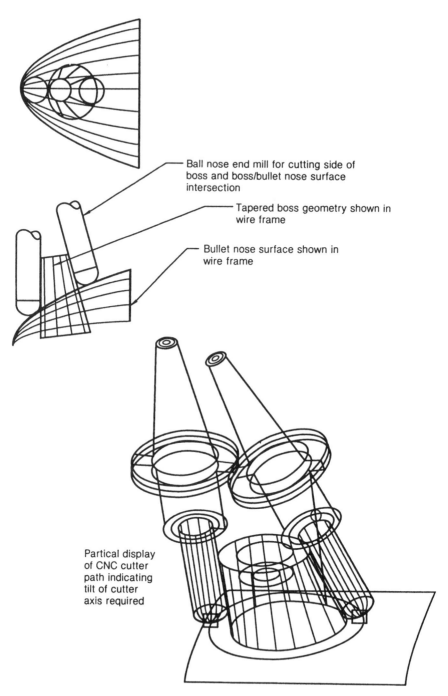

Figure 10.67 Example of five-axes tool path display on three-dimensional operation.

Figure 10.68 Cell phone design solids model computer image. (Courtesy of DELCAM plc & AxSys Incorporated.)

the computer models for machining. Solids software also allows for the creation of coordinate measuring machine programs to be created from solid model image so that parts and tools can be inspected, see Figure 10.73.

Solids Modeling brings powerful CAD benefits for 3D modeling of complex parts. Solutions have been brought to the toolmaking industry to create product designs for manufacturing. The ease of solid model creation allows programmers/designers to produce complex mold tools while starting with 2D drawings or incomplete 3D solids or surface models. The software today can calculate inside and outside of part geometry automatically for core and cavity tool development. Software today is built to accept geometry in all of the standard translators common to the industry such as IGES, DXF, CADL, SAT, and etc. Wireframe geometry to surfaces has been made much simpler through the use of geometry sweeps, rotates, blending, mirroring and easy trimming routines. Software is also capable of automatic surface gap and fill calculation. One might ask what else can be done in the design of product and tools? Designers can twist or raise specific pieces of geometry with the software automatically blending attached surfaces to the new geometry. Figure 10.74 shows the solids design image for a liquid product container and the windows type style interface used by DELCAM.

Solids Machining such as DELCAM's PowerMILL brings programmers a stand-alone 3D machining package. The new machining packages bring fast accurate, gouge free, roughing and finishing cutter paths from a menu and wizard based computer interface. Advances have also been greatly increased in the cutting tool geometry that can be used. Programming has moved from flat and ball nose endmills to additions of a variety of tapered mills and disk cutters. New machining strategies or patterns such as raster, radial, spiral, pattern profile, stitch corner finishing, and 3D offset are available. A further advantage is both wireframe and solids visual tool path verification as seen in Figures 10.75 and 10.76. Highspeed machining optimization has also been allowed for in newer software packages. Optimization includes leads and links, skim tool for less Z movement, rest roughing for even finish material removal, 3D offset finishing for constant cutting conditions, offset area clearance, and minimize full width cuts for higher feeds with less tool wear. Full descriptions of these options are available in the software training instructions.

Tool path images can also prove clearance for machining moves around work holding devices as demonstrated in the tombstone fixture, parts, and tool shown in Figure 10.77. The complex machining of a chainsaw cover is shown in the solids image in Figure 10.78.

Solids Inspection allows the creation of coordinate measuring machine programs from the solids images created see Figure 10.73. Manufactured product or tools can be compared to the computer model and either tabular or graphic reports can be generated, the speed that which this operation occurs minimizes disruption to production. In the use of DELCAM's PowerINSPECT the CAD model is downloaded and aligned to the part and the coordinated measuring machine starts its inspection path. In real time the software will display and print tables or graphical profiles, tables are also linked to microsoft excel as well Figure 10.79.

CopyCAD is a reverse engineering package in solids that allows the creation of a solids image from physical models. Option allows for computer surface creation, rapid prototyping product visualization, copy milling programs, feature analysis or animation. Touch probes, Figure 10.73, or laser scanners are used along with answering the software wizard questions to collect data points creating the data file. Software will then create the 3D model and allow the programmer to trim and manipulate the image. The programmer creates an accurate model from the construction profiles of the data collected, review Figure 10.80 to see this process. The software today is so powerful that it can wrap decorative 2D images around a solids model and emboss this surface with the design.

The last area of solids to be covered is **ArtCAM,** which is a fast and flexible method to penetrate 3D relief on computer images from 2D artwork. Complex asymmetrical reliefs to more simple symmetrical shapes can be performed. Sign making using 3D images and lettering becomes easy, see Figure 10.72 for examples. The system software makes it easy to assign set depths and 3D shapes to the various color patterns of the solids model. Complete surface texturing from a menu or custom texture is also available by image color.

(a)

(b)

Figure 10.69 (a) and (b) Camera and tooling to produce, created using solids images. (Courtesy of DELCAM plc & AxSys Incorporated.)

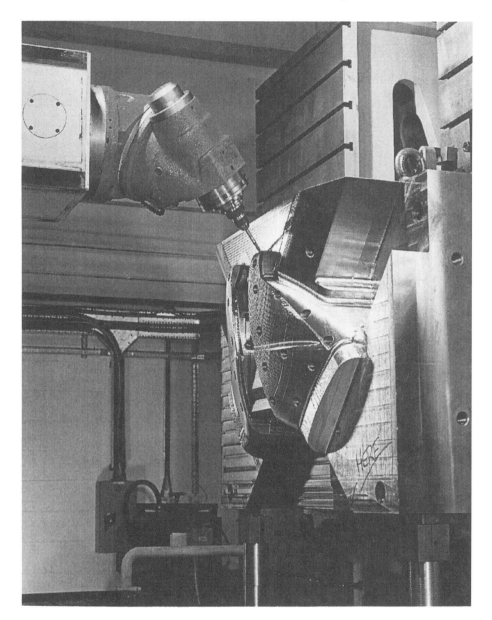

Figure 10.70 Five axis machine shown machining mold tooling. (Courtesy of DELCAM plc & AxSys Incorporated.)

Figure 10.71(a) Computer image of product jug created using solids modeling. (Courtesy of DELCAM plc & AxSys Incorporated.)

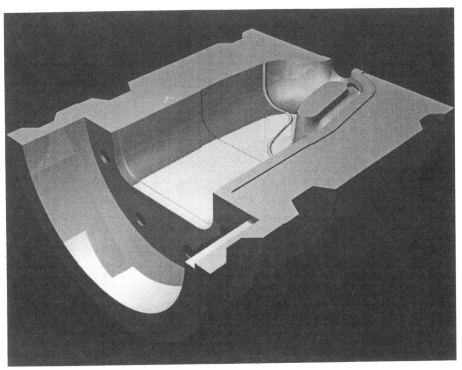

Figure 10.71(b) Mold Tool Insert for Product Jug created using solids modeling. (Courtesy of DELCAM plc & AxSys Incorporated.)

(a)

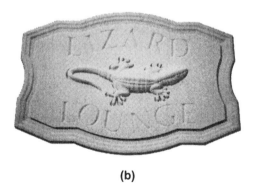

(b)

Figure 10.72 (a) and (b) Artwork and engraving samples created using solids modeling. (Courtesy of DELCAM plc & AxSys Incorporated.)

Figure 10.73 Coordinate measuring machine inspecting spiral impeller.
(Courtesy of DELCAM plc & AxSys Incorporated.)

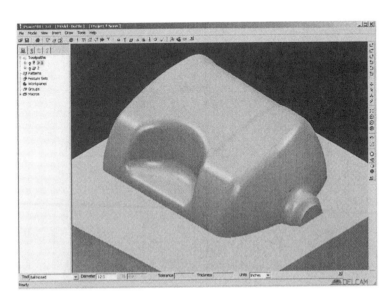

Figure 10.74 Solids image of liquid product jug. (Courtesy of DELCAM plc
& AxSys Incorporated.)

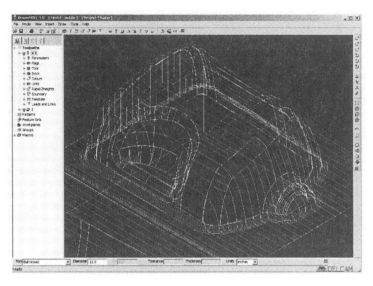

Figure 10.75 Wire frame image of product and windows style interface. (Courtesy of DELCAM plc & AxSys Incorporated.)

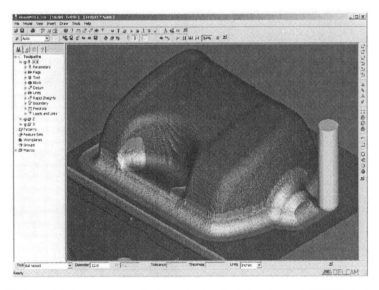

Figure 10.76 Solids image of product and tool path. (Courtesy of DELCAM plc & AxSys Incorporated.)

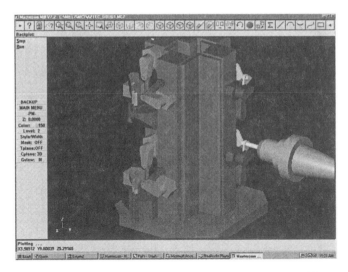

Figure 10.77 Solids image of tombstone fixture, parts, and tooling. (Courtesy of DELCAM plc & AxSys Incorporated.)

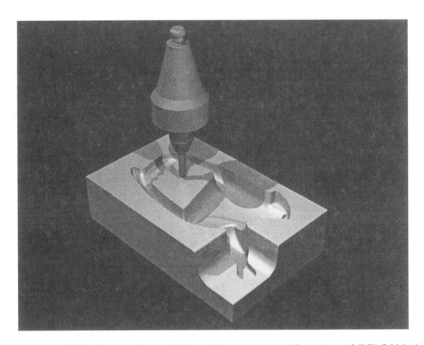

Figure 10.78 Solids image of machining chainsaw cover. (Courtesy of DELCAM plc & AxSys Incorporated.)

Project

j6666

Quality Department

Delcam UK		
Talbot Way	Quality Department: **0121 683 1075**	
	Toolroom: **0121 683 1070**	E-mail: **rlt@delcam.com**
Small Heath Business Park	Tooling Services: **0121 683 1060**	Web Site: **http://www.delcam.com**
Birmingham B10 0HJ, UK	Fax: **0121 766 5511**	

Report No.   **XYZ 345**

Description **DEMO TeST PIECE**	Customer **RYFORD**
Part No. **RESIN MODEL**	Customer contact **lez**
Drawing Number **dec145**	Customer phone No. **0121 766 5544**
Datum **AS CAD**	Customer fax No. **0121 766 5511**

AKU-1

Surface Points

Number	Name	Offset	Lo. Tol.	Hi. Tol.	X	Y	Z	dX	dY	dZ	DL
1000	AKU-1	0.000	-0.300	0.300	-5.020	35.655	-16.103	0.002	-0.005	0.016	
1001	AKU-2	0.000	-0.300	0.300	12.607	4.477	-21.149	-0.019	-0.008	0.148	
1002	AKU-3	0.000	-0.300	0.300	4.386	-4.168	-21.692	-0.002	0.004	0.100	
1003	AKU-4	0.000	-0.300	0.300	-13.355	-11.750	-20.735	0.002	0.003	0.030	
1004	AKU-5	0.000	-0.300	0.300	-36.734	-12.672	-18.324	-0.006	-0.005	-0.040	
1005	AKU-6	0.000	-0.300	0.300	-43.679	2.473	-8.793	-0.333	0.310	-0.260	-0.524
1006	AKU-7	0.000	-0.300	0.300	-33.999	7.419	-12.864	-0.102	0.085	-0.180	
1007	AKU-8	0.000	-0.300	0.300	-28.106	5.596	-16.023	-0.050	0.052	-0.165	
1008	AKU-9	0.000	-0.300	0.300	-58.418	-10.876	-8.845	-0.133	0.017	-0.052	
1009	AKU-10	0.000	-0.300	0.300	-48.161	-22.971	-12.676	-0.487	-0.575	-0.304	-0.812
1010	AKU-11	0.000	-0.300	0.300	-44.869	-24.156	-17.412	0.000	0.000	0.167	
1011	AKU-12	0.000	-0.300	0.300	-28.036	-32.045	-11.983	-0.017	-0.063	-0.036	
1012	AKU-13	0.000	-0.300	0.300	-7.547	-25.735	-11.231	-0.001	-0.170	-0.016	
1013	AKU-14	0.000	-0.300	0.300	16.306	-21.548	-19.037	-0.012	0.022	0.127	
1014	AKU-15	0.000	-0.300	0.300	23.820	-13.791	-19.182	-0.035	0.015	0.196	
1015	AKU-16	0.000	-0.300	0.300	37.663	-18.271	-16.559	-0.012	0.007	0.081	
1016	AKU-17	0.000	-0.300	0.300	50.921	-18.832	-14.398	-0.040	0.015	0.235	
1017	AKU-18	0.000	-0.300	0.300	63.407	-16.821	-12.190	-0.053	0.017	0.260	
1018	AKU-19	0.000	-0.300	0.300	75.141	-13.472	-9.880	-0.049	0.004	0.234	
1019	AKU-20	0.000	-0.300	0.300	84.069	-6.833	-8.313	-0.005	-0.001	0.092	
1020	AKU-21	0.000	-0.300	0.300	85.175	6.109	-8.410	0.004	0.000	0.035	
1021	AKU-22	0.000	-0.300	0.300	85.687	22.037	-8.443	-0.007	-0.003	0.091	
1022	AKU-23	0.000	-0.300	0.300	81.830	35.851	-8.406	-0.017	-0.003	0.173	
1023	AKU-24	0.000	-0.300	0.300	80.225	45.843	-11.016	-0.192	-0.526	0.592	0.815
1024	AKU-25	0.000	-0.300	0.300	63.327	49.934	-12.019	-0.168	-0.693	0.582	0.920
1025	AKU-26	0.000	-0.300	0.300	49.553	49.015	-12.525	0.113	0.999	0.679	1.213
1026	AKU-27	0.000	-0.300	0.300	39.433	53.464	-12.881	-0.099	-0.867	0.659	1.093
1027	AKU-28	0.000	-0.300	0.300	28.225	54.282	-13.074	-0.055	-0.944	0.716	1.186
1028	AKU-29	0.000	-0.300	0.300	20.712	50.993	-12.535	0.012	0.528	0.294	0.604
1029	AKU-30	0.000	-0.300	0.300	16.027	54.804	-12.813	0.009	-0.527	0.386	0.654
1030	AKU-31	0.000	-0.300	0.300	7.029	51.469	-14.874	-0.009	0.003	-0.009	
1031	AKU-32	0.000	-0.300	0.300	-4.808	51.828	-7.304	-0.020	0.057	-0.056	
1032	AKU-33	0.000	-0.300	0.300	-15.750	48.168	-5.880	-0.107	0.179	-0.133	

Figure 10.79 Table/report of part from solids software program. *Note:* profile graphs may also be created. (Courtesy of DELCAM plc & AxSys Incorporated.)

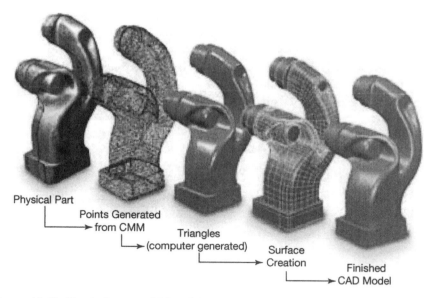

Figure 10.80 Physical part to CAD solids model process steps. (Courtesy of DELCAM plc & AxSys Incorporated.)

QUESTIONS

1 List the advantages of computer aided part programming when compared with manual part programming.

2 List and briefly describe the main stages in the CAPP process.

3 Make a block diagram to illustrate a basic 'stand-alone' CAPP system.

4 Explain what is meant by 'time-sharing' and list the advantages and disadvantages of using such a facility.

5 Describe three methods that may be used for menu selection from a digitizing tablet.

6 Describe three methods of cursor control that may be used to identify graphic features on a CRT screen.

7 Describe three general methods for geometrically defining a point, a straight line and a circle or curve.

8 List the various data that would be included as tool change data statements during the preparation of a part program.

9 Explain what is meant by "cutter location data."

10 Explain the function of "postprocessing" and state how a range of machines having a variety of control systems would be accommodated.

11 Describe two ways in which computer graphics are used as an aid to part programming.

12 Describe briefly the meaning of CAD/CAM.

Chapter 11

ADVANCED TECHNIQUES

The power of a computer's calculation ability continues to grow at a constant rate. With the computer's growth comes added programming techniques for CNC equipment. This chapter will give an overview of some of the additional programming abilities that exist today. One needs to follow the computer industry news in order to keep abreast of new developments and stay current in the field of programming.

Parametric Programming

A parameter is a quantity that is constant in one particular case but variable in others. A simple engineering example of a parameter is the length of a bolt. One version of the bolt will have a certain length; all other versions will be identical, that is, they will have the same thread form, diameter, and hexagon head, but they will all vary in length. Thus the length of the bolt is a parameter, constant in one particular case but variable in others.

Parametric programming involves defining parameters and then using those parameters as the basis for one part program that may be used to machine not only the original component but a number of variations as well.

Figure 11.1(a) shows a component the dimensional features of which have been defined as parameters using the symbol # and a number: #1, #2, #3, and so on.

Figures 11.1(b)–11.1(g) show six variations of the component, the variations being indicated. A range of components such as this is referred to as a family of parts.

The machine movements necessary to machine each of the variations are all included in the original component. Some components require exactly the same movements, but with varying lengths of travel. Other components do not require all of the movements to be made. Using the more usual programming techniques, the production of each component would require a separate part program. Using the parametric part programming technique, instead of defining each dimensional movement individually in the X and Z axes, the parametric reference is programmed. Thus, to turn along the stepped diameter, the entry in the main program, referred to as the "macro," would read as follows:

$$\text{N07 \quad G01 \quad X \#4 \quad Z \#2}$$

This entry would suffice for all components requiring a stepped diameter. Equally, one entry using parametric identification would suffice for facing all the components to length or drilling the hole.

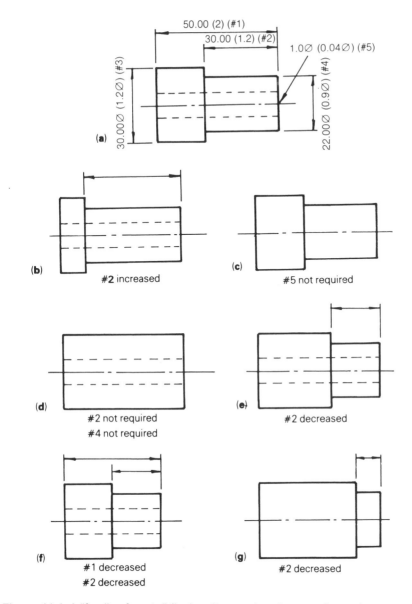

Figure 11.1 A "family of parts." (Inch units are given in parentheses.)

Having programmed all movements and the sequence in which they are to occur, it remains to dimensionally define them. The dimensional details are entered as a list at the start of the part program. Thus the parameters and their dimensional values for the original components would read as follows (in metric units):

$$
\begin{aligned}
\#1 &= -50.00 \\
\#2 &= -30.00 \\
\#3 &= 30.00 \\
\#4 &= 22.00 \\
\#5 &= 10.00
\end{aligned}
$$

As each parameter is called in the program, the dimensional entry made previously will be invoked.

To machine any of the variations in the family of parts requires a simple amendment of the original parametric values. The parameters (in metric units) to machine the component shown in Figure 11.1(b) would be:

$$#1 = -50.00$$
$$#2 = -40.00 \text{ (amended)}$$
$$#3 = 30.00$$
$$#4 = 22.00$$
$$#5 = 10.00$$

and to machine the component in Figure 11.1(f):

$$#1 = -40.00 \text{ (amended)}$$
$$#1 = -20.00 \text{ (amended)}$$
$$#3 = 30.00$$
$$#4 = 22.00$$
$$#5 = 10.00$$

Now consider the components where the programmed movements necessary for machining the basic component are not required. By using a relatively simple programming technique, the control unit can be caused to skip the redundant blocks. The necessary program entry involves the use of certain conditional expressions in which assigned abbreviations are used, such as the following:

$$EQ = \text{equal to}$$
$$NE = \text{not equal to}$$
$$GT = \text{greater than}$$
$$LT = \text{less than}$$
$$GE = \text{greater than or equal to}$$
$$LE = \text{less than or equal to}$$

Consider Figure 11.1(d) and assume the #1 and #3 have been machined. In the program the next call will be to machine the stepped diameter. To avoid this, blocks must be skipped so an entry in the program will read as follows:

N15 IF [#4 EQ 0] GO TO N18

This statement says that if #4 is zero, move on to block number 18. Since #4 is nonexistent in the component, the parametric value will be entered as zero and, consequently, the control unit will move ahead.

The preceding description of the use of the parametric programming technique is a very simple one. It is in fact a very powerful concept and its full application is quite complex. For instance, parameters may be mathematically related, that is, they may be added together, subtracted from one another, and so on.

In addition, the parametric principle may be extended to include speeds and feeds, when all the likely variations for roughing, finishing, etc. may be given a parametric identity and called into the program as and when required.

Parametric-type programming although not uncommon is not standardized in its methods between machines or programming systems, so vendor manuals should be consulted.

Digitizing

Digitizing is the name given to a technique used to obtain numerical data direct from a drawing or model. To obtain numerical data from a drawing, which may or may not be dimensioned, it is placed on a special tablet, or table, and a probe is traced over the drawing outline. This movement is received by a computer and is transformed into digital or dimensional values. Only two-dimensional data can be obtained from a drawing. For three-dimensional data a model of the component is required, and a probe, which is an electronic probe or laser beam in operation, is traced over the surface of the model, this movement being recorded by the computer as before.

Numerical data obtained by digitizing can be used as the basis of a numerical control program. The numerical data entered into a computer, on the other hand, can be used to create the geometric data for a three-dimensional data base. This data base can then be used to create three-dimensional contouring cutter paths, using CAM/surfacing programming. The technique is only suitable for certain types of machining, such as profile milling, but the concept is likely to be developed to cater to a wider range of machine-shop activity.

Flexible Manufacturing System

A flexible manufacturing system (FMS) is a computer-controlled machining arrangement which will cater to a variety of continuous metal-cutting operations on a range of components without manual intervention. The objective of such a system is to produce components at the lowest possible cost, and in particular components that are required only in small quantities. Thus a prime requirement of such a system is flexibility, that is, the capacity to switch from one type of component to another, or from one type of machining to another, without interruption in the production process.

Production costs per unit item decrease as the number of components required increases. Large production runs justify extensive capital expenditure on special-purpose machinery that does a particular job very efficiently and quickly. Machines of this type, however, are rarely adaptable to other types of work: they lack flexibility. When flexibility does exist—one skilled worker and one machine, for instance, where single components can be handled in random order—the production rate is slow and therefore costly. Modern flexible manufacturing systems aim to bridge the gap between these two extremes.

Flexible manufacturing systems have been made possible by the fact that modern machine control units can store in the computer memory a number of part programs which can be activated via a master computer program in random order, a system referred to as direct numerical control (DNC). The same master computer is also able to control the supply of workpieces to the machine. The third important factor, tooling, will be controlled by the part program itself, but if a wide range of machining is to be carried out the tooling magazine will be required to accommodate a large number of tools; for milling operations at least 60 and perhaps more than 100 may be necessary. To solve the problems of tool search time and maintenance of large tool conveyors some machine tool builders have made the conveyors themselves changeable.

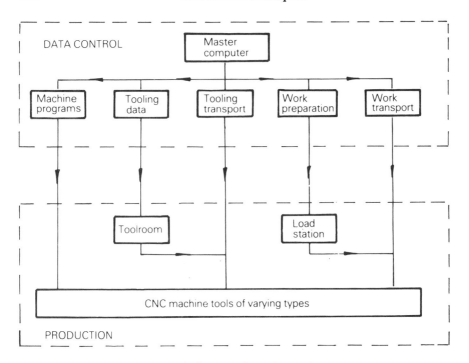

Figure 11.2 Computerized control of a manufacturing system.

A flexible manufacturing system will include at least two machines. When just two or three machines are involved, the arrangement is sometimes referred to as a "machining cell." A fully integrated system will include more machines than this and they will vary in type. Figure 11.2 illustrates the principle. Installations of this nature are, of course, very costly, but are becoming commonly used, at present. However, the modular approach to building such a system, that is, starting with two machines and then adding additional machines as and when investment funds are available, would suggest that the concept is set to become a dominant feature of manufacturing process engineering.

The automatic supply of work to each machine is an essential feature of any system, large or small. The use of pallets is the most favored method, particularly for machining centers as opposed to turning centers, although they are also used for turning work. When pallets are used for turning work, the final loading of the machine usually involves a robot. Figure 11.3 shows how one robot may be positioned to service two machines.

The way pallets are used for milling operations will vary according to the type of work being handled and the space available. Figure 11.4 illustrates the use of a rack or storage retrival system. Such a system as this is relatively simple and capable of modification and extension as and when required. More complex systems involve the use of pallet conveyors and automatic guided vehicles (AGV) moving about the factory along predetermined routes, guided by inductive control wires buried in the workshop floor or computerized programmed controls. Each machine will have its own load/unload station and there will be a master load/unload station to which each pallet or AGV returns at the end of a journey. Figure 11.5 illustrates the principle.

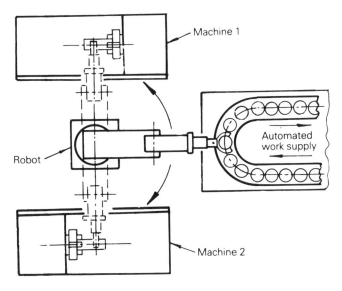

Figure 11.3 Robot loading of turning centers.

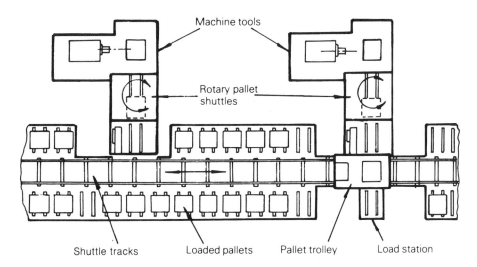

Figure 11.4 Flexible manufacturing system using racked palletized work supply.

Pallets may be fed to the machines in a predetermined order which means their positioning in the work queue is critical, otherwise a workpiece may be subjected to the wrong machining cycle! More commonly today, though, they are fed to the machine in random order and identified, usually by a photoelectric device responding to a bar code number attached to the pallet, when they arrive at the machine. On being identified the correct machining program for that workpiece will be called.

The preparation of work pallets is generally a manual operation. Their positioning and clamping in the machine are totally automated and, as a result, monitoring of their

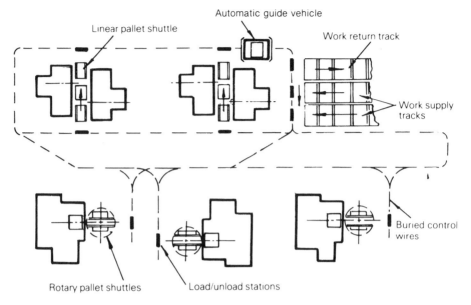

Figure 11.5 Flexible manufacturing system using remote controlled AGV work supply.

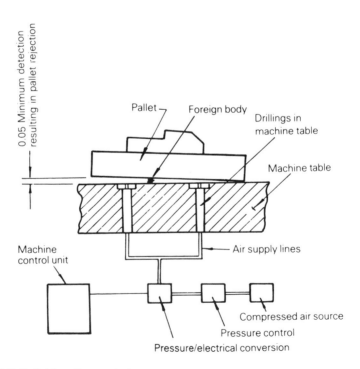

Figure 11.6 Pallet location control.

installation is necessary before machining commences. Limit switches or proximity sensors are a common feature of such control, and one method involving a combination of pneumatic and electrical principles is illustrated in Figure 11.6. Photoelectric cells, mechanical limit switches, and tactical sensors are also commonly used to check pallet and part locations.

Mention was made earlier of the high cost of flexible manufacturing systems which has, to date, limited their introduction. An intermediate approach to total automation is the use of automatic pallet-loaders dedicated to one machine. The pallet pool may involve two or more pallets and be designed in parallel rail, rectangular, oval or round form and when fully loaded will provide for an extended unsupervised production run lasting several hours, perhaps overnight or throughout a weekend. Figure 11.7 illustrates such an arrangement, referred to as a "processing center" by the manufacturers; its flexibility is indicated by the range of components shown in position on the pallets. Figure 11.8 shows a robot-loaded turning center where work chutes provide a similar capability. Due to the costly nature of automation/machining cells computer software has been developed to draw up a complete animated system for testing. This software is called simulation software and allows for completely analyzing the system for bottlenecks and problems before the system is engineered and built.

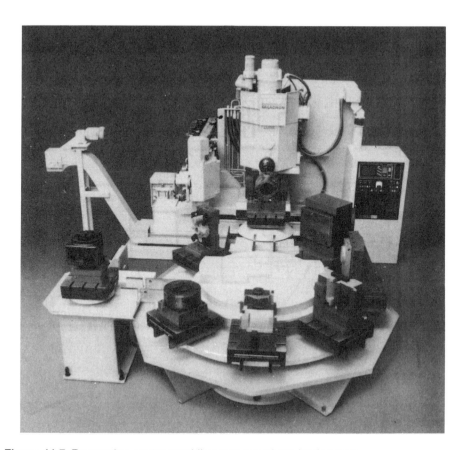

Figure 11.7 Processing center providing unmanned production runs.

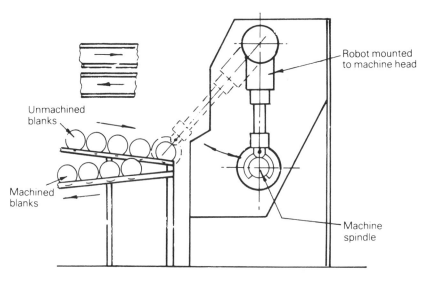

Figure 11.8 Robot loading facility providing unmanned production runs on a turning center.

Adaptive Control

Adaptive control is the term used to describe the facility that enables a machine control unit to recognize certain variations from the original conditions which may occur during a machining process and to make a compensating response. Unless such a response is made, the effect of the variations may be to damage the machine, tooling, workpiece, or cause the part to go out of prescribed tolerance. Adaptive control is basically a data "feedback system" rather like the closed-loop facility described in Chapter 1, which monitored slide positioning.

A number of unacceptable things can occur during a metal-cutting operation. For example, a tool may lose its cutting edge. On manually operated machines this would immediately be obvious to the operator, who would react accordingly. It is this type of response that adaptive control endeavours to emulate.

Now supposing the tool becomes dull on an automatic machining process. What is the likely effect? At least three things are likely to occur. First, the power necessary to turn the machine spindle is likely to increase, that is, there would be a torque variation. Second, there is likely to be a build-up in temperature between the cutting tool and the workpiece, as the tool tends to rub rather than cut. Finally, the tool itself is likely to deflect. By monitoring, that is, measuring, these variations and taking corrective action damage can be averted, and good parts consistently produced.

Torque monitoring of spindle and servo motors is one method of adaptive control that is used. The power consumption is monitored electronically and the application of the technology involves programming the control unit with data that will define the maximum and minimum torque values permitted for any particular operation. Assume that during a metal-cutting sequence the maximum torque value at the cutting tool is reached, indicating perhaps that the tool is dull or the component material is harder than anticipated. The control unit will respond to the feedback signal by lowering the feedrate and/or varying the spindle speed.

Consider another situation where, after modifications to feed and spindle speed, the torque continues to increase to a point where the spindle is overloaded. In this case the control unit would inhibit the sequence and indicate a "warning" signal on the CRT screen. The problem can then be investigated and the conditions rectified.

The torque monitoring feature can also be used to detect the minimum torque that is programmed to occur after a certain length of slide travel. If the programmed torque does not occur, there may be two possible reasons. One is that the cutting tool is broken and has not made contact, a broken drill for example; the other is that the workpiece itself is not in position. Total inhibition of the machining process may be the necessary response, or alternatively a duplicate tool, referred to as a "sister" tool, already in the magazine or turret could be called.

Torque monitoring taken to its extreme means that spindle speeds and feeds can be omitted from part programs. Provided the control unit is programmed with the values of the maximum permitted speeds and feedrates, it is possible for the adaptive control to adjust them to suit the prevailing cutting conditions. For instance, when the torque is high, the feed would reduce, but when it is low, as for example when no cutting is taking place, the feed would be rapid.

Another approach to adaptive control is one which concerns itself with monitoring the presence of workpieces by the use of surface-sensing probes. Such a probe is illustrated in Figure 11.9 and is used in milling operations. The probe is mounted in the tool magazine alongside the cutting tools and can be called into operation via the part program, in the same way as a cutting tool, and be mounted in the machine spindle. The probe is electronic in operation and the stylus is interchangeable to accommodate different applications. It can be programmed to detect the presence, by touching on, of a surface in three axes and, if the surface is not present, it will inhibit the machining cycle.

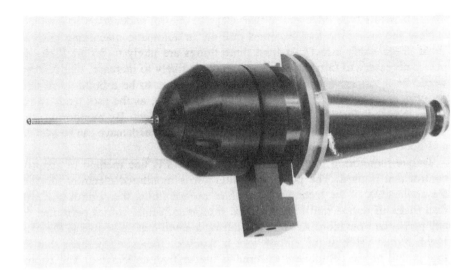

Figure 11.9 Precision surface sensing probe.

Probes can also be programmed to check stock size and automatically cause the work datums to be offset to locate the finished part within the bounds of the stock material, thus ensuring that the final work surface is completely machined. If insufficient stock is present, the machining is not performed. This facility is particularly useful when machining castings or forgings.

Another application of a probe is to speed up a cycle by preventing nonmetal-cutting passes of the cutting tool. For example, when machining casting or forgings, the part program will need to cater for all possibilities and may well include passing cuts that will be necessary only when there is excessive stock to be removed. If the probe detects that no metal is present, the feedrate will automatically be maximized or a program block may be skipped.

An interesting method of detecting the presence of cutting tools is a device that combines pneumatic or light, and electronic principles. It is designed primarily for use on machining centers to monitor small-diameter drills, taps, and reamers, which are very prone to break. The device is in the form of a simple caliper, which is positioned at a convenient point on the machine bed. The location of the caliper is predetermined and after use the cutting tool is moved via the part program so that it positions within the caliper. When in position, a jet of air is blown or light beam is shown from one side of the caliper and if the cutting tool is missing this jet of air or light beam will blow on to a pressure-sensitive/light-sensitive electrical device housed in the opposite arm of the caliper. This will generate a signal to the machine control unit that will result in either the machining process being halted or the tool being replaced in the program by a sister tool already housed in the magazine. If the tool is present, then there will be no air flow between the two arms of the caliper and the tool will automatically be replaced in the tool magazine to await a further call. Figure 11.10 illustrates the technique.

Another method of detecting broken or dull tooling involves the use of sound sensors. A cutting tool that is cutting properly will emit a certain sound. If the tool loses its edge or breaks, the sound it makes as it attempts to cut metal will be different from the original. The sound sensors detect the variation and will cause the program to be stopped or, alternatively, will call in a sister tool to replace the original.

Adaptive control is an area of computerized numerically controlled machining that is the subject of much research and experiment, and it is an area in which there are likely to be further very interesting developments.

In-Process Measurement

In-process measurement is the term used to describe the automatic measurement or gauging of a component while it is in position on the machine, and while the correction of errors is still possible. It is not a new concept. The need for automatic measurement went hand in hand with the development of automatic machining processes, and fully automated machines performing a variety of operations were around long before the advent of computerized numerical control.

In-process measurement presents many difficulties. A machining area, with its accumulation of chips and coolant, is not an ideal place to carry out precision measurement involving delicate instruments or monitoring devices. Nevertheless, a number of very

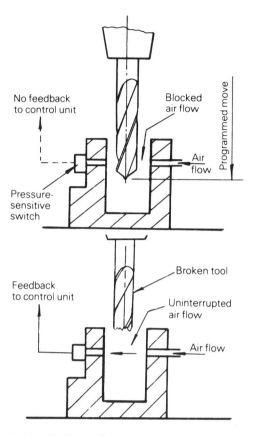

Figure 11.10 Broken tool detection unit.

successful devices have been developed over the years, their method of operation being based on mechanical, pneumatic, optical, laser, and electronic principles.

Many of the earlier devices, though not all, were "open loop," that is, there was no feedback of data to the machine controls and so there was no automatic adjustment of the machine setting to compensate for unacceptable size variations. Correction was possible only by manual intervention, but at least this was usually possible without halting the machining process.

On modern CNC machines the accuracy with which slide movements are generally made and monitored can, in the case of some classes of work, eliminate the need for further control, since the slide movements, and therefore the relative tool movements, are made to an accuracy which may well be within the dimensional tolerances of the component. In other cases this degree of control is insufficient and, as was stated in Chapter 2, transducers which monitor slide movement or leadscrew rotation may not give an accurate indication of the tool and work relationship. For instance, a tool may wear, thus affecting the dimensional size of the component, but this will have no connection with slide movement and no compensation will be made. Similarly, the workpiece may not be precisely located, or may be impossible to locate precisely, so again some monitoring and correction of movement may be necessary to ensure that surfaces are relatively positioned. These are the sorts of situations that in-process measuring can monitor. ·

The modern in-process measuring device is electronic in operation. It consists of a probe, laser or vision, and is capable of monitoring positional variations in three axes. The way in which it is applied will depend on the machine type, but it can be applied to the measurement of internal and external diameters, lengths, depths of slots, hole centers, and so on. Programmed air blasts are used to clean the work prior to measurement.

One method of using touch sensors requires reference to be made to an established datum, which may be a surface which is part of the machine structure, for example a tailstock barrel, or a surface on the component. The program will bring the sensor into contact with the reference face and record its position as zero. It will then be moved to the surface being checked and the resulting move will be compared by the machine control unit with a pre-programmed value. If there is a variation, a compensation in the relative tool offset will be made.

Features such as a bored hole diameter can be measured by touching it on each side of the hole, and the resulting movement, plus the stylus diameter of the probe, will indicate the hole size. The necessary calculation will be made by the control unit and again a comparison will be made with a pre-programmed value and tool offsets initiated as required. The technique is illustrated in Figure 11.11.

Measurement of this nature is not completely divorced from the machine slide movement, and its accuracy can never be better than the resolution, that is, the smallest increment that can be determined by the control unit of the machine.

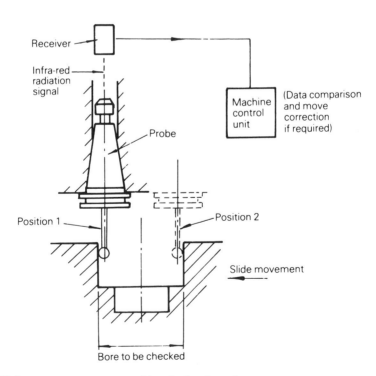

Figure 11.11 In-process measurement by electronic probe.

Computer Integrated Manufacturing (CIM)

It has been shown that computers are all around us in the CNC manufacturing area: Design "CAD," engineering analysis, CNC programming "CAM," simulation of machining and manufacturing cells, and adaptive controls. We also know that computers are used in the area of business and management for accounting, order processing, forecasting, sales analysis, production schedule planning, inventory management, materials requirements planning, machine capacity requirements planning, production control and costing, purchasing, production monitoring, payroll, financial analysis, general ledger, and accounts payable.

Computer-integrated manufacturing (CIM) is the concept of a totally automated factory in which all business, engineering, and manufacturing processes are linked and controlled by a computer system. See Figure 11.12 for a graphic representation. CIM enables managers, production planners and schedulers, shop floor floremen, and accountants to all use the same database as production designers and engineers. Owing to the short lead times and complexity of manufacturing, all areas of a business must work together to make a profit.

The enterprise model of a computer system, which allows business, engineering, and manufacturing to share information and work together, is shown in Figure 11.13. The inner ring depicts the computer hardware, software, and database. The middle ring indicates the decision making level of management and computer support staff (report generation). The outer ring indicates the users and suppliers of information that must work together. All areas of business are indicated in the three rings, and information can flow between any of

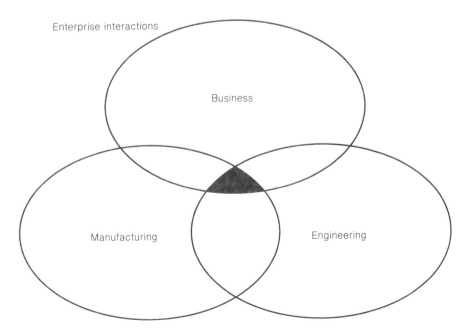

Figure 11.12 The three areas of a corporation that must work together and share data in order to make a profit.

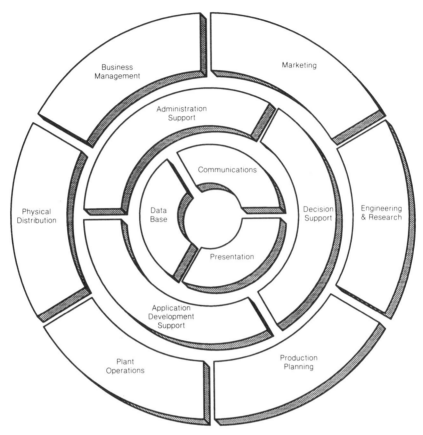

Figure 11.13 The three rings of computer information. (Courtesy of IBM.)

the areas. As in any business venture there should be improvements or goals to achieve. In implementing a CIM plan one would be looking for gains in the following areas:

- A reduction in product lead time.

- Faster, more reliable availability of quality information.

- The ability of process monitoring and tracking.

- Improved product delivery information and quality.

- Improved supplier performance and the ability to track historical performance and make predictions.

- Faster information flow and simultaneous engineering to reduce product cost.

- Improved communication of business plans to employees creating improved attitudes and quality consciousness.

The idea of CIM revolves around the center ring of shared information and people working in teams, simultaneously. The old method of passing information from department to department upon task completion is outdated and slow. To be responsive

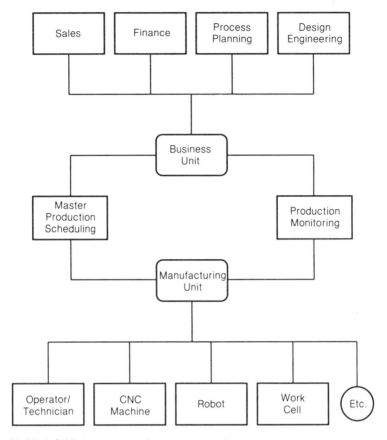

Figure 11.14 A CIM view: the business, engineering, and manufacturing units.

manufacturers we must keep from duplicating efforts and help each other for the common good of supplying products in a short period of time. Figure 11.14 shows in simple terms the interaction of information within a business.

In Chapter 10 we discussed the use of a CAD/CAM system for part design and CNC programming. The tasks involved in product design, tool design, and manufacturing engineering are much more involved than that. A product must be conceived first but then it must be analyzed for failure and determined how best to make it. It is here that the product, tool, and manufacturing engineers need to work together and share information to solve all the problems to get a product manufactured. At the same time marketing and sales need to be involved in order to see if the product will sell. As sales are projected, we then need to make plans and order materials to build the product. When orders come in, the product needs to be tracked through its processes so, as delays occur and changes must be made, the right people in engineering, business, and manufacturing are informed. As the end product leaves the manufacturing arena and is distributed to customers, billing must occur. During this whole time accounting and payroll continue. Now you can see the advantage of maintaining one shared computer database for all. Figure 11.15 shows the entire workflow of an enterprise, and it is easy to see how complex the information flow would be using paper instead of computers.

Looking further into business planning (Figure 11.16), we see three levels of management planning that the computer can help with. The top or first level of management deals with the future business plans, sales forecasting, and setting of future production levels. The second level is operations management, which takes care of monthly master schedules for production, makes plans for material needs, and checks capacity requirements (production equipment availability) to the master production schedule. The third level of management is operations execution at the production floor. This final level

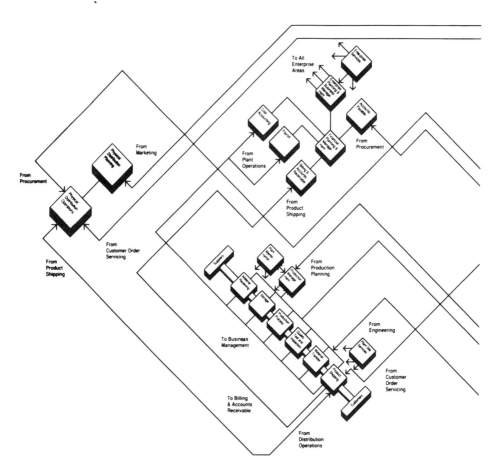

Figure 11.15 The Enterprise workflow. (Courtesy of IBM.)

schedules the production floor day to day in order to supply the proper product at the right time. This person is in charge of initial quality and wants to know about daily deliveries of vendor parts. A common computer database for all these management levels makes sure everyone has the same information for planning and problem solving.

In Figure 11.17 are the modules of a computer software package developed by IBM to take care of the previously mentioned business tasks in a company's development of CIM. The package diagrammed is called MAPICS (Manufacturing Accounting and

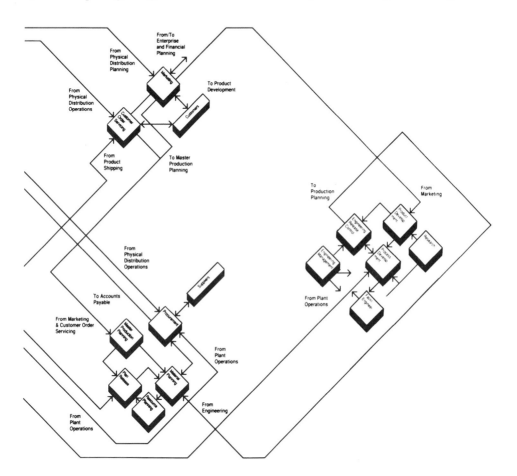

Figure 11.15 The Enterprise workflow. (Courtesy of IBM.)

Production Information Control System) and is made up of 16 modules, which can be broken down into four major areas. The diagram shows you how various types of information will cross applications in the database use.

The first application is Plant Operations, which is made up of inventory management, production control and costing, production monitoring and control, and purchasing. Inventory management improves plant productivity through reduced and improved accuracy of parts inventory. Production Control and Costing allows management to track production orders. The computer will highlight excessive material and labor costs for correction, pinpoint part locations, show production time remaining, and report daily quantities completed. This module will allow daily priority reports to be created so work can be sequenced for meeting delivery requirements. Production Monitoring and Control through timely and accurate shop reporting helps ensure work is progressing, and orders are met promptly. This application receives orders that can be added to, modified, or split, and then print shop instruction packets. The Purchasing section allows for maintaining valid quotes giving buyers more time to negotiate, and analyzes vendor performance. The system also allows for the tracking of purchase orders and validating of vendor invoices.

The second MAPICS area of application is Marketing and Physical Distribution, which is made up of the Order Entry and Invoicing, Sales Analysis, and Forecasting modules. The order entry point is the key starting point of a manufacturing organization. Detailed reports can improve cash flow, help manage inventory costs, and analyze product performance. The order entry updates both inventory and accounts receivable records. From sales records analysis reports can be generated to forecast/predict future sales and needs. This software will help ensure reasonable ship dates, coordinate inventory and production requirements, and automatically price customer orders.

The third MAPICS application is Production Planning made up of Master Production Schedule Planning, Material Requirements Planning, Capacity Requirements Planning, and Product Data Management. Production planning supplies information for optimizing resources and minimizing costs, so production stays on schedule and meets forecasts. Master production schedule planning allows production plans to be analyzed according to inventory levels, sales projections, and resource projections so that a master production schedule can be generated. Material requirements planning software creates a purchasing or manufacturing order recommendation report to be able to meet the master production schedule. Capacity requirements planning is used to calculate the future demands on machinery and manpower, both long and short range, to help reduce bottlenecks. Product data management is used to maintain the information database for engineering, manufacturing, and accounting. This file maintains information on all part numbers, bill of materials, work stations, and routings. With the product data information, cost simulations and analyses can be performed.

The last MAPICS application is Financial Management and Business Control made up of General Ledger, Financial Analysis, Accounts Payable, Payroll, and Accounts Receivable. It is here that up to date financial information is maintained for management decision making. This financial database gives tighter controls while making sure everyone gets the same fast, accurate information. General ledger allows you to get clear reports on the company's operating performance. Financial analysis will report on significant trends so additional production planning can occur. Accounts payable gives accurate, timely information on invoice due dates, vendors, and amounts. Accounts payable software is a flexible way to manage cash outflow and analyze vendor performance. The payroll unit performs all payroll tasks as well as attendance reporting and

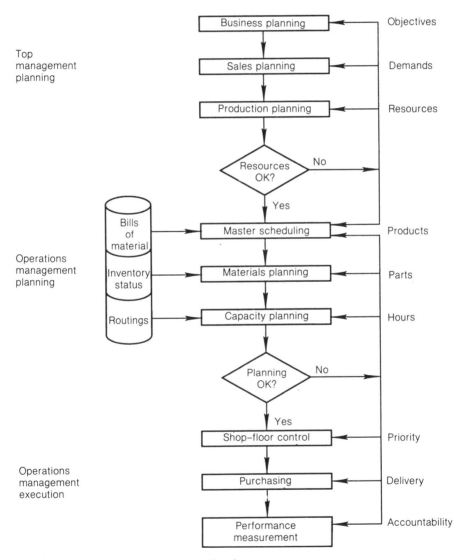

Figure 11.16 Business management levels.

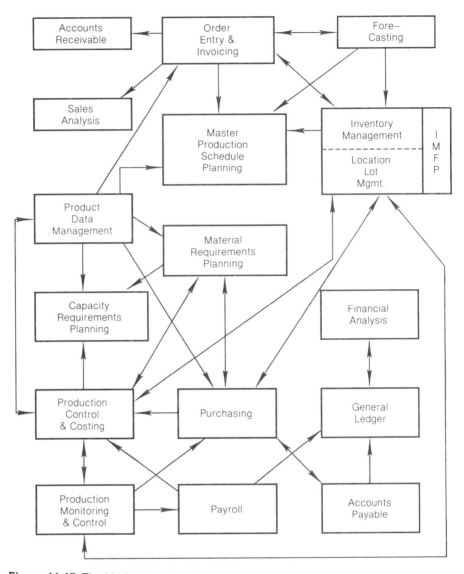

Figure 11.17 The MAPICS applications (showing major interfaces only).

payroll cost monitoring. Accounts receivable helps minimize collection periods, monitor cash flow in, and maintain records of good and bad customers.

It is easily seen that it would be a major advantage to have one computer system and database to control all the business functions. Everyone has the same up to date information to do their own planning and report generation. This IBM product runs on a midrange business computer. It should be noted that other companies also supply similar forms of software. The size of the computer running the software will have an effect on its capabilities. Software for some or all of these abilities are available on computer systems from personal size to main frames.

Remember, it is when we combine business control systems, engineering computer systems (CAD/CAM and computer-aided engineering analysis) and automated plant floor systems that we actually have true CIM. Many companies start out with pieces of CIM and will be building a system over a number of years. It is the computer that puts speed and ease into integration but it will take human integration also for the process to work.

QUESTIONS

1 What is a flexible manufacturing system?

2 What characteristic of computer technology makes the concept of FMS feasible?

3 What do you understand by the term in-process measurement? Explain how it might be applied to checking the size of a turned diameter.

4 What is torque monitoring? State two instances where its application may be useful in an automated machining process.

5 How are sound sensors used to monitor cutting-tool condition?

6 What is a sister tool?

7 Describe the technique of digitizing.

8 Describe parametric programming and explain the advantages of the technique.

9 Write a brief description of CIM.

10 What three major areas of a company make up the three rings of CIM?

11 What is it that takes place in a computerized business control system such as MAPICS?

Appendix A

Electronics Industries Association Specification

EIA Standards RS-274-D, "Interchangeable Variable Block Data Format for Positioning, Contouring, and Contouring/Positioning Numerically Controlled Machines," and RS-358-B, "Sublet of American National Standard Code for Information Interchange for Numerical Machine Control Perforated Tape" are two standards that contain useful information pertinent to the subject matter of this book. Copies of these standards may be obtained from the Electronic Industries Association, 200 Eye Street, N.W., Washington, DC 20006.

Appendix B

Cutting Speed and Feed Information, Carbide Grades, and Power Requirements Formulas

Metalcutting Safety

(Please read this before using products appearing in this catalog.)

Modern metalcutting operations involve high energy, high spindle or cutter speeds, and high temperatures and cutting forces. Hot, flying chips may be projected from the workpiece during metalcutting. Although advanced cutting tool materials are designed and manufactured to withstand the high cutting forces and temperatures that normally occur in these operations, they are susceptible to fragmentating in service, particularly if they are subjected to over-stress, severe impact or are otherwise abused. Therefore, precautions should be taken to adequately protect workers, observers and equipment against hot, flying chips, fragmented cutting tools, broken workpieces or other similar projectiles. Machines should be fullly guarded and personal protective equipment should be used at all times.

When grinding carbide or other advanced cutting tool materials, a suitable means for collection and disposal of dust, mist or sludge should be provided. Overexposure to dust or mist containing metallic particles can be hazardous to health, particularly if exposure continues over an extended period of time, and may cause eye, skin and mucous membrane irritation and temporary or permanent respiratory disease. Certain existing pulmonary and skin conditions may be aggravated by exposure to dust or mist. Adequate ventilation, respiratory protection and eye protection should be provided when grinding and workers should avoid breathing of and prolonged skin contact with dust or mist. General Industry Safety and Health Regulations, Part 1910, U.S. Department of Labor, published in Title 29 of the Code of Federal Regulation should be consulted. Obtain from Kennametal and read the applicable Material Safety Data Sheet before grinding.

Cutting tools are only one part of the worker-machine tool system. Many variables exist in machining operations, including: metal removal rate; workpiece size, shape, strength and rigidity; chucking and fixturing; the load carrying capability of centers; cutter and spindle speed and torque limitations; the holder and boring bar overhang; available power, and the condition of the tooling and the machine. A safe metalcutting operation must take all of these variables, and others, into consideration.

Kennametal has no control over the end use of its products or the environment into which those products are placed. Kennametal urges that its customers adhere to the recommended standards of use of their metalcutting machines and tools, and that they follow procedures that ensure safe metalcutting operations.

For more information, we suggest you write for Kennametal's Metalcutting Safety booklet, if you do not already have one. Quantities are available, free, for distribution to your operating personnel by contacting Kennametal at 724/539-5157. You may also obtain Material Safety Data Sheets on Kennametal products by calling the same number.

Information Sheet

How to calculate revolutions per minute when the cutting speed is given (surface feet per minute)

From the past experience and tests, the following values of cutting speeds (CS) for the materials and operation shown in the tables will be used as *maximum values* in this shop. These values are given to use for *high-speed-steel tools*:

$$RPM = \frac{4(CS)}{D} \qquad CS = \frac{D(RPM)}{4}$$

D = diameter of tool.

Material	Turning	Drilling	Shaping & Milling	Reaming
Mild Steel or Cold Rolled Steel	90 ft/min	80 ft/min	70 ft/min	40 ft/min
S. A. E. 1144	100 ft/min	90 ft/min	90 ft/min	50 ft/min
S. A. E. 4130	50 ft/min	45 ft/min	40 ft/min	25 ft/min
1% Carbon Steel	50 ft/min	45 ft/min	40 ft/min	25 ft/min
High Speed Steel	45 ft/min	40 ft/min	40 ft/min	20 ft/min
Rolled Brass	150–200 ft/min	120 ft/min	125 ft/min	70 ft/min
Cast Brass	100–125 ft/min	100 ft/min	100 ft/min	50 ft/min
Cast Iron	75 ft/min	70 ft/min	60 ft/min	35 ft/min
Cast Aluminum	250 ft/min	250 ft/min	200 ft/min	100 ft/min
Wrought Aluminum	400 ft/min	400 ft/min	400 ft/min	200 ft/min

Lathe cutting speeds for carbide tools (surface feet per minute)

Material Machined	Depth of Cut (in.)	Feed per Revolution (in.)	Surface Feet per Minute
Aluminum	.005–.015	.002–.005	700–1000
	.020–.090	.005–.015	450–700
	.100–.200	.015–.030	300–450
	.300–.700	.030–.090	100–200
Brass, bronze	.005–.015	.002–.005	700–800
	.020–.090	.005–.015	600–700
	.100–.200	.015–.030	500–600
	.300–.700	.030–.090	200–400
Cast iron (medium)	.005–.015	.002–.005	350–450
	.020–.090	.005–.015	250–350
	.100–.200	.015–.030	200–250
	.300–.700	.030–.090	75–150
Machine steel	.005–.015	.002–.005	700–1000
	.020–.090	.005–.015	550–700
	.100–.200	.015–.030	400–550
	.300–.700	.030–.090	150–300
Tool steel	.005–.015	.002–.005	500–750
	.020–.090	.005–.015	400–500
	.100–.200	.015–.030	300–400
	.300–.700	.030–.090	100–300
Stainless steel	.005–.015	.002–.005	375–500
	.020–.090	.005–.015	300–375
	.100–.200	.015–.030	250–300
	.300–.700	.030–.090	75–175
Titanium alloys	.005–.015	.002–.005	300–400
	.020–.090	.005–.015	200–300
	.100–.200	.015–.030	175–200
	.300–.700	.030–.090	50–125

Note: Cutting speeds obtained depend on operation setup and machine tool.

Suggested feed per tooth for *high speed* steel milling cutters

Material	Face Mills	Helical Mills	Slotting and Side Mills	End Mills	Form Relieved Cutters	Circular Saws
Plastic	.013	.010	.008	.007	.004	.003
Magnesium and Alloys	.022	.018	.013	.011	.007	.005
Aluminum and Alloys	.022	.018	.013	.011	.007	.005
Free Cutting Brasses and Bronzes	.022	.018	.013	.011	.007	.005
Medium Brasses and Bronzes	.014	.011	.008	.007	.004	.003
Hard Brasses and Bronzes	.009	.007	.006	.005	.003	.002
Copper	.012	.010	.007	.006	.004	.003
Cast Iron, Soft (150–180 B. H.)	.016	.013	.009	.008	.005	.004
Cast Iron, Medium (180–220 B. H.)	.013	.010	.007	.007	.004	.003
Cast Iron, Hard (220–300 B. H.)	.011	.008	.006	.006	.003	.003
Malleable Iron	.012	.010	.007	.006	.004	.003
Cast Steel	.012	.010	.007	.006	.004	.003
Low Carbon Steel, Free Machining	.012	.010	.007	.006	.004	.003
Low Carbon Steel	.010	.008	.006	.005	.003	.003
Medium Carbon Steel	.010	.008	.006	.005	.003	.003
Alloy Steel, Annealed (180–220 B. H.)	.008	.007	.005	.004	.003	.002
Alloy Steel, Tough (220–300 B. H.)	.006	.005	.004	.003	.002	.002
Alloy Steel, Hard (300–400 B. H.)	.004	.003	.003	.002	.002	.004
Stainless Steels, Free Machining	.010	.008	.006	.005	.003	.002
Stainless Steels	.006	.005	.004	.003	.002	.002
Monel Metals	.008	.007	.005	.004	.003	.002

Courtesy of Carboloy Inc., A Seco Tools Co.

Suggested feed per tooth—milling

Material	Face Mills		Helical Mills		Slotting & Side Mills		End Mills		Form Relieved Cutters		Circular Saws	
	Hss	Carb	Hss	Carb	Hss	Carb	Hss	Carb	Hss	Carb	Hss	Carb
Plastics	.013	.015	.010	.012	.008	.009	.007	.007	.004	.005	.003	.004
Magnesium and Alloys	.022	.020	.018	.016	.013	.012	.011	.010	.007	.006	.005	.005
Aluminum and Alloys	.022	.020	.018	.016	.013	.012	.011	.010	.007	.006	.005	.005
Free Cutting Brasses and Bronzes	.022	.020	.018	.016	.013	.012	.011	.010	.007	.006	.005	.005
Medium Brasses and Bronzes	.014	.012	.011	.010	.008	.007	.007	.006	.004	.004	.003	.003
Hard Brasses and Bronzes	.009	.010	.007	.008	.006	.006	.005	.005	.003	.003	.002	.003
Copper	.012	.012	.010	.009	.007	.007	.006	.006	.004	.004	.003	.003
Cast Iron, Soft (150–180 B. H.)	.016	.020	.013	.016	.009	.012	.008	.010	.005	.006	.004	.005
Cast Iron, Medium (180–220 B. H.)	.013	.015	.010	.013	.007	.010	.007	.008	.004	.005	.003	.004
Cast Iron, Hard (220–300 B. H.)	.001	.012	.008	.010	.006	.007	.006	.006	.003	.004	.003	.003
Malleable Iron	.012	.014	.010	.011	.007	.008	.006	.007	.004	.004	.003	.004
Cast Steel	.012	.014	.010	.011	.007	.008	.006	.007	.004	.005	.003	.004
Low Carbon Steel, Free Machining	.012	.016	.010	.013	.007	.009	.006	.008	.004	.005	.003	.004
Low Carbon Steel	.010	.014	.008	.011	.006	.008	.005	.007	.003	.004	.003	.004
Medium Carbon Steel	.010	.014	.008	.011	.006	.008	.005	.007	.003	.004	.003	.004
Alloy Steel, Annealed (180–220 B. H.)	.008	.014	.007	.011	.005	.008	.004	.007	.003	.004	.002	.004
Alloy Steel, Tough (220–300 B. H.)	.006	.012	.005	.010	.004	.007	.003	.006	.002	.004	.002	.003
Alloy Steel, Hard (300–400 B. H.)	.004	.010	.003	.008	.003	.006	.002	.005	.002	.003	.001	.003
Stainless Steels, Free Machining	.010	.014	.008	.011	.006	.008	.005	.007	.003	.004	.002	.004
Stainless Steels	.006	.010	.005	.008	.004	.006	.003	.005	.002	.003	.002	.003
Monel Metals	.008	.010	.007	.008	.005	.006	.004	.005	.003	.003	.002	.003

Courtesy of Carboloy Inc., A Seco Tools Co.

Suggested feed per tooth for *sintered carbide* tipped cutters

Material	Face Mills	Helical Mills	Slotting and Side Mills	End Mills	Form Relieved Cutters	Circular Saws
Plastic	.015	.012	.009	.007	.005	.004
Magnesium and Alloys	.020	.016	.012	.010	.006	.005
Aluminum and Alloys	.020	.016	.012	.010	.006	.005
Free Cutting Brasses and Bronzes	.020	.016	.012	.010	.006	.005
Medium Brasses and Bronzes	.012	.010	.007	.006	.004	.003
Hard Brasses and Bronzes	.010	.008	.006	.005	.003	.003
Copper	.012	.009	.007	.006	.004	.003
Cast Iron, Soft (150–180 B. H.)	.020	.016	.012	.010	.006	.005
Cast Iron, Medium (180–220 B. H.)	.016	.013	.010	.008	.005	.004
Cast Iron, Hard (220–300 B. H.)	.012	.010	.007	.006	.004	.003
Malleable Iron	.014	.011	.008	.007	.004	.004
Cast Steel	.014	.011	.008	.007	.005	.004
Low Carbon Steel, Free Machining	.016	.013	.009	.008	.005	.004
Low Carbon Steel	.014	.011	.008	.007	.004	.004
Medium Carbon Steel	.014	.011	.008	.007	.004	.004
Alloy Steel, Annealed (180–220 B. H.)	.014	.011	.008	.007	.004	.004
Alloy Steel, Tough (220–300 B. H.)	.012	.010	.007	.006	.003	.003
Alloy Steel, Hard (300–400 B. H.)	.010	.008	.006	.005	.003	.003
Stainless Steels, Free Machining	.014	.011	.008	.007	.004	.004
Stainless Steels	.010	.008	.006	.005	.003	.003
Monel Metals	.010	.008	.006	.005	.003	.003

Courtesy of Carboloy Inc., A Seco Tools Co.

Cutting data for drilling (meters per minute)

(Reproduced by kind permission of Guhring Ltd.)

Material of Workpiece	Drill Type	Material of Drill	Point Angle	Cutting Speed m per min.	Feed Scale No. (See p. 468)	Coolant
Free-cutting mild steel hardness up to 500 N/mm²	N/GT 50	HSS	118°	30–50	4	Soluble oil
Non-alloyed carbon steel with ≤ 0.4% Carbon ≤ 800 N/mm	N	HSS	118°	20–30	4	Soluble oil
Non-alloyed carbon steel with > 0.4% carbon, hardness 800–1000 N/mm² and purified alloy steel with a hardness ≤ 700 N/mm²	N/GT 100	HSS	118°	16–20	3	Soluble oil
Non-alloyed tool steels with a hardness of 800–1000 N/mm² and refined alloy steels with a hardness of 700–1000 N/mm²	N/GT 100	HSS	118°	12–16	3	Soluble oil
Alloyed tool steels hardness 800–1000 N/mm² and refined alloy steels with a hardness of 1000–1200 N/mm²	N/GV	HSCO (HSS)	118° (130°)	10–16	2	Soluble oil
Refined alloy steels with a hardness of > 1200 N/mm²	N/GV	HSCO	130°	5–8	1	Soluble oil, cutting oil
Chrome-molybdenum, stainless steel	N	HSCO	130°	8–12	1	Soluble oil, cutting oil
Stainless, austenitic, nickel-chrome, heat resisting steels	N/Ti (Specials)	HSCO	130°	3–8	1	Cutting oil or cutting oil with molybdenum disulphide additives
Manganese steels containing up to 10% molybdenum	H (Specials)	HSCO	130°	3–5	1	Dry: preheat to 200–300
Spring steels	N/GV	HSCO (HSS)	130°	5–10	1	Soluble oil, cutting oil
Nimonic alloys	W/Ti (Specials)	HSCO	130°	3–8	1	Cutting oil or cutting oil with molybdenum disulphide additives
Ferro-tic	N/Ti	HSCO	118°/130°	3–5	1	Dry: compressed air
Titanium and titanium alloys	Ti (Specials)	HSCO	130°	3–5	1	Cutting oil or cutting oil with molybdenum disulphide additives
Grey cast iron up to GG 26 and malleable iron	N	HSS (HSCO) (double angle point)	118°/90°	16–25	5	Dry: soluble oil
Hard cast iron up to 350 brinell	N	HSCO (double angle point)	118°/90°	8–12	4	Dry: soluble oil
Brass to MS 58	H	HSS	118°	60–80	6	Dry: cutting oil
Brass from MS 60	H(N)	HSS	118°	30–60	5	Soluble oil, cutting oil
Red copper	W/GT 50	HSS	130°	30–60	5	Soluble oil, cutting oil
Electrolytic copper	N	HSS	130°	20–30	5	Soluble oil, cutting oil
German silver	N	HSS	118°	20–30	3	Soluble oil, cutting oil
Copper nickel and copper-tin alloys	N	HSS	130°	20–30	3	Soluble oil, cutting oil
Copper-aluminium alloys	N	HSS	130°	10–30	3	Soluble oil, cutting oil
Alloys of copper and beryllium	H	HSS	130°	10–16	2	Soluble oil, cutting oil
Copper-manganese and copper-silicon alloys	N	HSS	130°	25–30	3	Soluble oil, cutting oil
Pure aluminium	W/GT 50	HSS	130°	40–60	5	Soluble oil
Aluminium-manganese and aluminium-chrome alloys	W/GT 50	HSS	130°	40–60	5	Soluble oil
Aluminium alloyed with lead, antimony or tin	W/GT 50	HSS	130°	60–100	5	Soluble oil

Cutting data for drilling (meters per minute) (*Continued*)

Material of Workpiece	Drill Type	Material of Drill	Point Angle	Cutting Speed m per min.	Feed Scale No. (See p. 468)	Coolant
Aluminium-copper alloys containing silicon, magnesium, lead, tin, titanium or beryllium	W/GT 50	HSS	130°	40–60	5	Soluble oil
Aluminium-silicon alloys containing copper, magnesium, manganese or chrome	W/GT 50	HSS	130°	40–60	5	Soluble oil
Aluminium-magnesium alloys with silicon, manganese or chrome	W/GT 50	HSS	130°	60–100	5	Soluble oil
Magnesium and magnesium alloys (Electron)	W/GT 50	HSS	130°	80–100	5	Dry
Zinc, Zamac	N	HSS	118°	30–40	4	Soluble oil
Hard duroplastics	H	HSS/HM	80°	10–20/50–100	3/4	Dry: Compressed air
Soft thermoplastics	W/GT 50	HSS	130°	16–40	3	Water: Compressed air
Hardboard and the like	W/H*	HSS	130°	16–25	3	Dry: Compressed air
Eternit, slate, marble	H	HSS (HM)	80°	3–5	from hand	Dry: Compressed air
Graphite	N	HSS (HM)	80°	3–5	from hand	Dry: Compressed air
Ebonite, Vulcanite	H	HSS	80°	16–30	6	Dry: Compressed air
Perspex	H	HSS	130°	16–25	3	Water

*) W = Drilling in the direction of the layers
    H = Drilling at right angles to the layers

N.B. The foregoing recommendations hold good only if the following conditions are met with:

a) uniform consistency of the material to be drilled;
b) drills are to B. S. 328 and Din 338;
c) Guhring drills of HSS and HSCO quality are used;
d) maximum depth does not exceed 3 times the drill diameter;
e) good machine condition and rigid mounting of the workpiece;
f) no drilling bushes are used;
g) correct quality of coolant and sufficient flow;
h) no excessive run-out of the machine spindle or drill.

Bearing these points in mind the figures in the tables may be increased or reduced accordingly.

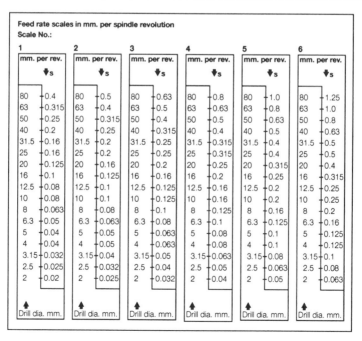

Feed rate scales in mm. per spindle revolution

Scale No.: 1	2	3	4	5	6
mm. per rev.	mm. per rev.	mm. per rev.	mm. per rev.	mm. per rev.	mm. per rev.
80 — 0.4	80 — 0.5	80 — 0.63	80 — 0.8	80 — 1.0	80 — 1.25
63 — 0.315	63 — 0.4	63 — 0.5	63 — 0.63	63 — 0.8	63 — 1.0
50 — 0.25	50 — 0.315	50 — 0.4	50 — 0.5	50 — 0.63	50 — 0.8
40 — 0.2	40 — 0.25	40 — 0.315	40 — 0.4	40 — 0.5	40 — 0.63
31.5 — 0.16	31.5 — 0.2	31.5 — 0.25	31.5 — 0.315	31.5 — 0.4	31.5 — 0.5
25 — 0.16	25 — 0.2	25 — 0.25	25 — 0.315	25 — 0.4	25 — 0.5
20 — 0.125	20 — 0.16	20 — 0.2	20 — 0.25	20 — 0.315	20 — 0.4
16 — 0.1	16 — 0.125	16 — 0.16	16 — 0.2	16 — 0.25	16 — 0.315
12.5 — 0.08	12.5 — 0.1	12.5 — 0.125	12.5 — 0.16	12.5 — 0.2	12.5 — 0.25
10 — 0.08	10 — 0.1	10 — 0.125	10 — 0.16	10 — 0.2	10 — 0.25
8 — 0.063	8 — 0.08	8 — 0.1	8 — 0.125	8 — 0.16	8 — 0.2
6.3 — 0.05	6.3 — 0.063	6.3 — 0.08	6.3 — 0.1	6.3 — 0.125	6.3 — 0.16
5 — 0.04	5 — 0.05	5 — 0.063	5 — 0.08	5 — 0.1	5 — 0.125
4 — 0.04	4 — 0.05	4 — 0.063	4 — 0.08	4 — 0.1	4 — 0.125
3.15 — 0.032	3.15 — 0.04	3.15 — 0.05	3.15 — 0.063	3.15 — 0.08	3.15 — 0.1
2.5 — 0.025	2.5 — 0.032	2.5 — 0.04	2.5 — 0.05	2.5 — 0.063	2.5 — 0.08
2 — 0.02	2 — 0.025	2 — 0.032	2 — 0.04	2 — 0.05	2 — 0.063
Drill dia. mm.	Drill dia. mm.	Drill dia. mm.	Drill dia. mm.	Drill dia. mm.	Drill dia. mm.

Cutting data for turning (meters per minute)

(Reproduced by kind permission of Anderson Strathclyde PLC)

MATERIAL	SPEED FT/MIN M/MIN			FEED INS/REV MM/REV			DEPTH INS MM			GRADE	
	ROUGH		FINISH	ROUGH		FINISH	ROUGH		FINISH	ROUGH	FINISH
ALUMINUM ALLOYS	800	1600	2500	.04	.02	.008	.25	.18	.01	CG	CF
	250	500	750	1.	.5	.2	6.5	4.5	.25		
ALUMINUM CASTINGS	800	1600	2500	.04	.02	.008	.25	.18	.01	CG	CF
	250	500	750	1.	.5	.2	6.5	4.5	.25		
ALUMINUM CASTINGS, HT. TREATED	300	600	1600	.04	.02	.008	.25	.18	.01	CG	CF
	90	180	500	1.	.5	.2	6.5	4.5	.25		
BRASS	600	750	1000	.04	.02	.008	.25	.18	.01	CG	CF
	180	230	300	1.	.5	.2	6.5	4.5	.25		
BRONZE, PHOSPHOR	300	600	800	.04	.02	.008	.25	.18	.01	CG	CF
	90	180	250	1.	.5	.2	6.5	4.5	.25		
CAST IRON, ALLOY	150	350	500	.04	.02	.008	.25	.18	.01	CR	CG
	45	105	150	1.	.5	.2	6.5	4.5	.25		
CAST IRON, CHILLED 400B	30	60	100	.04	.02	.008	.25	.18	.01	CG	CG
	9	18	30	1.	.5	.2	6.5	4.5	.25		
CAST IRON, CHILLED 600B	25	50	60	.04	.02	.008	.25	.18	.01	CG	CG
	8	15	18	1.	.5	.2	6.5	4.5	.25		
CAST IRON, GREY	250	550	650	.04	.02	.008	.3	.2	.01	CR	CG
	75	165	190	1.	.5	.2	7.5	5.	.25		
CAST IRON, NODULAR, FERRITIC	150	300	500	.04	.02	.008	.2	.1	.01	CR	CG
	45	90	150	1.	.5	.2	5.	2.5	.25		
CAST IRON, NODULAR, PEARLITIC	150	300	450	.04	.02	.008	.2	.1	.01	CR	CG
	45	90	135	1.	.5	.2	5.	2.5	.25		
COPPER	600	1100	2000	.04	.02	.008	.25	.18	.01	CR	CG
	180	330	600	1.	.5	.2	6.5	4.5	.25		
FIBRE	300	500	700	.04	.02	.008	.25	.18	.01	CG	CF
	90	150	210	1.	.5	.2	6.5	4.5	.25		
HARD RUBBER, ASBESTOS	600	800	1000	.04	.02	.008	.3	.2	.01	CF	CF
	180	250	300	1.	.5	.2	7.5	5.	.25		
LEAD BRONZE, ALLOY	750	1000	1500	.04	.02	.008	.25	.18	.01	CW	CG
	230	300	450	1.	.5	.2	6.5	4.5	.25		
MALLEABLE IRON, LONG CHIP	150	500	650	.04	.02	.008	.3	.2	.01	M1	M1
	45	150	190	1.	.5	.2	7.5	5.	.25		
MALLEABLE IRON, SHORT CHIP	250	400	600	.04	.02	.008	.3	.2	.01	M1/1	M1/1
	75	120	180	1.	.5	.2	7.5	5.	.25		
PORCELAIN	50	60	80	.04	.02	.008	.1	.01	.003	CF	CF
	15	18	25	1.	.5	.2	2.5	.25	.08		
RIGID PLASTICS, WOOD	600	800	1300	.04	.02	.008	.3	.2	.01	CW	CF
	180	250	390	1.	.5	.2	7.5	5.	.25		

Cutting data for turning (meters per minute) (*Continued*)

MATERIAL	SPEED FT/MIN M/MIN			FEED INS/REV MM/REV			DEPTH INS MM			GRADE	
	ROUGH	FINISH		ROUGH	FINISH		ROUGH	FINISH		ROUGH	FINISH
STEEL, ALLOY, ANNEALED	300 90	500 150	650 190	.03 .75	.01 .25	.004 .1	.5 13.	.25 6.5	.015 .4	SG	SF
STEEL, ALLOY HARDENED 250B	250 75	400 120	600 180	.03 .75	.01 .25	.004 .1	.3 7.5	.2 5.	.01 .25	SG	SF
STEEL, ALLOY, HARDENED 300B	200 60	300 90	500 150	.03 .75	.01 .25	.004 .1	.25 6.5	.18 4.5	.01 .25	SG	SF
STEEL, ALLOY, HARDENED 400B	150 45	250 75	350 100	.03 .75	.01 .25	.004 .1	.25 6.5	.18 4.5	.01 .25	SG	SF
STEEL, CARBON NORMALISED 125B	600 180	800 250	1100 330	.03 .75	.01 .25	.004 .1	.5 13.	.25 6.5	.015 .4	SG	SF
STEEL, CARBON NORMALISED 150B	400 120	650 190	1000 300	.03 .75	.01 .25	.004 .1	.5 13.	.25 6.5	.015 .4	SG	SF
STEEL, CARBON NORMALISED 250B	300 90	500 150	650 190	.03 .75	.01 .25	.004 .1	.3 7.5	.2 5.	.01 .25	SG	SF
STEEL, CAST 150B	200 60	300 90	500 150	.05 1.25	.01 .25	.006 .15	.5 13.	.25 6.5	.015 .4	SG	SF
STEEL, CAST 250B	150 45	250 75	350 100	.05 1.25	.01 .25	.006 .15	.3 7.5	.2 5.	.01 .25	SG	SF
STEEL, MANGANESE	60 18	100 30	200 60	.04 1.	.02 .5	.008 .2	.3 7.5	.2 5.	.01 .25	CW	CG
STEEL, STAINLESS, AUSTENTIC	300 90	400 120	500 150	.08 2.	.015 .4	.008 .2	.25 6.5	.18 4.5	.01 .25	CW	CW
STEEL, STAINLESS, MARTENSITIC	300 90	400 120	600 180	.08 2.	.015 .4	.008 .2	.25 6.5	.18 4.5	.01 .25	SG	SF
STEEL, TOOL, HARDENED	30 9	60 18	100 30	.04 1.	.02 .5	.008 .2	.2 5.	.1 2.5	.01 .25	SG	SF
STONE, HARD GRANITE	25 8	35 10	50 15	.04 1.	.02 .5	.008 .2	.2 5.	.1 2.5	.01 .25	CR	CR
STONE, SOFT MARBLE	150 45	200 60	250 75	.04 1.	.02 .5	.008 .2	.2 5.	.1 2.5	.01 .25	CF	CF

Kennamax™ Cutting Material Grade Selection

(side tab labels: Inserts, Face Mills, End Mills & Kits, Slotting Cutters, Die & Cavity Mills, Thread Milling & Grooving, Special Cutters, Milling Adapters, Spare Parts, Technical Section, Index)

Kennametal Metalcutting Insert Grades

Kennametal provides a wide variety of top quality inserts to satisfy any machining need with reliable and consistent service backing our product. Kennametal grade selection includes uncoated, CVD coated and PVD coated carbides as well as ceramic, cermet and polycrystalline superhard materials. For most machining operations, coated grades are the best choice because coatings reduce frictional forces at the tool tip, add chemical stability and have hot hardness at the elevated temperatures encountered in metalcutting.

PVD Coated Carbide Grades

PVD (physical vapor deposition) coatings have technical advantages that make them well suited for a variety of metalcutting applications in a wide range of workpiece materials. In particular, PVD grades offer outstanding performance in milling, threading, grooving, cutoff and finish turning. They operate well at low to medium cutting speeds and have a stable, relatively sharp cutting edge. These coatings are applied to the carbide substrate at lower temperatures, which preserves edge strength and enables coating of sharp edges. Tailored carbide substrates meet the needs of different machining conditions.

PVD coatings have a relatively smooth surface that generates less frictional heat, lower cutting forces and resists edge build-up that can lead to insert chipping. PVD coatings are fine grained and very hard, so they resist abrasive wear mechanisms. The cutting edges are sharp, or only slightly honed, resulting in less chatter, fewer burrs, finer surface finishes and better dimensional control on the insert itself. Chip loads can be as low as .001 ipt.

CVD Coated Carbide Grades

CVD (chemical vapor deposition) coated carbide grades are the grades of choice for most metalcutting applications involving ferrous workpiece materials. These coatings are applied to the carbide substrate at a high temperature which causes interdiffusion of the coating with the substrate to assure a strong bond. The CVD process also permits deposition of multi-layer coatings that combine different coating compounds. This enables Kennametal to provide coatings that can suppress both crater wear and flank wear, thereby expanding the range of tool application.

CVD grades also offer cobalt-enriched substrates, an advancement Kennametal pioneered. Cobalt-enrichment produces a cutting edge with excellent edge strength and fracture resistance while maintaining deformation resistance in the bulk of the insert.

CVD is currently the only coating process that can efficiently apply alumina (Al_2O_3) to carbide substrates. Alumina coatings permit higher cutting speeds and are the best coatings to combat both abrasive and crater wear.

CVD coated carbide inserts require heavier hones on the cutting edge and chip loads over .003 ipt are recommended.

Ceramic Grades

Ceramic cutting tool materials can be divided into two basic families: **alumina based (Al_2O_3)** and **silicon nitride based (Si_3N_4)**. These cutting tools can be extremely effective and productive when higher speeds can be used in the machining process. They machine cast irons, ductile irons, high-temperature alloys (nickel and iron based) and hardened steels, stainless steels and irons.

Cermet Grades

Cermet grades are comprised of mostly titanium carbonitride (TiCN) with nickel binder. They are chemically and thermally stable which leads to high wear resistance. Cermets are most successfully used for higher speed semi-finish and finish machining of most types of steels and stainless steels.

Cermets are able to hold a sharp cutting edge at high speeds and temperatures which enables them to produce exceptionally good surface finishes. Cermets are less suitable than carbides for heavy roughing.

The technical features of each grade group are explained in their respective part of this section. When making a grade choice, base your decision upon the workpiece material and configuration, speeds, feeds, the machine tool capabilities, surface finish requirements and most importantly, your productivity objectives.

Uncoated Carbide Grades

Uncoated carbides still have a place in machining applications. They work well when surface speeds are very low, when diffusion of the coating material into the workpiece is a concern, or when machining short run jobs. The cutting edges are usually sharp.

Uncoated carbides are generally classified into two groups: unalloyed and alloyed. The main application for unalloyed grades is for non-ferrous materials, where abrasive wear is the primary tool failure mechanism. Alloyed grades are applied mainly on ferrous materials where crater wear is the primary tool failure mechanism. The higher the binder content, the tougher the grade. The finer the grain size, the better the wear resistance.

Polycrystalline Grades

The **polycrystalline family** of cutting tool materials is divided into two basic groups: **diamond** and **cubic boron nitride**. Both types of materials are relatively expensive on a per unit basis, but can pay off handsomely by providing extraordinarily high productivity and tool life. This benefits the user with very low per unit manufacturing cost. Rigid machine tools and workholding fixtures are a must and as always, follow good machining practices.

Diamonds are the hardest cutting tool material available and are applied mostly on non-ferrous materials at very high speeds. They possess extremely good abrasion resistance and strength. Diamonds have high thermal conductivity to aid heat dissipation when used at high speeds.

Polycrystalline Cubic Boron Nitride (PCBN) grades can be further divided into two groups: **low CBN content** and **high CBN content** grades.

Of the two groups, **low CBN content grades** have lower thermal conductivity and comparatively higher compressive strength. These features enable low CBN content grades to promote self-induced hot cutting by combining high cutting speeds and negative rake tool geometries to soften the workpiece material and efficiently remove it from the part. These characteristics make low CBN content grades ideal for finish machining of hardened steels.

High CBN content grades possess extremely high thermal conductivity and toughness and can operate at high speeds and in severely interrupted cuts. High CBN content grades are tool materials of choice for rough cutting of hardened steel, where severe mechanical edge loading is likely to occur. The very high hardness of these cutting tools translates into excellent abrasion resistance. High PCBN content grades are very good cutting tool materials for fully pearlitic gray cast iron.

Cutting Material Grade Selection

The Kennametal grade system consists of four basic material groups: tungsten carbide, cermet, ceramic and polycrystalline. Each group contains a variety of cutting grades to accommodate various metalcutting needs.

tungsten carbide
This group consists of uncoated, CVD coated (chemical vapor deposition) and PVD coated (physical vapor deposition) materials. Each coated grade is made with various substrates of unalloyed (straight WC/Co), and alloyed (WC/TaC/TiC/NbC/Co) compositions.

cermet
Cermets contain mostly titanium carbide (TiC) and titanium nitride (TiN) with a metallic binder.

ceramic
Ceramic cutting tools can be divided into two basic families: alumina-base (aluminum oxide) and silicon nitride-base (sialon) compositions.

diamond
This material can also be divided into two basic families: polycrystalline diamond (PCD) and thin film diamond coatings.

Carbide Grades

uncoated—carbide

grade	composition and application	ISO
K313	**composition:** An uncoated WC/Co fine-grained grade. **application:** Exceptional edge wear resistance, combined with very high edge strength and abrasion resistance, delivers high-speed metal removal rates with lighter chip loads when machining non-metals and non-ferrous metals including aluminum, stainless steels and titanium.	K05-K15 M10-M20

coated—tri-phase CVD

grade	composition and application	ISO
KC850	**composition:** TiC/TiCN/TiN coating on a strengthened, cobalt-enriched substrate. **application:** Milling of carbon, alloy and certain stainless steels in a variety of feed and speed combinations. Balance of wear resistance and toughness is due to enriched substrate.	M25-M40 P25-P45

coated—alumina CVD

grades	composition and application	ISO
KC992M	**composition:** A multi-layered TiCN/Al$_2$O$_3$ CVD coated carbide. **application:** For milling of gray cast iron, with or without coolant, at medium feeds and speeds. Inserts with T-land geometries can machine nodular irons. Chip loads will be equivalent to those found when machining cast irons.	K10-K25
KC994M	**composition:** CVD Al$_2$O$_3$ coating on a tough carbide substrate. **application:** For wet or dry milling of high tensile nickel alloys and ductile irons. Tough, high wear resistant companion to KC730.	K10-K35 M15-M35

Cutting Material Grade Selection

Carbide Grades (Cont'd.)

coated—titanium nitride PVD

grades	composition and application	ISO
KC610M	**composition:** PVD TiN coated carbide grade with a deformation resistant substrate. Has superior edge wear characteristics. **application:** Developed for high productivity thread milling and grooving of most carbon, alloy and stainless steels at medium to high speeds.	P10-P30
KC620M	**composition:** PVD TiN coated carbide grade with a tough, thermal shock resistant substrate. **application:** Excellent thread milling and grooving grade for non-ferrous alloys, cast iron, high-temperature alloys and aluminum. Thermal and mechanical shock resistance, along with superior edge strength, gives this grade a good combination of properties for thread milling of difficult-to-machine materials.	K10-K20 M15-M25
KC705M	**composition:** PVD TiAlN coated carbide on a deformation resistant substrate. **application:** Primarily designed for milling hardened steel. However, exceptional heat and wear resistance qualities make this grade an excellent choice for milling of hardened steel, cast iron and heat-resistant alloys.	K01-K10 M01-M15
KC709M	**composition:** PVD TiAlN coating with superior hot hardness and chemical inertness. **application:** Designed for milling of all ductile iron materials with or without coolant. Capable of higher metal removal rates than conventional CVD coated carbides.	K05-K20
KC715M	**composition:** PVD TiCN coated carbide grade with excellent toughness and wear resistance. **application:** Long and consistent tool life in milling of carbon and alloy steels at moderate to high speeds, preferably without coolant. The hard PVD TiCN coating provides compressive residual strength for abrasion resistance and edge security.	M15-M25 P15-P25
KC720	**composition:** A tough, durable PVD TiN coated carbide grade. **application:** Developed for cutting high-temperature alloys, stainless steels and low-carbon steels at low to moderate speeds. Its unique mechanical and thermal shock resistant properties, and resistance to edge build-up, enable KC720 to deliver superior performance and reliability on difficult operations, in severe interrupted cuts and when milling high-temperature alloys with coolant.	K25-K35 M30-M40 P25-P45
KC721M	**composition:** New generation PVD TiAlN coating on a tough, thermal shock resistant carbide substrate. **application:** The synergistic combination of tough carbide substrate and highly wear resistant TiAlN coating provides long and reliable tool life when milling titanium, hard stainless steels and other high-temperature alloys. Can be applied with or without coolant.	M15-M35 P20-P35
KC725M	**composition:** A patented, multi-layer PVD TiN/TiCN/TiN coated carbide. **application:** A new milling grade engineered for high productivity wet and dry milling of carbon, alloy and austenitic stainless steels. The high thermal shock resistance of the tough carbide substrate, combined with the patented multi-layer coating, provides long and reliable tool life in aggressive milling operations with or without coolant. It is the higher speed companion to KC720 in wet milling of steel.	M15-M35 P20-P35
KC730	**composition:** A PVD TiN coated carbide grade. **application:** For milling cast and ductile irons, high-temperature alloys, aerospace materials, refractory metals, and 200 and 300 series stainless steels. The substrate offers superior thermal deformation resistance, depth of cut notch resistance and edge strength. The uniformly dense PVD coating increases wear resistance, reduces problems with edge build-up and provides an unusually good combination of properties for machining difficult-to-machine materials and aluminum.	K05-K15 M05-M15
KC792M	**composition:** A PVD-CVD coated carbide grade. **application:** Developed for milling of steels at higher speeds. Its unique substrate design, with cobalt-enriched periphery, provides maximum wear resistance combined with the chipping resistance needed for high-speed milling operations. Applying the patented PVD coating over a CVD coated insert allows application of thicker coatings than are possible with other CVD coatings. This provides desirable compressive strength in the coatings to delay thermal crack initiation. KC792M is the higher speed companion to KC710 for dry steel milling.	M25-M30 P30

Inserts

Face Mills

End Mills & Kits

Slotting Cutters

Die & Cavity Mills

Thread Milling & Grooving

Special Cutters

Milling Adapters

Spare Parts

Technical Section

Index

Cutting Material Grade Selection

Cermet Grades

	uncoated carbonitride materials	
grades	**composition and application**	**ISO**
KT175	**composition:** Titanium carbonitride based grade. **application:** Medium-to high-speed milling of steels when wear resistance and toughness requirements are balanced against light to medium chip loads at moderate to high speeds. Resists built-up edge formation.	P10-P20 M10-M20
KT195M	**composition:** Titanium carbonitride based grade. **application:** Maximum toughness and edge chipping resistance in dry milling applications on carbon and alloy steels, and stainless steels at moderate speeds and medium chip loads. Excellent hardness, strength and oxidation resistance at higher temperatures. Resists built-up and provides excellent surface finish.	P10-P30 M15-M25

Ceramic Grades

	alumina-base ceramics	
grade	**composition and application**	**ISO**
K090	**composition:** A composite (black) ceramic composed of alumina and 30% TiC. **application:** High toughness and thermal shock resistance for milling carbon steels, alloy steels, tool steels and stainless steels to 60 HRc.	K01-K10 M10 P01-P20

	silicon nitride-base ceramics	
grade	**composition and application**	**ISO**
Kyon 3500	**composition:** An extremely tough and pure silicon nitride grade. **application:** Superior edge strength ceramic for high-speed rough milling of gray and some ductile irons.	K10-K25

Diamond Grades

	diamond (PCD) and thin film diamond coating	
grades	**composition and application**	**ISO**
KD100	**composition:** This material is a polycrystalline diamond (PCD) tip brazed on a standard carbide insert. **application:** An ultra-hard grade with excellent wear resistance for improved size control (workpiece tolerance) and surface finish. It's unsurpassed for superior tool life when milling highly abrasive non-metals and non-ferrous metals.	K01-K10 M10

Kennametal Grade Application Guide–Milling

ANSI classification	characteristics of the cut and cutting tool material	ISO classification	Kennametal milling grade systems				
			uncoated carbide	CVD coated	PVD coated	cermet	*PCD and ceramic
C8	increasing speed and wear resistance / increasing feed and toughness / ferrous metals with long chips	01 P					K090
C7		10			KC792M	HT7 / KC792M	KD200
C6		20			KC721M / KC610M / KC715M / KC725M		
C5		30	CG4 / KC850		KC720		
C5		40					
C6 / C5	increasing speed and wear resistance / increasing feed and toughness / ferrous alloy metals with long or short chips and non-ferrous metals with high tensile strength properties	10 M			KC705M / KC730		K090 / KD100
C6 / C5		20	K313	KC994M	KC715M / KC620M	HT7	KT195M
C5		30	CG4 / KC850		KC725M / KC721M		
C5		40			KC720		
C4	increasing speed and wear resistance / increasing feed and toughness / ferrous metals with short chips, non-ferrous metals, and non-metals	01 K	K313		KC705M / KC730		K090 / KD100
C3		10		KC994M / KC992MCH2	KC620M / KC709M		KY3500
C2		20	CG4		KC720 / KC725M	HT7	
C1		30					

NOTE: Grades shown in **bold italic type** are recommended first choice grades.
*Advanced materials recommended for high-speed milling applications.

Inserts

Face Mills

End Mills & Kits

Slotting Cutters

Die & Cavity Mills

Thread Milling & Grooving

Special Cutters

Milling Adapters

Spare Parts

Technical Section

Index

Kennametal Milling Insert Identification System

ANSI Inserts (Inch)

NOTE:

Kennametal's milling insert identification system is provided as a general reference. The dimensional tables associated with each insert should be used for specific values. This system is based on the latest ANSI and ISO insert identification guidelines.

Dimensions shown in this catalog are prior to supplemental coating and edge modifications.

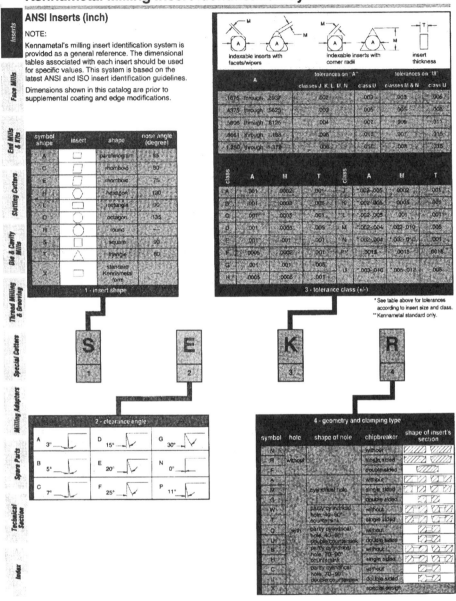

* See table above for tolerances according to insert size and class.
** Kennametal standard only.

Kennametal Milling Insert Identification System

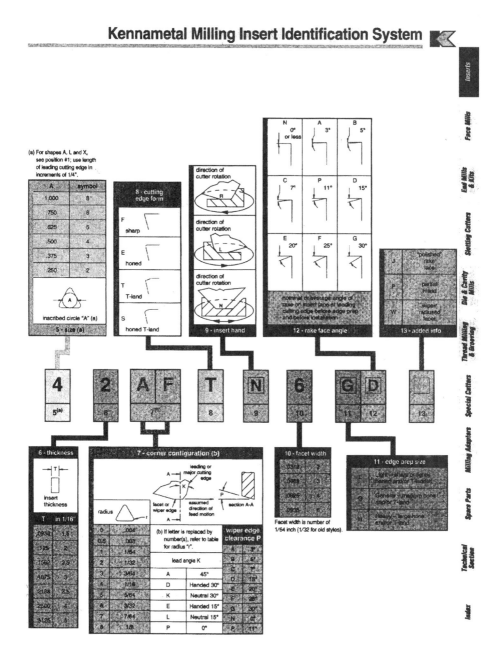

Kennametal Milling Insert Identification System

ISO Inserts (metric)

NOTE:

Kennametal's milling insert identification system is provided as a general reference. The dimensional tables associated with each insert should be used for specific values. This system is based on the latest ANSI and ISO insert identification guidelines.

Dimensions shown in this catalog are prior to supplemental coating and edge modifications.

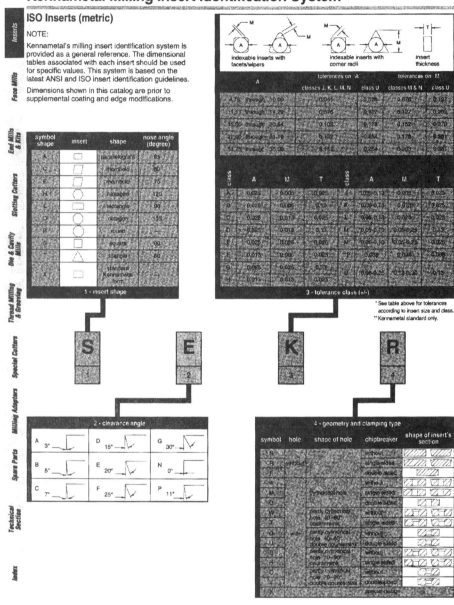

Kennametal Milling Insert Identification System

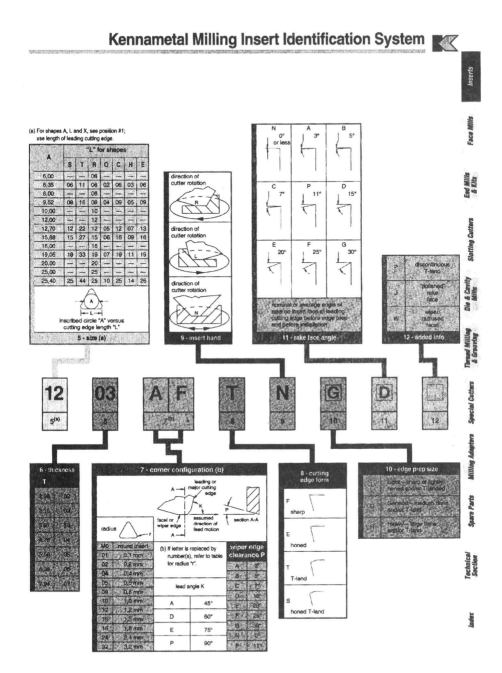

0° and 1/2° Face Mills

First Choice – High Performance
0° Lead Shear Angle – "SSM"
* screw-on inserts
* 10 mm, 1/2 and 5/8 IC
* .750 to 12.00 inch diameter range . . . . **pages 158-164**

0° Lead Shear Angle – NGE-II
* screw-on inserts
* various nose radii available
* 1.50 to 6.00 inch diameter range . . . . **page 165**

0° Lead Shear Angle – MCF-0°
* wedge insert clamping
* 3.00 to 12.00 inch diameter range
* accepts 1/2 and 5/8 IC inserts . . . . **pages 166-167**

General Purpose
* 1/2° lead angle double positive – wedge insert clamping
* 3.00 to 12.00 inch diameter range
* accepts carbide, ceramic and Kyon inserts . . . . **pages 168 and 187**

Light to Medium
* 0° lead double positive – screw-on inserts
* 2.00 to 3.00 inch diameter range . . . . **page 169**

Heavy Duty
* 0° lead positive... screw-on inserts
* 2.00 to 6.00 inch diameter range . . . . **page 170**

General Purpose
* 0° lead positive – wedge insert clamping
* 1.50 to 6.00 inch diameter range . . . . **page 171**

General Purpose
* 0° lead positive – high shear
* interchangeable adjustable cartridges... screw-on inserts
* 3.15 to 12.00 inch diameter range . . . . **pages 172-173**

General Purpose
* 0° lead utilizing – molded lock pin style inserts
* 1.50 to 6.00 inch diameter range . . . . **pages 174-175**

Aluminum Shoulder and
Face Milling – High Performance
* 0° lead high-velocity cutters
* indexable inserts or brazed PCD cartridge styles
* 2.50 to 12.00 inch diameter . . . . **pages 177-182**

FIX-PERFECT
* 0° lead, positive rake – series 305 and 306
* on-edge design insert
* 0° lead, shear angle – series 237, 311 and 313
* 0° lead, high shear angle – high performance
  for aluminum – series 312
* 1.50 to 12.00 inch diameter . . . . **pages 183-186**

Inserts
Face Mills
End Mills & Kits
Slotting Cutters
Die & Cavity Mills
Thread Milling & Grooving
Special Cutters
Milling Adapters
Spare Parts
Technical Section
Index

Kennametal Milling Cutter Identification System

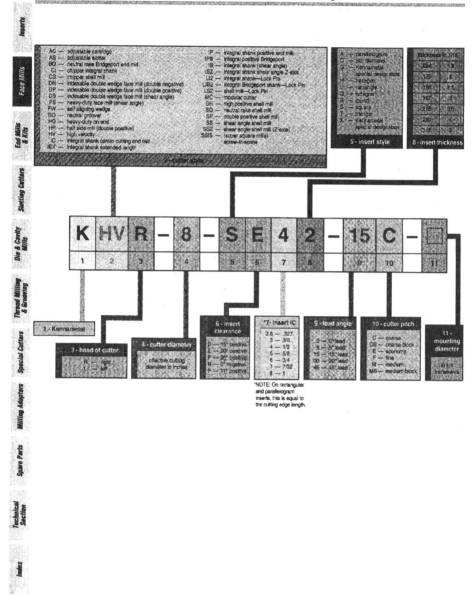

High-Performance Solid Carbide End Mills

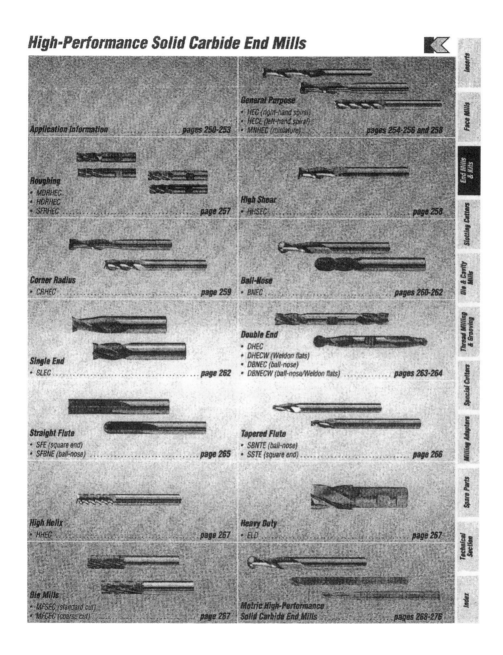

Application Information .... pages 250-253

General Purpose
- HEC (right-hand spiral)
- HECL (left-hand spiral)
- MNHEC (miniature) .... pages 254-256 and 258

Roughing
- MDRHEC
- HDRHEC
- SERHEC .... page 257

High Shear
- HHSEC .... page 258

Corner Radius
- CRHEC .... page 259

Ball-Nose
- BNEC .... pages 260-262

Single End
- SLEC .... page 262

Double End
- DHEC
- DHECW (Weldon flats)
- DBNEC (ball-nose)
- DBNECW (ball-nose/Weldon flats) .... pages 263-264

Straight Flute
- SFE (square end)
- SFBNE (ball-nose) .... page 265

Tapered Flute
- SBNTE (ball-nose)
- SSTE (square end) .... page 266

High Helix
- HHEC .... page 267

Heavy Duty
- ELD .... page 267

Die Mills
- MFSEC (standard cut)
- MFCEC (coarse cut) .... page 267

**Metric High-Performance
Solid Carbide End Mills** .... pages 268-276

Inserts | Face Mills | End Mills & Kits | Slotting Cutters | Die & Cavity Mills | Thread Milling & Grooving | Special Cutters | Milling Adapters | Spare Parts | Technical Section | Index

High-Performance Solid Carbide End Mills

Today's highly competitive industrial environment is the driving force behind the increasing use of solid carbide end mills. New machine tools, capable of milling workpieces at extremely high speeds and metal removal rates, require end mills that withstand harsh machining conditions. Kennametal carbide end mills are manufactured from state-of-the-art micrograin carbide grades that demonstrate maximum machining advantages over conventional carbide grades and high-speed end mills.

In addition, advances in PVD titanium nitride coating processes deliver performance levels beyond those attainable with conventional carbide end mills. Kennametal coated end mills offer high-speed capabilities, increased wear resistance and improved tool life. Moreover, the PVD coating provides increased lubricity for improved chip flow while reducing edge build-up.

Your payoff: improved surface finishes, reliable performance and maximum machining productivity.

Kennametal now offers eight different carbide end mill grades—one to suit your specific machining requirements.

grade K600

Our micrograin carbide composition is ideal for general purpose machining of all materials. Micrograin carbide helps produce an end mill with tough transverse rupture strength that withstands severe cutting pressures and provides maximum rigidity to minimize tool deflection, even under heavy cutting forces.

grade K605

This is the strongest grade available when uncoated carbide is preferred in machining titanium, high-temperature alloys and stainless steels. This ultra-fine, high-cobalt carbide is strong and maintains a sharp edge for positive cutting end mill geometries. Grade K605 is standard in the new 60° high helix geometry, style HHEC.

grade KC610

Increased speeds on all ferrous materials is possible with this Kennametal PVD titanium nitride coated grade. The cutting edges remain sharp and strong (after coating) to provide increased tool life, wear resistance and consistent performance. Kennametal grade KC610 can provide tool life improvements of as much as 3:1 over conventional uncoated carbide end mills.

grade KC615

This extremely wear resistant grade was engineered by Kennametal to address the machining of high-temperature alloys and stainless steels. Grade KC615 has a superior substrate structure and a PVD titanium nitride coating. It is specified as a standard offering in the new 60° high helix geometry, HHEC-style cutter.

grade KC625

High coating adhesion is achieved with this strong multi-layer TiCN grade. The extremely low friction and resistance to fatigue make this coating ideal for heavy stress operations involving abrasive materials or high-tensile alloys. Currently, this grade is only available on roughing end mills.

grade KC7215M

This is a micrograin composition with a PVD TiAIN coating that allows the cutting edge to remain sharp and strong, creating an edge that will wear consistently. It has been engineered to machine hardened steels from 45 to 62 Rc, and additional materials at higher speed and feed rates.

grade KMF

This uncoated, micrograin carbide is extremely tough and resists chipping. It is ideal for roughing and semi-finishing applications which require consistent edge wear. Its composition provides sharp edge capabilities along with uniform values both

physical and metallurgical. It is specified as a standard offering in the new DIN 6535 Shank Type A (straight) style end mills.

grade CS5

Grade CS5 was specially designed for the machining of general steels. Characterized by a high wear resistant PVD coating, its main advantage is providing better surface finishes and minimizing burrs. Grade CS5 is specified as a standard offering in the new DIN 6535 Shank Type A (straight) style end mills.

Application Information

workpiece

Establish a secure and rigid setup–cutting efficiency and quality surface finish are dependent upon it. Climb milling requires an extremely rigid setup.

end mill

*   Use end mills with the largest possible diameter, shortest possible flute and shortest possible overall length.
*   Use the correct feeds and speeds to suit the application and material being machined. Carbide end mills require much higher speeds than high-speed steel.
*   Verify adequate flute chip clearance for the type of workpiece material being cut and take appropriate action to avoid recutting of chips that can dull or chip the cutting edge.
*   Condition of the end mill should be closely monitored until reasonable tool life data figures have been established. At the first sign of dulling, the end mill should be replaced or reground; otherwise, the tool may fail beyond repair and damage the workpiece.

Wear signs include: — chip welding (increase speed)

— change in the sound of the cutting action

— changes in the shape or color of chips

— wear land development

toolholder

*   Accurate, well maintained single angle (TG) collet chucks and Powergrip milling chucks are the recommended holding methods for solid carbide end mills. These chucks hold better concentricity between the tool and machine spindle than conventional end mill adapters.
*   Cleanliness is mandatory with all types of end mill holders, if runout is to be held to a minimum. A spindle wiper should be used periodically to remove chips, lint, oil, sludge and coolants from the spindle taper to ensure proper adapter seating.

machine tool

*   The machine tool must have the necessary rigidity to minimize spindle deflection. It should also have sufficient horsepower to perform at recommended feeds and speeds. The spindle should be in excellent condition to avoid runout and chatter.
*   When increasing feed rates, overall machine condition, workpiece rigidity and cutting edge strength must be considered.
*   Climb mill whenever possible for roughing cuts— particularly where the finishing allowance is small.

coolant

*   Coolant is recommended when milling steel and high-temperature alloys. Coolant or jets of air direct chips away from the cutting tool and workpiece. This prevents recutting of chips that can damage the cutting edge. When machining titanium, coolant must be used in a heavy flow directed at the end mill cutting point to clear it of chips and reducing the hazard of fire.

Application Information

Starting Feed and Speed Guidelines for Uncoated, TiN and TiCN – High-Performance End Mills

workpiece material	cutter style	grade	speed (sfm)	cutter diameter and feed rates—chip load per tooth (ipt)					
				1/16	1/8	1/4	1/2	3/4	1
tool steel 42-50 Rc / tool steel annealed / P20 steel / die steel 32-42 Rc / die steel 52-60 Rc	HEC	KC610 CS5	150-250	.0001	.0002	.0005	.001	.002	.003
			175-275	.0005	.0006	.0015	.002	.004	.005
			275-500	.0005	.0006	.001	.003	.005	.008
			125-200	.0002	.0005	.0015	.002	.004	.006
			50-90	.0002	.0004	.0005	.001	.002	.003
low carbon steels annealed / medium carbon steels / hardened steels 48-52 Rc	HEC	KC610 CS5	250-400	.0004	.0005	.001	.003	.005	.007
			125-300	.0005	.0006	.0015	.002	.004	.005
			30-100	.0001	.0002	.0005	.001	.002	.003
stainless steel 400 series / stainless steel 300 series	HHEC	KC610 CS5	400-500	.0005	.0008	.001	.002	.004	.006
			300-400	.0005	.0008	.001	.002	.004	.006
cast iron 120-220 BHN / cast iron 220-320 BHN / ductile iron / malleable iron	HEC	K600 KMF	250-600	.0005	.001	.002	.003	.006	.008
			100-300	.0002	.0004	.0008	.002	.003	.004
			100-400	.0003	.0005	.001	.002	.004	.006
			250-500	.0003	.0005	.001	.003	.005	.007
aluminum / high silicon aluminum / brass, bronze and copper alloys / magnesium / plastics	HHSEC	K600 KMF	1000+	.0005	.001	.002	.004	.006	.008
			500-900	.0005	.001	.002	.004	.006	.008
			400-800	.0005	.001	.002	.003	.004	.005
			900+	.0005	.001	.002	.004	.006	.010
			1000+	.001	.0015	.003	.006	.010	.015
titanium alloys / high-temp. alloys (nickel base) / Monel high nickel steels	HHEC	K605 KC615 KC615	100-150	.0002	.0003	.0005	.001	.002	.004
			25-100	.0002	.0004	.0008	.001	.001	.002
			200-250	.0003	.0005	.001	.002	.003	.004

✪ Starting Feed and Speed Guidelines for TiAlN – High-Performance End Mills

workpiece material	cutter style	grade	speed (sfm)	cutter diameter and feed rates—chip load per tooth (ipt)					
				1/16	1/8	1/4	1/2	3/4	1
tool steel 42-50 Rc / tool steel annealed / P20 steel / die steel 32-42 Rc / die steel 52-60 Rc	HEC	KC7215	200-325	.0001	.0002	.0005	.001	.002	.003
			225-350	.0005	.0006	.0015	.002	.004	.005
			380-650	.0005	.0006	.001	.003	.005	.008
			160-260	.0002	.0005	.0015	.002	.004	.006
			70-120	.0002	.0004	.0005	.001	.002	.003
low-carbon steels annealed / medium carbon steels / hardened steels 48-52 Rc, (1045, forge steel)	HEC	KC7215	325-520	.0004	.0005	.001	.003	.005	.007
			215-390	.0005	.0006	.0015	.002	.004	.005
			70-130	.0001	.0002	.0005	.001	.002	.003
stainless steel 400 series / stainless steel 300 series	HHEC	KC7215	325-650	.0005	.0008	.001	.002	.004	.006
			350-520	.0005	.0008	.001	.002	.004	.006
cast iron 120-220 BHN / cast iron 220-320 BHN / ductile iron / malleable iron	HEC	KC7215	425-780	.0005	.001	.002	.003	.006	.008
			200-390	.0002	.0004	.0008	.002	.003	.004
			250-520	.0003	.0005	.001	.002	.004	.006
			375-650	.0003	.0005	.001	.003	.005	.007
aluminum / high silicon aluminum / brass, bronze and copper alloys / magnesium / plastics	HHSEC	KC7215	1000+	.0005	.001	.002	.004	.006	.008
			700-1170	.0005	.001	.002	.004	.006	.008
			600-1050	.0005	.001	.002	.003	.004	.005
			900+	.0005	.001	.002	.004	.006	.010
			1000+	.001	.0015	.003	.006	.010	.015
titanium alloys / high-temp. alloys (nickel base) / Monel high nickel steels	HHEC	KC7215	125-200	.0002	.0003	.0005	.001	.002	.004
			65-130	.0002	.0004	.0008	.001	.001	.002
			225-325	.0003	.0005	.001	.002	.003	.004

lighter radial depths of cut

Higher range of recommended surface speeds should be used.

greater radial depths of cut

Lower range of recommended surface speeds should be used.

slotting applications

Speeds should be reduced approximately 20% from the lowest range value shown.

axial depth of cut

Recommendations are not to exceed 1 1/2 times the cutter diameter.

reduce sfm as material hardness increases

When milling steels up to 60 Rc, chip color indicates correct feed and speed.

— A tan color indicates proper operating parameters.

— Blue or dark-color chips indicate speed should be reduced.

— White chips indicate speed should be increased.

NOTE: The above guidelines may require possible variations to achieve optimum results.

Application Information

Starting Feed and Speed Guidelines – Roughing End Mills

workplace material	cutter style	preferred grade	optional grade	speed (sfm)	cutter diameter and chip rates—chip load per tooth (ipt)					
					1/4	3/8	1/2	5/8	3/4	1
Free-machining steel	MDR	KC810	KC625	330-360	.0010/.0015	.0015/.0020	.0020/.0025	.0020/.0030	.0025/.0040	.0030/.0050
Low carbon steel	MDR	KC810	KC625	300-325	.0010/.0015	.0015/.0020	.0025/.0030	.0025/.0030	.0025/.0040	.0030/.0050
Medium carbon steel	MDR	KC810	KC625	220-320	.0010/.0015	.0010/.0020	.0020/.0025	.0020/.0030	.0025/.0030	.0030/.0050
Alloy steel	MDR	KC810	KC625	160-275	.0010/.0015	.0010/.0020	.0020/.0025	.0020/.0030	.0025/.0030	.0030/.0050
High strength alloy	MDR	KC810	KC625	140-215	.0010/.0015	.0010/.0020	.0020/.0025	.0020/.0030	.0025/.0030	.0030/.0050
Structural steel	MDR	KC810	KC625	215-250	.0010/.0015	.0010/.0020	.0020/.0025	.0020/.0030	.0025/.0030	.0025/.0035
Tool steel	MDR	KC810	KC625	200-250	.0010/.0015	.0010/.0015	.0020/.0025	.0020/.0025	.0025/.0030	.0025/.0040
Stainless steel	MDR	KC625	KC610	180-210	.0010/.0015	.0010/.0015	.0015/.0025	.0020/.0025	.0025/.0030	.0025/.0035
Cast iron	MDR	KC625	KC610	140-350	.0010/.0015	.0010/.0015	.0020/.0030	.0020/.0050	.0020/.0050	.0030/.0060
High temp alloys	HDR	KC610	KC625	40-60	.0010/.0015	.0010/.0015	.0015/.0025	.0020/.0025	.0020/.0030	.0020/.0040
Titanium	HDR	KC625	KC610	100-130	.0010/.0015	.0010/.0015	.0020/.0030	.0020/.0030	.0025/.0040	.0025/.0050
Aluminum & alum. alloys High silicon aluminum	SFR SFR	KC625	KC610	600-2000	.0010/.0015	.0015/.0025	.0020/.0045	.0030/.0050	.0030/.0080	.0030/.0100

- These recommendations are given as suggested starting points only.
- Maximum flood coolant suggested.
- Climb milling is preferred on CNC machining centers.
- If width of cut equals cutting diameter reduce feed rate by 50%.
- If width of cut equals 1/2 cutting diameter reduce feed rate by 25%.

Milling Adapters

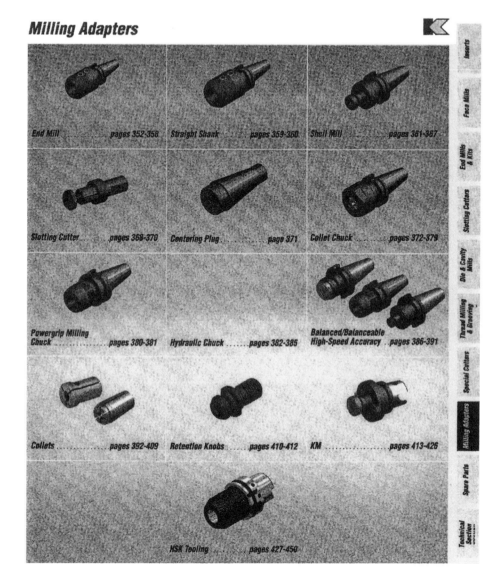

End Mill *pages 352-358*	**Straight Shank** *pages 359-360*	**Shell Mill** *pages 361-367*
Slotting Cutter *pages 368-370*	**Centering Plug** *page 371*	**Collet Chuck** *pages 372-379*
Powergrip Milling Chuck *pages 380-381*	**Hydraulic Chuck** *pages 382-385*	**Balanced/Balanceable High-Speed Accuracy** *pages 386-391*
Collets *pages 392-409*	**Retention Knobs** *pages 410-412*	**KM** *pages 413-426*
	HSK Tooling *pages 427-450*	

Inserts

Face Mills

End Mills & Kits

Slotting Cutters

Die & Cavity Mills

Thread Milling & Grooving

Special Cutters

Milling Adapters

Spare Parts

Technical Section

Kennametal Erickson Milling Adapter Systems

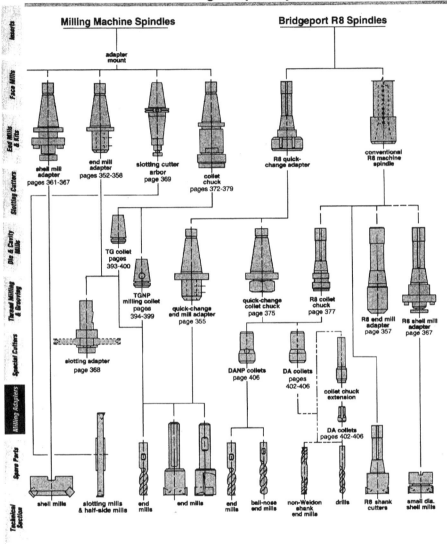

Kennametal Erickson Milling Adapter Systems

Machining Center Spindles

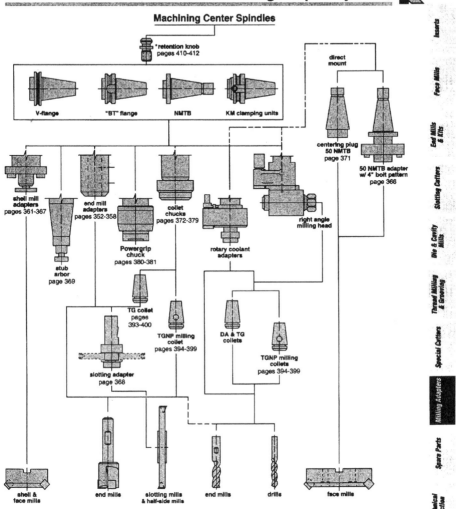

Workpiece Machinability Groups

Grade Optimization – Example

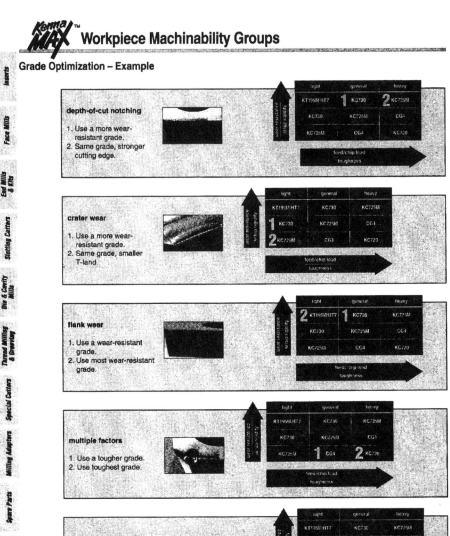

depth-of-cut notching

1. Use a more wear-resistant grade.
2. Same grade, stronger cutting edge.

crater wear

1. Use a more wear-resistant grade.
2. Same grade, smaller T-land.

flank wear

1. Use a wear-resistant grade.
2. Use most wear-resistant grade.

multiple factors

1. Use a tougher grade.
2. Use toughest grade.

chipping

1. Use a tougher grade.
2. Use toughest grade.

Troubleshooting

Introduction

Troubleshooting should be performed in a sequential method to identify and solve your milling problems. These problems can be recognized as premature insert edge failure, part appearance, machine noise or vibration and the cutter's appearance. Successful troubleshooting requires that we correctly identify the problem, then take the necessary corrective action one step at a time. The five key areas of concern are:

1. cutting tool material (indexable carbide inserts)
2. cutter/adapter
3. machine
4. workpiece
5. set-up/fixturing

This section will discuss possible causes and will recommend corrective actions for each of the five areas listed. Remember, if more than one step is taken concurrently, the real cause of the problem may never be discovered. Always perform one corrective measure at a time.

Indexable Carbide Insert

Edge Condition Problems and Solutions

1. **Chipping:** Appears like normal flank wear to the untrained eye. Actually, normal flank wear lands have a fine, smooth wear pattern, while a land formed by chipping has a saw-toothed, uneven surface. If chipping is not detected soon enough, it may be perceived as depth-of-cut notching.

   Chipping can also be caused by recutting of chips. A good example of this would be a slotting operation where chip clearance or chip gullet space does not allow the chips to evacuate cleanly. In this instance, packing of the chips also occurs.

   In most cases, by changing to a stronger grade and/or to a different edge preparation such as a larger hone or T-land, or from a 0° cutter geometry to a lead angle cutter geometry, will resolve the problem.

problem	cause	solution
chipping	• chatter	• Check system rigidity for proper part clamping. • Correct worn gibs/bearings. • Check for improper cutter mounting.
	• edge prep	• Use largest hone or T-land possible.
	• grade	• Use a tougher grade.
	• built-up edge	• Increase speed.
	• feed	• Reduce feed per tooth.
	• recutting chips	• Choose cutter geometry with correct pitch for chip clearance. • Use air blast or coolant to remove chips.

2. **Depth-of-Cut Notching:** Appears when chipping or localized wear at the depth-of-cut line on the rake face and flank of the insert occurs. Notching is primarily caused by the condition of the workpiece material. Material conditions prone to depth-of-cut notch include: an abrasive workpiece skin of scale, abrasive properties of high-temperature alloys like Inconel, a work-hardened outer layer resulting from a previous machining operation, or heat-treated material above 55 HRc.

problem	cause	solution
depth-of-cut notching	• cutter geometry	• Change to 15°, 30° or 45° lead cutters.
	• grade	• Use a more wear resistant grade of carbide.
	• lead	• Reduce feed per tooth.
	• speed	• Reduce speed.
	• edge-prep	• Use honed or T-land inserts.
	• programming	• Vary depth of cut on very abrasive materials.

Technical Data

Inserts

Face Mills

End Mills & Kits

Slotting Cutters

Die & Cavity Mills

Thread Milling & Grooving

Special Cutters

Milling Adapters

Spare Parts

Technical Section

Index

Indexable Carbide Insert
Edge Condition Problems and Solutions (Cont'd.)

3. **Thermal Cracks:** These cracks run perpendicular to the insert's cutting edge and are caused by the extreme temperature variations involved in milling. In one revolution of a milling cutter, the insert starts to cut and the temperature quickly rises as the insert enters the cut. The varying chip thickness also changes the temperature throughout the cut. When the insert comes out of the cut, air or coolant flow rapidly cools the insert before it reenters the cut.

   These temperature variations create heat stresses in the insert which can result in thermal cracks. To the untrained eye, advanced thermal cracking could appear as chipping.

problem	cause	solution
thermal cracks	• speed and feed	• Reduce cutting edge temperature by reducing the cutting speed and possibly the feed per tooth.
	• coolant	• Shut off coolant or be sure it is properly applied.
	• grade	• Use coated grade designed for wet milling.

4. **Built-Up Edge:** This condition involves the adhesion of layers of workpiece material to the top surface of the insert. Hardened pieces of the adhered material periodically break free leaving an irregularly shaped depression along the cutting edge. This causes damage to the part and insert. Cutting forces will also be increased due to built-up edge.

problem	cause	solution
built-up edge	• speed	• Increase sfm.
	• feed	• Increase feed per tooth.
	• coolant	• Use mist or flood coolant to avoid chips sticking to the insert when machining stainless and aluminum alloys.
	• grade	• Use sharp edge PVD inserts.
		• Higher speeds require diamond-tipped inserts or diamond coated inserts on certain alloys.
	• edge-prep	• Use sharp edge, positive rake PVD inserts or polished (J-polished) inserts.

5. **Crater Wear:** A relatively smooth, regular depression produced on the insert's rake face. Crater wear occurs in two ways:
   1. Material adhering to the insert's top surface is dislodged, carrying away minute fragments of the top surface of the insert.
   2. Frictional heat builds up resulting from the flow of chips over the top surface of the insert. Eventually, this frictional heat buildup will soften the insert behind the cutting edge and carries minute particles of the insert away until such time as a crater becomes noticeable.

   Crater wear is rarely encountered in milling, but can appear when machining certain steel and cast iron alloys. If crater wear becomes severe, there is a risk that the cutting edge will break, destroying the insert.

problem	cause	solution
crater wear	• grade	• Use a more wear-resistant grade.
	• speed	• Reduce cutting speed.
	• edge-prep	• Use smaller T-land or increase feed to proper range for T-land.

Indexable Carbide Insert
Edge Condition Problems and Solutions (Cont'd.)

6. **Flank Wear:** Uniform flank wear is the preferred method of insert failure because it can be predicted. Excessive flank wear increases cutting forces and gives rise to a loss of surface finish. When wear occurs at an unacceptable rate or becomes unpredictable, the key elements that must be investigated are speed, feed, grade and insert/cutter geometry.

NOTE: Inserts should be indexed when: roughing (.015 to .020 flank wear is reached) finishing (.010 to .015 flank wear or sooner).

problem	cause	solution
flank wear	• speed	• Check this area first. Recalculate sfm to assure correctness. • Speed should be reduced without changing feed rate.
	• feed	• Increase feed per tooth (feed should be high enough to avoid the pure rubbing which occurs with small chip thickness).
	• grade	• Use more wear-resistant grade. • Change to a coated grade if you are now using an uncoated grade.
	• insert geometry	• Inspect insert for proper style in the cutter used.

7. **Multiple Factors:** When wear, chipping, thermal cracking and breakage all occur at once, the machine operator must look beyond the normal feed, speed and depth-of-cut adjustments to find the root cause of the problem. Speed, feed and depth-of-cut parameters should be re-examined for accuracy, but the system's rigidity should also be closely inspected for loose or worn parts as well.

problem	cause	solution
multiple factors	• system rigidity	• Check system for loose cutter mounting. • Improve fixture and cutter rigidity. • Check for worn hardware or improper insert installation.
	• feed	• Reduce feed rate to relieve cutting forces.
	• cutter geometry	• If possible, use a lead angle cutter to redirect cutting forces away from the insert nose.
	• insert/grade	• If possible, use a larger nose radius. • Use T-land insert. • Use a tougher grade of carbide.

Inserts
Face Mills
End Mills & Kits
Slotting Cutters
Die & Cavity Mills
Thread Milling & Grooving
Special Cutters
Milling Adapters
Spare Parts
Technical Section
Index

Technical Data

Troubleshooting Matrix for Advanced Cutting Tool Materials

This matrix explains the specific areas where advanced cutting tool materials perform differently from uncoated and coated carbide grades during the troubleshooting identification process.

cutting tool material	problem	solution	comments
Cermets KT150 KT175 KT195M	• chipping	• Reduce feed per insert. • Turn off coolant. • Apply hone or T-land insert.	• Excellent resistance to built-up edge. • Dry milling grades, do not use coolant. • KT150 is recommended for high-speed finishing at extremely light chip loads. Excellent for wear and deformation resistance. • KT175 is recommended for medium- to high-speed milling when balanced with light-to-medium chip loads. • KT195M is noted for maximum toughness and edge chipping resistance at moderate speeds and medium chip loads.
	• breakage (fracture)	• Reduce depth of cut and chip load. • Increase speed. • Apply hone or T-land insert.	
Ceramic K090	• chipping and breakage	• Check system rigidity. • Increase hone or T-land. • Switch to thicker insert. • Increase speed. • Reduce feed from heavy to moderate/ light feed range. • Change to grade Kyon 2100 for nickel-base alloys. • Change to grades Kyon 3000 or 3500 for cast iron alloys.	• Coolant is not recommended when used for milling operations. • Use KFW-style cutter designed especially for ceramics, page 168. • Use lead angle cutters where possible.
	• wear	• Reduce speed. • Use KFW-style cutter.	
Sialon Kyon 2000 or Kyon 2100	• depth-of-cut notch	• Reduce hone or size of T-land edge preparation. • Use a lead angle cutter, if possible. • Pre-chamfer part to eliminate stress points on cutting edge of insert. • Vary depth of cut.	• Excellent for machining nickel-base materials over 35 HRc. • Available in positive rake inserts. • Can be used with coolant. • Use KFW-style cutters, page 168.
	• minor chipping	• Minor chipping is normal, especially on Inconel.	
	• flank wear	• Use .060 as indexing criterion.	
	• fracture	• Use thicker inserts. • Do not over-torque clamping.	
Silicon Nitride Kyon 3000 or Kyon 3500	• flank wear	• Reduce speed, increase feed. • Change to Kyon 3000, if using Kyon 3500.	• Use with or without coolant. • Will provide optimum combination of increased toughness and wear resistance in high-speed machining of cast irons. • Wide range of sfm. • Kyon 3000 is recommended for high-speed finishing at moderate-to-light feeds. Excellent abrasion resistance combined with good toughness and thermal shock resistance. • Kyon 3500, first choice for maximum toughness and edge chipping resistance at high-speed and heavy-to-moderate feeds.
	• chipping	• Change edge preparation. • Change to Kyon 3500, if using Kyon 3000. • Reduce chip load.	
	• breakage	• Use KFW-style cutter, page 168.	

Inserts • Face Mills • End Mills & Kits • Slotting Cutters • Die & Cavity Mills • Thread Milling & Grooving • Special Cutters • Milling Adapters • Spare Parts • Technical Section • Index

Technical Data

Troubleshooting Matrix for Advanced Cutting Tool Materials (Cont'd.)

cutting tool material	problem	solution	comments
Polycrystalline Diamond KD100 (tipped)	• chipping and breaking	• Check system rigidity. • Reduce chip load, increase sfm.	• Excellent wear resistance for improved size control and surface finish. • Unsurpassed tool life when machining aluminum alloys, non-ferrous and non-metallics at high sfm's. • Can be used with coolant. • Regrindable/resettable.
KCD25 diamond film coating	• burrs and finish	• Use a KD100 tipped insert in one or two pockets as a wiper insert.	• Roughing to semi-finishing grade. • Excellent tool life when machining aluminum alloys that have 12% or less silicon content. • Multiple cutting edges versus single-edge on tipped PCD. • Less expensive than ground, tipped KD100.
KD120 Cubic Boron Nitrides (tipped) and KD200 (solid) CBN's	• chipping and breaking	• Check system rigidity. • Additional edge preparation may be required (hone or T-land).	• Use on hardened tool steels, cast irons and some high-temperature alloys (Ni-base). • Applications on: Ni-hards, high-chrome irons, chill cast irons, hard alloys and hardened tool steels (50-65 Rc). • KD120 tipped CBN for finishing only. One cutting edge. • Regrindable/resettable. • KD200 solid CBN with high thermal conductivity and a low thermal coefficient; excellent for milling hardened materials. • Regrindable. • Multiple cutting edges versus single-tipped CBN. • Used with coolant.

Inserts

Face Mills

End Mills & Kits

Slotting Cutters

Die & Cavity Mills

Thread Milling & Grooving

Special Cutters

Milling Adapters

Spare Parts

Technical Section

Index

Technical Data

Solid Carbide and High-Speed Steel End Mills

Causes of Chipping

- rigidity
- chip load
- tool alloy
- recutting chips
- rake angle
- handling
- tir

Being a good tool detective requires problem identification and taking the necessary corrective action one step at a time. Remember, if more than one step is taken concurrently, then the real cause of the problem may never be discovered. Let's first look at problems and corrective actions for HSS cutters.

Chipping and nicked edges are uneven fragmentations of the cutting edge. They can be caused by a variety of factors.

- **Rigidity** - Check the rigidity of the system for improper fixture clamping, improper cutter mounting or worn gibs or bearings. Conventional mill if table has back lashing.
- **Chip Load** - Reduce feed per tooth.
- **Tool Alloy** - Use a tougher cutting tool: M42 or M7 over cobalt (M12) or T15 which is powdered metal.
- **Recutting Chips** - Check chip evacuation, reduce number of flutes for more chip clearance, increase coolant concentration and/or flow.
- **Rake Angle** - Use stronger rake angle, general purpose flute versus high helix flute.
- **Handling** - Improve storage and handling. Cutters should not be thrown unprotected into a drawer. This can chip the cutting edges.
- **tir** (Total Indicator Reading) - Check tool and toolholder for runout and/or play in the spindle.

Causes of Chatter

- chip load
- speed
- depth of cut
- rigidity
- fixturing

Chatter is a condition of vibration involving the machine and cutter. Once this condition arises, it tends to be self-sustaining.

Chatter can be identified by lines or grooves that appear at regular intervals in the workpiece, caused by the teeth of the end mill as they vibrate in and out of the work. Spacing depends on the frequency of vibration.

Eliminating this problem is largely a trial-and-error process. Let's look at the causes and solutions.

- **Chip Load** - Increase feed per tooth; load the tool.
- **Speed** - Decrease speed.
- **Rigidity** - Check for shortest and most accurate holder, use a Powergrip milling chuck.
  - Check machine for worn gibs and bearings;
  - Use shortest possible cutting tool.
- **Fixturing** - Check for part movement; clamp opposite direction of feed; change set-up to position the workpiece and cutter as close as possible to the spindle. Note that in a situation where the heavy radial and axial depth is combined with the right-hand helix on the cutter, the forces generated might overcome the pull-back force on the retention knob on a smaller (40 taper) machine. If so, the tool will bounce in spindle.

Technical Data

Solid Carbide and High-Speed Steel End Mills (Cont'd.)

Built-Up Edge and Chip Welding

- coolant
- tool finish
- speed
- chip load
- tool geometry

Built-up edge is the adhesion of layers of the workpiece material on the cutting edges of the tool.

Workhardened pieces of the adhered material break off and cause damage to the part and cutting tool (chipping).

Chip welding is the result of high heat and pressure. This is usually due to inadequate coolant flow.

- **Coolant** - Increase coolant concentration and/or flow (lubricity).
- **Tool Finish** - Rough ground finishes on edges and flutes of re-ground cutting tools increases drag, which will allow material to adhere to the cutting edge.
- **Speed** - For built-up edge, increase speed; for chipwelding, decrease speed.
- **Chip Load** - For built-up edge, increase chip load; for chip welding decrease chip load.
- **Tool Geometry** - A sharper penetration angle or increased rake angle can help reduce the tendency of softer materials to smear and cling to the cutting edges. Try a tool with greater clearance angles.

Causes of Breakage

- depth of cut
- rigidity
- dull tool
- chip load
- chip evacuation

Cutting tool breakage may be caused by too great a depth of cut, part movement, poor mounting, poor regrinding or improper programming.

Another common cause is chip packing, particularly when milling a slot.

- **Depth of Cut** - Reduce depth of cut. The basic rule of thumb is doc should not exceed 1/2 inch of the end mill diameter. For example, a 1 inch end mill, cutting its full diameter, should be set to a 1/2 inch maximum depth of cut.
- **Rigidity** - Check for work bearings and gibs in the machine, part deflection, reduce tool overhang ratio; use largest diameter end mill possible; use shortest end mill possible. What type of toolholder?
- **Dull Tool** - As the end mill teeth wear, frictional forces increase. More power is required to drive the end mill, resulting in more deflection. Failure to replace the end mill could result in tool breakage.
- **Chip Load** - Reduce chip load; too heavy of a chip load versus the number of available flutes in the tool will crowd chip removal space. This condition will lead to packing of chips, which will result in tool breakage.

Technical Data

Inserts

Face Mills

End Mills & Kits

Slotting Cutters

Die & Cavity Mills

Thread Milling & Grooving

Special Cutters

Milling Adapters

Spare Parts

Technical Section

Index

Solid Carbide and High-Speed Steel End Mills (Cont'd.)

Causes of Chip Packing

- inadequate number of flutes
- insufficient coolant when plunge cutting

Chip packing occurs when there is inadequate space in the flutes for chips to be evacuated; or when milling a pocket or slot, the chips are not evacuated from the area of the cut.

- **Inadequate Flutes** - Make sure flute space is adequate to promote clean chip removal. Two flutes are needed for roughing, plunging and slotting. Four or more flutes are required for finishing only. Three flutes are a good compromise where finish and chip clearance is important.
- **Insufficient Coolant** - Increase flow. Improper flow can cause both chip welding and packing.
- **When Plunge Cutting** - Use two-flute end mill for adequate chip clearance. On softer materials, use the two-flute hi-helix end mill (for aluminum).

Slotting

- chip load
- speed
- depth of cut
- rigidity
- fixturing

When periphery or slot milling, helical cutters can pull or push off location. The side wall will be angled or the slot will not be positioned where you wanted it to be.

- Use an end mill with a shorter flute length.
- Use an end mill adapter with a shorter projection length.
- Reduce feed rate to reduce cutting forces.
- Take multiple passes on axial depth.
- Make finish profiling passes.

Causes of Premature Wear

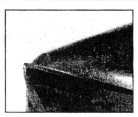

- speed
- feed
- tool alloy
- coolant

Wear is the dulling of the cutting tool edge resulting from cutting action, abrasion and heat.

Wear is the preferred method of cutting tool failure because it is predictable and repeatable.

When wear occurs at unacceptable rates or becomes unpredictable, there are key elements that must be investigated.

NOTE: HSS cutting tools should be removed for resharpening when the wear land reaches .010. This will eliminate grinding excess metal to restore a new edge (depends on application).

- **Speed** - Check to see if setting is correct for material being machined (heat).
- **Feed** - Check to see if chip load is in the proper range for material being machined (too low = rubbing).
- **Tool Alloy** - Make sure the cutting tool alloy is suitable for the material being machined; use a more wear resistant alloy.
- **Coolant** - Make sure coolant is directed at the cut and the mixture ratio is correct for the application. Coolant should be clean and of high quality.

Kennametal Grade System for Cutting Materials

PVD Coated Grades

grade	coating	insert styles	composition and application	C class	ISO class
KC6725	TiN	A3 deep grooving	**composition:** A PVD TiN coated grade with a tough ultra-fine grain, unalloyed substrate. **application:** Available only in the A3 tooling system. For general purpose machining of most steels, stainless steels, high-temperature alloys, titanium, irons, and non-ferrous materials. Speeds may vary from low to medium, and will handle interruptions and high feed rates. Cutting edges are lightly honed.	C2 C6	K15 - K25 M25 - M35 P25 - P40
KC710	TiN	threading grooving	**composition:** A PVD TiN coating over a general purpose alloyed substrate. **application:** Use to cut steel at medium to high speeds. Grade KC710 will greatly improve productivity, and allow higher speed capabilities in comparison to uncoated carbide. Available in threading and grooving geometries where upgrades from uncoated carbides are common. Most cutting edges are lightly honed. Positive rake Top Notch inserts are sharp.	C6 - C7	M15 - M30 P20 - P35
KC720	TiN	turning & boring profiling threading grooving cutoff	**composition:** A tough, durable PVD TiN coating over an unalloyed carbide substrate. **application:** Developed for cutting high-temperature alloys, most stainless steels, and titanium alloys at low to moderate speeds. Its unique mechanical and thermal shock resistant properties and resistance to edge build-up enable grade KC720 to deliver superior performance and reliability on difficult operations like cutoff and interrupted turning. Consider it to be your problem solving grade. Most ground periphery inserts have a sharp edge, others are lightly honed.	C1 C5	K25 - K35 M30 - M40 P25 - P45
KC722	TiN	threading cutoff face grooving	**composition:** A PVD TiN coating over a medium tough WC/Co unalloyed substrate. **application:** This grade was specifically developed for the Ranger face grooving system. Use in all types of steel, austenitic, ferritic, and martensitic stainless steel, tool steels, high-temperature alloys, and titanium. The fine grain substrate provides just the right amount of wear resistance and toughness for the intended applications. The coating contributes crater wear resistance and resistance to built-up edge, as well as higher speed capability when desired. Most inserts are lightly honed. Positive rake Top Notch inserts are sharp.	C2 C6	K15 - K25 M25 - M35 P25 - P40
KC730	TiN	turning & boring profiling threading grooving	**composition:** A PVD TiN coating over a very wear-resistant unalloyed substrate. **application:** For general purpose machining of high-temperature alloys, aerospace materials, refractory metals and 200 or 300 series stainless steels. The thin, uniformly dense, smooth coating increases wear resistance and reduces problems with built-up edge. It also provides an unusually good combination of properties for machining difficult-to-machine materials and aluminum. The substrate offers superior thermal deformation resistance, depth of cut notch resistance, and edge strength. Run at higher speeds than uncoated grades. Most ground periphery inserts have a sharp edge.	C2 - C4	K05 - K20 M10 - M25 P10 - P20
KC732	TiN TiCN TiN	turning & boring profiling grooving	**composition:** A CVD/PVD coating over a very wear-resistant unalloyed substrate. **application:** This grade was designed for semifinishing to finishing of high-temperature alloys and titanium. Grade KC732 benefits from the combined strengths of two coating processes. The CVD layer provides exceptional adherence to the substrate, and the PVD coating is crack free and very smooth. This patented grade allows higher cutting speeds than other PVD grades, which leads to greater productivity, reduced cycle times, and lower costs. Most ground periphery inserts have a sharp edge.	C3 - C4	K05 - K15 M10 - M20

Inserts
Toolholders
Boring Bars & Heads
Drills
Collet Chucks
Cartridges
Brazed Tools
Technical Data
Index

Kennametal Grade System for Cutting Materials

CVD Coated Carbide Grades					
grade	coating	insert styles	composition and application	C class	ISO class
KC8840	TiN TiCN	A3 deep grooving light profiling	**composition:** This grade has a wear resistant TiCN coating over a coarse grained and very tough substrate. **application:** Available exclusively in the A3 multipurpose tooling system. Designed for heavy duty grooving applications subject to severe mechanical edge loading. Use at low to medium speeds on most carbon, alloy, and stainless steels. Consider KC6840 to be your workhorse grade for steel applications. For medium cutting conditions, use grade KC6920.	C5	M30 - M40 P40 - P50
KC6920	TiN Al$_2$O$_3$ TiC TiCN	A3 deep grooving light profiling	**composition:** A moderately thick alumina coating over a hard substrate. **application:** Available exclusively in the A3 deep grooving system. Engineered for general purpose use on carbon steel, alloy steel, ductile iron and cast iron. The Al$_2$O$_3$ coating is highly abrasion resistant, allows higher speeds and offers better surface finishes. The coating layers allow economic use at a wide range of speeds and feeds. Use as your first grade choice for the above materials. Withstands moderate interruptions. For heavy interrupted cuts, use grade KC6840.	C6 - C7	K15 - K25 M10 - M20 P10 - P30
KC810	TiN TiCN TiC	turning & boring profiling threading grooving	**composition:** A multilayered coating over an alloyed carbide substrate. **application:** An economical choice for general steel machining at low to moderate speeds. For better tool life at moderate to higher speeds, consider upgrading to grade KC935.	C6 - C7	P10 - P30
KC820	TiN TiCN TiC	cutoff	**composition:** A multilayered CVD coating over a tough steel cutting substrate. **application:** Available exclusively in the Separator and Separator PL cutoff tools. For use on carbon and alloy steel, ductile iron, and ferritic and martensitic stainless steels. The CVD coating provides wear resistance, while the substrate provides the toughness required for cutoff applications. For most operations running at medium to higher cutting speeds, consider upgrading to grade KC935.	C5	M10 - M30 P20 - P35
KC850	TiN TiCN TiC	turning & boring profiling grooving	**composition:** A tri-phase coating on an extra strong, cobalt-enriched substrate. **application:** Grade KC850 has long been considered the industry's leading choice for general purpose machining of many workpiece materials. With the advent of higher machine tool spindle speeds, today it finds its best application in heavy cutting of low, medium, and high carbon steels, as well as medium hardness alloy and tool steels. Excellent thermal and mechanical shock resistance makes grade KC850 ideally suited for difficult applications with interruptions. Consider using grade KC935 for lighter cuts.	C5 - C6	M30 - M45 P25 - P45
KC9010	TiN Al$_2$O$_3$ TiCN	turning & boring profiling	**composition:** A thick alumina coated grade with a moderately hard, deformation resistant substrate. **application:** This is a great finishing grade for use in a large variety of workpiece materials including most steels, ferritic and martensitic stainless steel, and irons. The thick coating is the preferred choice for cast iron machining because it has outstanding abrasion resistance and maintains hardness at high cutting speeds. Best economy and productivity can be attained when used at high speeds. Can withstand some interruptions. For rougher cutting, use grade KC9025.	C3 C7	K10 - K20 M10 - M20 P01 - P20
KC9025	TiN Al$_2$O$_3$ TiCN	turning & boring profiling	**composition:** A thick alumina coated grade with a cobalt-enriched substrate. **application:** Grade KC9025 can be considered the industry's best high-speed, general purpose turning grade. Workpiece applications include most steels, ferritic and martensitic stainless steels, and irons. The smooth coating results in less microchipping, reduced frictional heat, and produces better surface finishes. The substrate maintains both toughness and edge strength. Performs well in moderately heavy roughing to semifinishing. Use grade KC9010 for the finish cut.	C2 - C3 C6 - C7	K15 - K25 M15 - M25 P15 - P35

Kennametal Grade System for Cutting Materials

Inserts
Toolholders
Boring Bars & Heads
Drills
Collet Chucks
Cartridges
Brazed Tools
Technical Data
Index

CVD Coated Carbide Grades (Cont'd)

grade	coating	insert styles	composition and application	C class	ISO class
KC9040	TiN Al₂O₃ TiC TiCN	turning & boring profiling	**composition:** An alumina coated grade with a tough cobalt-enriched substrate. **application:** For heavy roughing applications on all types of steels, stainless steels, and most other materials when tool edge strength is critical. A specially designed coating preparation assures prolonged tool life. Apply with confidence on tough jobs.	C5 - C6	M30 - M40 P30 - P45
KC9045	TiN Al₂O₃ TiC TiCN	turning & boring profiling	**composition:** An alumina coating over a coarse grained substrate that has a minimal amount of solid solution carbide. **application:** Designed for heavy to violent roughing of all types of materials where bulk toughness is essential. Reserve this grade for your most difficult interrupted cutting applications.	C5	M35 - M45 P35 - P50
KC9120	TiN Al₂O₃ TiCN	turning & boring profiling grooving	**composition:** A TiCN/Al₂O₃/TiN coating over a carefully chosen substrate. **application:** Grade KC9120 was specifically engineered for short-chipping ductile irons and gray irons. The newly developed tool coating cycle used for this grade preserves the substrate strength and reduces thermal cracks. The substrate and coating combination perform well in heavy interruptions as well as smooth cutting. Apply at speeds up to 1200 sfm in both high and low tensile strength materials.	C3	K10 - K30
KC910	Al₂O₃ TiC	turning & boring profiling grooving	**composition:** A thin alumina coating over a hard, deformation resistant substrate. **application:** This grade excels in two main application areas; high-speed finishing of gray cast irons, and medium-speed finishing of alloy steels that are in a hardness range of 35 to 50 HRc. The hard substrate prolongs tool life in these applications. The alumina coating allows higher cutting speeds. The TiC layer contributes abrasion resistance, which is important for intended uses. Can withstand light interruptions. For heavy interrupted cuts, use grade KC9025.	C3 C7	K01 - K20 M05 - M20 P01 - P20
KC935	Al₂O₃ TiC TiCN	turning & boring profiling cutoff	**composition:** A multilayered coating with optimized layer thickness over a cobalt-enriched substrate. **application:** Grade KC935 is fast becoming the favorite grade for soft and gummy workpiece materials. Successfully apply on most steels, ferritic, martensitic, and austenitic stainless steels, and heavier cutting in nickel base alloys. The TiCN/TiC coating layers are effective at low to medium speeds, and the outer alumina coating maintains hot hardness at medium to high speeds. The well balanced substrate maintains toughness and edge strength. The specially engineered coating surface provides a smooth, stable cutting edge that resists build-up and microchipping. If you like grade KC850, try grade KC935, and bring real flexibility to your metalcutting operations.	C2 C6	K20 - K30 M20 - M35 P20 - P40
KC950	TiN Al₂O₃ TiC	turning & boring profiling grooving	**composition:** A multilayered coating over a hard, cobalt-enriched substrate. **application:** Best applied in tough, fairly hard, 35 to 45 HRc, alloy and bearing steels. This unique grade offers a substrate that combines hardness and toughness, and a coating design that resists crater and abrasive wear. Can withstand interruptions. Use for moderate roughing to semifinishing at medium to high cutting speeds and feeds. Consider using grade KC9025 for general purpose use.	C3 - C4 C7 - C8	K10 - K20 M10 - M25 P05 - P20
KC990	TiN Al₂O₃ TiN Al₂O₃ TiN Al₂O₃ TiCN	turning & boring profiling	**composition:** A multilayered alumina coated grade with a high-strength substrate. Coated with TiCN and then alternating layers of Al₂O₃ and TiN. **application:** Engineered for finishing of carbon and alloy steels, and ductile, nodular, or malleable irons. The thin alumina coating layers are very hard. Best speed range is above 650 sfm in smooth cuts. In most applications, grade KC990 may be replaced by grade KC9010, with better machining results.	C3 C7	K05 - K20 P10 - P20

Kennametal Grade System for Cutting Materials

Alumina-based Ceramics

grade	coating	insert styles	composition and application	C class	ISO class
K060		turning & boring profiling	**composition:** A pure alumina-based ceramic grade (white). **application:** Most wear resistant alumina-based ceramic grade; used for finish machining of soft cast irons and steels to 35 HRc (330 BHN).	C4 C8	K01 - K05 P01 - P05
K090		turning & boring	**composition:** Alumina/TiC ceramic grade (black). **application:** Great combination of toughness and wear resistance; used for machining alloy steels, tool steels and stainless steels to 60 HRc (653 BHN).	C4 C8	K01 - K15 P01 - P05
KY4000		turning & boring	**composition:** Alumina-based ceramic grade with zirconium oxide and silicon carbide whiskers for added strength. **application:** Wear resistance, high toughness and mechanical shock resistance; used for machining medium carbon alloy steels and ductile or nodular cast irons.	C4 C8	K05 - K15 P05 - P10

Silicon Nitride-based Ceramics

grade	coating	insert styles	composition and application	C class	ISO class
KY2000		turning & boring profiling grooving	**composition:** An advanced sialon grade. **application:** Excellent combination of thermal shock resistance and fracture toughness; used for general purpose machining of high-temperature alloys.	C4	M10 - M25 K05 - K15
KY2100		turning & boring profiling grooving	**composition:** An advanced sialon grade. **application:** Good mechanical shock resistance combined with edge wear resistance; used for general purpose machining of high-temperature alloys.	C4	M05 - M20 K05 - K15
KY3000		turning & boring profiling grooving	**composition:** An advanced sialon grade. **application:** Maximum edge wear resistance; used for finishing to general purpose machining of gray cast iron and maximum toughness for roughing high-temperature alloys.	C4	K05 - K15 M10 - M30
KY3400	TiN Al₂O₃	turning & boring profiling	**composition:** CVD coated pure silicon nitride grade. **application:** Excellent combination of toughness and edge wear resistance; used for general purpose machining of gray cast irons and ductile or nodular cast irons.	C3	K10 - K30
KY3500		turning & boring profiling	**composition:** Pure silicon nitride grade. **application:** Maximum toughness; used at high feed rates for rough machining of gray cast iron, including machining through interruptions.	C2	K15 - K35 M15 - M30

Inserts   Toolholders   Boring Bars & Heads   Drills   Collet Chucks   Cartridges   Brazed Tools   Technical Data   Index

Kennametal Grade System for Cutting Materials

Cermet - (CERamics with METallic binders)

grade	coating	insert styles	composition and application	C class	ISO class
KT125		turning & boring	**composition:** A hard and very wear resistant TiC/TiN-base grade. **application:** Used for high-speed, precision turning and boring of carbon steels, alloy steels, stainless steels and ductile and malleable irons.	C4 C8	M10 P01 - P05
KT150		turning & boring	**composition:** A general purpose TiC/TiN-base grade. **application:** Used for high-speed, semifinish turning and boring of carbon steels, alloy steels, stainless steels and ductile and malleable irons.	C4 C8	M15 P01 - P10
KT175		turning & boring grooving	**composition:** A tougher TiC/TiN- base grade. **application:** Used for medium to high-speed, light roughing to semifinishing of carbon steels, alloy steels, stainless steels, and ductile and malleable irons.	C3 C7	M20 P05 - P15

Uncoated Carbide Grades

grade	coating	insert styles	composition and application	C class	ISO class
K21		brazed cutoff brazed tools	**composition:** A very tough, medium to high binder content, alloyed, medium grain size grade. **application:** This is a heavy duty grade for difficult applications that require good mechanical shock resistance, and less wear resistance. Use for roughing or interrupted cuts at relatively low surface speeds on steels.	C5	M20 - M35 P25 - P40
K313		turning & boring profiling threading grooving	**composition:** A hard, low binder content, unalloyed WC/Co fine-grained grade. **application:** Exceptional edge wear resistance combined with very high strength for machining titanium, cast irons, austenitic stainless steels, non-ferrous metals, nonmetals, and most high-temperature alloys. Superior thermal deformation and depth of cut notch resistance. The grain structure is well controlled for minimal pits and flaws which contributes to long, reliable service.	C3-C4	K05 - K20 M10 - M20
K420		threading grooving	**composition:** A medium binder content, alloyed, larger grain size grade. **application:** Grade K420 is a general purpose steel cutting grade. It has just the right balance of wear resistance and toughness. Available as a standard grade in the Top Notch threading and grooving line. Can withstand heavy chip loads in soft to moderately hard steels. Consider upgrading to grade KC710 for most uses.	C6	M25 - M35 P30 - P40
K6		cutoff brazed tools	**composition:** A medium hardness, low binder content, unalloyed WC/Co grade. **application:** Use for machining cast iron, ductile iron, austenitic stainless steel, aluminum, high-temperature alloys, titanium and non-metallic materials. Grade K6 has the wear resistance needed to machine these materials with added toughness for cutoff applications.	C3	K10 - K30 M15 - M25
K6225		A3 deep grooving	**composition:** A tough, high binder content, unalloyed WC/Co, ultra fine-grained grade. **application:** Available exclusively in the A3 tooling system. Choose this grade for machining aluminum, cast iron, high-temperature alloys and titanium. Well suited for demanding operations on aerospace materials. The high binder content imparts toughness, while the small grain structure provides wear resistance.	C2	K20 - K35 M20 -M35
K68		turning & boring profiling threading grooving	**composition:** A hard, low binder content, unalloyed grade WC/Co fine-grained grade. **application:** Grade K68 has excellent abrasion resistance for machining cast irons, austenitic stainless steels, non-ferrous metals, nonmetals and as an alternative to grade K313 on most high-temperature alloys. Use as a general purpose grade for non-ferrous materials.	C3	K05 - K20 M10 - M20

Inserts · Toolholders · Boring Bars & Heads · Drills · Collet Chucks · Cartridges · Brazed Tools · Technical Data · Index

Kennametal Grade System for Cutting Materials

PCD – CVD Thin Film Diamond Coated

grade	coating	insert styles	composition and application	C class	ISO class
KCD25	diamond	turning & boring profiling	**composition:** A highly abrasion resistant, pure diamond coating over a general purpose carbide substrate. **application:** This grade provides outstanding performance in roughing and semi-finishing operations, plus many finishing cuts. Recommended for free-machining low silicon content aluminum alloys, metal matrix composites, carbon and graphite composites, non-ferrous materials and non-metallics. May also be an economical choice for use on high silicon aluminum alloys (hypereutectic). Compared to conventional PCD grades, grade KCD25 provides the user with up to four cutting edges, and depth of cut limitations are no longer a concern. In addition, chip control geometries are now possible, the coating is more chemically stable, and higher cutting speeds are attainable. The cutting edge is slightly honed. This grade operates at medium- to ultra-high speeds.	C4	K03 - K15

PCD – Polycrystalline Diamond

grade	coating	insert styles	composition and application	C class	ISO class
KD100		turning & boring profiling grooving	**composition:** A polycrystalline diamond tip (PCD) brazed onto a carbide substrate. **application:** Grade KD100 is for general purpose turning. The cutting tool material contains a binder in addition to diamond particles. This makes the grade suitable for roughing to finishing all types of highly abrasive workpieces, including non-ferrous metals and non-metallics. Use as your first choice on high content silicon aluminum alloys (hypereutectic). Will produce generally good surface finishes. Provides the best mechanical shock resistance of the diamond tool materials. The cutting edge is sharp. This grade operates at very high speeds.	C4	K03 - K20

PCD – CVD Thick Film Diamond Sheet

grade	coating	insert styles	composition and application	C class	ISO class
KD105		turning & boring profiling	**composition:** An extremely abrasion resistant, pure diamond material, brazed onto a carbide substrate. **application:** This grade is intended for fine finishing cuts with little or no interruptions. Will retain edge sharpness longer than grade KD100 due to its 100% diamond content. Recommended for finishing free-machining low silicon content aluminum alloys, metal matrix composites, carbon and graphite composites, non-ferrous materials and non-metallics. May also work well in high silicon content aluminum alloys (hypereutectic). The cutting edge is sharp. This grade operates at very high speeds.	C4	K01 - K05

Inserts

Toolholders

Boring Bars & Heads

Drills

Collet Chucks

Cartridges

Brazed Tools

Technical Data

Index

Kennametal Grade System for Cutting Materials

PCBN — Polycrystalline Cubic Boron Nitride

grade	coating	insert styles	composition and application	C class	ISO class
KD050		turning & boring profiling	**composition:** A low CBN content, PCBN tip brazed onto a carbide insert. **application:** Designed for precision finishing of hardened steels (>45 HRc), the harder the better. Use on bearing steel, hot and cold work tool steels, high-speed steels, die steels, case hardened steels, carburized and nitrided irons, and some hard coatings. Do not apply on soft steel, rapid crater wear will result. When possible use negative rake tools. Available in mini tips and regular size tips, and various edge preps.	C8	K01 - K03
KD081		turning & boring profiling grooving	**composition:** A low CBN content, PCBN tip brazed onto a carbide insert. **application:** Designed for roughing to semi-finishing of hardened steels (>45 HRc). Like grade KD050, apply on bearing steel, hot and cold work tool steels, high-speed steels, die steels, case hardened steels, carburized and nitrided irons, and some hard coatings. Do not apply on soft steel, rapid crater wear will result. When possible use negative rake tools. Available in mini tips and regular size tips, and various edge preps.	C8	K03 - K05
KD120		turning & boring profiling grooving	**composition:** A high CBN content, PCBN tip brazed onto a carbide insert. **application:** The primary application area for high CBN content grades is in roughing to finishing of fully pearlitic gray cast iron, chilled irons, high chrome alloys steels, sintered powdered metals, and heavy cuts in hardened steels (>45 HRc). Also use for finishing chilled cast iron and fully pearlitic cast iron. Do not apply on finishing cuts in hardened steels, use grade KD050 or grade KD081 for that purpose. Available in regular size tips.	C8	K05 - K15
KD200		turning & boring	**composition:** A high CBN content, solid PCBN structure having multiple cutting edges. **application:** Grade KD200 is applied in the same machining parameters as grade KD120, however, the solid inserts offer better security and shock resistance than the tipped grade KD120 inserts. Multiple cutting edges are available on the solid grade KD200 inserts. Always apply solid PCBN's first, if the insert geometry and available toolholders will allow its use. Always use a T-land edge prep if possible.	C8	K05 - K15
KD240	TiN	turning & boring	**composition:** A high CBN content, solid PCBN structure having multiple cutting edges and a TiN coating. **application:** Grade KD240 is applied in the same machining parameters as the other high CBN content grades – KD120 and KD200. In addition, grade KD240 provides the user with a gold colored coating to aid in the identification of worn cutting edges. This feature is especially beneficial when using round insert shapes to get the maximum number of insert indexes. Always use a T-land edge prep if possible.	C8	K05 - K15

Kennametal Inserts

Turning and Boring Insert Identification System

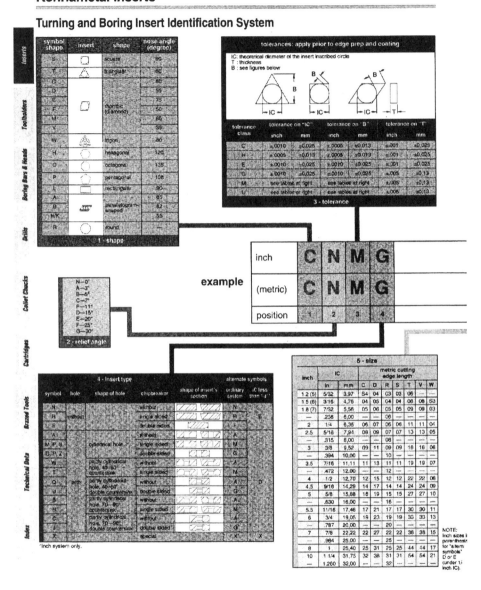

Kennametal Inserts

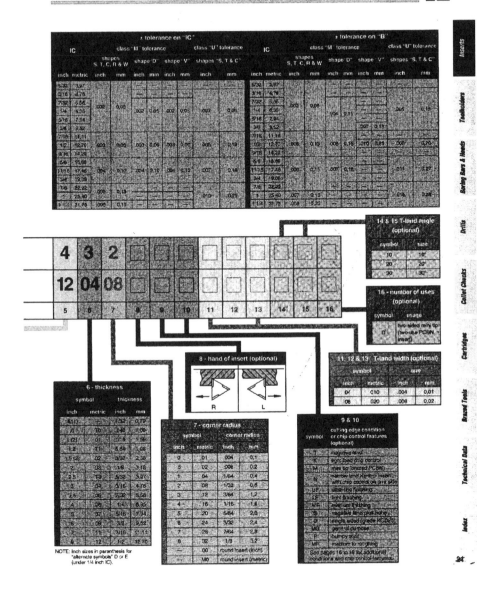

Kennametal Threading Systems

On-Edge Threading Insert Identification System

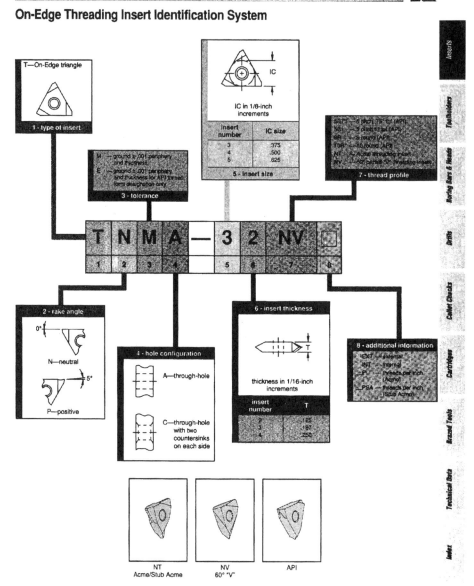

NT
Acme/Stub Acme

NV
60° "V"

API

Kennametal Grooving Systems

Top Notch Grooving Insert Identification System

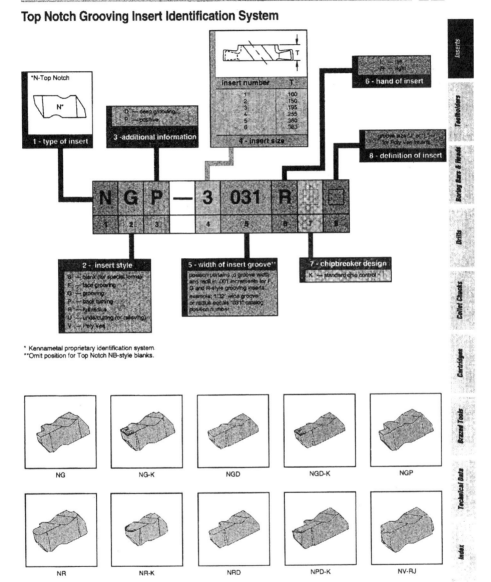

* Kennametal proprietary identification system.
**Omit position for Top Notch NB-style blanks.

| NG | NG-K | NGD | NGD-K | NGP |
| NR | NR-K | NRD | NPD-K | NV-RJ |

Kenloc Combination Toolholder Index

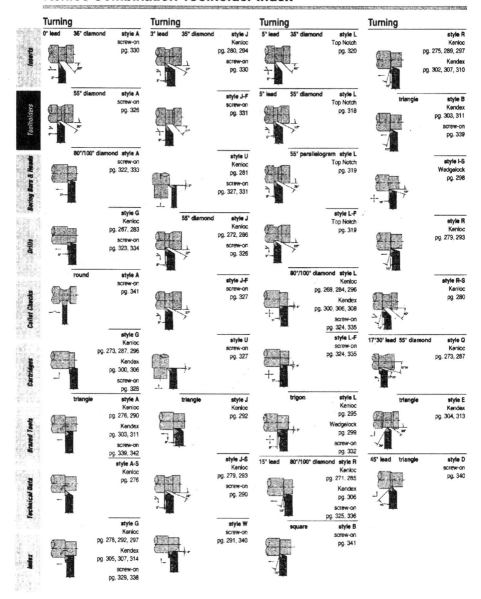

Inserts

Toolholders

Boring Bars & Heads

Drills

Collet Chucks

Cartridges

Braze Tools

Technical Data

Index

Turning

| 0° lead | 35° diamond | style A |
| screw-on |
| pg. 330 |

55° diamond | style A
screw-on
pg. 326

80°/100° diamond | style A
screw-on
pg. 322, 333

style G
Kenloc
pg. 267, 283
screw-on
pg. 323, 334

round | style A
screw-on
pg. 341

style G
Kenloc
pg. 273, 287, 296
Kendex
pg. 300, 306
screw-on
pg. 328

triangle | style A
Kenloc
pg. 276, 290
Kendex
pg. 303, 311
screw-on
pg. 339, 342

style A-S
Kenloc
pg. 276

style G
Kenloc
pg. 278, 292, 297
Kendex
pg. 305, 307, 314
screw-on
pg. 329, 338

Turning

3° lead | 35° diamond | style J
Kenloc
pg. 280, 294
screw-on
pg. 330

style J-F
screw-on
pg. 331

style U
Kenloc
pg. 281
screw-on
pg. 327, 331

55° diamond | style J
Kenloc
pg. 272, 286
screw-on
pg. 326

style J-F
screw-on
pg. 327

style U
screw-on
pg. 327

triangle | style J
Kenloc
pg. 292

style J-S
Kenloc
pg. 279, 293
screw-on
pg. 290

style W
screw-on
pg. 291, 340

Turning

5° lead | 35° diamond | style L
Kenloc
Top Notch
pg. 320

5° lead | 55° diamond | style L
Top Notch
pg. 318

55° parallelogram | style L
Top Notch
pg. 319

style L-F
Top Notch
pg. 319

80°/100° diamond | style L
Kenloc
pg. 269, 284, 296
Kendex
pg. 300, 306, 308
screw-on
pg. 324, 335

style L-F
screw-on
pg. 324, 335

trigon | style L
Kenloc
pg. 295
Wedgelock
pg. 299
screw-on
pg. 332

15° lead | 80°/100° diamond | style R
Kenloc
pg. 271, 285
Kendex
pg. 306
screw-on
pg. 325, 336

square | style B
screw-on
pg. 341

Turning

style R
Kenloc
pg. 275, 289, 297
Kendex
pg. 302, 307, 310

triangle | style B
Kendex
pg. 303, 311
screw-on
pg. 339

style I-S
Wedgelock
pg. 296

style R
Kenloc
pg. 279, 293

style R-S
Kenloc
pg. 280

17°30' lead | 55° diamond | style Q
Kenloc
pg. 273, 287

triangle | style E
Kendex
pg. 304, 313

45° lead | triangle | style D
screw-on
pg. 340

Kenloc Combination Toolholder Index

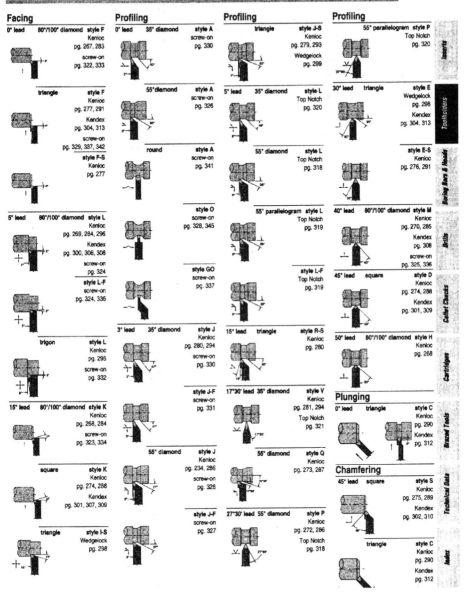

Facing

0° lead 80°/100° diamond **style F**	Kenloc pg. 267, 283
	screw-on pg. 322, 333
triangle **style F**	Kenloc pg. 277, 291
	Kendex pg. 304, 313
	screw-on pg. 329, 337, 342
style F-S	Kenloc pg. 277
5° lead 80°/100° diamond **style L**	Kenloc pg. 269, 284, 296
	Kendex pg. 300, 306, 308
	screw-on pg. 324
style L-F	screw-on pg. 324, 335
trigon **style L**	Kenloc pg. 295
	screw-on pg. 332
15° lead 80°/100° diamond **style K**	Kenloc pg. 268, 284
	screw-on pg. 323, 334
square **style K**	Kenloc pg. 274, 288
	Kendex pg. 301, 307, 309
triangle **style I-S**	Wedgelock pg. 298

Profiling

0° lead 35° diamond **style A**	screw-on pg. 330
55° diamond **style A**	screw-on pg. 326
round **style A**	screw-on pg. 341
style O	screw-on pg. 328, 345
style GO	screw-on pg. 337
3° lead 35° diamond **style J**	Kenloc pg. 280, 294
	screw-on pg. 330
style J-F	screw-on pg. 331
55° diamond **style J**	Kenloc pg. 234, 286
	screw-on pg. 326
style J-F	screw-on pg. 327

Profiling

triangle **style J-S**	Kenloc pg. 279, 293
	Wedgelock pg. 299
5° lead 35° diamond **style L**	Top Notch pg. 320
55° diamond **style L**	Top Notch pg. 318
55° parallelogram **style L**	Top Notch pg. 319
	style L-F Top Notch pg. 319
15° lead triangle **style R-S**	Kenloc pg. 280
17°30' lead 35° diamond **style V**	Kenloc pg. 281, 294
	Top Notch pg. 321
55° diamond **style Q**	Kenloc pg. 273, 287
27°30' lead 55° diamond **style P**	Kenloc pg. 272, 286
	Top Notch pg. 318

Profiling

55° parallelogram **style P**	Top Notch pg. 320
30° lead triangle **style E**	Wedgelock pg. 298
	Kendex pg. 304, 313
style E-S	Kenloc pg. 276, 291
40° lead 80°/100° diamond **style M**	Kenloc pg. 270, 285
	Kendex pg. 308
	screw-on pg. 325, 336
45° lead square **style D**	Kenloc pg. 274, 288
	Kendex pg. 301, 309
50° lead 80°/100° diamond **style H**	Kenloc pg. 268

Plunging

0° lead triangle **style C**	Kenloc pg. 290
	Kendex pg. 312

Chamfering

45° lead square **style S**	Kenloc pg. 275, 289
	Kendex pg. 302, 310
triangle **style C**	Kenloc pg. 290
	Kendex pg. 312

Inserts
Toolholders
Boring Bars & Heads
Drills
Collet Chucks
Cartridges
Brazed Tools
Technical Data
Index

Kenloc Combination Toolholders

Toolholder Identification System

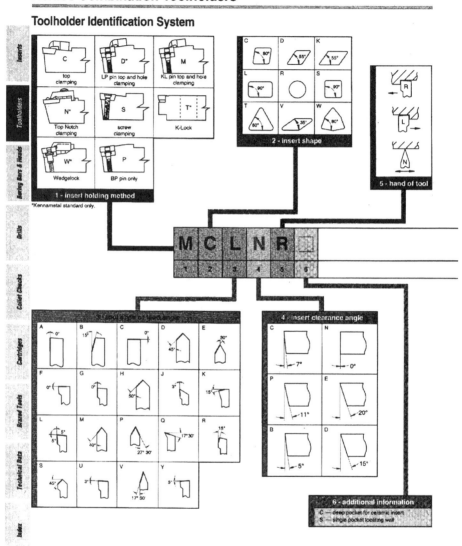

Kenloc Combination Toolholders

Toolholder Identification System

The seventh and eighth position shall be a significant two-digit number which indicates the holder cross section. For shanks 5/8" square and over, the number will represent the number of sixteenths of width and height. For shanks under 5/8" square, the number of sixteenths of cross section will be preceded by a zero. For rectangular holders, the first digit represents the number of eighths of width "A" and the second digit the number of quarters of height "B", except for a toolholder 1 1/4" x 1 1/2" which is given the number 91.

7 & 8 - shank dimensions

9 - insert size
number of 1/8ths of IC

10 - qualified surface and length

11 - shank modification*

*Kennametal standard only.

Threading and Grooving Index

Threading

3° lead   Top Notch   **style NE**
pg. 360

style NS
pg. 356, 357

style NAS
pg. 358

style NS-DH
pg. 359

style NSU
pg. 359

Threading

LT-laydown   **style LSA**
pg. 365

style LSS
pg. 365

style LSS-DH
pg. 366

on-edge   **style MTH**
pg. 369

style MTV
pg. 369

Grooving

3° lead   Top Notch   **style NE**
pg. 360

style NS
pg. 356, 357

style NAS
pg. 358

style NS-DH
pg. 359

style NSU
pg. 359

Grooving

style MTH
pg. 369

style MTV
pg. 369

Undercutting

45° lead   Top Notch   **style NR**
pg. 361

Top Notch Threading and Grooving Toolholders

Toolholder Identification System

side mount utility**

SU**

end

E

undercut

R

side mount, offset

S

side mount, no offset

AS

2 - insert location

N—Top Notch*

1 - insert holding method

4 - drop head

DH

Insert number	T
2	.150
3	.195
4	.255
5	.380
6	.385
8	.436

6 - insert size

N	S	R	—		—	16	4	D
1	2	3		4		5	6	7

5 - shank size

This position will show a significant two-digit number which indicates the holder cross section. For shanks 5/8" square and larger, the number will represent the number of sixteenths of width and height. For shanks under 5/8" square, the number of sixteenths of cross section will be preceded by a zero. For rectangular holders, the first digit represents the number of eighths of width and the second digit the number of quarters of height, except for a toolholder 1 1/4" x 1 1/2" which is given the number 91.

7 - qualified surface and length

A — qualified back and end, 4" long.
B — qualified back and end, 4.5" long
C — qualified back and end, 5" long
D — qualified back and end, 6" long
E — qualified back and end, 7" long
W — qualified back and end, 4.5" long

3 - hand of tool

end mount

R   L

side mount

R   L

qualified set dimensions

F ±.003

A

B

±.003 C

Toolholders are qualified over sharp corner of gage grooving insert.

Catalog numbers for qualified toolholders are overprinted with a shade of yellow.

Catalog numbers for utility toolholders are not overprinted with color.
Utility holder tolerances are ±.010 on "F" dimension and ±.125 on "C".

*Kennametal proprietary standard only.
**Side mount utility holder can only use NTU inserts.

Inserts
Toolholders
Boring Bars & Heads
Drills
Collet Chucks
Cartridges
Brazed Tools
Technical Data
Index

Boring Bar Index

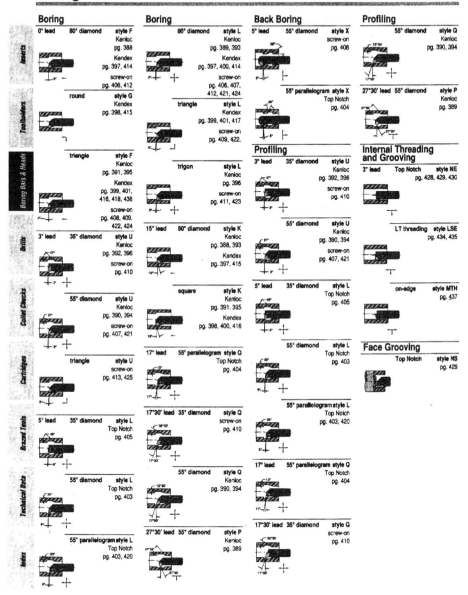

Inserts

Toolholders

Boring Bars & Heads

Drills

Collet Chucks

Cartridges

Brazed Tools

Technical Data

Index

Boring

0° lead	80° diamond	style F
		Kenloc
		pg. 388
		Kendex
		pg. 397, 414
		screw-on
		pg. 406, 412
	round	style G
		Kendex
		pg. 398, 415
	triangle	style F
		Kenloc
		pg. 391, 395
		Kendex
		pg. 399, 401,
		416, 418, 438
		screw-on
		pg. 408, 409,
		422, 424
3° lead	35° diamond	style U
		Kenloc
		pg. 392, 396
		screw-on
		pg. 410
	55° diamond	style U
		Kenloc
		pg. 390, 394
		screw-on
		pg. 407, 421
	triangle	style U
		screw-on
		pg. 413, 425
5° lead	35° diamond	style L
		Top Notch
		pg. 405
	55° diamond	style L
		Top Notch
		pg. 403
	55° parallelogram	style L
		Top Notch
		pg. 403, 420

Boring

	90° diamond	style L
		Kenloc
		pg. 389, 393
		Kendex
		pg. 397, 400, 414
		screw-on
		pg. 406, 407,
		412, 421, 424
	triangle	style L
		Kenloc
		pg. 399, 401, 417
		screw-on
		pg. 409, 422
	trigon	style L
		Kenloc
		pg. 396
		screw-on
		pg. 411, 423
15° lead	80° diamond	style K
		Kenloc
		pg. 388, 393
		Kendex
		pg. 397, 415
	square	style K
		Kenloc
		pg. 391, 395
		Kendex
		pg. 398, 400, 416
17° lead	55° parallelogram	style Q
		Top Notch
		pg. 404
17°30' lead	35° diamond	style Q
		screw-on
		pg. 410
	55° diamond	style Q
		Kenloc
		pg. 390, 394
27°30' lead	55° diamond	style P
		Kenloc
		pg. 389

Back Boring

5° lead	55° diamond	style X
		screw-on
		pg. 408
	55° parallelogram	style X
		Top Notch
		pg. 404

Profiling

3° lead	35° diamond	style U
		Kenloc
		pg. 392, 396
		screw-on
		pg. 410
	55° diamond	style U
		Kenloc
		pg. 390, 394
		screw-on
		pg. 407, 421
5° lead	35° diamond	style L
		Top Notch
		pg. 405
	55° diamond	style L
		Top Notch
		pg. 403
	55° parallelogram	style L
		Top Notch
		pg. 403, 420
17° lead	55° parallelogram	style Q
		Top Notch
		pg. 404
17°30' lead	35° diamond	style Q
		screw-on
		pg. 410

Profiling

	55° diamond	style Q
		Kenloc
		pg. 390, 394
27°30' lead	55° diamond	style P
		Kenloc
		pg. 389

Internal Threading and Grooving

3° lead	Top Notch	style NE
		pg. 428, 429, 430
	LT threading	style LSE
		pg. 434, 435
	on-edge	style MTH
		pg. 437

Face Grooving

	Top Notch	style NS
		pg. 429

Kennametal Boring Systems

Boring Bar and Head Identification System

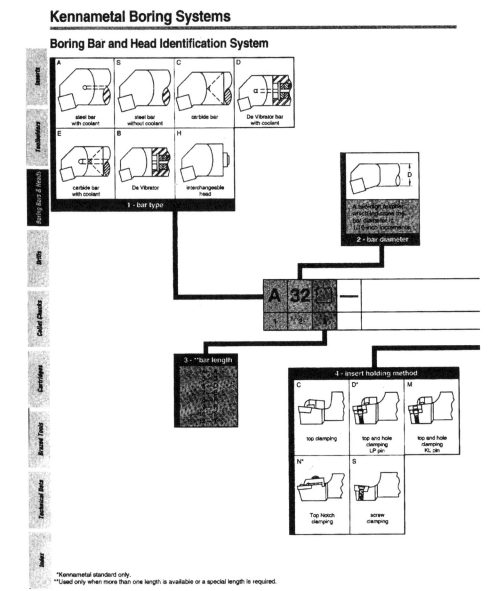

*Kennametal standard only.
**Used only when more than one length is available or a special length is required.

Kennametal Boring Systems

Boring Bar and Head Identification System

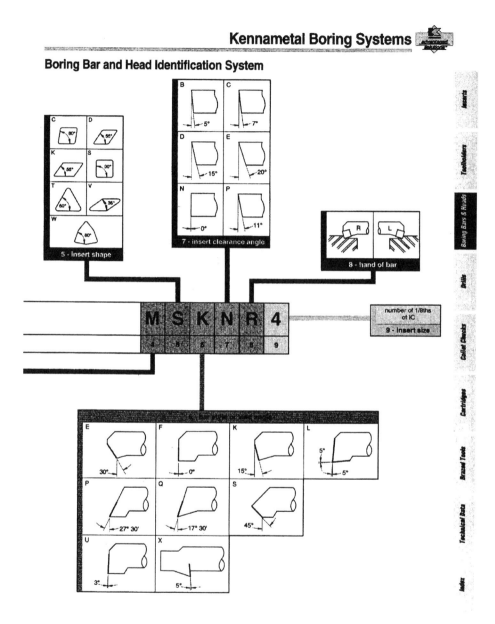

Cartridge Index

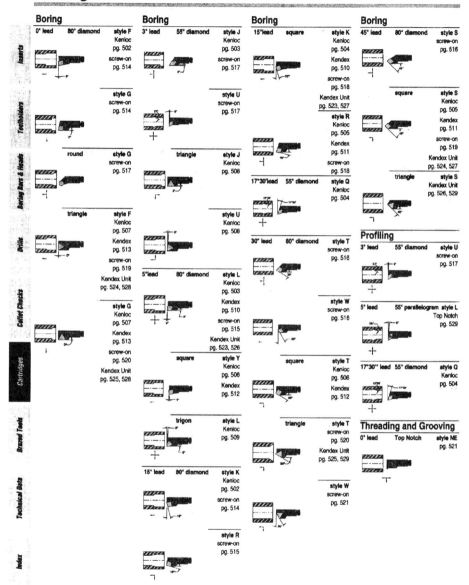

Boring

0° lead	80° diamond	style F
		Kenloc
		pg. 502
		screw-on
		pg. 514

		style G
		screw-on
		pg. 514

round		style G
		screw-on
		pg. 517

triangle		style F
		Kenloc
		pg. 507
		Kendex
		pg. 513
		screw-on
		pg. 519
		Kendex Unit
		pg. 524, 528

		style G
		Kenloc
		pg. 507
		Kendex
		pg. 513
		screw-on
		pg. 520
		Kendex Unit
		pg. 525, 528

Boring

3° lead	55° diamond	style J
		Kenloc
		pg. 503
		screw-on
		pg. 517

		style U
		screw-on
		pg. 517

triangle		style J
		Kenloc
		pg. 508

		style U
		Kenloc
		pg. 508

5°lead	80° diamond	style L
		Kenloc
		pg. 503
		Kendex
		pg. 510
		screw-on
		pg. 515
		Kendex Unit
		pg. 523, 526

square		style Y
		Kenloc
		pg. 508
		Kendex
		pg. 512

trigon		style L
		Kenloc
		pg. 509

15° lead	80° diamond	style K
		Kenloc
		pg. 502
		screw-on
		pg. 514

		style R
		screw-on
		pg. 515

Boring

15°lead	square	style K
		Kenloc
		pg. 504
		Kendex
		pg. 510
		screw-on
		pg. 518
		Kendex Unit
		pg. 523, 527

		style R
		Kenloc
		pg. 505
		Kendex
		pg. 511
		screw-on
		pg. 518

17°30'lead	55° diamond	style Q
		Kenloc
		pg. 504

30° lead	80° diamond	style T
		screw-on
		pg. 516

		style W
		screw-on
		pg. 516

square		style T
		Kenloc
		pg. 506
		Kendex
		pg. 512

triangle		style T
		screw-on
		pg. 520
		Kendex Unit
		pg. 525, 529

		style W
		screw-on
		pg. 521

Boring

45° lead	80° diamond	style S
		screw-on
		pg. 516

	square	style S
		Kenloc
		pg. 505
		Kendex
		pg. 511
		screw-on
		pg. 519
		Kendex Unit
		pg. 524, 527

	triangle	style S
		Kendex Unit
		pg. 526, 529

Profiling

3° lead	55° diamond	style U
		screw-on
		pg. 517

5° lead	55° parallelogram	style L
		Top Notch
		pg. 529

17°30'' lead	55° diamond	style Q
		Kenloc
		pg. 504

Threading and Grooving

| 0° lead | Top Notch | style NE |
| | | pg. 521 |

ANSI/ISO Cartridges

Cartridge Identification System

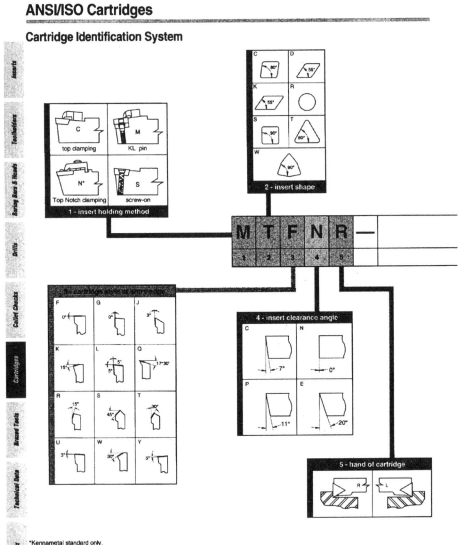

*Kennametal standard only.

NOTE: Threading and grooving cartridges are identified as NER or NEL with the next to last position in the identification system being the designated insert size of 2, 3 or 4 (e.g. NER 20CA-2A).

ANSI/ISO Cartridges

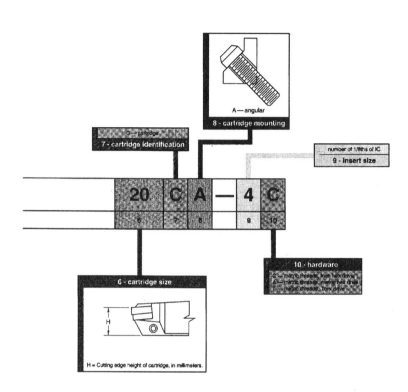

8 - cartridge mounting

A — angular

7 - cartridge identification

C — cartridge

9 - insert size

number of 1/8ths of IC

20 C A — 4 C

6 - cartridge size

H

H = Cutting edge height of cartridge, in millimeters.

10 - hardware

C — metric thread, Allen head drive
A — metric thread, wrench head drive
T — metric thread, Torx drive

Inserts
Toolholders
Boring Bars & Heads
Drills
Collet Chucks
Cartridges
Brazed Tools
Technical Data
Index

Technical Data - Easy 3 Step Insert Selection Guidelines

Medium and High Carbon Steels (> 0.3% C) (135 - 330 BHN) (≤ 35 HRc)

AISI: 1035, 1040, 1045, 1055, 1080, 1085, 1090, 1095, 1525, 1541, 1548, 1551, 1561, 1572

Material Characteristics

• higher carbon or manganese content	– more abrasive, lower cutting speeds and feeds, achieves surface finish easier

Common Tool Application Considerations

condition	remedy
• excessive crater wear	1. Reduce the speed.
	2. Reduce feed rate.
	3. Use thick alumina coated grades such as KC9010 or KC9025.
	4. Use more free-cutting chip control like the UF or LF geometries.
	5. Increase coolant pressure.
• excessive edge wear	1. Use a thick alumina coated grade such as KC9010 or KC9025.
	2. Increase feed rate.
	3. Increase depth of cut.

Common Tool Application Considerations (Cont'd)

condition	remedy
• thermal deformation	1. Reduce speed.
	2. Use a noncobalt enriched grade such as KC9010.
	3. Increase coolant concentration.
• built-up edge	1. If running low to medium speeds, in some cases a PVD coated grade like KC730, with a sharp edge, will resist build-up.
	2. When cutting with interruptions, increase speed, decrease feed, use a grade with good edge strength, like KC935 or KC850.

1st Step - Select the Insert Geometry

Kenloc Geometries (pages 24-89)

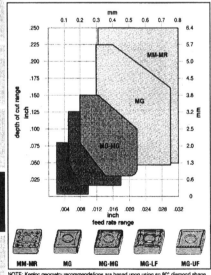

Screw-On Geometries (pages 112-141)

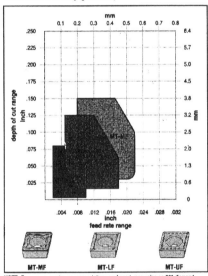

NOTE: Kenloc geometry recommendations are based upon using an 80° diamond shape, 1/2" IC, with a 1/32" nose radius. For more information about insert chip control designs see pages 16-19.

NOTE: Screw-on geometry recommendations are based upon using an 80° diamond shape, 3/8" IC, with a 1/32" nose radius. For more information about insert chip control designs see pages 16-19.

Technical Data - Easy 3 Step Insert Selection Guidelines

Medium and High Carbon Steels (> 0.3% C) (135 - 330 BHN) (≤ 35 HRc)

2nd Step - Select the Grade

insert geometry	🔧	🍩	⬤	⬤
	heavily interrupted	lightly interrupted	varied depth	smooth cut
MM-MR MG	KC850	KC935	KC9025	KC9025
MG-MG	KC9040	KC935	KC9025	KC9010
MT-MF	KC850	KC935	KC935	KC935

3rd Step - Select the Cutting Speed

speed – sfm (m/min)	100 (30)	300 (90)	500 (150)	700 (210)	900 (270)	1100 (330)	1300 (390)	general purpose starting conditions	
								sfm	m/min
KC9040								450	140
KC850								525	160
KC935								775	240
KC9025								875	265
KC9010								1000	300

NOTE: As depth of cut increases, decrease cutting speed.

Technical Data

Troubleshooting

Inserts

Toolholders

Boring Bars & Heads

Drills

Collet Chucks

Cartridges

Brazed Tools

Technical Data

Index

problem	cause	possible solution
thread with torn finish	• burrs	• Use positive rake or full profile insert.
		• Increase coolant concentration.
	• torn finish	• Alter infeed.
		• Use PVD grades.
		• Use positive rake inserts.
		• Increase sfm.
	• steps	• Check machine "Z" travel axis.
		• Check insert form.
		• Avoid recutting chips.
		• Check for correct shim in LT system.
chatter	• poor rigidity	• Minimize tool overhang.
		• Check for workpiece deflection.
	• incorrect speed	• Adjust sfm.
	• wrong edge prep	• Adjust hone level.
	• insert movement	• Check insert and clamp.
	• improper infeed	• Use modified feed angle.
	• off centerline	• Verify that tool cutting position is at workpiece centerline.
built-up edge	• speed too low	• Increase sfm.
	• insufficient coolant	• Increase coolant concentration and/or flow.
	• wrong edge prep	• Adjust hone size.
	• chip load	• Adjust infeed angle.
		• Adjust depth of cut per pass.
deformation	• speed too high	• Reduce sfm.
	• incorrect grade	• Use grade with a higher hot hardness.
	• improper infeed angle	• Alter infeed angle.
chipping	• light chip load	• Adjust chip load.
		• Increase or decrease number of passes.
	• wrong grade	• Use tougher grade.
	• improper infeed	• Alter infeed to modified flank.
	• incorrect speed	• Increase sfm if chipping on trailing edge.
		• Decrease sfm if chipping on leading edge.
	• wrong edge prep	• Increase hone size.
	• poor rigidity	• Minimize tool overhang.
		• Check for insert movement/check clamp.
		• Check for possible part deflection.
broken nose	• heavy chip load	• Decrease chip load.
	• small nose radius	• Use large nose radius if allowable.
	• wrong grade	• Use tougher grade.
	• wrong edge prep	• Increase hone size.
flank wear	• wrong grade	• Use a more wear-resistant grade.
	• insufficient coolant	• Increase coolant flow.
	• off centerline	• Check the centerline height of the tool
		(the smaller the diameter, the more critical the need for centerline accuracy).

Technical Data

Troubleshooting Matrix

problems	increase sfm	reduce sfm	increase chip load	decrease chip load where failure occurs	use tougher carbide grade	use harder carbide grade	apply coolant	use coated carbide	use topping insert	change infeed angle	check for insert movement and reseat	reduce tool overhang	reselect shim	apply chipbreaker style	reduce doc	adjust center height	begin cutting threads 1/2-inch before workpiece
chatter	•			•							•	•				•	
burr on crest	•							•									
short tool life		•	•	•		•		•									
chipped leading edge			•	•	•												
chipped trailing edge				•						•							
broken nose (first pass)	•														•	•	
broken nose (after first pass)			•	•						•			•				
build-up on cutting edge	•		•				•	•									
premature topping				•										•			
splitting threads																	•
poor chip evacuation														•			

Grooving Tool Detective

Practical Solutions to Some Common Grooving Problems

problem	remedy
burr	1. Assure tool center height.
	2. Use sharp tool (index more often).
	3. Use positive rake PVD coated insert.
	4. Use correct grade for workpiece material.
	5. Use correct geometry (e.g.-positive rake for workhardening material).
	6. Chamfer before grooving.
	7. Change tool path.
poor surface finish	1. Increase speed.
	2. Use sharp tool (index more often).
	3. Dwell tool in bottom 1-3 revolutions (max.).
	4. Use proper chip control geometry.
	5. Increase coolant flow/concentration.
	6. Assure proper setup (overhang, shank size).
	7. Use correct geometry (e.g.-positive rake for workhardening material).
groove bottom not flat	1. Use sharp tool (index more often).
	2. Dwell tool in bottom 1-3 revolutions (max.).
	3. Reduce tool overhang (increase rigidity).
	4. Assure correct tool alignment (see illustration at right).
	5. Reduce feed rate at groove bottom.
	6. Use a wider insert.
	7. Assure tool center height.
poor chip control	1. Use "K" chip control geometry insert.
	2. Use sharp tool (index more often).
	3. Increase coolant concentration.
	4. Adjust feed rate (usually increase first).
chatter	1. Reduce tool and workpiece overhang.
	2. Adjust speed (usually increase first).
	3. Adjust feed (usually increase first).
	4. Assure center height.
insert chipping	1. Use correct grade for workpiece material.
	2. Increase speed.
	3. Reduce feed.
	4. Use a stronger grade.
	5. Increase tool and setup rigidity.
built-up edge	1. Use positive rake PVD coated insert.
	2. Increase speed.
	3. Reduce feed.
	4. Increase coolant flow/concentration.
	5. Use cermets.
	6. For aluminum, use polycrystalline diamond insert.

problem	remedy
side walls not straight	1. Check tool alignment for square.
	2. Use correct insert hand.
	3. Reduce workpiece and tool overhang.
	4. Use sharp insert (index more often).

Holder Position for Grooving Operation

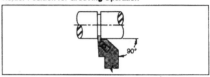

How to Cut a Groove Slightly Wider Than the Groove Tool

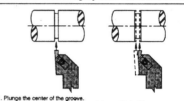

1. Plunge the center of the groove.
2. Plunge each side of the groove to get the specified width. Use a slower feed rate when cutting groove sides.

How to Cut Wider Grooves

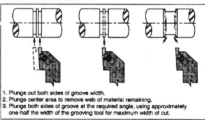

1. Plunge out both sides of groove width.
2. Plunge center area to remove web of material remaining.
3. Plunge both sides of groove at the required angle, using approximately one-half the width of the grooving tool for maximum width of cut.

Finish Turning the Groove

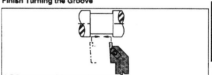

1. Follow recommendations explained above.
2. To avoid insert chipping and to achieve groove wall perpendicularity, follow the tool path outlined here.
3. Use the lightest depth of cut that still allows good chip breaking, tool life, and surface finishing.

Inserts

Toolholders

Boring Bars & Heads

Drills

Collet Chucks

Cartridges

Bizznel Tools

Technical Data

Index

Technical Data

Troubleshooting Guide for Indexable Drilling

Drill Misalignment

1. cutting wrong diameter (large or small)

A. If the drill is on center, it will cut the proper diameter.

B. If the drill is to the left of center, both inserts will move to the left and the diameter of the hole will increase. The center inserts will cut a smaller path and the gap between the outside and center insert will cause breakage.

C. If the drill is to the right of center, both inserts move to the right and the diameter of the hole will decrease. The center insert will cut a larger path, and the insert overlap could cause breakage. The smaller diameter could also cause rubbing on the steel at the outside diameter.

2. rubbing on the steel in the center of the drill

This condition could be caused by the drill being below center. It would cause the normally small .020 diameter core to increase. The larger core will rub in the center of the drill and cause the drill to deflect down and to the left, further increasing pressure on the drill.

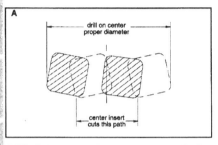

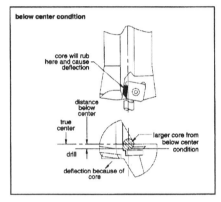

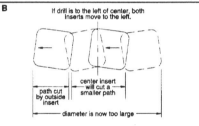

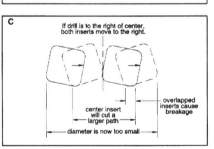

Technical Data

Troubleshooting Guide for Indexable Drilling

problem	possible cause	solution
insert chipping or breakage*	off-center drill due to misalignment	Maintain proper alignment. Concentricity not to exceed ±.005 tir.
	improper seating of tool in toolholder, spindle or turret	Check tool shank and socket for nicks and dirt. Check parting line between tool shank and socket with feeler gage. Make sure tool is locked tight.
	deflection due to too much overhang and lack of rigidity	Check with indicator to see if tool can be moved by hand. Check if tool can be held shorter.
	improper seating of inserts in pocket	Clean pockets whenever indexing or changing inserts. Check pockets for nicks and burrs. Make sure inserts rest completely on pocket bottoms.
	damaged insert screws	Check head and thread for nicks and burrs. Do not overtorque screws.
	improper speeds and feeds	Check recommended guidelines for given material.
	insufficient coolant supply	Check coolant flow.
	improper carbide grade used on inboard station	Use straight grade for multiple insert drills.
• grooving on back stroke • drill body rubbing hole wall • oversize or undersize holes	off-center drill	Restore drill to proper alignment and concentricity. Check bottom of hole or disk for center stub.
	deflection	Check setup rigidity. Check speed/feed guidelines.
rough cutting action (tool rumbles and deflects)	too much thrust feed rate too high	Lower feed and/or increase speed.
	recutting chips	Increase coolant flow. Add coolant grooves to tool.
poor hole surface finish	vibrations	Check setup and part rigidity. Check set in spindle or toolholder. Check speeds and feeds.
	insufficient coolant pressure and volume	Increase coolant pressure and flow. Check coolant flow for interruptions. Make sure coolant reaches inserts at all times.
	recutting chips causing drill to jump	Increase coolant flow. Add coolant grooves to tool.
	• poor chip control • chips trapped in hole	Modify speed or feed.
	chatter	Modify feed rate.
very short, thick, flat chips	feed rate too high in relation to cutting speed	Lower feed and/or increase speed.
long, stringy chips	feed rate too low in relation to cutting speed	Increase feed rate and/or decrease speed, or use dimple inserts.
cannot loosen insert locking screws	seized threads due to insufficient coolant or high heat buildup	Apply water and heat resistant lubricant to threads.

*If constant chipping occurs, especially on the inner insert, and operating conditions are optimum, try an uncoated carbide insert or a grade with higher transverse rupture strength.

Inserts · Toolholders · Boring Bars & Heads · Drills · Collet Chucks · Cartridges · Brazed Tools · **Technical Data** · Index

Tool Design Data Formula—thrust reaming—boring—core drilling

Reaming, Boring & Core Drilling Thrust
Thrust = 160,000 · K · FPR · (Width of cut)

$$\text{Thrust} = 160{,}000 \cdot K \cdot \text{FPR} \cdot \left(\frac{D\text{-}d}{2}\right) \times 1.5 \text{ (dull tool factor)}$$

Material	K	Material	K
Dow Metal	.20	1320 Steel	1.00
Bearing Bronze	.40	6140 Steel	1.00
Alum. Alloy	.48	1020 Steel	1.05
Cast Iron	.80	2320 Steel	1.05
Malleable C.I.	.90	3120 Steel	1.05
1112 Steel	.90	2345 Steel	1.10
1315 Steel	.95	1095 Steel	1.40
1120 Steel	.96	Ann Copper	1.15

Note: Use this formula when tool has lead angle.

Spotface and Counterboring Thrust
Thrust = 232,000 · K · FPR · (Width of cut)

$$\text{Thrust} = 232{,}000 \cdot K \cdot \text{FPR} \cdot \left(\frac{D\text{-}d}{2}\right) \times 1.5 \text{ (dull tool factor)}$$

Material	Brinell	K (Thrust)
Mag. H-Alloy	63	.27
Alum. Alloy 24 ST	154	.82
Alum. Alloy 2S	37	2.70
Leaded Brass	124	.21
Phos. Bronze	156	.82
Monel Metal	207	1.36
C.I. (40,000 PSI)	210	.71
1020 Steel C.D.	180	1.00
6150 Steel H.R.	195	1.72
6150 Steel H.T.	241	2.09
1095 Steel Ann.	156	3.04

Note: Use this formula when tool has no lead angle such as Spotface tool.

Tool Design Data—Formula-horsepower tapping

Tapping

$$\left(\frac{1/N \cdot RPM}{10}\right) \times \text{HP from chart} \times 1.3^* = \text{HP}$$

N = No. Thd's per inch

HP required for tapping various materials (approx.)

(to be use for estimating purposes only)

Note—tap drill sizes to give approx. 75% full thread

Tap Size	rpm	Drill size Frac.	Dec.	Class 1	Class 2	Class 3	Class 4	Class 5	Class 6
						HP for various materials based on a feed of 10″ per minute			
1/4 — 20	200	13/64	0.203	0.058	0.086	0.113	0.140	0.165	0.189
1/4 — 28	280	7/32	0.219	0.043	0.064	0.084	0.104	0.122	0.140
5/16 — 18	180	F	0.257	0.082	0.121	0.160	0.198	0.232	0.266
5/16 — 24	240	I	0.272	0.064	0.094	0.125	0.155	0.181	0.207
3/8 — 16	160	5/16	0.312	0.112	0.165	0.218	0.270	0.317	0.363
3/8 — 24	240	Q	0.332	0.078	0.114	0.151	0.188	0.219	0.251
7/16 — 14	140	U	0.368	0.150	0.221	0.292	0.362	0.426	0.486
7/16 — 20	200	W	0.386	0.109	0.161	0.212	0.263	0.308	0.353
1/2 — 13	130	27/64	0.422	0.185	0.272	0.360	0.447	0.523	0.600
1/2 — 20	200	29/64	0.453	0.125	0.184	0.243	0.302	0.353	0.405
9/16 — 12	120	31/64	0.484	0.227	0.334	0.441	0.548	0.641	0.735
9/16 — 18	180	33/64	0.516	0.157	0.231	0.305	0.379	0.444	0.508
5/8 — 11	110	17/32	0.531	0.275	0.405	0.534	0.664	0.777	0.890
5/8 — 18	180	37/64	0.578	0.176	0.259	0.342	0.425	0.497	0.570
3/4 — 10	100	21/32	0.656	0.366	0.539	0.711	0.883	1.034	1.184
3/4 — 16	160	11/16	0.687	0.237	0.349	0.460	0.572	0.669	0.767
7/8 — 9	90	49/64	0.766	0.477	0.702	0.926	1.151	1.347	1.544
7/8 — 14	140	13/16	0.812	0.317	0.467	0.616	0.765	0.895	1.026
1 — 8	80	7/8	0.875	0.614	0.903	1.192	1.481	1.734	1.987
1 — 14	140	15/16	0.937	0.327	0.481	0.635	0.789	0.924	1.058
1-1/8 — 7	70	63/64	0.984	0.780	1.146	1.513	1.879	2.20	2.521
1-1/8 — 12	120	1-3/64	1.047	0.518	0.762	1.006	1.250	1.463	1.676
1-1/4 — 7	70	1-7/64	1.109	0.874	1.286	1.697	2.108	2.468	2.828
1-1/2 — 6	60	1-11/32	1.343	1.238	1.821	2.404	2.986	3.500	4.00
1-1/2 — 12	120	1-27/64	1.422	0.700	1.030	1.359	1.689	1.977	2.265

Note: HP values for all other materials can be based on machinability value for tapping.

*Add 30.5% to horsepower for dull tools and machine friction.

Select class designation from following sheet

Example 1/2–13 tap 1040 material

$$\left(\frac{1/13 \cdot 425}{10}\right) \times 0.523 \times 1.3 = 2.225 \text{ HP}$$

Tool Design Data
Formula—Horsepower classification of material

Classifications of materials for computing horsepower required for tapping

Class 1	Class 4
Aluminum—Rod; Cast; Die-Cast	Iron—Malleable
Brass—Bar; Cast	Steel—1010; 1035; 1112
Zinc—Die-Cast	X-1340 Cast

Class 2	Class 5
Brass—Stamping; tubing	Iron, Wrought
Bronze, Phosphor; Tubing; Cast	Steel—1040; 1095
Bar; Maganese	T-1330–T-1350; Stamping
Cast Aluminum	
Copper; German Silver	

Class 3	Class 6
Brass—Forging	Monel Metal
Bronze—Naval	Steel—5120–5210
Iron—Cast; Nickel	6115–6195
Steel—Semi; Casting	4130–4820
	2015–2515
	3115–3450
	Forging; Nitralloy
	Stainless—Free

Determining Power Requirements in Machining†

TABLE 17.2–1 Shop Formulas for Turning, Milling, Drilling and Broaching—English Units

PARAMETER	TURNING	MILLING	DRILLING	BROACHING
Cutting speed, fpm	$V_c = .262 \times D_t \times rpm$	$V_c = .262 \times D_m \times rpm$	$V_c = .262 \times D_d \times rpm$	V_c
Revolutions per minute	$rpm = 3.82 \times \dfrac{V_c}{D_t}$	$rpm = 3.82 \times \dfrac{V_c}{D_m}$	$rpm = 3.82 \times \dfrac{V_c}{D_d}$	—
Feed rate, in/min	$f_m = f_r \times rpm$	$f_m = f_r \times n \times rpm$	$f_m = f_r \times rpm$	—
Feed per tooth, in	—	$f_t = \dfrac{f_m}{n \times rpm}$	—	f_t
Cutting time, min	$t = \dfrac{L}{f_m}$	$t = \dfrac{L}{f_m}$	$t = \dfrac{L}{f_m}$	$t = \dfrac{L}{12\,V_c}$
Rate of metal removal, in³/min	$Q = 12 \times d \times f_r \times V_c$	$Q = w \times d \times f_m$	$Q = \dfrac{\pi D^2}{4} \times f_m$	$Q = 12 \times w \times d_t \times V_c$
Horsepower required at spindle*	$hp_s = Q \times P$	$hp_s = Q \times P$	$hp_s = Q \times P$	—
Horsepower required at motor*	$hp_m = \dfrac{Q \times P}{E}$	$hp_m = \dfrac{Q \times P}{E}$	$hp_m = \dfrac{Q \times P}{E}$	$hp_m = \dfrac{Q \times P}{E}$
Torque at spindle	$T_s = \dfrac{63030\ hp_s}{rpm}$	$T_s = \dfrac{63030\ hp_s}{rpm}$	$T_s = \dfrac{63030\ hp_s}{rpm}$	—

SYMBOLS:
D_t = Diameter of workpiece in turning, inches
D_m = Diameter of milling cutter, inches
D_d = Diameter of drill, inches
d = Depth of cut, inches
d_t = Total depth per stroke in broaching, inches
E = Efficiency of spindle drive
f_m = Feed rate, inches per minute
f_r = Feed, inches per revolution
f_t = Feed, inches per tooth
hp_m = Horsepower at motor

hp_s = Horsepower at spindle
L = Length of cut, inches
n = Number of teeth in cutter
P = Unit power, horsepower per cubic inch per minute
Q = Rate of metal removed, cubic inches per minute
rpm = Revolutions per minute of work or cutter
T_s = Torque at spindle, inch-pounds
t = Cutting time, minutes
V_c = Cutting speed, feet per minute
w = Width of cut, inches

*Unit power data are given in table 17.2-3 for turning, milling and drilling, and in figure 17.2-1 for broaching.
†Reprinted by permission from *Machining Data Handbook*, 3rd edition, © 1980, Metant Research Associates, Inc.

Determining Power Requirements in Machining[†]

TABLE 17.2–3 Average Unit Power Requirements for Turning, Drilling and Milling—English Units

MATERIAL	HARDNESS	UNIT POWER° hp/in³/min					
		TURNING P_t HSS AND CARBIDE TOOLS (feed .005-.020 ipr)		DRILLING P_d HSS DRILLS (feed .002-.008 ipr)		MILLING P_m HSS AND CARBIDE TOOLS (feed .005-.012 ipt)	
	Bhn	Sharp Tool	Dull Tool	Sharp Tool	Dull Tool	Sharp Tool	Dull Tool
STEELS, WROUGHT AND CAST	85-200	1.1	1.4	1.0	1.3	1.1	1.4
Plain Carbon	35-40 R_c	1.4	1.7	1.4	1.7	1.5	1.9
Alloy Steels Tool Steels	40-50 R_c	1.5	1.9	1.7	2.1	1.8	2.2
	50-55 R_c	2.0	2.5	2.1	2.6	2.1	2.6
	55-58 R_c	3.4	4.2	2.6	3.2[*]	2.6	3.2
CAST IRONS	110-190	0.7	0.9	1.0	1.2	0.6	0.8
Gray, Ductile and Malleable	190-320	1.4	1.7	1.6	2.0	1.1	1.4
STAINLESS STEELS, WROUGHT AND CAST	135-275	1.3	1.6	1.1	1.4	1.4	1.7
Ferritic, Austenitic and Martensitic	30-45 R_c	1.4	1.7	1.2	1.5	1.5	1.9
PRECIPITATION HARDENING STAINLESS STEELS	150-450	1.4	1.7	1.2	1.5	1.5	1.9
TITANIUM	250-375	1.2	1.5	1.1	1.4	1.1	1.4
HIGH TEMPERATURE ALLOYS Nickel and Cobalt Base	200-360	2.5	3.1	2.0	2.5	2.0	2.5
Iron Base	180-320	1.6	2.0	1.2	1.5	1.6	2.0
REFRACTORY ALLOYS Tungsten	321	2.8	3.5	2.6	3.3[*]	2.9	3.6
Molybdenum	229	2.0	2.5	1.6	2.0	1.6	2.0
Columbium	217	1.7	2.1	1.4	1.7	1.5	1.9
Tantalum	210	2.8	3.5	2.1	2.6	2.0	2.5
NICKEL ALLOYS	80-360	2.0	2.5	1.8	2.2	1.9	2.4
ALUMINUM ALLOYS	30-150 500 kg	0.25	0.3	0.16	0.2	0.32	0.4
MAGNESIUM ALLOYS	40-90 500 kg	0.16	0.2	0.16	0.2	0.16	0.2
COPPER	80 R_B	1.0	1.2	0.9	1.1	1.0	1.2
COPPER ALLOYS	10-80 R_B 80-100 R_B	0.64 1.0	0.8 1.2	0.48 0.8	0.6 1.0	0.64 1.0	0.8 1.2

°Power requirements at spindle drive motor, corrected for 80% spindle drive efficiency.
* Carbide
†Reprinted by permission from *Machining Data Handbook*, 3rd edition, ©1980, Metcut Research Associates, Inc.

PROGRAMMING EXERCISES

Ideally, any part programming exercise should be supported by program proving and production of the component. Most of the inch and metric exercises that follow will fall within the capacity of equipment now generally available in educational institutions, and it is likely that most benefit will be gained if the exercises are completed with that equipment in mind.

To cater to students who do not have access to suitable equipment two imaginary machine types follow together with their control systems. These alternative systems are fairly typical and are illustrative of the way manufacturers summarize the capabilities of machines and control systems in their promotional literature and instruction manuals.

It is anticipated, if the exercises are attempted using the alternative systems, that, as when using college-based equipment, the student will receive further guidance and advice from his or her lecturer. Partially completed programs for Exercises 1, 2, 9, and 10 are included at the end of the chapter.

Details of the machining, tooling and programming requirements are included alongside each detail drawing with the exception of the last exercise of each type, where the intention is that the student should complete all stages from detail drawing to finished product, making decisions relating to work holding, tooling, feeds and speeds followed by part programming and, in cases where the programming has been related to equipment available, by program proving and final machining.

Appropriate speeds and feeds may be selected from the data given in Chapter 7, Appendix B, or from a *Machining Data Handbook.*

The components have been dimensioned according to traditional standards in some cases, and in others the method of dimensioning which is increasingly being favored for numerical control is used. Students will be able to judge for themselves which is the more appropriate conventional or coordinate.

The direction diagrams included on Exercises 1, 2, 9, and 10 indicate relative tool movement, that is, the directions shown will be those used in the part program. The diagrams relating to the turning exercise assume a rear mounted tool post.

*(Additional tool position calculation formulas can be found in Appendix E.)

EXERCISE NO.	1

Machining
Center drill and drill
five holes 0.625∅ in sequence
P1 to P5

Counterbore two holes 0.812∅ ×
0.40 deep in sequence
P3 to P5

Tooling
HSS No. 2 center drill
HSS drill – .625∅
HSS counterbore .812∅

Programming
Absolute dimensions
Point-to-point positioning
Linear interpolation
Z datum clearance 0.100
Time dwell (to clear counterbore)
Flood coolant
Spindle speed rev/min
Feed inches
Allocate tool offsets
Do *not* use drill cycle

Counterbore two holes
0.812∅ × 0.40

XY zero datum

Drill five holes 0.625∅

Material: mild steel
Inch Programming
Exercise
(see example program 1)

EXERCISE NO.	2

Machining

Mill 12 slot, P1 start

Center drill and drill three
  holes 5∅ in sequence
  P2 to P4

Tooling

HSS 12∅ end mill

HSS No. 2 center drill

HSS drill 5∅

Programming

Incremental dimensions

Linear interpolation

Point-to-point positioning

Quill clamp (when milling slot)

Drill cycle

Spray mist coolant

Spindle speed rev/min

Feed mm/min

Allocate tool offsets

Z datum clearance 4 mm

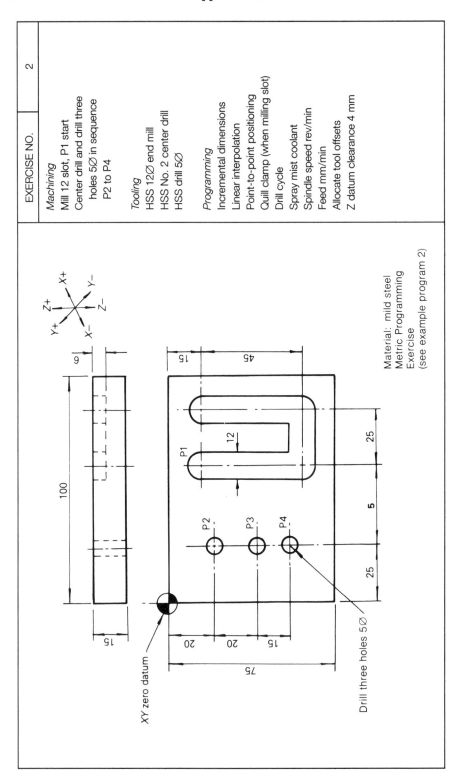

Material: mild steel

Metric Programming

Exercise

(see example program 2)

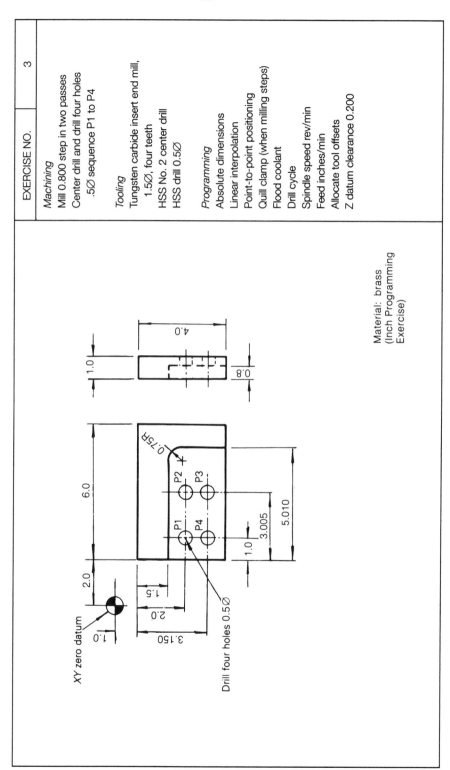

| EXERCISE NO. | 3 |

Machining
Mill 0.800 step in two passes
Center drill and drill four holes
.5∅ sequence P1 to P4

Tooling
Tungsten carbide insert end mill,
   1.5∅, four teeth
HSS No. 2 center drill
HSS drill 0.5∅

Programming
Absolute dimensions
Linear interpolation
Point-to-point positioning
Quill clamp (when milling steps)
Flood coolant
Drill cycle
Spindle speed rev/min
Feed inches/min
Allocate tool offsets
Z datum clearance 0.200

Material: brass
(Inch Programming
Exercise)

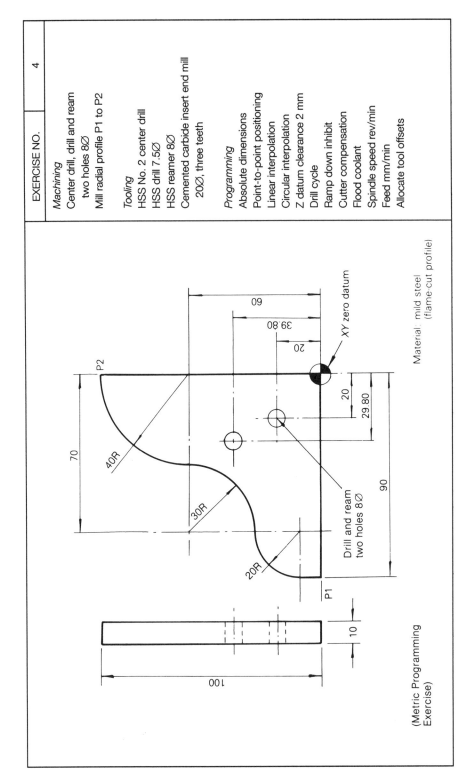

EXERCISE NO.	4

Machining
Center drill, drill and ream
 two holes 8⌀
Mill radial profile P1 to P2

Tooling
HSS No. 2 center drill
HSS drill 7.5⌀
HSS reamer 8⌀
Cemented carbide insert end mill
 20⌀, three teeth

Programming
Absolute dimensions
Point-to-point positioning
Linear interpolation
Circular interpolation
Z datum clearance 2 mm
Drill cycle
Ramp down inhibit
Cutter compensation
Flood coolant
Spindle speed rev/min
Feed mm/min
Allocate tool offsets

Material: mild steel
 (flame-cut profile)

P2

P1

70

40R

30R

20R

60

39.80

20

20

29.80

90

XY zero datum

Drill and ream
two holes 8⌀

100

10

(Metric Programming
Exercise)

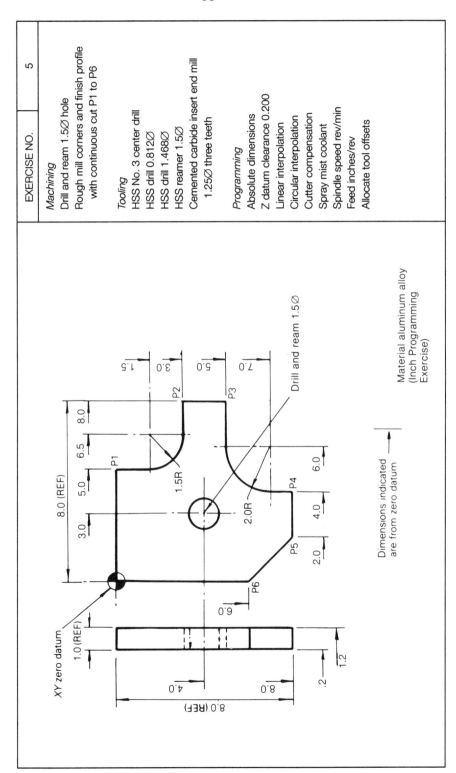

EXERCISE NO. 5

Machining
Drill and ream 1.5∅ hole
Rough mill corners and finish profile
  with continuous cut P1 to P6

Tooling
HSS No. 3 center drill
HSS drill 0.812∅
HSS drill 1.468∅
HSS reamer 1.5∅
Cemented carbide insert end mill
  1.25∅ three teeth

Programming
Absolute dimensions
Z datum clearance 0.200
Linear interpolation
Circular interpolation
Cutter compensation
Spray mist coolant
Spindle speed rev/min
Feed inches/rev
Allocate tool offsets

Material aluminum alloy
(Inch Programming
Exercise)

Drill and ream 1.5∅

Dimensions indicated
are from zero datum

XY zero datum

8.0 (REF)

1.0 (REF)

P1 P2 P3 P4 P5 P6

1.5R   2.0R

3.0   5.0   6.5   8.0

1.5   3.0   5.0   7.0

2.0   4.0   6.0

4.0   8.0

.2   1.2

6.0

8.0 (REF)

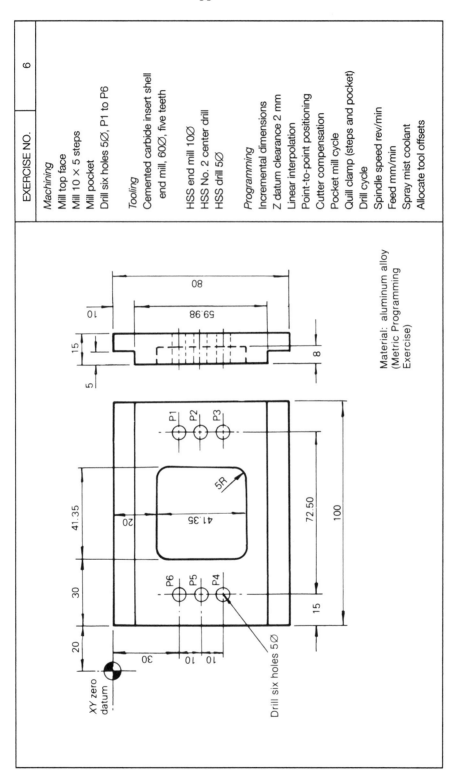

EXERCISE NO.   6

Machining
Mill top face
Mill 10 × 5 steps
Mill pocket
Drill six holes 5∅, P1 to P6

Tooling
Cemented carbide insert shell
end mill, 60∅, five teeth

HSS end mill 10∅
HSS No. 2 center drill
HSS drill 5∅

Programming
Incremental dimensions
Z datum clearance 2 mm
Linear interpolation
Point-to-point positioning
Cutter compensation
Pocket mill cycle
Quill clamp (steps and pocket)
Drill cycle
Spindle speed rev/min
Feed mm/min
Spray mist coolant
Allocate tool offsets

Material: aluminum alloy
(Metric Programming
Exercise)

Drill six holes 5∅

XY zero
datum

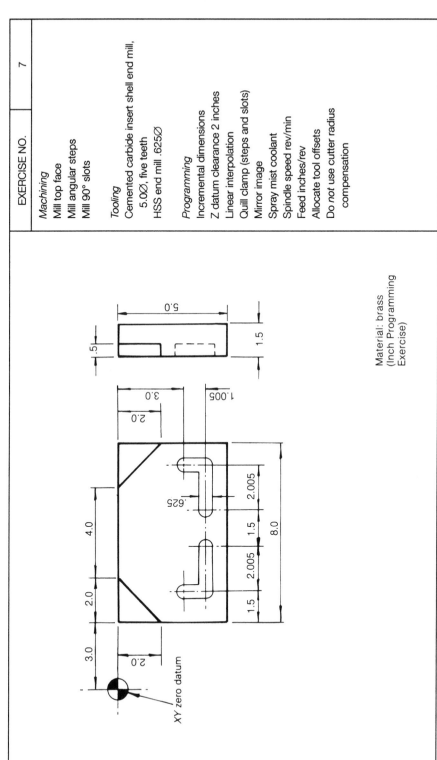

EXERCISE NO.	7

Machining
Mill top face
Mill angular steps
Mill 90° slots

Tooling
Cemented carbide insert shell end mill,
5.0∅, five teeth
HSS end mill .625∅

Programming
Incremental dimensions
Z datum clearance 2 inches
Linear interpolation
Quill clamp (steps and slots)
Mirror image
Spray mist coolant
Spindle speed rev/min
Feed inches/rev
Allocate tool offsets
Do *not* use cutter radius
    compensation

Material: brass
(Inch Programming
Exercise)

XY zero datum

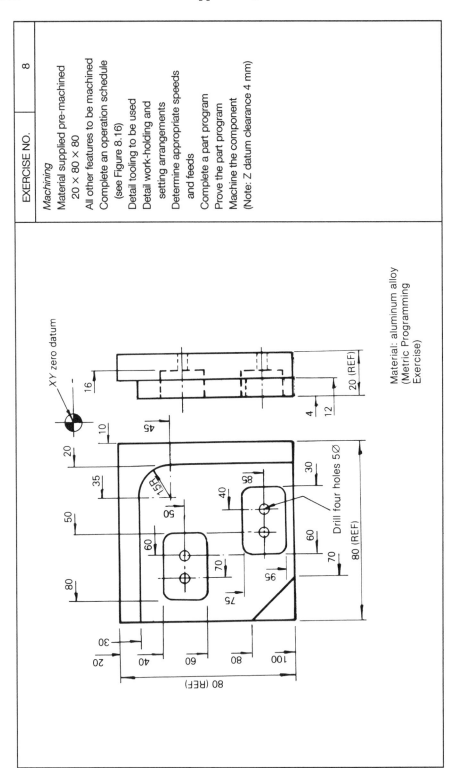

EXERCISE NO.	8

Machining
Material supplied pre-machined
  20 × 80 × 80
All other features to be machined
Complete an operation schedule
  (see Figure 8.16)
Detail tooling to be used
Detail work-holding and
  setting arrangements
Determine appropriate speeds
  and feeds
Complete a part program
Prove the part program
Machine the component
(Note: Z datum clearance 4 mm)

Material: aluminum alloy
(Metric Programming
Exercise)

XY zero datum

Drill four holes 5∅

EXERCISE NO.	9

Machining

Stock material 5.0∅ hand loaded and positioned

Face one end

Turn 4.5∅, 3.5∅ and 2.5∅, two passes per diameter

Part off to length

Tooling

Light turning and facing, cemented carbide insert

Parting off, cemented carbide insert .125 wide

Programming

Absolute positioning

Linear interpolation

Feed inches/rev

Spindle speed rev/min

Spray mist coolant

Allocate tool offset numbers

Ignore tool-tip radius

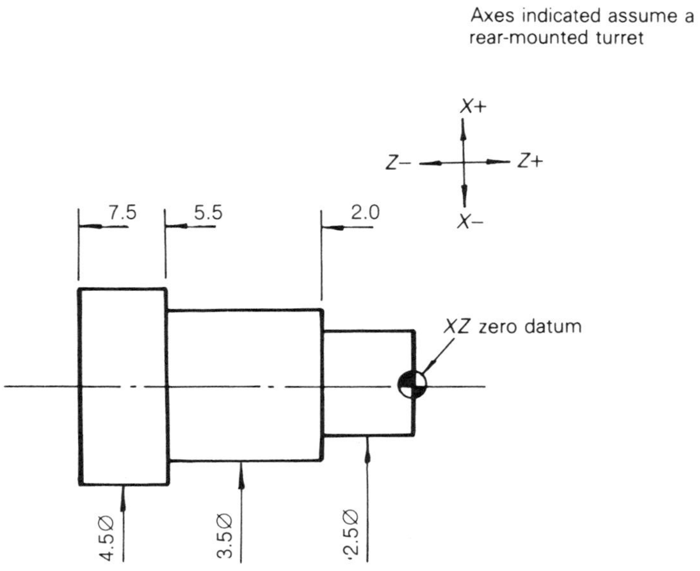

Axes indicated assume a rear-mounted turret

Material: brass
(Inch Programming
Exercise; See Example Program 9)

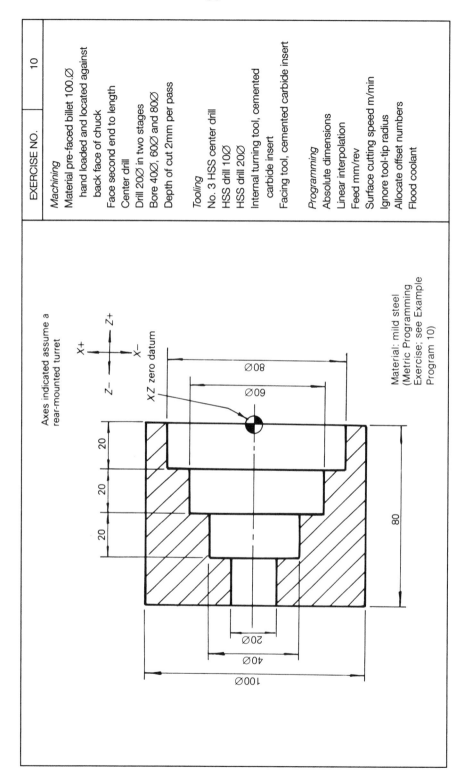

EXERCISE NO.	10

Machining

Material pre-faced billet 100.∅
hand loaded and located against
back face of chuck

Face second end to length

Center drill

Drill 20∅ in two stages

Bore 40∅, 60∅ and 80∅

Depth of cut 2mm per pass

Tooling

No. 3 HSS center drill

HSS drill 10∅

HSS drill 20∅

Internal turning tool, cemented
carbide insert

Facing tool, cemented carbide insert

Programming

Absolute dimensions

Linear interpolation

Feed mm/rev

Surface cutting speed m/min

Ignore tool-tip radius

Allocate offset numbers

Flood coolant

Axes indicated assume a
rear-mounted turret

X+

Z+

Z−

X−

XZ zero datum

∅08

∅09

20

20

20

80

∅20

∅40

∅100

Material: mild steel
(Metric Programming
Exercise; see Example
Program 10)

EXERCISE NO.	11

Machining

Stock material 4.0∅ hand loaded
   and positioned

Face one end

Center drill

Drill 0.4∅

Rough turn to profile

Finish turn with continuous cut

Part off

Tooling

Light turning and facing tool,
   cemented carbide insert

HSS No. 2 center drill

HSS drill .4∅

Parting–off tool, cemented carbide
   insert 0.125 wide

Programming

Absolute dimensions

Linear interpolation

Feed inch/rev varied for roughing and
   finishing cuts

Surface cutting speed feet/min varied
   for roughing and finishing cuts

Flood coolant

Peck drill cycle

Ignore tool-tip radius

Allocate tool offset numbers

Material: brass
(Inch Programming
Exercise)

EXERCISE NO.	12

Machining

Material pre–faced billet 70∅ hand loaded and located against back face of chuck

Face second end to length

Center drill

Drill in two stages

Ream

Rough turn to profile

Finish turn profile

Tooling

Light turning and facing tool, cemented carbide insert, tip radius 2.0 mm

HSS No. 3 center drill

HSS drill 6∅

HSS drill 11.5∅

HSS reamer 12∅

Programming

Absolute dimensions

Linear interpolation

Circular interpolation

Cutter radius compensation

Feed mm/rev, varied for roughing and finishing cuts

Surface cutting speed m/min varied for roughing and finishing cuts

Mist coolant

Peck drill cycle for initial drilling

Allocate tool offset numbers

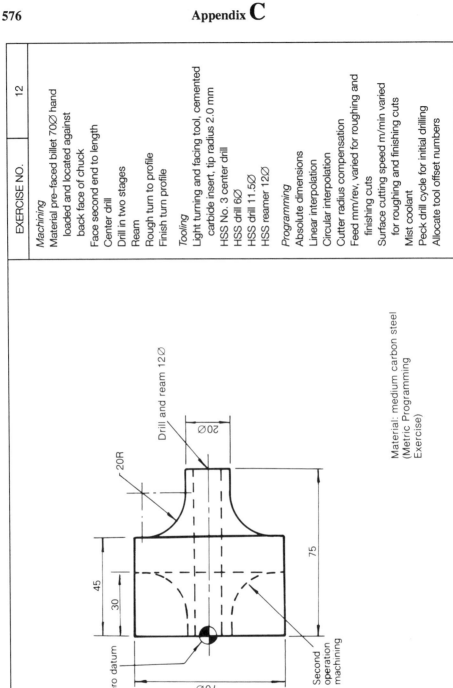

20R

Drill and ream 12∅

∅20

45

30

75

XZ zero datum

∅70

Second operation machining

Material: medium carbon steel (Metric Programming Exercise)

EXERCISE NO.	13

Machining

Material pre–faced billet 8.0∅
hand loaded and located against
back face of chuck
Face second end to length
Rough turn 4.0∅ and 2.0∅
Finish turn complete profile in one pass

Tooling

Roughing tool, cemented carbide insert,
tip radius 0.200
Light turning and facing tool, cemented
carbide insert, tip radius 0.100

Programming

Absolute dimensions
Linear interpolation
Circular interpolation
Cutter radius compensation
Feed inches/rev varied for roughing and
finishing cuts
Surface cutting speed feet/min varied
for roughing and finishing
Mist coolant
Allocate tool offset numbers

Material: mild steel
(Inch Programming
Exercise)

2.0∅

2.0R

10.3

8.3

0.2R

6.0

∅4.0

1.0R

4.0

3.0

∅6.0

∅8.0

XZ zero datum

EXERCISE NO.	14

Machining
Material pre–faced billet 100∅, hand
loaded and located against back
face of chuck
Face second end to length
Center drill
Drill 18∅ in two stages
Machine end radius in three passes
Rough machine to profile
Finish machine profile
with continuous cut

Tooling
Light turning and facing tool, cemented
carbide insert, tip radius 0.8 mm
Roughing tool, cemented carbide insert,
tip radius 2 mm
HSS No. 4 center drill
HSS drill 8∅
HSS drill 18∅
Internal turning tool, tip radius 1 mm

Programming
Absolute dimensions
Linear interpolation
Circular interpolation
Cutter radius compensation
Feed mm/rev varied for roughing and
finishing cuts
Surface cutting speed m/min
varied for roughing and finishing cuts
Flood coolant
Allocate tool offset numbers

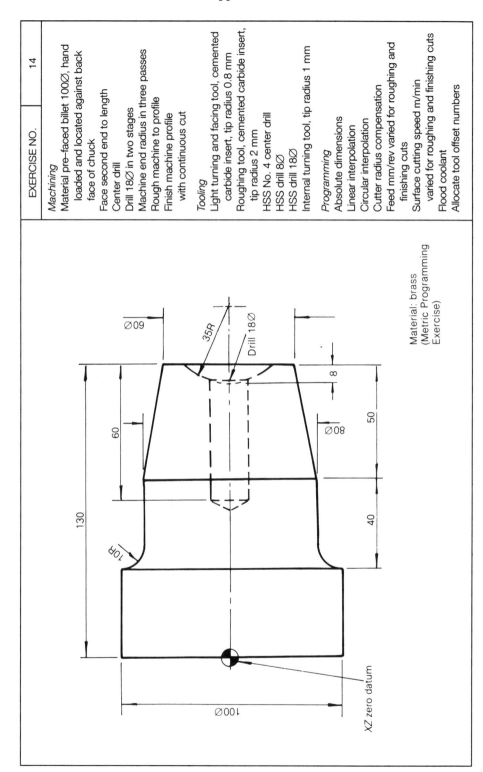

Material: brass
(Metric Programming
Exercise)

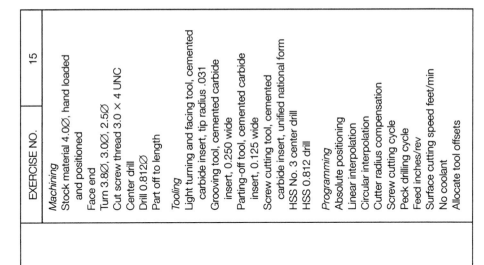

EXERCISE NO.	15

Machining

Stock material 4.0⌀, hand loaded and positioned
Face end
Turn 3.8⌀, 3.0⌀, 2.5⌀
Cut screw thread 3.0 × 4 UNC
Center drill
Drill 0.812⌀
Part off to length

Tooling

Light turning and facing tool, cemented carbide insert, tip radius .031
Grooving tool, cemented carbide insert, 0.250 wide
Parting-off tool, cemented carbide insert, 0.125 wide
Screw cutting tool, cemented carbide insert, unified national form
HSS No. 3 center drill
HSS 0.812 drill

Programming

Absolute positioning
Linear interpolation
Circular interpolation
Cutter radius compensation
Screw cutting cycle
Peck drilling cycle
Feed inches/rev
Surface cutting speed feet/min
No coolant
Allocate tool offsets

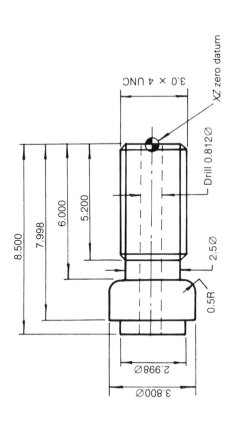

Material: brass
(Inch Programming Exercise)

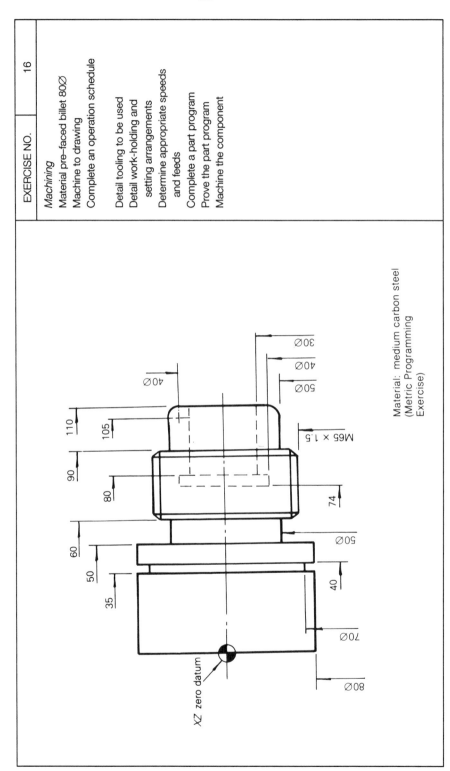

EXERCISE NO.	16

Machining

Material pre-faced billet 80∅
Machine to drawing
Complete an operation schedule

Detail tooling to be used
Detail work-holding and
  setting arrangements
Determine appropriate speeds
  and feeds
Complete a part program
Prove the part program
Machine the component

Material: medium carbon steel
(Metric Programming
Exercise)

Assigned miscellaneous functions:	M plus two digits
M00	Programmed stop. Stops all slide movement, spindle rotation and coolant
M01	Optional stop. Ignored unless activated manually from control console.
M02	End of program
M03	Spindle on clockwise
M04	Spindle on counter-clockwise
M05	Spindle off
M07	Coolant on (mist)
M08	Coolant on (flood)
M09	Coolant off
M10	Quill clamp on
M11	Quill clamp off
M30	End of program. Rewind tape.
Axis movement commands:	End point in *X*, *Y* and *Z*
	Start point of arcs relative to circle center
	I, *J* and *K*
	Dimensional values in 3/2 format metric, that is, three digits before and two digits after the decimal point; 2/3 format inch. Do not program the decimal point and omit leading zeros.
	Plus (+) signs are not required but (−) signs must be included.
Other functions:	
Feed	F plus four digits
	Feed/min in 1 mm or 0.1 in. steps
	Feed/rev in 0.001 mm or 0.001 in. steps
	Do not program decimal point or leading zeros
Spindle speed	S plus four digits
Tool identification	T plus two digits
	T01 to T16. With offsets use four digits, first two tool number, second two offset number, offsets 00 to 32.
Dwell	D plus three digits in 0.1 s (Do not program decimal point.)
	Slash delete. Messages ignored when 'slash delete' switch on the control unit console is activated. They are obeyed when switch is off.
%	Rewind stop
*	End of block

Programming Notes Relating to Milling and Drilling Exercises

Pocket Clearance Cycle (G28)

1. Position the cutter over the center point of the pocket.
2. Program the appropriate movement in the Z axis.
3. Program G28 with X and Y values indicating pocket dimensions. Cutter radius compensation and the step-over value will be automatically determined and implemented.
4. Cancel the cycle by programming G80.

(Note this code is not available or standard on all machines.)

Mirror Image (G31)

1. Program G31 together with the axis or axes to be mirrored. For example, G31 X will mirror in the X axis only; G31 XY will mirror in the X and Y axes. No other data are to be included in this block.
2. Program the original axes commands.
3. Cancel by programming G30.

(Note this is not a standard code that is available on all machines, some machines will use a manual switch.)

Cutter Radius Compensation (G41, G42)

1. Program G41 or G42 in the same block as G01 or G00 when making the approach move to the profile to be machined. The cutter will offset by the appropriate radius.
2. Cancel G41 or G42 by programming G40 in the withdrawal move.

(Note some machines will require this code to be programmed in a separate block before the move.)

Drill Cycle (G81)

1. Program G81 when making the approach move to the first hole position. The block must also contain the Z depth to be drilled and Z clearance position. The drill cycle will activate at the end of the positional move and will be repeated at the end of each subsequent positional move until cancelled.
2. Cancel G81 by programming G80 in the withdrawal move.

Peck Drill Cycle (G83)

1. Program G83 when making the approach move to the first hole position. The block must also contain the Z depth to be drilled, the Z clearance position and the peck distance as a *W* or *K* increment. The drill cycle will activate at the end of the positional move and will be repeated at the end of each subsequent positional move until cancelled.
2. Cancel G83 by programming G80 in the withdrawal move.

Alternative Machine Specification and Control System for Programming Exercises 1 to 8: Milling and Drilling

Machine Type and Specification

Vertical machining center with three-axis control

Traverse:	*X* longitudinal 600 mm (24 in.)
	Y transverse 400 mm (16 in.)
	Z vertical 450 mm (18 in.)
Spindle speed:	10–3300 rev/min infinitely variable
Working surface:	1000 mm × 300 mm (40 in. × 12 in.)
Feeds:	1–5000 mm/min (0.1–198 in/min)
Tool changing:	Manual

Control System

Program format:	Word address
Axes controlled:	*X*, *Y* and *Z* singly or simultaneously
Interpolation:	Linear *X*, *Y* and *Z*
	Circular *XY*, *YZ* and *ZX* planes
Command system:	Incremental or absolute
Data input:	MDI or perforated eight-track tape
Tape code:	ISO or EIA via tape sensing

Programming Information

Block numbers:	N plus one to three digits
Preparatory functions:	G plus two digits
G00	Rapid traverse at machine maximum (modal)
G01	Linear interpolation, programmed feed (modal)
G02	Clockwise circular interpolation (modal)
G03	Counter-clockwise circular interpolation (modal)
G08	Ramp down inhibit (modal)
G09	Cancels G08
G28	Pocket clearance cycle (modal)
G30	Cancels mirror image

G31	Mirror image with axis command (modal)
G40	Cutter offset cancel
G41	Cutter radius compensation left (modal)
G42	Cutter radius compensation right (modal)
G70	Inch programming (modal)
G71	Metric programming (modal)
G80	Cancels all fixed cycles
G81	Drill cycle (modal)
G83	Peck drill cycle (modal)
G90	Absolute programming (modal)
G91	Incremental programming (modal)
G93	Inverse time feedrate (V/D) (modal)
G94	Feed inch (mm)/min (modal)
G95	Feed inch (mm)/rev (modal)
G96	Constant surface speed
G97	Spindle speed rev/min (modal)

Alternative Machine Specification and Control System for Programming Exercises 9 to 16: Turning

Machine Type and Specification

Precision turning center with two-axis control
Traverse:	X transverse 160 mm (6.3 in.)
	Z longitudinal 450 mm (17.7 in.)
Spindle speed:	50–3800 rev/min
Feed:	0–400 mm/min, 0–200 inch/min
Tooling:	Indexable turret providing eight tool stations

Control System

Program format:	Word address
Axes controlled:	X and Z singly or simultaneously
Interpolation:	Linear X and Z axes
	Circular XZ plane
Command system:	Absolute
Data input:	MDI and magnetic tape

Programming Information

Block numbers:	N plus one to three digits
Preparatory functions:	G plus two digits
G00	Rapid traverse at machine maximum (modal)
G01	Linear interpolation, programmed feed (modal)
G02	Clockwise circular interpolation (modal)

G03	Counter-clockwise circular interpolation (modal)
G08	Ramp down inhibit (modal)
G09	Cancels G08
G33	Threading cycle
G40	Cutter offset cancel
G41	Cutter radius compensation left (modal)
G42	Cutter radius compensation right (modal)
G70	Inch programming (modal)
G71	Metric programming (modal)
G80	Cancels all fixed cycles
G81	Drill cycle (modal)
G83	Peck drill cycle (modal)
G90	Absolute programming (modal)
G91	Incremental programming (modal)
G92	Preset axes command
G93	Feed inverse time (V/D)
G94	Feed inch or mm/min (modal)
G95	Feed inch or mm/rev (modal)
G96	Surface cutting speed feet or meters/min
G97	Surface speed rev/min
Assigned miscellaneous functions.	M plus two digits
M00	Programmed stop. Stops all slide movement, spindle rotation and coolant.
M01	Optional stop. Ignored unless activated manually from control console.
M02	End of program
M03	Clockwise spindle rotation
M04	Counter-clockwise spindle rotation
M05	Spindle off
M06	Tool change
M07	Coolant on (mist)
M08	Coolant on (flood)
M09	Coolant off
M30	End of program. Tape rewind.
Axis movement commands:	End point in X and Z
	Start point of arcs relative to circle center/and K (see pp. 128–136)
	Dimensional values in 3/2 format metric, that is, three figures before and two after the decimal point; 2/4 format inch. Program the decimal point but no leading or trailing zeros.
	Plus (+) signs are not required but (−) signs must be included.
	X values to be programmed as a diameter.
Other functions:	
Feed	F plus four digits
	Feed/min in 1 mm or 0.1 in. steps
	Feed/rev in 0.001 mm or 0.001 in. steps
	Do not program decimal point
Spindle speed	S plus four digits

Surface speed	S plus three digits
Tool identity	T plus two digits, T01 to T10. With offsets program four digits, offsets 00 to 24, first two digits tool number/second two offset number.
%Rewind stop	Slash delete. Messages ignored when 'slash delete'
*End of block	switch on the control unit console is activated. They are obeyed when switch is off.

Programming Notes Relating to Turning Exercises

Tooling System and Turret Indexing

The tooling system comprises an eight-station turret mounted at 90° to the machine spindle axis, the tooling positions being numbered 1 to 8. (See following figure.) It illustrates the way the tooling is arranged in relation to the workpiece.

Turret indexing is achieved as follows:

1. In the block following the end of a machining sequence program M06 (tool change). No other data are to be included in this block. The turret will withdraw to a pre-set safe indexing position.
2. In the next block program the required tool number and, if applicable, its related tool offset number. The turret will index by the shortest route to that tool position.
3. In the next block program a rapid move to the next pre-cutting position, which should be approximately 2 mm or 0.100 in. clear of the workpiece.
4. Finally, continue to program moves at a controlled feedrate.

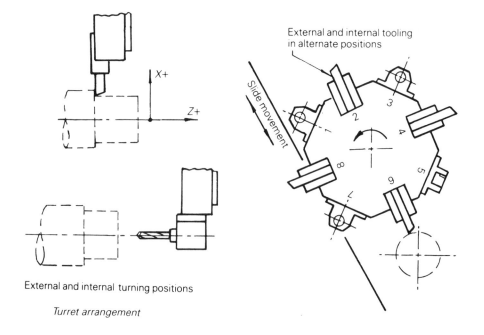

External and internal turning positions

Turret arrangement

Note tool changes for various machines will program differently and machinery manuals should be consulted.

Screw-cutting Cycle (G33)

The movement sequence of the screw-cutting cycle is illustrated in the following figure.

1. Tool moves rapidly to programmed X value.
2. Thread is cut to programmed Z value.
3. Rapid traverse to initial position in X axis.
4. Rapid traverse to initial position in Z axis.
5.

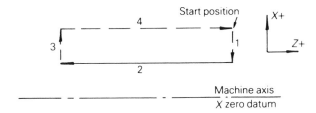

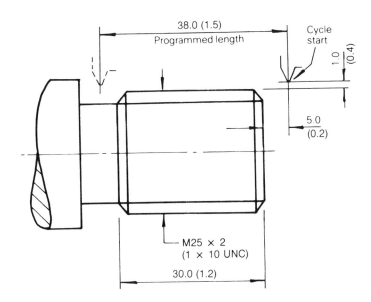

Component detail. (Inch units are given in parentheses.)

The final thread depth is reached by a series of rough and finish pass cuts as indicated in the part program below, which refers to the preceding figure.

The pitch is programmed as a K value.

Allow an approach distance of 0.250 inches in the Z axis when cutting threads.

(Inch)	N	G	X	Z	I	K	F	S	T	M	*
	35	0	2.7	.25							*
	40	33	2.48	−3.8		2		490	0404		*
	45		2.46								*
	50		2.44								*
	55		2.42								*
	60		2.4								*
	65		2.38								*
	70		2.36								*

Allow an approach distance of 5 mm in the Z axis when cutting threads.

(Metric)	N	G	X	Z	I	K	F	S	T	M	*
	35	0	26	5							*
	40	33	24.8	−38		2		490	0404		*
	45		24.6								*
	50		24.4								*
	55		24.2								*
	60		24								*
	65		23.8								*
	70		23.6								*

The X values are continually reduced until the full thread depth is reached. Two passes of the final cut should be made to reduce tool pressure for finishing.

The Z axis move is programmed as an incremental value from the start position.

The cycle is cancelled by programming G80.

Drill Cycles (G81 and G83)

1. Position drill at start point in the Z axis on X zero datum.
2. Program G81 or G83 together with Z depth to be drilled. G83 requires the peck distance to be programmed as a special coded increment. (Refer to machine manual for address used.)
3. Cancel G81 or G83 by programming G80.

Cutter Radius Compensation (G41 and G42)

Common to both turning and milling exercises.

Partially Completed Exercises Using Alternative Control Systems

Exercise 1 (Inch Program)

PART PROGRAM — EXERCISE NO. 1
MACHINE As book — COMPILED BY A. Programmer
CONTROL As book — DATE 28.3.84

N	G	X	Y	Z	I	J	K	F	S	T	M	*	REMARKS
01												*	Rewind stop
05	70						%					*	Inch units
10	90											*	Absolute
15	94											*	Feed inch/min
20	97											*	Speed rev/min
25	00	8000	4500	100						0101		*	Rapid to Z clear /P1
30									2000		03	*	Spindle/coolent on
35	01			−1300				200			08	*	Feed to Z depth
40	00			100								*	Rapid to Z clear
45			1300									*	Rapid to P2
50	01			−1300								*	Feed to Z depth
55	00			100								*	Rapid to Z clear
60		4000										*	Rapid to P3
65	01			−1300								*	Feed to Z depth
70	00			100								*	Rapid to Z clear
75			3000									*	Rapid to P4
80	01			−1300								*	Feed to Z depth
85	00			100								*	Rapid to Z clear
90			4500									*	Rapid to P5
95	01			−1300								*	Feed to Z depth
100	00			100								*	Rapid to Z clear
		0	0	2000								*	Rapid to base datum
						(Manual tool change)					00	*	Program stop

Exercise 2 (Metric Program)

PART PROGRAM — EXERCISE NO. 2
MACHINE As book — COMPILED BY A. Programmer
CONTROL As book — DATE 8.5.84

N	G	X	Y	Z	I	J	K	F	S	T	M	*	REMARKS
						%						*	Rewind stop
01	71											*	Metric units
02	91											*	Incremental
03	95											*	Feed mm/min
04	97											*	Speed rev/min
05	00	6000	−1500							0101		*	Rapid to P1/Z0
06									750		03	*	Spindle/coolent on
07	01			−1000				225			07	*	Feed to Z depth
08							D20				10	*	Dwell, Quill clamp
09			−4500									*	Feed in Y axis
10		2500										*	Feed in X axis
11			4500										Feed in Y axis
12											11	*	Quill clamp off
13				20000									Rapid lift
	00										00	*	Program stop

(Manual tool change)

Exercise 9 (Inch Program Example, Decimal Point Programming)

PART PROGRAM — EXERCISE NO. 9
MACHINE As book   **COMPILED BY** A. Programmer
CONTROL As book   **DATE** 20.6.84

N	G	X	Y	Z	I	J	K	F	S	T	M	*	REMARKS
01							%					*	Rewind stop
05	70											*	Inch units
10	95											*	Feed inches/rev.
15	90											*	Absolute
20	97											*	Speed rev/min.
25										0202		*	Tool/offset
30	00	5.1		0								*	Rapid to start
35									2300		03		Spindle on
40	01	0						.007			07	*	Feed to X0 coolant on
45	00			.1								*	Clear face
50		4.5										*	Return in X axis
55	01			-7.625					.010			*	Feed in Z axis
60	00	4.6										*	Clear diam.
65				.1								*	Return to start
70		4.0										*	Rapid in X axis
75	01			-5.5					.010			*	Feed in Z axis
80	00	4.1										*	Clear diam.
85			.1	.1								*	Return to start
90		3.5										*	Rapid in X axis
95	01			-5.5					.010			*	Feed in Z axis
100	00	3.6										*	Clear diam.
105				.1								*	Return to start

Exercise 10 (Metric Programming Example)

PART PROGRAM — EXERCISE NO. 10
MACHINE As book — COMPILED BY A. Programmer
CONTROL As book — DATE 5.6.84

N	G	X	Y	Z	I	J	K	F	S	T	M	*	REMARKS
01												*	Rewind stop
05	71						%					*	Metric
10	95											*	Feed mm/rev.
15	96											*	Speed m/min.
20										0202		*	Tool and offset
25	00	104		0								*	Rapid to start
30											03		Spindle/on
	01							250	170		08	*	Feed to X0, coolant on
35	00			2								*	Clear face
40											06	*	Tool change
45		0		2						0101		*	Index to c/drill
50	01											*	Rapid to start
55	00	0		-5				80	28			*	Center drill
60				2								*	Return to start
65											06	*	Tool change
70										0303		*	Index to drill 10∅
75	01	0		2								*	Rapid to start
80	83			-85			w20	180				*	Peck drill 10∅
85	80											*	Cancel cycle
90											06	*	Tool change
95										0505		*	Index to drill 20∅
100	00	0		2								*	Rapid to start
101	81			-85				300				*	Drill 20∅

Appendix D

GDT SYMBOLS

Geometric Tolerances

Geometrical Tolerance Symbols

SYMBOL	CHARACTERISTIC	APPLICATION
—	STRAIGHTNESS	Applied to an edge line or axis. For an edge or line the tolerance zone is the area between two parallel straight lines containing the edge or line. The tolerance value is the distance between the two lines.
▱	FLATNESS	Applied to a surface. The tolerance zone is the space between two parallel planes. The tolerance value is the distance between the two planes.
○	ROUNDNESS	Applied to the cross-section of a cylinder, cone or sphere. The tolerance zone is the angular space between two concentric circles lying in the same plane. The tolerance value is the distance between the two circles.
⌭	CYLINDRICITY	Applied to the surface of a cylinder. Combines roundness, straightness and parallelism. The tolerance zone is the angular space between two coaxial cylinders. The tolerance zone is the radial distance between the two cylinders.
⌒	PROFILE OF A LINE	Applied to a profile. The tolerance zone is an area defined by two lines that have a constant width normal to the stated profile. The tolerance is the diameter of a series of circles contained between the two lines. The tolerance may be unilateral or bilateral.
⌓	PROFILE OF A SURFACE	Applied to a surface. The tolerance zone is a space contained between two surfaces normal to the stated surface. The tolerance value is the diameter of a series of spheres enveloped by the two surfaces. The tolerance may be unilateral or bilateral.
//	PARALLELISM	Applied to a line, surface or cylinder. The tolerance zone is the area between two parallel lines or planes, or the space between two parallel cylinders, which must be parallel to the datum feature. The tolerance is the distance between the two lines or planes or, in the case of a cylinder, the diameter of the cylinder.
⊥	SQUARENESS	Applied to a line, surface or cylinder. For a line or surface the tolerance zone is the area between two parallel lines or planes which are perpendicular to the datum surface. The tolerance is the distance between the lines or planes. For a cylinder the tolerance zone is the space within a cylinder equal in diameter to the tolerance value and perpendicular to the datum plane.
∠	ANGULARITY	Applied to a line, surface or cylinder. For a line or surface the tolerance is the area or space between two parallel lines or planes inclined at a specified angle to the datum features. For a cylinder the tolerance zone is the space within a cylinder equal in diameter to the tolerance value and inclined at a specified angle to the datum feature.
⊕	POSITION	Applied to a circle or cylinder. The tolerance zone is the space within a cylinder equal in diameter to the tolerance value and coaxial with the datum axis. The tolerance limits the deviation of the datum axis from its true position.
◎	CONCENTRICITY	Applied to parallel lines or surfaces. The tolerance zone is the area of space between the lines or surfaces symmetrically disposed in relation to a datum feature. The tolerance value is the distance between the lines or planes.
⚌	SYMMETRY	Applied to a point, axis, line or plane. The tolerance zone definition varies according to the feature. The tolerance value will limit the positional deviation from the specified true position.
⟋	RUN OUT	Applied to the surface of a solid of revolution or to a face perpendicular to the axis. The tolerance value indicates the permissible indicator movement during one revolution.
○	MAXIMUM MATERIAL CONDITION	MMC exists when the component or feature contains the maximum amount of material permitted by its dimensional tolerances. When M is included in a tolerance frame the tolerance value need only be applied rigorously when the component or feature is in that condition. When not in that condition the geometric tolerance may be increased up to the difference between the MMC limit and the actual finished sized.

Geometric Tolerance Frames

1. Tolerance relating to a single datum:

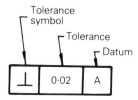

2. Tolerance relating to more than one datum:

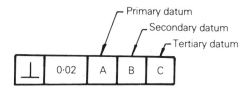

Appendix E

FORMULAS

Formula #1

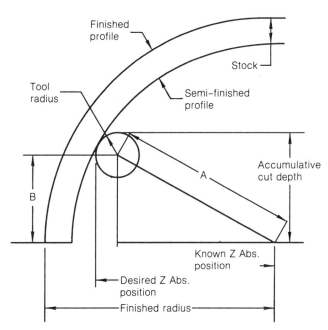

A = Finished radius–stock–tool radius
B = Accumulative cut depth–tool radius
Desired Z Abs. = Known Z Abs. − $\sqrt{A^2 - B^2}$ − tool radius

Formula #2

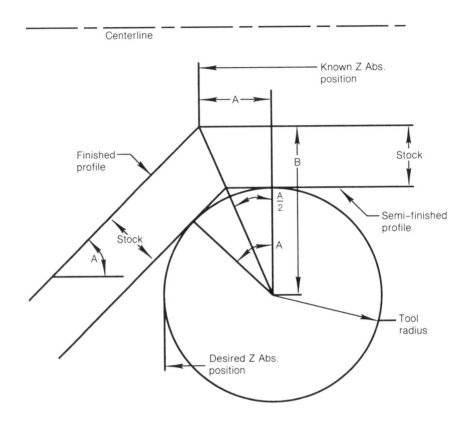

B = Stock + tool radius
A = Tan $\frac{A}{2}$ × B
Desired Z Abs. = Known Z Abs. − (tool radius − A)

Formula #3

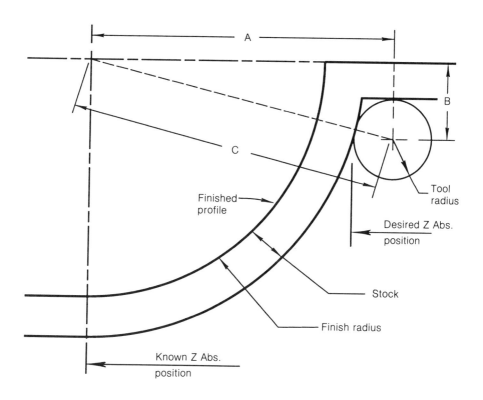

B = Tool radius + stock
C = Finish radius + stock + tool radius
A = $\sqrt{C^2 - B^2}$
Desired Z Abs. = Known Z Abs. + A − tool radius

Formula #4

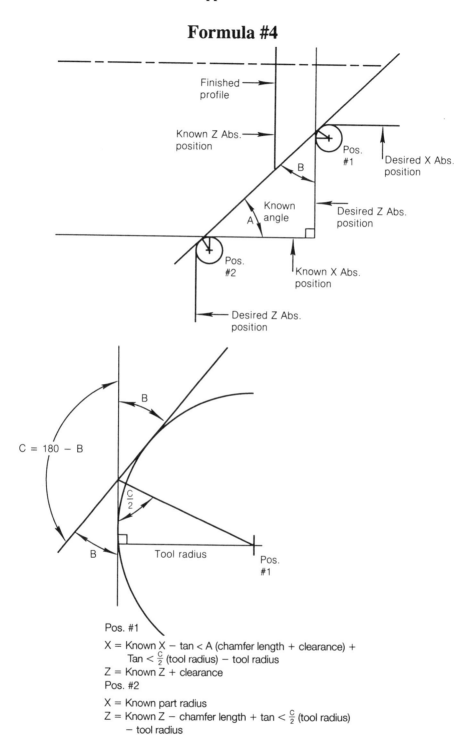

Pos. #1

X = Known X − tan < A (chamfer length + clearance) +
     Tan < $\frac{C}{2}$ (tool radius) − tool radius

Z = Known Z + clearance

Pos. #2

X = Known part radius

Z = Known Z − chamfer length + tan < $\frac{C}{2}$ (tool radius)
     − tool radius

Index

A118167